Applied Finite Mathematics

Edmond C. Tomastik | Janice L. Epstein

Australia • Brazil • Japan • Korea • Mexico • Singapore • Spain • United Kingdom • United States

CENGAGE
Learning™

Applied Finite Mathematics

Edmond C. Tomastik | Janice L. Epstein

Executive Editors:
 Michele Baird
 Maureen Staudt
 Michael Stranz

Project Development Manager:
 Linda deStefano

Senior Marketing Coordinators:
 Sara Mercurio
 Lindsay Shapiro

Production/Manufacturing Manager:
 Donna M. Brown

PreMedia Services Supervisor:
 Rebecca A. Walker

Rights & Permissions Specialist:
 Kalina Hintz

Cover Image:
 Getty Images*

© 2008 Cengage Learning

For product information and technology assistance, contact us at
Cengage Learning Customer & Sales Support, 1-800-354-9706

For permission to use material from this text or product,
submit all requests online at **cengage.com/permissions**
Further permissions questions can be emailed to
permissionrequest@cengage.com

ISBN-13: 978-0-495-83960-6

ISBN-10: 0-495-83960-4

Cengage Learning
5191 Natorp Boulevard
Mason, Ohio 45040
USA

Cengage Learning is a leading provider of customized learning solutions with office locations around the globe, including Singapore, the United Kingdom, Australia, Mexico, Brazil, and Japan. Locate your local office at:
international.cengage.com/region

Cengage Learning products are represented in Canada by Nelson Education, Ltd.

For your lifelong learning solutions, visit **custom.cengage.com**

Visit our corporate website at **cengage.com**

Printed in the United States of America

Contents

Preface   **v**

1   Systems of Linear Equations and Models   **2**
1.1   Mathematical Models 3
1.2   Systems of Linear Equations 20
1.3   Gauss Elimination for Systems of Linear Equations 31
1.4   Systems of Linear Equations With Non-Unique Solutions 50
1.5   Method of Least Squares 68
      Review 80

2   Matrices   **86**
2.1   Introduction to Matrices 87
2.2   Matrix Multiplication 97
2.3   Inverse of a Square Matrix 114
2.4   Additional Matrix Applications 126
      Review 139

3   Linear Programming: The Graphical Method   **142**
3.1   Linear Programming Problems 143
3.2   Graphing Linear Inequalities 156
3.3   Graphical Solution of Linear Programming Problems 168
      Review 181

4   Sets and Probability   **184**
4.1   Introduction to Sets 185
4.2   The Number of Elements in a Set 194
4.3   Sample Spaces and Events 201
4.4   Basics of Probability 209
4.5   Rules for Probability 216
4.6   Conditional Probability 225
4.7   Bayes' Theorem 238
      Review 246

5   Counting and Probability   **254**
5.1   The Multiplication Principle and Permutations 255
5.2   Combinations 265
5.3   Probability Applications of Counting Principles 272
5.4   Bernoulli Trials 278
5.5   Binomial Theorem 284
      Review 288

6   Probability Distributions and Statistics   **290**
   6.1   Random Variables and Histograms 291
   6.2   Measures of Central Tendency 303
   6.3   Measures of Spread 316
   6.4   The Normal Distribution 329
   6.5   Normal Approximation to the Binomial Distribution 339
         Review 347

F   Finance   **352**
   F.1   Simple Interest and Discount 353
   F.2   Compound Interest 359
   F.3   Annuities and Sinking Funds 368
   F.4   Present Value of Annuities and Amortization 376
         Review 386

Area Under a Normal Curve   **390**

Answers to Selected Exercises   **392**

Bibliography   **407**

Index   **410**

Preface

Applied Finite Mathematics is designed for a finite mathematics course aimed at students majoring in business, management, economics, or the life or social sciences. The text can be understood by the average student with one year of high school algebra. A wide range of topics is included, giving the instructor considerable flexibility in designing a course. Optional technology material is available where relevant.

Applications truly play a central and prominent role in the text. This is because the text is written for *users* of mathematics. Thus, for example, a concrete applied problem is presented first as a motivation before developing a needed mathematical topic. After the mathematical topic has been developed, further applications are given so that the student understands the practical need for the mathematics. This is done so consistently and thoroughly that after going completing some chapters, the student should come to believe that mathematics is everywhere. Indeed, countless applications are drawn from actual referenced examples extracted from journals and other professional texts and papers.

No other skill is more important than the ability to translate a real-life problem into an appropriate mathematical format for finding the solution. Students often refer to this process as "word problems." Whereas linear systems of equations, linear programming problems, and financial problems, for example, can easily be solved using modern technology, no calculator or computer, now or in the foreseeable future, can translate these applied problems into the necessary mathematical language. Thus students, in their jobs, will most likely use their mathematical knowledge to translate applied problems into necessary mathematical models for solution by computers.

To develop these needed skills many word problems, requiring the writing of one linear equation, are given in the introductory sections. This prepares the student for the many word problems that require creating systems of linear equations. The word problems continue in subsequent chapters, for example, on linear programming.

✧ Important Features

The text can be understood by the average student with a minimum of outside assistance. Material on a variety of topics is presented in an interesting, informal, and student-friendly manner without compromising the mathematical content and accuracy. Concepts are developed gradually, always introduced intuitively, and culminate in a definition or result. Where possible, general concepts are presented only after particular cases have been presented.

Historical Boxes Scattered throughout the text, and set-off in boxes, are historical and anecdotal comments. The historical comments are not only interesting in themselves, but also indicate that mathematics is a continually developing subject.

Connections   The Connection boxes relate the material to contemporary problems. This makes the material more relevant and interesting.

Applications   The text includes many meaningful applications drawn from a variety of fields. For example, every section opens by posing an interesting and relevant applied problem using familiar vocabulary, which is then solved later in the section after the appropriate mathematics has been developed. Applications are given for all the mathematics that are presented and are used to motivate the student.

Worked Examples   About 300 worked examples, including about 100 self-help exercises mentioned below, have been carefully selected to take the reader progressively from the simplest idea to the most complex. All the steps needed for the complete solutions are included.

Self-Help Exercises   Immediately preceding each exercise set is a set of Self-Help Exercises. These approximately 100 exercises have been very carefully selected to bridge the gap between the exposition in the chapter and the regular exercise set. By doing these exercises and checking the complete solutions provided, students will be able to test or check their comprehension of the material. This, in turn, will better prepare them to do the exercises in the regular exercise set.

Exercises   The text contains over 2000 exercises. Each set begins with drilling problems to build skills, and then gradually increases in difficulty. The exercise sets also include an extensive array of realistic applications from diverse disciplines. Technology exercises are included.

End of Chapter Projects   Most chapters contain an in-depth exportation of an important concept taught in the chapter. This provides strong connections to real applications or a treatment of the material at a greater depth than in the main part of the chapter.

Flexibility and Technology   The text does not require any technology. However, important material on how to use technology is included. This material is tucked out of the way of a reader not interested in using technology, being placed at the end of a section as technology notes and also within green boxes in the margin.

✧ Technology

For those finite math classes that are taught with a graphing calculator or a spreadsheet, this text has abundant resources for the student and the instructor. The most accessible resource is the green margin boxes with the **Technology Option**. These are designed for students who are familiar with a graphing calculator and wish to see how the current example is worked using the calculator. For those students who need step-by-step directions, the **Technology Corner** provides details on using a graphing calculator or a spreadsheet to carry out the mathematical operations discussed in the section. While the text focuses on the use of a TI-83/84 and Microsoft Excel, other technology help is available upon request.

✧ Student Aids

- Boldface cyan text is used when new terms are defined.

- **Boxes** are used to highlight definitions, theorems, results, and procedures.

- **Remarks** are used to draw attention to important points that might otherwise be overlooked.

- **Titles** for worked examples help to identify the subject.

- **Chapter summary outlines** at the end of each chapter conveniently summarize all the definitions, theorems, and procedures in one place.

- **Review exercises** are found at the end of each chapter.

- **Answers** to odd-numbered exercises and to all the review exercises are provided at the end of each chapter.

- A student's **solution manual** that contains completely worked solutions to all odd-numbered exercises and to all chapter review exercises is available.

✧ Instructor Aids

- An **instructor's manual** with completely worked solutions to all the exercises is available free to adopters.

- **WebAssign** A selection of questions from every section of the text will be available for online homework on the WebAssign system. These homework questions are algorithmically generated and computer graded.

✧ Content Overview

Chapter 1. An introduction to the theory of the firm with some necessary economics background is provided to take into account the students' diverse backgrounds. The next three sections cover linear systems of equations. The last (optional) section on least squares provides other examples and applications of the use of linear equations.

Chapter 2. The first three sections cover the basic material on matrices. Although many applications are included in the first three sections, the fourth (optional) section is entirely devoted to input–output analysis, which is an application of linear systems and matrices used in economics.

Chapter 3. The first section is an introduction to linear programming with the emphasis on translating applied problems into a mathematical format for solving them. The next two sections then develop the necessary mathematics needed to solve the linear programming problems. This includes graphing systems of linear equations and using a geometric method of finding solutions. The final (optional) section considers a post-optimal analysis, including determining excess resources and shadow prices.

Chapter 4. The first two sections give an introduction to sets and counting the number of elements in a set. The third section then sets the background for probability by considering sample spaces and events. The next two sections then introduce the basics of probability and their rules. The next two sections cover conditional probability and Bayes' theorem.

Chapter 5. This chapter involves counting and probability. The first four sections cover the multiplication principle, permutations, combinations, probability applications of counting principles, and Bernoulli trials. The last (optional) section considers the binomial theorem.

Chapter 6. The first section revisits probability distributions and introduces histograms. The next two sections look at the measure of central tendency and the measure of the spread of data. The next sections consider the normal distribution, the approximation of the binomial distribution by a normal distribution, and finally the Poisson distribution.

Chapter F. This chapter covers finance. The first two sections cover simple and compound interest. The next two sections cover annuities, sinking funds, present value, and amortization. This chapter on finance does not depend on any of the other material and can be covered at any point in the course.

Chapter S. The first section presents the simplex method for standard maximization problems. The second section shows how to solve minimization problems by solving the dual problem, while the third section considers more general linear programming problems. Finally, the last section looks at post-optimal analysis.

Chapter M. The basic material on Markov processes, covering both regular and absorbing Markov processes, is presented in this chapter.

Chapter G. Game theory and its important connection to linear programming is presented in this chapter. This material gives the basics on the extensive interrelationship between linear programming and the celebrated theory of games developed by von Neumann and important in economic theory.

Chapter L. This chapter covers the basic topics in logic with an application in the last section to switching networks.

✧ Some Additional Comments on the Contents

In Chapter 1 when solving systems of linear equations with an infinite number of solutions we will have free variables as parameters. We make it clear that in a list of variables, such as x, y, z, and u, the last variable need not be the free one. Rather, any of the variables can be a free variable. This requires us to develop a solution plan that can address this issue.

Also when solving a system of linear equations with an infinite number of solutions in an applied application, the parameter may require some constraints. For example, the parameter may need to be an integer, or an even integer, or have a bound above and below. Furthermore, it is possible in an applied problem that there is no acceptable solution, even though there are an infinite number of solutions of the abstract mathematical system.

Suppose there are three equations and three unknowns, say x, y, and z, in a system of linear equations. When using the augmented matrix to solve the system, the normal procedure is to first reduce this matrix to a matrix with ones down the diagonal and zeros below the diagonal. Students invariably notice that we now have found the z value, so why not substitute this into the previous equation, solve for y, and then use these two values to substitute into the first equation in order to find x. This is formally called backward substitution. Since this is such a natural way of solving the system, we follow backward substitution in this text. In fact, software used to solve systems follow just this plan. (See "Matrix Computations" by Gene H. Golub and Charles F. van Loan.) It does not require any more calculations than some other methods that are sometimes taught.

We also indicate in an optional subsection that following the solving plan for systems of linear equations given in this text is actually more efficient and in general requires fewer calculations than any other solving plan found in some other texts.

Acknowledgments

At the University of Connecticut we are thankful for the support offered by Michael Neumann, Jeff Tollefson, Gerald Leibowitz, and David Gross. At Texas A&M University we are thankful for the support of G. Donald Allen and the feedback of Kathryn Bollinger, Kendra Kilmer, and Heather Ramsey were invaluable. We wish to express our sincere appreciation to each of the following reviewers for their many helpful suggestions.

Marti Mclard, University of Tennessee, Knoxville

John Herron, University of Montevallo

Fritz Keineut, Iowa State University

On a personal level, we both are grateful to our families for their patience and support.

Edmond C. Tomastik, University of Connecticut

Janice L. Epstein, Texas A&M University

April, 2008

Applied Finite Mathematics

CHAPTER 1

Systems of Linear Equations and Models

CONNECTION

Demand for Televisions

As sleek flat-panel and high-definition television sets became more affordable, sales soared during the holidays. Sales of ultra-thin, wall-mountable LCD TVs rose over 100% in 2005 to about 20 million sets while plasma-TV sales rose at a similar pace, to about 5 million sets. Normally set makers and retailers lower their prices after the holidays, but since there was strong demand and production shortages for these sets, prices were kept high.

Source: http://biz.yahoo.com

1.1 Mathematical Models

APPLICATION
Cost, Revenue, and Profit Models

A firm has weekly fixed costs of $80,000 associated with the manufacture of dresses that cost $25 per dress to produce. The firm sells all the dresses it produces at $75 per dress. Find the cost, revenue, and profit equations if x is the number of dresses produced per week. See Example 3 for the answer.

We will first review some basic material on functions. An introduction to the mathematical theory of the business firm with some necessary economics background is provided. We study mathematical business models of cost, revenue, profit, and depreciation, and mathematical economic models of demand and supply.

✧ Functions

HISTORICAL NOTE

**Augustin Cournot
(1801–1877)**

The first significant work dealing with the application of mathematics to economics was Cournot's *Researches into the Mathematical Principles of the Theory of Wealth*, published in 1836. It was Cournot who originated the supply and demand curves that are discussed in this section. Irving Fisher, a prominent economics professor at Yale University and one of the first exponents of mathematical economics in the United States, wrote that Cournot's book "seemed a failure when first published. It was far in advance of the times. Its methods were too strange, its reasoning too intricate for the crude and confident notions of political economy then current."

Mathematical modeling is an attempt to describe some part of the real world in mathematical terms. Our models will be functions that show the relationship between two or more variables. These variables will represent quantities that we wish to understand or describe. Examples include the price of gasoline, the cost of producing cereal, or the number of video games sold. The idea of representing these quantities as variables in a function is central to our goal of creating models to describe their behavior. We will begin by reviewing the concept of functions. In short, we call any rule that assigns or corresponds to each element in one set precisely one element in another set a function.

For example, suppose you are going a steady speed of 40 miles per hour in a car. In one hour you will travel 40 miles; in two hours you will travel 80 miles; and so on. The distance you travel depends on (corresponds to) the time. Indeed, the equation relating the variables distance (d), velocity (v), and time (t), is $d = v \cdot t$. In our example, we have a constant velocity of $v = 40$, so $d = 40 \cdot t$. We can view this as a correspondence or rule: Given the time t in hours, the rule gives a distance d in miles according to $d = 40 \cdot t$. Thus, given $t = 3$, $d = 40 \cdot 3 = 120$. Notice carefully how this rule is unambiguous. That is, given any time t, the rule specifies one and only one distance d. This rule is therefore a function; the correspondence is between time and distance.

Often the letter f is used to denote a function. Thus, using the previous example, we can write $d = f(t) = 40 \cdot t$. The symbol $f(t)$ is read "f of t." One can think of the variable t as the "input" and the value of the variable $d = f(t)$ as the "output." For example, an input of $t = 4$ results in an output of $d = f(4) = 40 \cdot 4 = 160$ miles. The following gives a general definition of a function.

Definition of a Function
A function f from D to R is a rule that assigns to each element x in D one and only one element $y = f(x)$ in R. See Figure 1.1.

Figure 1.1
A function as a mapping

The set D in the definition is called the domain of f. We might think of the domain as the set of inputs. We then can think of the values $f(x)$ as outputs.

The set of outputs, R is called the range of f. Another helpful way to think of a function is shown in Figure 1.2. Here the function f accepts the input x from the conveyor belt, operates on x, and outputs (assigns) the new value $f(x)$.

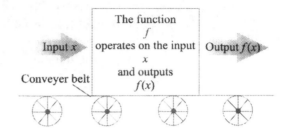

Figure 1.2
A function as a process

The letter representing elements in the domain is called the independent variable and the letter representing the elements in the range is called the dependent variable. Thus, if $y = f(x)$, x is the independent variable, and y is the dependent variable, since the value of y depends on x. In the equation $d = 40t$, we can write $d = f(t) = 40t$ with t as the independent variable. The dependent variable is d, since the distance depends on the spent time t traveling. We are free to set the independent variable t equal to any number of values in the domain. The domain for this function is $t \geq 0$ since only nonnegative time is allowed.

REMARK: The domain in an application problem will always be those values that are allowed for the independent variable in the particular application. This often means that we are restricted to nonnegative values or perhaps we will be limited to the case of whole numbers only, as in the next example.

EXAMPLE 1   Steak Specials   A restaurant serves a steak special for $12. Write a function that models the amount of revenue made from selling these specials. How much revenue will 10 steak specials earn?

Solution   We first need to decide if the independent variable is the price of the steak specials, the number of specials sold, or the amount of revenue earned. Since the price is fixed at $12 per special and revenue depends on the number of specials sold, we choose the independent variable, x, to be the number of specials sold and the dependent variable, $R = f(x)$ to be the amount of revenue. Our rule will be $R = f(x) = 12x$, where x is the number of steak specials sold and R is the revenue from selling these specials in dollars. Note that x must be a whole number, so the domain is $x = 0, 1, 2, 3, \ldots$. To determine the revenue made on selling 10 steak specials, plug $x = 10$ into the model:

$$R = f(10) = 12(10) = 120$$

So the revenue is $120.   ◆

⊘ Technology Option

Example 1 is solved using a graphing calculator in Technology Note 1 on page 12.

Recall that lines satisfy the equation $y = mx + b$. Actually, we can view this as a function. We can set $y = f(x) = mx + b$. Given any number x, $f(x)$ is obtained by multiplying x by m and adding b. More specifically, we call the function $y = f(x) = mx + b$ a linear function.

> **Definition of Linear Function**
> A linear function f is any function of the form,
>
> $$y = f(x) = mx + b$$
>
> where m and b are constants.

EXAMPLE 2   Linear Functions   Which of the following functions are linear?

a. $y = -0.5x + 12$

b. $5y - 2x = 10$

c. $y = \dfrac{1}{x} + 2$

d. $y = x^2$

Solution

a. This is a linear function. The slope is $m = -0.5$ and the y-intercept is $b = 12$.

b. Rewrite this function first as,

$$5y - 2x = 10$$
$$5y = 2x + 10$$
$$y = (2/5)x + 2$$

Now we see it is a linear function with $m = 2/5$ and $b = 2$.

c. This is not a linear function. Rewrite $1/x$ as x^{-1} and this shows that we do not have a term mx and so this is not a linear function.

d. x is raised to the second power and so this is not a linear function.   ✦

 Technology Option

You can graph the functions on a calculator to verify your results. Linear functions will be a straight line in any window.

✧ Mathematical Modeling

When we use mathematical modeling we are attempting to describe some part of the real world in mathematical terms, just as we have done for the distance traveled and the revenue from selling meals. There are three steps in mathematical modeling: formulation, mathematical manipulation, and evaluation.

Formulation

First, on the basis of observations, we must state a question or formulate a hypothesis. If the question or hypothesis is too vague, we need to make it precise. If it is too ambitious, we need to restrict it or subdivide it into manageable parts. Second, we need to identify important factors. We must decide which quantities and relationships are important to answer the question and which can be ignored. We then need to formulate a mathematical description. For example, each important quantity should be represented by a variable. Each relationship should be represented by an equation, inequality, or other mathematical construct. If we obtain a function, say, $y = f(x)$, we must carefully identify the input variable *x* and the output variable *y* and the units for each. We should also indicate the interval of values of the input variable for which the model is justified.

Mathematical Manipulation   After the mathematical formulation, we then need to do some mathematical manipulation to obtain the answer to our original question. We might need to do a calculation, solve an equation, or prove a theorem. Sometimes the mathematical formulation gives us a mathematical problem that is impossible to solve. In such a case, we will need to reformulate the question in a less ambitious manner.

Evaluation   Naturally, we need to check the answers given by the model with real data. We normally expect the mathematical model to describe only a very limited aspect of the world and to give only approximate answers. If the answers are wrong or not accurate enough for our purposes, then we will need to identify the sources of the model's shortcomings. Perhaps we need to change the model entirely, or perhaps we need to just make some refinements. In any case, this requires a new mathematical manipulation and evaluation. Thus, modeling often involves repeating the three steps of formulation, mathematical manipulation, and evaluation.

We will next create linear mathematical models by finding equations that relate cost, revenue, and profits of a manufacturing firm to the number of units produced and sold.

✧ Cost, Revenue, and Profit

Any manufacturing firm has two types of costs: fixed and variable. Fixed costs are those that do not depend on the amount of production. These costs include real estate taxes, interest on loans, some management salaries, certain minimal maintenance, and protection of plant and equipment. Variable costs depend on the amount of production. They include the cost of material and labor. Total cost, or simply cost, is the sum of fixed and variable costs:

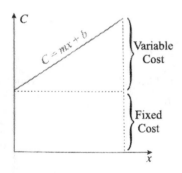

Figure 1.3
A linear cost function

$$\text{cost} = \text{variable cost} + \text{fixed cost}$$

Let *x* denote the number of units of a given product or commodity produced by a firm. (Notice that we must have $x \geq 0$.) The units could be bales of cotton, tons of fertilizer, or number of automobiles. In the linear cost model we assume that the cost *m* of manufacturing one unit is the same no matter how many units are produced. Thus, the variable cost is the number of units produced times the cost of each unit:

$$\text{variable cost} = (\text{cost per unit}) \times (\text{number of units produced})$$
$$= mx$$

If *b* is the fixed cost and $C(x)$ is the cost, then we have the following:

$$C(x) = \text{cost}$$
$$= (\text{variable cost}) + (\text{fixed cost})$$
$$= mx + b$$

Notice that we must have $C(x) \geq 0$. In the graph shown in Figure 1.3, we see that the *y*-intercept is the fixed cost and the slope is the cost per item.

CONNECTION
What Are Costs?

> Isn't it obvious what the costs to a firm are? Apparently not. On July 15, 2002, Coca-Cola Company announced that it would begin treating stock-option compensation as a cost, thereby lowering earnings. If all companies in the Standard and Poor's 500 stock index were to do the same, the earnings for this index would drop by 23%.
>
> *Source*: The Wall Street Journal, July 16, 2002

In the linear revenue model we assume that the price p of a unit sold by a firm is the same no matter how many units are sold. (This is a reasonable assumption if the number of units sold by the firm is small in comparison to the total number sold by the entire industry.) Revenue is always the price per unit times the number of units sold. Let x be the number of units sold. For convenience, we always assume that the number of units sold equals the number of units produced. Then, if we denote the revenue by $R(x)$,

$$R(x) = \text{revenue}$$
$$= (\text{price per unit}) \times (\text{number sold})$$
$$= px$$

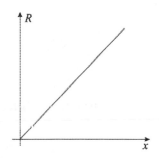

Figure 1.4
A linear revenue function

Since $p > 0$, we must have $R(x) \geq 0$. Notice in Figure 1.4 that the straight line goes through $(0,0)$ because nothing sold results in no revenue. The slope is the price per unit.

CONNECTION
What Are Revenues?

> The accounting practices of many telecommunications companies, such as Cisco and Lucent, have been criticized for what the companies consider revenues. In particular, these companies have loaned money to other companies, which then use the proceeds of the loan to buy telecommunications equipment from Cisco and Lucent. Cisco and Lucent then book these sales as "revenue." But is this revenue?

Regardless of whether our models of cost and revenue are linear or not, profit P is always revenue less cost. Thus

$$P = \text{profit}$$
$$= (\text{revenue}) - (\text{cost})$$
$$= R - C$$

Recall that both cost $C(x)$ and revenue $R(x)$ must be nonnegative functions. However, the profit $P(x)$ can be positive or negative. Negative profits are called losses.

Let's now determine the cost, revenue, and profit equations for a dress-manufacturing firm.

EXAMPLE 3   Cost, Revenue, and Profit Equations   A firm has weekly fixed costs of $80,000 associated with the manufacture of dresses that cost $25 per dress to produce. The firm sells all the dresses it produces at $75 per dress.

a. Find the cost, revenue, and profit equations if x is the number of dresses produced per week.

b. Make a table of values for cost, revenue, and profit for production levels of 1000, 1500, and 2000 dresses and discuss what is the table means.

Solution

a. The fixed cost is $80,000 and the variable cost is 25x. So

$$C = (\text{variable cost}) + (\text{fixed cost})$$
$$= mx + b$$
$$= 25x + 80,000$$

See Figure 1.5a. Notice that $x \geq 0$ and $C(x) \geq 0$.

b. The revenue is just the price $75 that each dress is sold for multiplied by the number x of dresses sold. So

$$R = (\text{price per dress}) \times (\text{number sold})$$
$$= px$$
$$= 75x$$

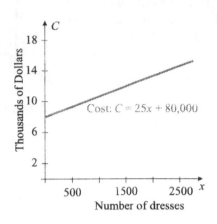

Figure 1.5a

See Figure 1.5b. Notice that $x \geq 0$ and $R(x) \geq 0$. Also notice that if there are no sales, then there is no revenue, that is, $R(0) = 0$.

Profit is always revenue less cost. So

$$P = (\text{revenue}) - (\text{cost})$$
$$= R - C$$
$$= (75x) - (25x + 80,000)$$
$$= 50x - 80,000$$

See Figure 1.5c. Notice in Figure 1.5c that profits can be negative.

c. When 1000 dresses are produced and sold $x = 1000$ so we have

$$C(1000) = 25(1000) + 80,000 = 105,000$$
$$R(1000) = 75(1000) = 75,000$$
$$P(1000) = 75,000 - 105,000 = -30,000$$

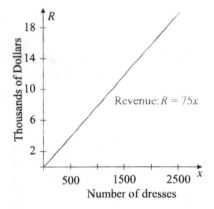

Figure 1.5b

Thus, if 1000 dresses are produced and sold, the cost is $105,000, the revenue is $75,000, and there is a negative profit or loss of $30,000. Doing the same for 1500 and 2000 dresses, we have the results shown in Table 1.1.

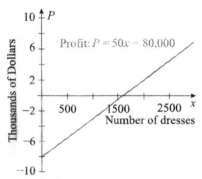

Figure 1.5c

Number of Dresses Made and Sold	1000	1500	2000
Cost in dollars	105,000	117,500	130,000
Revenue in dollars	75,000	112,500	150,000
Profit (or loss) in dollars	−30,000	−5,000	20,000

Table 1.1

We can see in Figure 1.5c or in Table 1.1, that for smaller values of x, $P(x)$ is negative; that is, the firm has losses as their costs are greater than their revenue. For larger values of x, $P(x)$ turns positive and the firm has (positive) profits.   ◆

✧ Supply and Demand

In the previous discussion we assumed that the number of units produced and sold by the given firm was small in comparison to the number sold by the industry. Under this assumption it was reasonable to conclude that the price, p, was constant and did not vary with the number x sold. But if the number of units sold by the firm represented a large percentage of the number sold by the entire industry, then trying to sell significantly more units could only be accomplished by lowering the price of each unit. Since we just stated that the price effects the number sold, you would expect the price to be the independent variable and thus graphed on the horizontal axis. However, by custom, the price is graphed on the vertical axis and the quantity x on the horizontal axis. This convention was started by English economist Alfred Marshall (1842–1924) in his important book, *Principles of Economics*. We will abide by this custom in this text.

For most items the relationship between quantity and price is a decreasing function (there are some exceptions to this rule, such as certain luxury goods, medical care, and higher eduction, to name a few). That is, for the number of items to be sold to increase, the price must decrease. We assume now for mathematical convenience that this relationship is linear. Then the graph of this equation is a straight line that slopes downward as shown in Figure 1.6.

We assume that x is the number of units produced and sold by the entire industry during a given time period and that $p = D(x) = -cx + d$, $c > 0$, is the price of one unit if x units are sold; that is, $p = -cx + d$ is the price of the xth unit sold. We call $p = D(x)$ the **demand equation** and the graph the **demand curve**.

Estimating the demand equation is a fundamental problem for the management of any company or business. In the next example we consider the situation when just two data points are available and the demand equation is assumed to be linear.

EXAMPLE 4   Finding the Demand Equation   Timmins estimated the municipal water demand in Delano, California. He estimated the demand x, measured in acre-feet (the volume of water needed to cover one acre of ground at a depth of one foot), with price p per acre-foot. He indicated two points on the demand curve, $(x, p) = (1500, 230)$ and $(x, p) = (5100, 50)$. Use this data to estimate the demand curve using a linear model. Estimate the price when the demand is 3000 acre-feet.

Source: Timmins 2002

Solution   Figure 1.7 shows the two points $(x, p) = (1500, 230)$ and $(x, p) = (5100, 50)$ that lie on the demand curve. We are assuming that the demand curve is a straight line. The slope of the line is

$$m = \frac{50 - 230}{5100 - 1500} = -0.05$$

Now using the point-slope equation for a line with $(1500, 230)$ as the point on the line, we have

$$p - 230 = m(x - 1500)$$
$$= -0.05(x - 1500)$$
$$p = -0.05x + 75 + 230$$
$$= -0.05x + 305$$

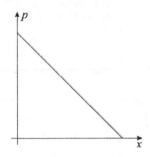

Figure 1.6
A linear demand function

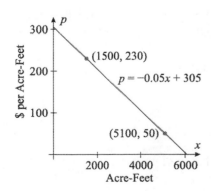

Figure 1.7

When demand is 3000 acre-feet, then $x = 3000$, and

$$p = -0.05(3000) + 305 = 155$$

or $155 per acre-foot. Thus, according to this model, if 3000 acre-feet is demanded, the price of each acre-foot will be $155. ✦

CONNECTION
Demand for Apartments

The figure shows that during the minor recession of 2001, vacancy rates for apartments increased, that is, the demand for apartments decreased. Notice in the figure that as demand for apartments decreased, rents also decreased. For example, in San Francisco's South Beach area, a two-bedroom apartment that had rented for $3000 a month two years before saw the rent drop to $2100 a month.

Source: Wall Street Journal, April 11, 2002

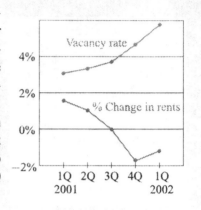

The supply equation $p = S(x)$ gives the price p necessary for suppliers to make available x units to the market. The graph of this equation is called the **supply curve**. A reasonable supply curve rises, moving from left to right, because the suppliers of any product naturally want to sell more if the price is higher. (See Shea 1993 who looked at a large number of industries and determined that the supply curve does indeed slope upward.) If the supply curve is linear, then as shown in Figure 1.8, the graph is a line sloping upward. Note the positive y-intercept. The y-intercept represents the **choke point** or lowest price a supplier is willing to accept.

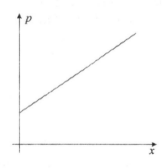

Figure 1.8
A supply equation

EXAMPLE 5   Finding the Supply Equation   Antle and Capalbo estimated a spring wheat supply curve. Use a mathematical model to determine a linear curve using their estimates that the supply of spring wheat will be 50 million bushels at a price of $2.90 per bushel and 100 million bushels at a price of $4.00 per bushel. Estimate the price when 80 million bushels is supplied.

Source: Antle and Capalbo 2001

Solution   Let x be in millions of bushels of wheat. We are then given two points on the linear supply curve, $(x, p) = (50, 2.9)$ and $(x, p) = (100, 4)$. The slope is

$$m = \frac{4 - 2.9}{100 - 50} = 0.022$$

The equation is then given by

$$p - 2.9 = 0.022(x - 50)$$

or $p = 0.022x + 1.8$. See Figure 1.9 and note that the line rises.

When supply is 80 million bushels, $x = 80$, and we have

$$p = 0.022(80) + 1.8 = 3.56$$

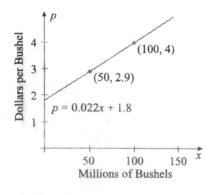

Figure 1.9

This gives a price of $3.56 per bushel.   ✦

On May 2, 2002, the U.S. House of Representatives passed a farm bill that promises billions of dollars in subsidies to cotton farmers. With the prospect of a greater supply of cotton, cotton prices dropped 1.36 cents to 33.76 cents per pound.

Source: The Wall Street Journal, May 3, 2002.

✧ Straight-Line Depreciation

Many assets, such as machines or buildings, have a finite useful life and furthermore depreciate in value from year to year. For purposes of determining profits and taxes, various methods of depreciation can be used. In straight-line depreciation we assume that the value V of the asset is given by a linear equation in time t, say, $V = mt + b$. The slope m must be negative since the value of the asset decreases over time. The y-intercept is the initial value of the item and the slope gives the rate of depreciation (how much the item decreases in value per time period).

EXAMPLE 6   Straight-Line Depreciation   A company has purchased a new grinding machine for $100,000 with a useful life of 10 years, after which it is assumed that the scrap value of the machine is $5000. Use straight-line depreciation to write an equation for the value V of the machine, where t is measured in years. What will be the value of the machine after the first year? After the second year? After the ninth year? What is the rate of depreciation?

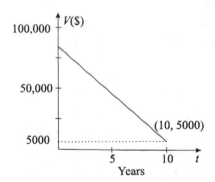

Figure 1.10

Solution   We assume that $V = mt + b$, where m is the slope and b is the V-intercept. We then must find both m and b. We are told that the machine is initially worth $100,000, that is, when $t = 0$, $V = 100,000$. Thus, the point $(0, 100,000)$ is on the line, and $100,000$ is the V-intercept, b. See Figure 1.10 and note the domain of t is $0 \leq t \leq 10$.

Since the value of the machine in 10 years will be $5000, this means that when $t = 10$, $V = 5000$. Thus, $(10, 5000)$ is also on the line. From Figure 1.10, the slope can then be calculated since we now know that the two points $(0, 100,000)$ and $(10, 5000)$ are on the line. Then

$$m = \frac{5000 - 100,000}{10 - 0} = -9500$$

Then, using the point-slope form of a line,

$$V = -9500t + 100,000$$

where the time t is in years since the machine was purchased and V is the value in dollars. Now we can find the value at different time periods,

$$V(1) = -9500(1) + 100,000 = 90,500 \text{ or } \$90,500$$
$$V(2) = -9500(2) + 100,000 = 81,000 \text{ or } \$81,000$$
$$V(9) = -9500(9) + 100,000 = 14,500 \text{ or } \$14,500$$

The rate of depreciation is the slope of the line, –$9500/year.   ✦

✧ Technology Corner

⑨ Technology Note 1 **Example 1 on a Graphing Calculator**

Begin by pressing the Y= button on the top row of your calculator. Enter 12 from the keypad and the variable X using the X,T,θ,n button. The result is shown in Screen 1. Next choose the viewing window by pressing the WINDOW button along the top row of buttons. The smallest value for x is 0 (no steak specials sold), so enter 0 for Xmin. To evaluate the function for 12 steak specials, or $x = 12$, choose an Xmax that is greater than 12. We have chosen Xmax=20 and Xscl=5 (to have a tick mark is placed every 5 units on the X-axis). The range of values for y must be large enough to view the function. The Y range was set as Ymin=0, Ymax=200 and Yscl=10. The Xres setting can be left at 1 to have the full resolution on the screen. Screen 2 shows the window settings.

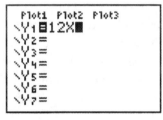

Screen 1

Screen 2

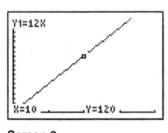

Screen 3

$[0, 20] \times [0, 200]$

Later the graphs will have the window listed under the graph as [Xmin, Xmax] × [Ymin, Ymax]. The choice of the Xscl and Yscl will be left to the reader. Press the GRAPH button to see the function displayed. To find the value of our function at a particular x-value, choose the CALC menu (above the TRACE button). Avoid the trace function as it will not go to an exact x-value. Choose the first option, 1:value and then enter the value 10. Pressing ENTER again to evaluate, we see in Screen 3 the value of the function at $x = 10$ is 120.

⑨ Technology Note 2 **Example 6 on a Graphing Calculator**

The depreciation function can be graphed as done in Technology Note 1 above. Screen 4 shows the result of graphing $Y_1 = -9500X + 100000$ and finding the value at X=2. We were asked to find the value of the grinding machine at several different times; the table function can be used to simplify this task. Once a function is entered, go to the TBLSET feature by pressing 2ND and then WINDOW (see Screen 5). We want to start at X=0 and count by 1's, so set TblStart = 0 and ΔTbl=1. To see the table, press 2ND and then GRAPH to access the TABLE function (see Screen 6).

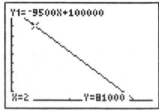

Screen 4

$[0, 12] \times [0, 100000]$

Screen 5

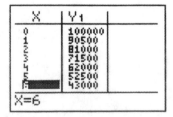

Screen 6

REMARK: You can also find a window by entering `Xmin=0` and `Xmax=10`, the known domain of this function, and then pressing `ZOOM` and scrolling to choose `0:ZoomFit`. This useful feature will evaluate the functions to be graphed from `Xmin` to `Xmax` and choose the values for `Ymin` and `Ymax` to allow the functions to be seen.

Self-Help Exercises 1.1

1. Rogers and Akridge of Purdue University studied fertilizer plants in Indiana. For a typical medium-sized plant they estimated fixed costs at $400,000 and estimated the cost of each ton of fertilizer was $200 to produce. The plant sells its fertilizer output at $250 per ton.

   a. Find and graph the cost, revenue, and profit equations.

   b. Determine the cost, revenue, and profits when the number of tons produced and sold is 5000, 7000, and 9000 tons.

   Source: Rogers and Akridge 1996

2. The excess supply and demand curves for wheat worldwide were estimated by Schmitz and coworkers to be

   Supply: $p = 7x - 400$

   Demand: $p = 510 - 3.5x$

   where p is price in dollars per metric ton and x is in millions of metric tons. Excess demand refers to the excess of wheat that producer countries have over their own consumption. Graph these two functions. Find the prices for the supply and demand models when x is 70 million metric tons. Is the price for supply or demand larger? Repeat these questions when x is 100 million metric tons.

   Source: Schmitz, Sigurdson, and Doering 1986

1.1 Exercises

In Exercises 1 and 2 you are given the cost per item and the fixed costs. Assuming a linear cost model, find the cost equation, where C is cost and x is the number produced.

1. Cost per item = $3, fixed cost=$10,000

2. Cost per item = $6, fixed cost=$14,000

In Exercises 3 and 4 you are given the price of each item, which is assumed to be constant. Find the revenue equation, where R is revenue and x is the number sold.

3. Price per item = $5

4. Price per item = $.10

5. Using the cost equation found in Exercise 1 and the revenue equation found in Exercise 3, find the profit equation for P, assuming that the number produced equals the number sold.

6. Using the cost equation found in Exercise 2 and the revenue equation found in Exercise 4, find the profit equation for P, assuming that the number produced equals the number sold.

In Exercises 7 to 10, find the demand equation using the given information.

7. A company finds it can sell 10 items at a price of $8 each and sell 15 items at a price of $6 each.

8. A company finds it can sell 40 items at a price of $60 each and sell 60 items at a price of $50 each.

9. A company finds that at a price of $35, a total of 100 items will be sold. If the price is lowered by $5, then 20 additional items will be sold.

10. A company finds that at a price of $200, a total of 30 items will be sold. If the price is raised $50, then 10 fewer items will be sold.

In Exercises 11 to 14, find the supply equation using the given information.

11. A supplier will supply 50 items to the market if the price is $95 per item and supply 100 items if the price is $175 per item.

12. A supplier will supply 1000 items to the market if the price is $3 per item and supply 2000 items if the price is $4 per item.

13. At a price of $60 per item, a supplier will supply 10 of these items. If the price increases by $20, then 4 additional items will be supplied.

14. At a price of $800 per item, a supplier will supply 90 items. If the price decreases by $50, then the supplier will supply 20 fewer items.

In Exercises 15 to 18, find the depreciation equation and corresponding domain using the given information.

15. A calculator is purchased for $130 and the value decreases by $15 per year for 7 years.

16. A violin bow is purchased for $50 and the value decreases by $5 per year for 6 years.

17. A car is purchased for $15,000 and is sold for $6000 six years later.

18. A car is purchased for $32,000 and is sold for $23,200 eight years later.

Applications

19. Wood Chipper Cost A contractor needs to rent a wood chipper for a day for $150 plus $10 per hour. Find the cost function.

20. Truck Rental Cost A builder needs to rent a dump truck for a day for $75 plus $.40 per mile. Find the cost function.

21. Sewing Machine Cost A shirt manufacturer is considering purchasing a sewing machine for $91,000 and it will cost $2 to sew each of their standard shirts. Find the cost function.

22. Copying Cost At Lincoln Library there are two ways to pay for copying. You can pay 5 cents a copy, or you can buy a plastic card for $5 and then pay 3 cents a copy. Let x be the number of copies you make. Write an equation for your costs for each way of paying.

23. Assume that the linear cost model applies and fixed costs are $1000. If the total cost of producing 800 items is $5000, find the cost equation.

24. Assume that the linear cost model applies. If the total cost of producing 1000 items at $3 each is $5000, find the cost equation.

25. When 50 silver beads are ordered they cost $1.25 each. If 100 silver beads are ordered, they cost $1.00 each. How much will each silver bead cost if 250 are ordered?

26. You find that when you order 75 magnets, the average cost per magnet is $.90 and when you order 200 magnets, the average cost per magnet is $.80. What is the cost equation for these custom magnets?

27. Assume that the linear revenue model applies. If the total revenue from selling 600 items is $7200, find the revenue equation.

28. Assume that the linear revenue model applies. If the total revenue from selling 1000 items is $8000, find the revenue equation.

29. Assume that the linear cost and revenue model applies. An item sells for $10. If fixed costs are $2000 and profits are $7000 when 1000 items are made and sold, find the cost equation.

30. Assume that the linear cost and revenue models applies. An item that costs $3 to make sells for $6. If profits of $5000 are made when 2000 items are made and sold, find the cost equation.

31. Assume that the linear cost and revenue models applies. Each additional item costs $3 to make. If fixed costs are $1000 and profits are $7000 when 1000 items are made and sold, find the revenue equation.

32. Assume that the linear cost and revenue models applies. An item costs $7 to make. If fixed costs are $1500 and profits are $1700 when 200 items are made and sold, find the revenue equation.

33. Demand for Blueberries A grocery store sells 27 packages of blueberries daily when the price is $3.18 per package. If the price is decreased by $.25 per package, then the store will sell an additional 5 packages every day. What is the demand equation for blueberries?

34. Demand for Bagels A bakery sells 124 bagels daily when the price is $1.50 per bagel. If the price is

increased by $.50, the bakery will sell 25 fewer bagels. What is the demand equation for bagels?

35. **Supply of Basil** A farmer is willing to supply 15 packages of organic basil to a market for $2 per package. If the market offers the farmer $1 more per package, the farmer will supply 20 more packages of organic basil. What is the supply equation for organic basil?

36. **Supply of Roses** A grower is willing to supply 200 long-stemmed roses per week to a florist for $.85 per rose. If the florist offers the grower $.20 less per rose, then the grower will supply 50 fewer roses. What is the supply equation for these long-stemmed roses?

37. **Machine Depreciation** Consider a new machine that costs $50,000 and has a useful life of nine years and a scrap value of $5000. Using straight-line depreciation, find the equation for the value V in terms of t, where t is in years. Find the value after one year and after five years.

38. **Building Depreciation** A new building that costs $1,100,000 has a useful life of 50 years and a scrap value of $100,000. Using straight-line depreciation, find the equation for the value V in terms of t, where t is in years. Find the value after 1 year, after 2 years, and after 40 years.

Referenced Applications

39. **Cotton Ginning Cost** Misra and colleagues estimated the cost function for the ginning industry in the Southern High Plains of Texas. They give a (total) cost function C by $C(x) = 21x + 674,000$, where C is in dollars and x is the number of bales of cotton. Find the fixed and variable costs.

Source: Misra, McPeek, and Segarra 2000

40. **Fishery Cost** The cost function for wild crayfish was estimated by Bell to be a function $C(x)$, where x is the number of millions of pounds of crayfish caught and C is the cost in millions of dollars. Two points that are on the graph are $(x, C) = (8, 0.157)$ and $(x, C) = (10, 0.190)$. Using this information and assuming a linear model, determine a cost function.

Source: Bell 1986

41. **Fender Costs** Saur and colleagues did a careful study of the cost of manufacturing automobile fenders. The fenders were made from five different materials: steel, aluminum, and three injection-molded polymer blends: rubber-modified polypropylene (RMP), nylon-polyphenylene oxide (NPN), and polycarbonate-polybutylene terephthalate (PPT). The following table gives the fixed and variable costs of manufacturing each pair of fenders.

Costs	Steel	Aluminum	RMP	NPN
Variable	$5.26	$12.67	$13.19	$9.53
Fixed	$260,000	$385,000	$95,000	$95,000

Write down the cost function associated with each of the materials.

Source: Saur, Fava, and Spatari 2000

42. **Cost of Raising a Steer** Kaitibie and colleagues estimated the costs of raising a young steer purchased for $428 and the variable food cost per day for $.67. Determine the cost function based on the number of days this steer is grown.

Source: Kaitibie, Epplin, Brorsen, Horn, Eugene G. Krenzer, and Paisley 2003

43. **Revenue for red wine grapes in Napa Valley** Brown and colleagues report that the price of red varieties of grapes in Napa Valley was $2274 per ton. Determine a revenue function and indicate the independent and dependent variables.

Source: Brown, Lynch, and Zilberman 2002

44. **Revenue for wine grapes in Napa Valley** Brown and colleagues report that the price of certain wine grapes in Napa Valley was $617 per ton. They estimated that 6 tons per acre was yielded. Determine a revenue function using the independent variable as the number of acres.

Source: Brown, Lynch, and Zilberman 2002

45. **Ecotourism Revenue** Velazquez and colleagues studied the economics of ecotourism. A grant of $100,000 was given to a certain locality to use to develop an ecotourism alternative to destroying forest and the consequent biodiversity. The community found that each visitor spent $40 on average. If x is the number of visitors, find a revenue function. How many visitors are needed to reach the initial $100,000 invested? (This community was experiencing about 5000 visits per year.)

Source: Velazquez, Bocco, and Torres 2001

46. **Heinz Ketchup Revenue** Besanko and colleagues reported that a Heinz ketchup 32-oz size yielded a

price of $.043 per ounce. Write an equation for revenue as a function of the number of 32-oz bottles of Heinz ketchup.

Source: Besanko, Dubé, and Gupta 2003

47. **Fishery Revenue** Grafton created a mathematical model for revenue for the northern cod fishery. We can see from this model that when 150,000 kilograms of cod were caught, $105,600 of revenue were yielded. Using this information and assuming a linear revenue model, find a revenue function R in units of $1000 where x is given in units of 1000 kilograms.

Source: Grafton, Sandal, and Steinhamn 2000

48. **Shrimp Profit** Kekhora and McCann estimated a cost function for a shrimp production function in Thailand. They gave the fixed costs per hectare of $1838 and the variable costs per hectare of $14,183. The revenue per hectare was given as $26,022

    a. Determine the total cost for 1 hectare.
    b. Determine the profit for 1 hectare.

Source: Kekhora and McCann 2003

49. **Rice Production Profit** Kekhora and McCann estimated a cost function for the rice production function in Thailand. They gave the fixed costs per hectare of $75 and the variable costs per hectare of $371. The revenue per hectare was given as $573.

    a. Determine the total cost for 1 hectare.
    b. Determine the profit for 1 hectare.

Source: Kekhora and McCann 2003

50. **Profit for Small Fertilizer Plants** In 1996 Rogers and Akridge of Purdue University studied fertilizer plants in Indiana. For a typical small-sized plant they estimated fixed costs at $235,487 and estimated that it cost $206.68 to produce each ton of fertilizer. The plant sells its fertilizer output at $266.67 per ton. Find the cost, revenue, and profit equations.

Source: Rogers and Akridge 1996

51. **Profit for Large Fertilizer Plants** In 1996 Rogers and Akridge of Purdue University studied fertilizer plants in Indiana. For a typical large-sized plant they estimated fixed costs at $447,917 and estimated that it cost $209.03 to produce each ton of fertilizer. The plant sells its fertilizer output at $266.67 per ton. Find the cost, revenue, and profit equations.

Source: Rogers and Akridge 1996

52. **Demand for Recreation** Shafer and others estimated a demand curve for recreational power boating in a number of bodies of water in Pennsylvania. They estimated the price p of a power boat trip including rental cost of boat, cost of fuel, and rental cost of equipment. For the Lake Erie/Presque Isle Bay Area they collected data indicating that for a price (cost) of $144, individuals made 10 trips, and for a price of $50, individuals made 20 trips. Assuming a linear model determine the demand curve. For 15 trips, what was the cost?

Source: Shafer, Upneja, Seo, and Yoon 2000

53. **Demand for Recreation** Shafer and others estimated a demand curve for recreational power boating in a number of bodies of water in Pennsylvania. They estimated the price p of a power boat trip including rental cost of boat, cost of fuel, and rental cost of equipment. For the Three Rivers Area they collected data indicating that for a price (cost) of $99, individuals made 10 trips, and for a price of $43, individuals made 20 trips. Assuming a linear model determine the demand curve. For 15 trips, what was the cost?

Source: Shafer, Upneja, Seo, and Yoon 2000

54. **Demand for Cod** Grafton created a mathematical model for demand for the northern cod fishery. We can see from this model that when 100,000 kilograms of cod were caught the price was $.81 per kilogram and when 200,000 kilograms of cod were caught the price was $.63 per kilogram. Using this information and assuming a linear demand model, find a demand function.

Source: Grafton, Sandal, and Steinhamn 2000

55. **Demand for Rice** Suzuki and Kaiser estimated the demand equation for rice in Japan to be $p = 1,195,789 - 0.1084753x$, where x is in tons of rice and p is in yen per ton. In 1995, the quantity of rice consumed in Japan was 8,258,000 tons.

    a. According to the demand equation, what was the price in yen per ton?
    b. What happens to the price of a ton of rice when the demand increases by 1 ton. What has this number to do with the demand equation?

Source: Suzuki and Kaiser 1998

56. **Supply of Childcare** Blau and Mocan gathered data over a number of states and estimated a supply curve that related quality of child care with price.

For quality q of child care they developed an index of quality and for price p they used their own units. In their graph they gave $q = S(p)$, that is, the price was the independent variable. On this graph we see the following points: $(p,q) = (1,2.6)$ and $(p,q) = (3,5.5)$. Use this information and assuming a linear model, determine the supply curve.

Source: Blau and Mocan 2002

57. **Oil Production Technology** The economics of conversion to saltwater injection for inactive wells in Texas was studied by D'Unger and coworkers. (By injecting saltwater into the wells, pressure is applied to the oil field, and oil and gas are forced out to be recovered.) The expense of a typical well conversion was estimated to be $31,750. The monthly revenue as a result of the conversion was estimated to be $2700. If x is the number of months the well operates after conversion, determine a revenue function as a function of x. How many months of operation would it take to recover the initial cost of conversion?

Source: D'Unger, Chapman, and Carr 1996

58. **Rail Freight** In a report of the Federal Trade Commission (FTC) an example is given in which the Portland, Oregon, mill price of 50,000 board square feet of plywood is $3525 and the rail freight is $0.3056 per mile.

   a. If a customer is located x rail miles from this mill, write an equation that gives the total freight f charged to this customer in terms of x for delivery of 50,000 board square feet of plywood.

   b. Write a (linear) equation that gives the total c charged to a customer x rail miles from the mill for delivery of 50,000 board square feet of plywood. Graph this equation.

   c. In the FTC report, a delivery of 50,000 board square feet of plywood from this mill is made to New Orleans, Louisiana, 2500 miles from the mill. What is the total charge?

Source: Gilligan 1992

Extensions

59. **Understanding the Revenue Equation** Assuming a linear revenue model, explain in a complete sentence where you expect the y-intercept to be. Give a reason for your answer.

60. **Understanding the Cost and Profit Equations** Assuming a linear cost and revenue model, explain in complete sentences where you expect the y-intercepts to be for the cost and profit equations. Give reasons for your answers.

61. **Demand Area** In the figure we see a demand curve with a point (a,b) on it. We also see a rectangle with a corner on this point. What do you think the area of this rectangle represents?

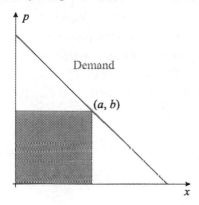

62. **Demand Curves for Customers** Price and Connor studied the difference between demand curves between loyal customers and nonloyal customers in ready-to-eat cereal. The figure shows two such as demand curves. (Note that the independent variable is the quantity.) Discuss the differences and the possible reasons. For example, why do you think that the p-intercept for the loyal demand curve is higher than the other? Why do you think the loyal demand is above the other? What do you think the producers should do to make their customers more loyal?

Source: Price and Connor 2003

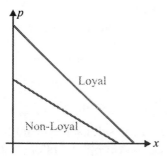

63. **Cost of Irrigation Water** Using an argument that is too complex to give here, Tolley and Hastings argued that if c is the cost in 1960 dollars per acre-foot of water in the area of Nebraska and x is the acre-feet of water available, then $c = 12$ when $x = 0$. They also noted that farms used about 2 acre-feet of water in the Ainsworth area when this water was free. If we assume (as they did) that the relationship

between c and x is linear, then find the equation that c and x must satisfy.

Source: Tolley and Hastings 1960

64. Kinked and Spiked Demand and Profit Curves Stiving determined demand curves. Note that a manufacturer can decide to produce a durable good with a varying quality.

  a. The figure shows a demand curve for which the quality of an item depends on the price. Explain if this demand curve seems reasonable.

  b. Notice that the demand curve is kinked and spiked at prices at which the price ends in the digit, such at $39.99. Explain why you think this could happen.

Source: Stiving 2000

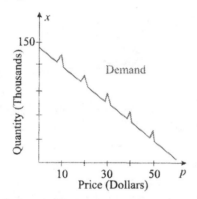

65. Profits for Kansas Beef Cow Farms Featherstone and coauthors studied 195 Kansas beef cow farms. The average fixed and variable costs are found in the following table.

Variable and Fixed Costs	
Costs per cow	
Feed costs	$261
Labor costs	$82
Utilities and fuel costs	$19
Veterinary expenses costs	$13
Miscellaneous costs	$18
Total variable costs	$393
Total fixed costs	$13,386

The farm can sell each cow for $470. Find the cost, revenue, and profit functions for an average farm. The average farm had 97 cows. What was the profit for 97 cows? Can you give a possible explanation for your answer?

Source: Featherstone, Langemeier, and Ismet 1997

66. Profit on Corn Roberts formulated a mathematical model of corn yield response to nitrogen fertilizer in high-yield response land given by $Y(N)$, where Y is bushels of corn per acre and N is pounds of nitrogen per acre. They estimated that the farmer obtains $2.42 for a bushel of corn and pays $.22 a pound for nitrogen fertilizer. For this model they assume that the only cost to the farmer is the cost of nitrogen fertilizer.

  a. We are given that $Y(20) = 47.8$ and $Y(120) = 125.8$. Find $Y(N)$.

  b. Find the revenue $R(N)$.

  c. Find the cost $C(N)$.

  d. Find the profit $P(N)$.

Source: Roberts, English, and Mahajashetti 2000

67. Profit in the Cereal Manufacturing Industry Cotterill estimated the costs and prices in the cereal-manufacturing industry. The table summarizes the costs in both pounds and tons in the manufacture of a typical cereal.

Item	$/lb	$/ton
Manufacturing cost:		
Grain	0.16	320
Other ingredients	0.20	400
Packaging	0.28	560
Labor	0.15	300
Plant costs	0.23	460
Total manufacturing costs	1.02	2040
Marketing expenses:		
Advertising	0.31	620
Consumer promo (mfr. coupons)	0.35	700
Trade promo (retail in-store)	0.24	480
Total marketing costs	0.90	1800
Total variable costs	1.92	3840

The manufacturer obtained a price of $2.40 a pound, or $4800 a ton. Let x be the number of tons of cereal manufactured and sold and let p be the price of a ton sold. Nero estimated fixed costs for a typical plant to be $300 million. Let the cost, revenue, and profits be given in thousands of dollars. Find the cost, revenue, and profit equations. Also make a table of values for cost, revenue, and profit for production levels of 200,000, 300,000 and 400,000 tons and discuss what the table of numbers is telling you.

Source: Cotterill and Haller 1997 and Nero 2001

Solutions to Self-Help Exercises 1.1

1. Let x be the number of tons of fertilizer produced and sold.

   a. Then the cost, revenue and profit equations are, in dollars,

   $$C(x) = (\text{variable cost}) + (\text{fixed cost}) = 200x + 400,000$$
   $$R(x) = (\text{price per ton}) \times (\text{number of tons sold}) = 250x$$
   $$P(x) = R - C = (250x) - (200x + 400,000) = 50x - 400,000$$

   The cost, revenue, and profit equations are graphed below.

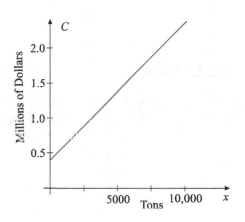 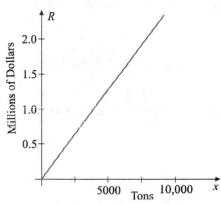 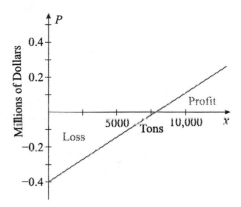

   b. If $x = 5000$, then

   $$C(5000) = 200(5000) + 400,000 = 1,400,000$$
   $$R(5000) = 250(5000) = 1,250,000$$
   $$P(5000) = 1,250,000 - 1,400,000 = -150,000$$

   If 5000 tons are produced and sold, the cost is $1,400,000, the revenue is $1,250,000, and there is a loss of $150,000. Doing the same for some other values of x, we have the following,

x	5000	7000	9000
Cost	1,400,000	1,800,000	2,200,000
Revenue	1,250,000	1,750,000	2,250,000
Profit (or loss)	−150,000	−50,000	50,000

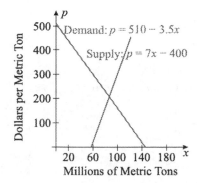

Millions of Metric Tons

2. The graphs are shown in the figure. When $x = 70$, we have

   supply: $p = 7(70) - 400 = 49$

   demand: $p = 510 - 3.5(70) = 265$

   Demand is larger. When $x = 100$, we have

   supply: $p = 7(100) - 400 = 300$

   demand: $p = 510 - 3.5(100) = 160$

   Supply is larger.

1.2   Systems of Linear Equations

APPLICATION
Cost, Revenue, and Profit Models

In Example 3 in the last section we found the cost and revenue equations in the dress-manufacturing industry. Let x be the number of dresses made and sold. Recall that cost and revenue functions were found to be $C(x) = 25x + 80,000$ and $R(x) = 75x$. Find the point at which the profit is zero. See Example 2 for the answer.

We now begin to look at systems of linear equations in many unknowns. In this section we first consider systems of two linear equations in two unknowns. We will see that solutions of such a system have a variety of applications.

✧ Two Linear Equations in Two Unknowns

In this section we will encounter applications that have a unique solution to a system of two linear equations in two unknowns. For example, consider two lines,

$$L_1 : y = m_1 x + b_1$$
$$L_2 : y = m_2 x + b_2$$

If these two linear equations are not parallel ($m_1 \neq m_2$), then the lines must intersect at a unique point, say (x_0, y_0) as shown in Figure 1.11.   This means that (x_0, y_0) is a solution to the two linear equations and must satisfy both of the equations

$$y_0 = m_1 x_0 + b_1$$
$$y_0 = m_2 x_0 + b_2$$

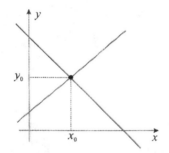

Figure 1.11

EXAMPLE 1   Intersection of Two Lines   Find the solution (intersection) of the two lines.

$$L_1 : y = 7x - 3$$
$$L_2 : y = -4x + 9$$

Solution   Set the two lines equal to each other, $L_1 = L_2$,

$$y_0 = y_0$$
$$7x_0 - 3 = 4x_0 + 9$$
$$11x_0 = 12$$
$$x_0 = \frac{12}{11}$$

To find the value of y_0, substitute the x_0 value into either equation,

$$y_0 = 7\left(\frac{12}{11}\right) - 3 = \frac{51}{11}$$

$$y_0 = 4\left(\frac{12}{11}\right) + 9 = \frac{51}{11}$$

Technology Option

Example 1 is solved using a graphing calculator in Technology Note 1 on page 25

So, the solution to this system is the intersection point $(12/11, 51/11)$.   ✦

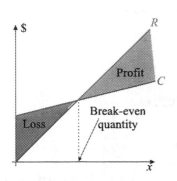

Figure 1.12

> 🖉 **Technology Option**
>
> Example 2 is solved using a graphing calculator in Technology Note 2 on page 25

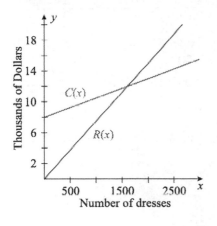

Figure 1.13

✧ Decision Analysis

In the last section we considered linear mathematical models of cost, revenue, and profit for a firm. In Figure 1.12 we see the graphs of two typical cost and revenue functions. We can see in this figure that for smaller values of x, the cost line is above the revenue line and therefore the profit P is negative. Thus the firm has losses. As x becomes larger, the revenue line becomes above the cost line and therefore the profit becomes positive. The value of x at which the profit is zero is called the break-even quantity. Geometrically, this is the point of intersection of the cost line and the revenue line. Mathematically, this requires us to solve the equations $y = C(x)$ and $y = R(x)$ simultaneously.

EXAMPLE 2 Finding the Break-Even Quantity In Example 3 in the last section we found the cost and revenue equations in a dress-manufacturing firm. Let x be the number of dresses manufactured and sold and let the cost and revenue be given in dollars. Then recall that the cost and revenue equations were found to be $C(x) = 25x + 80,000$ and $R(x) = 75x$. Find the break-even quantity.

Solution To find the break-even quantity, we need to solve the equations $y = C(x)$ and $y = R(x)$ simultaneously. To do this we set $R(x) = C(x)$,

$$R(x) = C(x)$$
$$75x = 25x + 80,000$$
$$50x = 80,000$$
$$x = 1600$$

Thus, the firm needs to produce and sell 1600 dresses to break even (i.e., for profits to be zero). See Figure 1.13. ◆

REMARK: Notice that $R(1600) = 120,000 = C(1600)$ so it costs the company $120,000 to make the dresses and they bring in $120,000 in revenue when the dresses are all sold.

In the following example we consider the total energy consumed by automobile fenders using two different materials. We need to decide how many miles carrying the fenders result in the same energy consumption and which type of fender will consume the least amount of energy for large numbers of miles.

EXAMPLE 3 Break-Even Analysis Saur and colleagues did a careful study of the amount of energy consumed by each type of automobile fender using various materials. The total energy was the sum of the energy needed for production plus the energy consumed by the vehicle used in carrying the fenders. If x is the miles traveled, then the total energy consumption equations for steel and rubber-modified polypropylene (RMP) were as follows:

$$\text{Steel: } E = 225 + 0.012x$$
$$\text{RPM: } E = 285 + 0.007x$$

Graph these equations, and find the number of miles for which the total energy consumed is the same for both fenders. Which material uses the least energy for 15,000 miles?

Source: Saur, Fava, and Spatari 2000

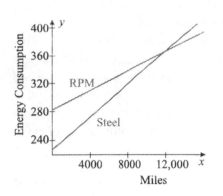

Figure 1.14

Solution   The total energy using steel is $E_1(x) = 225 + 0.012x$ and for RMP is $E_2(x) = 285 + 0.007x$. The graphs of these two linear energy functions are shown in Figure 1.14. We note that the graphs intersect. To find this intersection we set $E_1(x) = E_2(x)$ and obtain

$$E_1(x) = E_2(x)$$
$$225 + 0.012x = 285 + 0.007x$$
$$0.005x = 60$$
$$x = 12,000$$

So, 12,000 miles results in the total energy used by both materials being the same.

Setting $x = 0$ gives the energy used in production, and we note that steel uses less energy to produce these fenders than does RMP. However, since steel is heavier than RMP, we suspect that carrying steel fenders might require more total energy when the number of pair of fenders is large. Indeed, we see in Figure 1.14 that the graph corresponding to steel is above that of RMP when $x > 12,000$. Checking this for $x = 15,000$, we have

$$\text{steel:} \qquad E_1(x) = 225 + 0.012x$$
$$E_1(15,000) = 225 + 0.012(15,000)$$
$$= 405$$
$$\text{RMP:} \qquad E_2(x) = 285 + 0.007x$$
$$E_2(15,000) = 285 + 0.007(15,000)$$
$$= 390$$

So for traveling 15,000 miles, the total energy used by RMP is less than that for steel.   ◆

✧ Supply and Demand Equilibrium

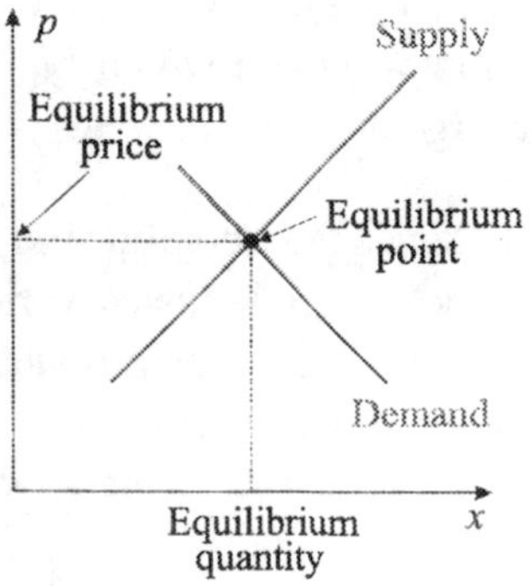

The best-known law of economics is the law of supply and demand. Figure 1.15 shows a demand equation and a supply equation that intersect. The point of intersection, or the point at which supply equals demand, is called the equilibrium point. The x-coordinate of the equilibrium point is called the equilibrium quantity, x_0, and the p-coordinate is called the equilibrium price, p_0. In other words, at a price p_0, the consumer is willing to buy x_0 items and the producer is willing to supply x_0 items.

EXAMPLE 4   **Finding the Equilibrium Point**   Tauer determined demand and supply curves for milk in this country. If x is billions of pounds of milk and p is in dollars per hundred pounds, he found that the demand function for milk was $p = D(x) = 56 - 0.3x$ and the supply function was $p = S(x) = 0.1x$. Graph the demand and supply equations. Find the equilibrium point.

Source: Tauer 1994

Figure 1.15

Solution   The demand equation $p = D(x) = 56 - 0.3x$ is a line with negative slope -0.3 and y-intercept 56 and is graphed in Figure 1.16. The supply equation $p = S(x) = 0.1x$ is a line with positive slope 0.1 with y-intercept 0. This is also graphed in Figure 1.16.

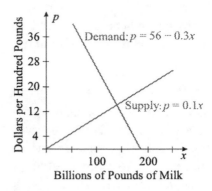

Figure 1.16

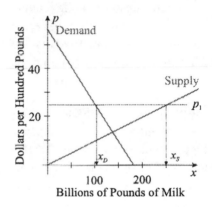

Figure 1.17a

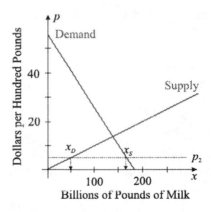

Figure 1.17b

To find the point of intersection of the demand curve and the supply curve, set $S(x) = D(x)$ and solve:

$$S(x) = D(x)$$
$$0.1x = 56 - 0.3x$$
$$0.4x = 56$$
$$x = 140$$

Then since $p(x) = 0.1x$,

$$p(140) = 0.1(140) = 14$$

We then see that the equilibrium point is $(x, p) = (140, 14)$. That is, 140 billions pounds of milk at \$14 per hundred pounds of milk. ✦

EXAMPLE 5   Supply and Demand   Refer to Example 4. What will consumers and suppliers do if the price is $p_1 = 25$ shown in Figure 1.17a? What if the price is $p_2 = 5$ as shown in Figure 1.17b?

Solution   If the price is at $p_1 = 25$ shown in Figure 1.17a, then let the supply of milk be denoted by x_S. Let us find x_S.

$$p = S(x_S)$$
$$25 = 0.1x_S$$
$$x_S = 250$$

That is, 250 billion pounds of milk will be supplied. Keeping the same price of $p_1 = 25$ shown in Figure 1.17a, then let the demand of milk be denoted by x_D. Let us find x_D. Then

$$p = D(x_D)$$
$$25 = 56 - 0.3x_D$$
$$x_D \approx 103$$

So only 103 billions of pounds of milk are demanded by consumers. There will be a surplus of $250 - 103 = 147$ billions of pounds of milk. To work off the surplus, the price should fall toward the equilibrium price of $p_0 = 14$.

If the price is at $p_2 = 5$ shown in Figure 1.17b, then let the supply of milk be denoted by x_S. Let us find x_S. Then

$$p = S(x_S)$$
$$5 = 0.1x_S$$
$$x_S = 50$$

That is, 50 billion pounds of milk will be supplied. Keeping the same price of $p_2 = 5$ shown in Figure 1.17b, then let the demand of milk be denoted by x_D. Let us find x_D. Then

$$p = D(x_D)$$
$$5 = 56 - 0.3x_D$$
$$x_D \approx 170$$

So 170 billions of pounds of milk are demanded by consumers. There will be a shortage of $170 - 50 = 120$ billions of pounds of milk, and the price should rise toward the equilibrium price. ✦

CONNECTION
Demand for Steel Outpaces Supply

In early 2002 President George W. Bush imposed steep tariffs on imported steel to protect domestic steel producers. As a result millions of tons of imported steel were locked out of the country. Domestic steelmakers announced on March 27, 2002, that they had been forced to ration steel to their customers and boost prices because demand has outpaced supply.
Source: Wall Street Journal

✧ Enrichment: Decision Analysis Complications

In the following example we look at the cost of manufacturing automobile fenders using two different materials. We determine the number of pairs of fenders that will be produced by using the same cost. However, we must keep in mind that we do not produce fractional numbers of fenders, but rather only whole numbers. For example, we can produce one or two pairs of fenders, but not 1.43 pairs.

EXAMPLE 6 **Decision Analysis for Manufacturing Fenders** Saur and colleagues did a careful study of the cost of manufacturing automobile fenders using two different materials: steel and a rubber-modified polypropylene blend (RMP). The following table gives the fixed and variable costs of manufacturing each pair of fenders.

Variable and Fixed Costs of Pairs of Fenders

Costs	Steel	RMP
Variable	$5.26	$13.19
Fixed	$260,000	$95,000

Graph the cost function for each material. Find the number of fenders for which the cost of each material is the same. Which material will result in the lowest cost if a large number of fenders are manufactured?
Source: Saur, Fava, and Spataru 2000

Solution The cost function for steel is $C_1(x) = 5.26x + 260,000$ and for RMP is $C_2(x) = 13.19x + 95,000$. The graphs of these two cost functions are shown in Figure 1.18.

For a small number of fenders, we see from the graph that the cost for steel is greater than that for RMP. However, for a large number of fenders the cost for steel is less. To find the number of pairs that yield the same cost for each material, we need to solve $C_2(x) = C_1(x)$.

$$C_2(x) = C_1(x)$$
$$13.19x + 95,000 = 5.26x + 260,000$$
$$7.93x = 165,000$$
$$x = 20,807.062$$

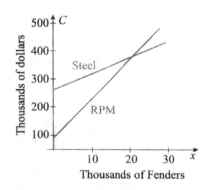

Figure 1.18

This is a real application, so only an integer number of fenders can be manufactured. We need to round off the answer given above and obtain 20,807 pair of fenders.   ◆

REMARK: Note that $C_2(20,807) = 369,444.44$ and $C_1(20,807) = 369,444.82$. The two values are not exactly equal.

✦ Technology Corner

⑨Technology Note 1   **Example 1 on a Graphing Calculator**

Begin by entering the two lines as Y_1 and Y_2. Choose a window where the intersection point is visible. To find the exact value of the intersection, go to CALC (via 2nd TRACE) and choose 5:intersect. You will be prompted to select the lines. Press ENTER for "First curve?", "Second curve?", and "Guess?". The intersection point will be displayed as in Screen 1. To avoid rounding errors, the intersection point must be converted to a fraction. To do this, QUIT to the home screen using 2ND and MODE . Then press X,T,θ,n , then the MATH button, as shown in Screen 2. Choose 1:▷Frac and then ENTER to convert the x-value of the intersection to a fraction, see Screen 3. To convert the y-value to a fraction, press ALPHA then 1 to get the variable Y. Next the MATH and 1:▷Frac to see Y as a fraction.

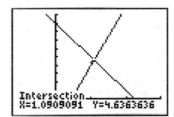

Screen 1

$[-1,\ 3] \times [-1,\ 10]$

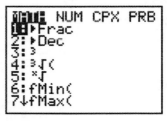

Screen 2

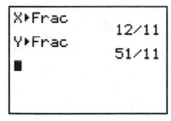

Screen 3

⑨Technology Note 2   **Example 2 on a Graphing Calculator**

You can find the break-even quantity in Example 2 on your graphing calculator by finding where $P = 0$ or by finding where $C = R$. Begin by entering the revenue and cost equations into Y_1 and Y_2. You can subtract these two on paper to find the profit equation or have the calculator find the difference, as shown in Screen 1.10. To access the names Y_1 and Y_2, press the VARS , then right arrow to Y-VARS and ENTER to select 1:Function then choose Y_1 or Y_2, as needed.

The intersection can be found in the same manner as Technology Note 1. To find where the profit is zero, return to the CALC menu and choose 2:zero. Note you will initially be on the line Y_1. Use the down arrow twice to be on Y_3. Then use the left or right arrows to move to the left side of the zero of Y_3 and hit ENTER to answer the question "Left Bound?". Right arrow over to the right side of the place where Y_3 crosses the x-axis and hit ENTER to answer the question "Right Bound?". Place your cursor between these two spots and press ENTER to answer the last question, "Guess?". The result is shown in Screen 6.

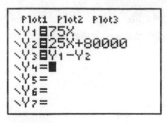

Screen 4

$[0, 2500] \times [-80000, 160000]$

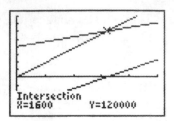

Screen 5

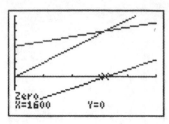

Screen 6

Self-Help Exercises 1.2

1. Rogers and Akridge of Purdue University studied fertilizer plants in Indiana. For a typical medium-sized plant they estimated fixed costs at $400,000 and estimated that it cost $200 to produce each ton of fertilizer. The plant sells its fertilizer output at $250 per ton. Find the break-even point. (Refer to Self-Help Exercise 1 in Section 1.1.)

Source: Rogers and Akridge 1996

2. The excess supply and demand curves for wheat worldwide were estimated by Schmitz and coworkers to be

Supply: $p = S(x) = 7x - 400$

Demand: $p = D(x) = 510 - 3.5x$

where p is price per metric ton and x is in millions of metric tons. Excess demand refers to the excess of wheat that producer countries have over their own consumption. Graph and find the equilibrium price and equilibrium quantity.

Source: Schmitz, Sigurdson, and Doering 1986

1.2 Exercises

Exercises 1 through 4, show linear cost and revenue equations. Find the break-even quantity.

1. $C = 2x + 4$, $R = 4x$

2. $C = 3x + 10$, $R = 6x$

3. $C = 0.1x + 2$, $R = 0.2x$

4. $C = 0.03x + 1$, $R = 0.04x$

In Exercises 5 through 8, you are given a demand equation and a supply equation. Find the equilibrium point.

5. Demand: $p = -x + 6$, supply: $p = x + 3$

6. Demand: $p = -3x + 12$, supply: $p = 2x + 5$

7. Demand: $p = -10x + 25$, supply: $p = 5x + 10$

8. Demand: $p = -0.1x + 2$, supply: $p = 0.2x + 1$

Applications

9. **Break-Even for Purses** A firm has weekly fixed costs of $40,000 associated with the manufacture of purses that cost $15 per purse to produce. The firm sells all the purses it produces at $35 per purse. Find the cost, revenue, and profit equations. Find the break-even quantity.

10. **Break-Even for Lawn Mowers** A firm has fixed costs of $1,000,000 associated with the manufacture of lawn mowers that cost $200 per mower to produce. The firm sells all the mowers it produces at $300 each. Find the cost, revenue, and profit equations. Find the break-even quantity.

11. **Rent or Buy Decision Analysis** A forester has the need to cut many trees and to chip the branches. On the one hand he could, when needed, rent a large wood chipper to chip branches and logs up to 12 inches in diameter for $320 a day. Since he has a large amount of work to do, he is considering purchasing a new 12-inch wood chipper for $28,000. He estimates that he will need to spend $40 on maintenance per every day of use.

a. Let d be the number of days he will use a wood chipper. Write a formula that gives him the total cost of renting for d days.

b. Write a formula that gives him the total cost of buying and maintaining the wood chipper for d days of use.

c. If the forester estimates he will need to use the chipper for 120 days, should he buy or rent?

d. Determine the number of days of use before the forester can save as much money by buying the chipper as opposed to renting.

12. **Decision Analysis for Making Copies** At Lincoln Library there are two ways to pay for copying. You can pay 5 cents a copy, or you can buy a plastic card for $5 and then pay 3 cents a copy. Let x be the number of copies you make. Write an equation for your costs for each way of paying.

a. How many copies do you need to make before buying the plastic card is the same as cash?

b. If you wish to make 300 copies, which way of paying has the least cost?

13. **Energy Decision Analysis** Many home and business owners in northern Ohio can successfully drill for natural gas on their property. They have the choice of obtaining natural gas free from their own gas well or buying the gas from a utility company. A garden center would need to buy $5000 worth of gas each year from the local utility company to heat their greenhouses. They determine that the cost of drilling a small commercial gas well for the garden center will be $40,000 and they assume that their well will need $1000 of maintenance each year.

a. Write a formula that gives the cost of the natural gas bought from the utility for x years.

b. Write a formula that gives the cost of obtaining the natural gas from their well over x years.

c. How many years will it be before the cost of gas from the utility equals the cost of gas from the well?

> **CONNECTION:** We know an individual living in a private home in northern Ohio who had a gas and oil well drilled some years ago. The well yields both natural gas and oil. Both products go into a splitter that separates the natural gas and the oil. The oil goes into a large tank and is sold to a local utility. The natural gas is used to heat the home and the excess is fed into the utility company pipes, where it is measured and purchased by the utility.

14. **Compensation Decision Analysis** A salesman for carpets has been offered two possible compensation plans. The first offers him a monthly salary of $2000 plus a royalty of 10% of the total dollar amount of sales he makes. The second offers him a monthly salary of $1000 plus a royalty of 20% of the total dollar amount of sales he makes.

a. Write a formula that gives each compensation package as a function of the dollar amount x of sales he makes.

b. Suppose he believes he can sell $15,000 of carpeting each month. Which compensation package should he choose?

c. How much carpeting will he sell each month if he earns the same amount of money with either compensation package?

15. **Truck Rental Decision Analysis** A builder needs to rent a dump truck from Acme Rental for $75 plus $.40 per mile or the same one from Bell Rental for $105 plus $.25 per mile. Find a cost function for using each rental firm.

a. Find the number of miles for which each cost function will give the same cost.

b. If the builder wants to rent a dump truck to use for 150 miles, which rental place will cost less?

16. **Wood Chipper Rental Decision Analysis** A contractor wants to rent a wood chipper from Acme Rental for a day for $150 plus $10 per hour or from Bell Rental for a day for $165 plus $7 per hour. Find a cost function for using each rental firm.

a. Find the number of hours for which each cost function will give the same cost.

b. If the contractor wants to rent the chipper for 8 hours, which rental place will cost less?

17. **Make or Buy Decision** A company includes a manual with each piece of software it sells and is trying to decide whether to contract with an outside

supplier to produce it or to produce it in-house. The lowest bid of any outside supplier is $.75 per manual. The company estimates that producing the manuals in-house will require fixed costs of $10,000 and variable costs of $.50 per manual. Find the number of manuals resulting in the same cost for contracting with the outside supplier and producing in-house. If 50,000 manuals are needed, should the company go with outside supplier or go in-house?

18. **Decision Analysis for a Sewing Machine** A shirt manufacturer is considering purchasing a standard sewing machine for $91,000 and for which it will cost $2 to sew each of their standard shirts. They are also considering purchasing a more efficient sewing machine for $100,000 and for which it will cost $1.25 to sew each of their standard shirts. Find a cost function for purchasing and using each machine.

    a. Find the number of hours for which each cost function will give the same cost.

    b. If the manufacturer wishes to sew 10,000 shirts, which machine should they purchase?

19. **Equilibrium Point for Organic Carrots** A farmer will supply 8 bunches of organic carrots to a restaurant at a price of $2.50 per bunch. If he can get $.25 more per bunch, he will supply 10 bunches. The restaurant's demand for organic carrot bunches is given by $p = D(x) = -0.1x + 6$, where x is the number of bunches of organic carrots. What is the equilibrium point?

20. **Equilibrium Point for Cinnamon Rolls** A baker will supply 16 jumbo cinnamon rolls to a cafe at a price of $1.70 each. If she is offered $1.50, then she will supply 4 fewer rolls to the cafe. The cafe's demand for jumbo cinnamon rolls is given by $p = D(x) = -0.16x + 7.2$. What is the equilibrium point?

Referenced Applications

21. **Break-Even Quantity for Rice Production in Thailand** Kekhora and McCann estimated a cost function for the rice production function in Thailand. They gave the fixed costs per hectare of $75 and the variable costs per hectare of $371. The revenue per hectare was given as $573. Suppose the price for rice went down. What would be the minimum price to charge per hectare to determine the break-even quantity?

Source: Kekhora and McCann 2003

22. **Break-Even Quantity for Shrimp Production in Thailand** Kekhora and McCann estimated a cost function for a shrimp production function in Thailand. They gave the fixed costs per hectare of $1838 and the variable costs per hectare of $14,183. The revenue per hectare was given as $26,022. Suppose the price for shrimp went down. What would be the revenue to determine the break-even quantity?

Source: Kekhora and McCann 2003

23. **Break-Even Quantity for Small Fertilizer Plants** In 1996 Rogers and Akridge of Purdue University studied fertilizer plants in Indiana. For a typical small-sized plant they estimated fixed costs at $235,487 and estimated that it cost $206.68 to produce each ton of fertilizer. The plant sells its fertilizer output at $266.67 per ton. Find the break-even quantity.

Source: Rogers and Akridge 1996

24. **Break-Even Quantity for Large Fertilizer Plants** In 1996 Rogers and Akridge of Purdue University studied fertilizer plants in Indiana. For a typical large-sized plant they estimated fixed costs at $447,917 and estimated that it cost $209.03 to produce each ton of fertilizer. The plant sells its fertilizer output at $266.67 per ton. Find the break-even quantity.

Source: Rogers and Akridge 1996

25. **Break-Even Quantity on Kansas Beef Cow Farms** Featherstone and coauthors studied 195 Kansas beef cow farms. The average fixed and variable costs are in the following table.

Variable and Fixed Costs	
Costs per cow	
Feed costs	$261
Labor costs	$82
Utilities and fuel costs	$19
Veterinary expenses costs	$13
Miscellaneous costs	$18
Total variable costs	$393
Total fixed costs	$13,386

The farm can sell each cow for $470. Find the break-even quantity.

Source: Featherstone, Langemeier, and Ismet 1997

In Exercises 26 and 27 use the following information. In the Saur study of fenders mentioned in Exercise 41 of Section 1.1, the amount of energy consumed by each type of fender was also analyzed. The total energy was the sum of the energy needed for production plus the energy consumed by the vehicle used in carrying the fenders. If x is the miles traveled, then the total energy consumption equations for steel, aluminum, and NPN were as follows:

Steel: $E = 225 + 0.012x$

Al: $E = 550 + 0.007x$

NPN: $E = 565 + 0.007x$

26. Find the number of miles traveled for which the total energy consumed is the same for steel and NPN fenders. If 6000 miles is traveled, which material would use the least energy?

27. Find the number of miles traveled for which the total energy consumed is the same for steel and aluminum fenders. If 5000 miles is traveled, which material would use the least energy?

For Exercises 28 and 29 refer to the following information. In the Saur study of fenders mentioned in Example 3, the amount of CO_2 emissions in kg per 2 fenders of the production and utilization into the air of each type of fender was also analyzed. The total CO_2 emissions was the sum of the emissions from production plus the emissions from the vehicle used to carry the fenders. If x is the miles traveled, then the total CO_2 emission equations for steel, aluminum, and NPN were as follows:

Steel: $CO_2 = 21 + 0.00085x$

Aluminum: $CO_2 = 43 + 0.00045x$

NPN: $CO_2 = 23 + 0.00080x$

28. Find the number of miles for which the total CO_2 emissions is the same for both steel and aluminum fenders. If 60,000 miles are traveled, which material would yield the least $CO2_2$

29. Find the number of miles for which the total CO_2 emissions is the same for both steel and NPN fenders. If 30,000 miles are traveled, which material would yield the least CO_2?

30. **Supply and Demand for Milk** Demand and supply equations for milk were given by Tauer. In this paper he estimated demand and supply equations for bovine somatotropin-produced milk. The demand equation is $p = 55.9867 - 0.3249x$, and the supply equation is $p = 0.07958x$, where again p is the price in dollars per hundred pounds and x is the amount of milk measured in billions of pounds. Find the equilibrium point.

Source: Tauer 1994

31. **Facility Location** A company is trying to decide whether to locate a new plant in Houston or Boston. Information on the two possible locations is given in the following table. The initial investment is in land, buildings, and equipment.

	Houston	Boston
Variable cost	$.25 per item	$.22 per item
Fixed costs	$4,000,000	$4,210,000
Initial investment	$17,200,000	$20,000,000

a. Find which city has the lower annual total costs, not counting the initial investment, when 5,000,000 and 10,000,000 items are produced each year.

b. Find the number of items that yield the same cost for each city, when not counting the initial investment.

32. **Facility Location** Use the information found in the previous exercise.

a. Determine which city has the lower total cost over five years, counting the initial investment if 10,000,000 items are produced each year.

b. Find the number of items yielding the same cost for each city counting the initial investment.

Extensions

For Exercises 33 through 36, consider the following study. As mentioned in Example 3 Saur and colleagues did a careful study of the cost of manufacturing automobile fenders using five different materials: steel, aluminum (Al), and three injection-molded polymer blends: rubber-modified polypropylene (RMP), nylon-polyphenylene oxide (NPN), and polycarbonate-polybutylene terephthalate (PPT). The following table gives the fixed and variable costs of manufacturing each pair of fenders. Note that only an integer number of pairs of fenders can be counted.

Variable and Fixed Costs of Pairs of Fenders

Costs	Steel	Al	RMP	NPN	PPT
Variable	$5.26	$12.67	$13.19	$9.53	$12.55
Fixed	$260,000	$385,000	$95,000	$95,000	$95,000

33. How many pairs of fenders are required for the cost of the aluminum ones to equal the cost of the RMP ones?

34. How many pairs of fenders are required for the cost of the steel ones to equal the cost of the NPN ones?

35. How many pairs of fenders are required for the cost of the steel ones to equal the cost of the PPT ones?

36. How many pairs of fenders are required for the cost of the steel ones to equal the cost of the RMP ones?

37. **Process Selection and Capacity** A machine shop needs to drill holes in a certain plate. An inexpensive manual drill press could be purchased that will require large labor costs to operate, or an expensive automatic press can be purchased that will require small labor costs to operate. The following table summarizes the options.

Machine	Annual Fixed Costs	Variable Labor Costs	Production plates/hr
Manual	$1000	$16.00/hour	10
Automatic	$8000	$2.00/hour	100

Suppose these are the only fixed and variable costs.

a. What does it cost to make 10,000 plates in a year using the manual drill press and using the automatic drill press?

b. Find the number of plates produced per year for which the manual and automatic drill presses will cost the same.

38. **Decision Analysis** Roberts formulated a mathematical model of corn yield response to nitrogen fertilizer in high-yield response land and low-yield response land. They estimated a profit equation $P = f(N)$ that depended only on the number of pounds of nitrogen fertilizer per acre used. For the high-yield response land they estimated that $P = H(N) = 0.17N + 96.6$ and for the low-yield response land they estimated that $P = L(N) = 0.48N + 26.0$. A farmer has both types of land in two separate fields but does not have the time to use both fields. How much nitrogen will result in each response land yielding the same profit? Which field should be selected if 250 pounds of nitrogen is used?

Source: Roberts, English, and Mahajashetti 2000

Solutions to Self-Help Exercises 1.2

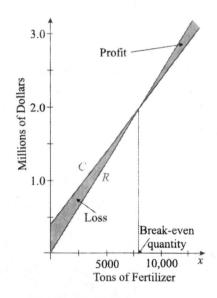

Millions of Dollars — Tons of Fertilizer

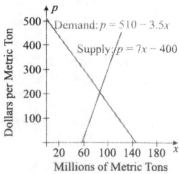

Dollars per Metric Ton — Millions of Metric Tons

1. Let x be the number of tons of fertilizer produced and sold. Then the cost and revenue equations are

$$C(x) = (\text{variable cost}) + (\text{fixed cost}) = 200x + 400{,}000$$
$$R(x) = (\text{price per ton}) \times (\text{number of tons sold}) = 250x$$

The cost and revenue equations are graphed in the figure. To find the break-even quantity set $C(x) = R(x)$ and solve for x:

$$R(x) = C(x)$$
$$250x = 200x + 400{,}000$$
$$50x = 400{,}000$$
$$x = 8000$$

Thus, the plant needs to produce and sell 8000 tons of fertilizer to break-even (i.e., for profits to be zero).

2. The graphs are shown in the figure. To find the equilibrium price, set $D(p) = S(p)$ and obtain

$$D(p) = S(p)$$
$$510 - 3.5x = 7x - 400$$
$$10.5x = 910$$
$$x \approx 86.7$$

With $x = 86.7$, $p = D(86.7) = 510 - 3.5(86.7) \approx 207$. The equilibrium price is $207 per metric ton, and the equilibrium quantity is 86.7 million metric tons.

1.3 Gauss Elimination for Systems of Linear Equations

In the previous section we considered systems of linear equations that had two variables and two equations. In this section we look at larger systems of linear equations that have unique solutions. Systems with no solution or non-unique solutions are covered in Section 1.4. To solve these larger systems we will develop the method of Gauss elimination, an efficient and systematic manner of finding the solution to systems of linear equations. For example, consider the following system of linear equations:

$$\begin{aligned} x + 2y + 7z &= 14 \\ x - 3y + 2z &= 4 \\ 2x - y - 3z &= -5 \end{aligned}$$

Our method is to first eliminate the x variable from all the equations below the first. Then eliminate the y variable from the equation below the second, and so forth. After this, we are left with a system like the following:

$$\begin{aligned} x + 2y + 7z &= 14 \\ y - z &= 2 \\ z &= 1 \end{aligned}$$

We notice that we have found that $z = 1$. We now use backward substitution. That is, the value for z substituted into the next to the last equation. We can solve for the y variable and then substitute the values for y and z into the first equation and solve for x. In the discussion below we will determine an efficient and systematical manner of preparing the system for backward substitution.

✧ Creating Systems of Linear Equations

In the first example we examine how to translate English sentences into equations. Nearly all word problems follow a similar format. First you are given some information and then you are asked "How much?" or "How many?". Always begin your work on a word problem by clearly defining your variables — they are the answer to the "How much?" or "How many?" question you were asked. The next step is to take the given information and translate it into an equation using the variables you defined. A table or diagram is often helpful to organize the information.

EXAMPLE 1 Document Scheduling An insurance company has two types of documents to process: contracts and leases. Each contract needs to be examined for 2 hours by the accountant and 3 hours by the attorney, while each lease needs to be examined for 4 hours by the accountant and 1 hour by the attorney. If the accountant has 40 hours and the attorney 30 hours each week to spend working on these documents, how many documents of each type can they process?

Solution The question asked is "how many documents of each type?". This indicates what the unknowns are: the number of contracts and the number of leases. So let

$$x = \text{the number of contracts}$$
$$y = \text{the number of leases}$$

Since there are x contracts and the accountant spends 2 hours per week on each of these, the accountant spends $2x$ hours per week on contracts. The attorney spends $3x$ hours per week on contracts. There are y leases and the accountant spends 4 hours per week on each of these, so the accountant spends $4y$ hours per week on leases and the attorney spends y hours per week on leases.

Let us now create a table that summarizes all of the given information. When we organize information in a table note that we have written the conditions we must obey in a row. The first row in the table summarizes in mathematical notation how the accountant spends her time and the second row summarizes how the attorney spends his time.

	Contracts	Leases	Total
Accountant time	$2x$	$4y$	40 hours
Attorney time	$3x$	y	30 hours

The accountant spends $2x + 4y$ hours on these two documents and this must equal the total available accountant time which is 40. So the first equation must be

$$2x + 4y = 40$$

The attorney spends $3x + y$ hours on these two documents and this must equal the total available attorney time which is 30. So the second equation must be

$$3x + y = 30$$

We then have the system of equations

$$2x + 4y = 40 \quad \text{accountant hours}$$
$$3x + y = 30 \quad \text{attorney hours}$$

The solution of this system will then tell us the number contracts and leases processed per week. ◆

✧ Gauss Elimination With Two Equations

Let us now solve this system we found in Example 1. There are several basic ways of solving such a system. First, we could solve each equation for y and have $y = -(1/2)x + 10$ and $y = -3x + 30$. As in the last section we can set $-(1/2)x + 10 = -3x + 30$ and solve for x. This method will only work for systems with two variables.

Another basic way of solving this system of equations is to use substitution. For example, we could solve for y in the second equation and obtain $y = 30 - 3x$. Then substitute this into the first equation to obtain $2x + 4(30 - 3x) = 40$. Now solve for x. We then find y, since $y = 30 - 3x$. The method works well when we have two equations with two unknowns, but becomes cumbersome and not very useful when applied to systems with more than two equations and two unknowns.

We need a systematic method that will always work, no matter how complicated the system. Such a method is Gauss elimination with backward substitution. This method will serve us well in subsequent sections. The strategy begins with eliminating x from the second equation. To make this easier, we wish to have the coefficient of x in the first equation equal to 1. To do this simply divide the first equation by 2 to get the system S1,

$$x + 2y = 20$$
$$3x + y = 30 \tag{S1}$$

Now we more readily see how to eliminate x from the second equation. We multiply the first equation by -3, written -3(first), and add this to the second equation to get a new second equation. We have

$$-3(\text{first}) : -3x - 6y = -60$$
$$+(\text{second}) : 3x + y = 30$$
$$\overline{ - 5y = -30}$$

This last equation is the new second equation. We now have the system as

$$x + 2y = 20$$
$$ - 5y = -30$$

Notice that we have eliminated the x variable from the second equation. We then divide the last equation by -5 and obtain

$$x + 2y = 20$$
$$y = 6$$

We have $y = 6$. Now substitute this back into the first equation and obtain

$$x + 2y = 20$$
$$x + 2(6) = 20$$
$$x - 20 - 12 = 8$$

We then have the solution $(x,y) = (8,6)$. This means that eight of the contracts documents can be processed and six of the leases.

When we manipulated the equations in Example 1, we followed three basic rules that allowed us to change the system of equations from one form to another form with the same solution as the original system. But it was easy to determine the solution in the new system. For convenience we will denote the first equation by E_1, the second equation by E_2, the third equation by E_3, and so forth. The rules that must be followed are below.

Elementary Equation Operations

1. Two equations can be interchanged, $E_i \leftrightarrow E_j$.

2. An equation may be multiplied by a non-zero constant,

   $kE_i \rightarrow E_i$.

3. A multiple of one equation may be added to another equation, $E_i + kE_j \rightarrow E_i$.

Gauss elimination is the systematic use of these three allowed operations to put the system of equations into an easily solved form.

✦ Gauss Elimination

We will now develop Gauss elimination for a system with any number of equations with any number of unknowns. In this section we continue to restrict ourselves to examples for which there is a unique solution. We will consider the case when there is no solution or are infinitely many solutions in the next section. First we solve a system of three equations with three unknowns.

EXAMPLE 2 Scheduling Shirts A firm produces three products, a dress shirt, a casual shirt, and a sport shirt, and uses a cutting machine, a sewing machine, and a packaging machine in the process. To produce each gross[1] of dress shirts requires 3 hours on the cutting machine and 2 hours on the sewing machine. To produce each gross of casual shirts requires 5 hours on the cutting machine and 1 hour on the sewing machine. To produce each gross of sport shirts requires 7 hours on the cutting machine and 3 hours on the sewing machine. It takes 2 hours to package each gross of each type of shirt. If the cutting machine is available for 480 hours, the sewing machine for 170 hours, and the packaging machine for 200 hours, how many gross of each type of shirt should be produced to use all of the available time on the three machines?

Solution We are asked "how many gross of each type of shirt should be produced?" So begin by defining the variables. Let

x = the number of gross of dress shirts made
y = the number of gross of casual shirts made
z = the number of gross of sport shirts made

We then create a table that summarizes all of the given information. Once again we will have each row of the table represent how a condition is fulfilled. The first row shows how the time is used on the packaging machine, the second shows the time on the cutting machine, and the third row shows the time used on the sewing machine. Organizing the information in this way will make it easier to form the equations needed to answer the question.

	Dress Shirts	Casual Shirts	Sport Shirts	Total Hours Available
Hours on packaging machine	$2x$	$2y$	$2z$	200
Hours on cutting machine	$3x$	$5y$	$7z$	480
Hours on sewing machine	$2x$	y	$3z$	170

Since each gross of each style of shirt requires 2 hours on the packaging machine, and this machine is available for 200 hours, we must have

$$2x + 2y + 2z = 200$$

Since the number of hours on the cutting machine is $3x + 5y + 7z$, while the total hours available is 480, we must have

$$3x + 5y + 7z = 480$$

Looking at the time spent and available on the sewing machine gives

$$2x + y + 3z = 170$$

---

[1] A gross is a dozen dozen, or 144.

Together, these three equations gives the system of linear equations

$$2x + 2y + 2z = 200 \text{ packaging machine hours}$$
$$3x + 5y + 7z = 480 \text{ cutting machine hours}$$
$$2x + y + 3z = 170 \text{ sewing machine hours}$$

Begin by dividing the first equation by 2 so that the coefficient of x in the first equation is 1. Doing this gives the system

$$\begin{cases} E_1: & x + y + z = 100 \\ E_2: & 3x + 5y + 7z = 480 \\ E_3: & 2x + y + 3z = 170 \end{cases}$$

We need to use the first equation to eliminate x from the second and third equations. We do this one equation at a time. Start by using the first equation to eliminate x from the second equation. We can do this by multiplying -3 times the first equation and add this to the second equation to become our new second equation. That is, $E_2 - 3E_1 \rightarrow E_2$. We have

$$\begin{array}{rl} -3E_1: & -3x - 3y - 3z = -300 \\ E_2: & 3x + 5y + 7z - 480 \\ \hline E_2 - 3E_1: & 2y + 4z = 180 \end{array}$$

Now we use the first equation to eliminate x from the third equation. We can do this by multiplying -2 times the first equation and add this to the third equation ($E_3 - 2E_1 \rightarrow E_3$) to form our new third equation. We have

$$\begin{array}{rl} -2E_1: & 2x - 2y - 2z = -200 \\ E_3: & 2x + y + 3z = 170 \\ \hline E_3 - 2E_1: & -y + z = -30 \end{array}$$

Using the new second and third equations from above in the bracketed system we have

$$\begin{cases} E_1: & x + y + z = 100 \\ E_2: & 2y + 4z = 180 \\ E_3: & -y + z = -30 \end{cases}$$

Pause for a moment to see what we have accomplished. We started with a system of three equations with three unknowns. But if we just look at the new second and third equations,

$$\begin{cases} E_2: & 2y + 4z = 180 \\ E_3: & -y + z = -30 \end{cases}$$

we see that we now have *two* equations with the *two* unknowns y and z as we have eliminated x from the last two equations. This is much simpler and we solve these two equations as we did in Example 1, while, for now, leaving the first equation unchanged. Begin by dividing the second equation by 2 (that is, $\frac{1}{2}E_2 \rightarrow E_2$) to have a y-coefficient of 1 and obtain

$$\begin{cases} E_1: & x + y + z = 100 \\ E_2: & y + 2z = 90 \\ E_3: & -y + z = -30 \end{cases}$$

Now we use the second equation to eliminate the y variable from the third equation. We replace the third equation with the sum of the second and third equations

$(E_2 + E_3 \rightarrow E_3)$. We have

$$
\begin{array}{rl}
E_2: & y + 2z = 90 \\
E_3: -\, y + & z = -30 \\
\hline
E_2 + E_3: & 3z = 60
\end{array}
$$

This last equation is the new third equation. We now have

$$
\begin{cases}
E_1: x + y + z = 100 \\
E_2: y + 2z = 90 \\
E_3: 3z = 60
\end{cases}
$$

Finally, we divide the last equation by 3 ($\frac{1}{3}E_3 \rightarrow E_3$) and our system is

$$
\begin{cases}
E_1: x + y + z = 100 \\
E_2: y + 2z = 90 \\
E_3: z = 20
\end{cases}
$$

with the value $z = 20$. Now we backward substitute.

$$
E_3: \qquad\qquad z = 20
$$

$$
\begin{aligned}
E_2: \qquad\qquad y + 2z &= 90 \\
y + 2(20) &= 90 \\
y &= 50
\end{aligned}
$$

$$
\begin{aligned}
E_3: \qquad x + y + z &= 100 \\
x + (50) + (20) &= 100 \\
x &= 30
\end{aligned}
$$

So the solution is $(x, y, z) = (30, 50, 20)$. Thus, the firm should produce 30 gross of dress shirts, 50 gross of casual shirts, and 20 gross of sport shirts to use all of the available time on the three machines.   ◆

✧ Gauss Elimination Using the Augmented Matrix

Let us continue by solving the following system of equations.

$$
\begin{aligned}
x + 2y - 2z &= 1 \\
2x + 7y + 2z &= -1 \\
x + 6y + 7z &= -3
\end{aligned}
$$

It is convenient to write this system in the abbreviated form as

$$
\left[
\begin{array}{ccc|c}
1 & 2 & -2 & 1 \\
2 & 7 & 2 & -1 \\
1 & 6 & 7 & -3
\end{array}
\right]
$$

Such a rectangular array of numbers is called a matrix. We refer to this matrix as the augmented matrix for the system. The only difference between this augmented matrix and the original system is that in the augmented matrix the symbols x, y, z, and $=$ have been dropped. This spares us the work of always writing these symbols for each step of the solution. Now if we wish to interchange two equations in the system, we interchange the two corresponding rows in the augmented matrix. If we wish to multiply a constant times each side of one equation, we multiply the constant times each member of the corresponding row, etc. In general we have the following.

Elementary Row Operations

1. Interchange the ith row with the jth row ($R_i \leftrightarrow R_j$).

2. Multiply each member of the ith row by a nonzero constant
k ($kR_i \rightarrow R_i$).

3. Replace each element in the ith row with the corresponding element in the ith row plus k times the corresponding element in the jth row ($R_i + kR_j \rightarrow R_i$).

Notice that our notation using elementary row operations is similar to that for equations. So, for example, the row R_i corresponds to the equation E_i.

EXAMPLE 3   Using the Augmented Matrix   Solve the system of linear equations using the augmented matrix.

$$\begin{cases} E_1: & x + 2y - 2z = 1 \\ E_2: 2x + 7y + 2z = -1 \\ E_3: & x + 6y + 7z = -3 \end{cases}$$

Technology Option

Example 3 is solved using a graphing calculator in Technology Note 1 on page 42

Solution   As usual, we first want the coefficient of x in the first equation to be 1. This is the same as having a 1 in the first row and first column of the augmented matrix. This we already have. Now we wish to eliminate x from the second and third equations. This corresponds to wanting zeros as the first element in each of the second and third rows. We write each equation as a row and proceed as before, but with the augmented matrix and row operations.

$$\left[\begin{array}{ccc|c} 1 & 2 & -2 & 1 \\ 2 & 7 & 2 & -1 \\ 1 & 6 & 7 & -3 \end{array}\right] \begin{array}{l} R_2 - 2R_1 \rightarrow R_2 \\ R_3 - R_1 \rightarrow R_3 \end{array} \rightarrow \left[\begin{array}{ccc|c} 1 & 2 & -2 & 1 \\ 0 & 3 & 6 & -3 \\ 0 & 4 & 9 & -4 \end{array}\right] \frac{1}{3}R_2 \rightarrow R_2$$

$$\rightarrow \left[\begin{array}{ccc|c} 1 & 2 & -2 & 1 \\ 0 & 1 & 2 & -1 \\ 0 & 4 & 9 & -4 \end{array}\right] R_3 - 4R_2 \rightarrow R_3$$

$$\rightarrow \left[\begin{array}{ccc|c} 1 & 2 & -2 & 1 \\ 0 & 1 & 2 & -1 \\ 0 & 0 & 1 & 0 \end{array}\right]$$

Notice that we have created a diagonal of 1's with zeros below each of the 1's in the matrix. This augmented matrix corresponds to a system of equations that is ready for backward substitution,

$$\begin{array}{ll} E_1: x + 2y - 2z = & 1 \\ E_2: y + 2z = -1 \\ E_3: z = 0 \end{array}$$

This gives $z = 0$. Now backward substitute and obtain

$$E_2: \qquad\qquad y + 2z = -1$$
$$y + 2(0) = -1$$
$$y = -1$$

$$E_1: \qquad x + 2y - 2z = 1$$
$$x + 2(-1) - 2(0) = 1$$
$$x = 3$$

The solution is $(x, y, z) = (3, -1, 0)$. ◆

EXAMPLE 4   Gauss Elimination With Four Equations   Solve the following system of equations.

$$\begin{cases} E_1: & 3x & + & 6y & + & 3z & + & 3u & = & 450 \\ E_2: & 2x & + & 6y & + & 4z & + & 4u & = & 500 \\ E_3: & & & 3y & + & 5z & + & 7u & = & 480 \\ E_4: & & & 2y & + & z & + & 3u & = & 170 \end{cases}$$

Solution   The augmented matrix is

$$\left[\begin{array}{cccc|c} 3 & 6 & 3 & 3 & 450 \\ 2 & 6 & 4 & 4 & 500 \\ 0 & 3 & 5 & 7 & 480 \\ 0 & 2 & 1 & 3 & 170 \end{array} \right]$$

Begin by making the coefficient of the first variable in the first row 1 by dividing the first row by 3,

$$\left[\begin{array}{cccc|c} 3 & 6 & 3 & 3 & 450 \\ 2 & 6 & 4 & 4 & 500 \\ 0 & 3 & 5 & 7 & 480 \\ 0 & 2 & 1 & 3 & 170 \end{array} \right] \begin{array}{c} \frac{1}{3}R_1 \to R_1 \\ \\ \to \end{array} \left[\begin{array}{cccc|c} 1 & 2 & 1 & 1 & 150 \\ 2 & 6 & 4 & 4 & 500 \\ 0 & 3 & 5 & 7 & 480 \\ 0 & 2 & 1 & 3 & 170 \end{array} \right]$$

We need to place a zero in the second row and first column. We have

$$\left[\begin{array}{cccc|c} 1 & 2 & 1 & 1 & 150 \\ 2 & 6 & 4 & 4 & 500 \\ 0 & 3 & 5 & 7 & 480 \\ 0 & 2 & 1 & 3 & 170 \end{array} \right] \begin{array}{c} R_2 - 2R_1 \to R_2 \\ \\ \to \end{array} \left[\begin{array}{cccc|c} 1 & 2 & 1 & 1 & 150 \\ 0 & 2 & 2 & 2 & 200 \\ 0 & 3 & 5 & 7 & 480 \\ 0 & 2 & 1 & 3 & 170 \end{array} \right]$$

This corresponds to

$$\begin{cases} E_1: x + 2y + z + u = 150 \\ E_2: \qquad 2y + 2z \quad 2u = 200 \\ E_3: \qquad 3y + 5z + 7u = 480 \\ E_4: \qquad 2y + z + 3u = 170 \end{cases}$$

Notice how we began with a complicated system with four equations with four unknowns, and now the last three equations are just three equations with three unknowns.

$$\begin{cases} E_2: \quad 2y + 2z \quad 2u = 200 \\ E_3: \quad 3y + 5z + 7u = 480 \\ E_4: \quad 2y + z + 3u = 170 \end{cases}$$

This is much simpler. As usual we ignore the first equation for now and just work with the last three. But notice that the last three equations are the same as the three equations we solved in Example 2! Only the variables are labeled differently. So we can use this observation and recalling the solution to Example 2 we see that $y = 30$, $z = 50$, and $u = 20$. Now we backward substitute this into E_1 and obtain

$$E_1 : x + \quad 2y + \quad z + \quad u = 150$$
$$x + (30) + (50) + (20) = 150$$
$$x = \quad 50$$

The solution is $(x, y, z, u) = (50, 30, 50, 20)$.   ◆

EXAMPLE 5   Gauss Elimination With Three Equations   Solve the following system of equations.

$$y - 3z = 1$$
$$x + y - 2z = 2$$
$$x + y - \quad z = 1$$

Solution   The augmented matrix is

$$\begin{bmatrix} 0 & 1 & -3 & | & 1 \\ 1 & 1 & -2 & | & 2 \\ 1 & 1 & -1 & | & 1 \end{bmatrix}$$

 Technology Option

Example 5 is solved using a graphing calculator in Technology Note 2 on page 44

Our normal procedure would be to use the first equation to eliminate x from the second equation. But since the coefficient of x in the first equation is zero, this is not possible. The simple solution is to switch the first equation with another equation that has a nonzero coefficient of x. In this case we may pick the second or the third equation. We pick the second. Then

$$\begin{bmatrix} 0 & 1 & -3 & | & 1 \\ 1 & 1 & -2 & | & 2 \\ 1 & 1 & -1 & | & 1 \end{bmatrix} \begin{array}{c} R_1 \leftrightarrow R_2 \\ \rightarrow \end{array} \begin{bmatrix} 1 & 1 & -2 & | & 2 \\ 0 & 1 & -3 & | & 1 \\ 1 & 1 & -1 & | & 1 \end{bmatrix} R_3 - R_1 \rightarrow R_3$$

$$\rightarrow \begin{bmatrix} 1 & 1 & -2 & | & 2 \\ 0 & 1 & -3 & | & 1 \\ 0 & 0 & 1 & | & -1 \end{bmatrix}$$

We now have an augmented matrix with 1's along the diagonal and zeros below each 1, and so we are ready to write out the system of equations. This augmented matrix corresponds to

$$E_1 : x + y - 2z = \quad 2$$
$$E_2 : \quad y - 3z = \quad 1$$
$$E_3 : \quad z = -1$$

We have $z = -1$, then backward substitution gives

$$E_2 : \qquad y - 3z = 1$$
$$y - 3(-1) = 1$$
$$y = 1 - 3 = -2$$

$$E_1 : \qquad x + y - 2z = 2$$
$$x + (-2) - 2(-1) = 2$$
$$x = 2 + 2 - 2 = 2$$

So the solution is $(x, y, z) = (2, -2, -1)$.   ◆

✧ Additional Applications

EXAMPLE 6   Investment Allocation   A fund manager has been given a total of $900,000 by a client to invest in certain types of stocks and bonds. The client requires that twice as much money be in bonds as in stocks. Also stocks must be restricted to a certain class of low-risk stocks and another class of medium-risk stocks. Furthermore, the client demands an annual return of 8%. The fund manager assumes from historical data that the low-risk stocks should return 9% annually, the medium-risk stocks 11% annually, and the bonds 7%. How should the fund manager allocate funds among the three groups to meet all the demands of the client?

Solution   Begin by defining the variables needed to answer the question. Let
x = the amount of money in dollars allocated to low-risk stocks
y = the amount of money in dollars allocated to medium-risk stocks
z = the amount of money in dollars allocated to bonds

The total invested is $x + y + z$ dollars and this must equal 900,000. Thus, our first equation is

$$x + y + z = 900,000$$

Low-risk stocks will earn 9% per year, so $0.09x$ is the number of dollars low-risk stocks will return in one year. Medium-risk will earn 11% per year, so $0.11y$ is the number of dollars medium-risk stocks will return in one year. Bonds will earn 7% per year, so $0.07z$ is the number of dollars bonds will return in one year. These three returns must add to the return the client has demanded, which is $0.08 \times 900,000 = 72,000$. Thus,

$$0.07x + 0.11y + 0.07z = 72,000$$

Finally, we must have twice as much money in bonds as in stocks. The amount we have in stocks is $x + y$ and the amount in bonds is z. To see this ratio we can look at Figure 1.19.

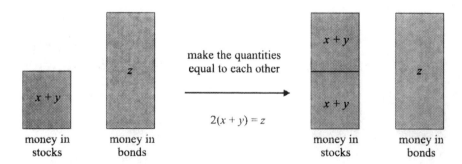

Figure 1.19

Or we can organize our information in a table and look for a pattern in how the variables are related to each other as shown in the table below.

$x+y$	1	2	3	...	$x+y$
z	2	4	6	...	$2(x+y)$

Therefore, we must have $z = 2(x+y)$. For Gauss Elimination the variables must be on the left, so write this equation as

$$2x + 2y - z = 0$$

Our three equations are then

$$\begin{array}{rcll} x + y + z & = & 900,000 & \text{total dollars invested} \\ 0.09x + 0.11y + 0.07z & = & 72,000 & \text{total return} \\ 2x + 2y - z & = & 0 & \text{ratio of stocks to bonds} \end{array}$$

The augmented matrix is

$$\left[\begin{array}{ccc|c} 1 & 1 & 1 & 900,000 \\ 0.09 & 0.11 & 0.07 & 72,000 \\ 2 & 2 & -1 & 0 \end{array}\right]$$

Proceeding with the Gauss elimination we have

$$\left[\begin{array}{ccc|c} 1 & 1 & 1 & 900,000 \\ 0.09 & 0.11 & 0.07 & 72,000 \\ 2 & 2 & -1 & 0 \end{array}\right] \begin{array}{l} R_2 - 0.09R_1 \to R_2 \\ R_3 - 2R_1 \to R_3 \end{array} \to \left[\begin{array}{ccc|c} 1 & 1 & 1 & 900,000 \\ 0 & 0.02 & -0.02 & -9000 \\ 0 & 0 & -3 & -1,800,000 \end{array}\right] \begin{array}{l} 50R_2 \to R_2 \\ -\frac{1}{3}R_3 \to R_3 \end{array}$$

$$\to \left[\begin{array}{ccc|c} 1 & 1 & 1 & 900,000 \\ 0 & 1 & -1 & -450,000 \\ 0 & 0 & 1 & 600,000 \end{array}\right]$$

This corresponds to

$$\begin{array}{rcr} x + y + z & = & 900,000 \\ y - z & = & -450,000 \\ z & = & 600,000 \end{array}$$

Backward substituting gives

$$E_3: \qquad\qquad z = 600,000$$

$$E_2: \qquad\qquad \begin{aligned} y - z & = -450,000 \\ y - 600,000 & = -450,000 \\ y & = 150,000 \end{aligned}$$

$$E_1: \qquad\qquad \begin{aligned} x + y + z & = 900,000 \\ x + 150,000 + 600,000 & = 900,000 \\ x & = 150,000 \end{aligned}$$

The client places \$150,000 in each type of stock and \$600,000 in bonds. ✦

✧ Introduction to Gauss-Jordan (Optional)

Recall in Example 3 that we ended with the matrix

$$\left[\begin{array}{ccc|c} 1 & 2 & -2 & 1 \\ 0 & 1 & 2 & -1 \\ 0 & 0 & 1 & 0 \end{array}\right]$$

which we then solved by backward substitution. It is possible, however, to continue to perform row operations to reduce this matrix to a simple form that allows us to read off the solution. Keep in mind, however, that the amount of calculations that we will do is no more nor less than what we did in backward substitution.

We start with the one that is circled in the first augmented matrix below. We use this one and the row it is in to perform row operations with the goal of obtaining zeros in the column above the circled one. We repeat this procedure using the circled one in the second augmented matrix.

Technology Option

Example 3 is solved using a graphing calculator in Technology Note 4 on page 44

$$
\left[\begin{array}{ccc|c} 1 & 1 & -2 & 2 \\ 0 & 1 & 2 & -1 \\ 0 & 0 & ① & 0 \end{array}\right]
\begin{array}{l} R_1 + 2R_3 \to R_1 \\ R_2 - 2R_3 \to R_2 \\ \to \end{array}
\left[\begin{array}{ccc|c} 1 & 2 & 0 & 1 \\ 0 & ① & 0 & -1 \\ 0 & 0 & 1 & 0 \end{array}\right]
R_1 - 2R_2 \to R_1
$$

$$
\to \left[\begin{array}{ccc|c} 1 & 0 & 0 & 3 \\ 0 & 1 & 0 & -1 \\ 0 & 0 & 1 & 0 \end{array}\right]
$$

This can then be written as the following system.

$$
\begin{aligned}
x &= 3 \\
y &= -1 \\
z &= 0
\end{aligned}
$$

As before, we have $z = 0$. But now we see that we immediately have $y = -1$ and $x = 3$. The solution is then $(x, y, z) = (3, -1, 0)$ as before.

We outline how the Gauss-Jordan method could be used on the following augmented matrix.

$$
\left[\begin{array}{cccc|c} 1 & x & x & x & x \\ 0 & 1 & x & x & x \\ 0 & 0 & 1 & x & x \\ 0 & 0 & 0 & 1 & d \end{array}\right]
\to
\left[\begin{array}{cccc|c} 1 & x & x & 0 & x \\ 0 & 1 & x & 0 & x \\ 0 & 0 & 1 & 0 & c \\ 0 & 0 & 0 & 1 & d \end{array}\right]
\to
\left[\begin{array}{cccc|c} 1 & x & 0 & 0 & x \\ 0 & 1 & 0 & 0 & b \\ 0 & 0 & 1 & 0 & c \\ 0 & 0 & 0 & 1 & d \end{array}\right]
\to
\left[\begin{array}{cccc|c} 1 & 0 & 0 & 0 & a \\ 0 & 1 & 0 & 0 & b \\ 0 & 0 & 1 & 0 & c \\ 0 & 0 & 0 & 1 & d \end{array}\right]
$$

So, the solution is seen to be (a, b, c, d).

✦ Technology Corner

Technology Note 1   Example 3 on a Graphing Calculator

Begin by entering the matrix in the calculator. Matrices are accessed via the MATRX button on the TI-83. On the TI-83Plus and all TI-84s, the matrix commands are accessed with the 2ND and x^{-1} buttons. Either way, you will see Screen 1 for the matrix commands. To enter the matrix, right arrow to the EDIT command and press ENTER to edit matrix [A]. Now you are in the matrix edit menu. Enter 3 and 4 from the keypad to create a 3x4 matrix and then proceed to enter the matrix elements, as shown in Screen 2. To return to the home screen and see the matrix, do 2ND MODE to quit, then access the matrix commands and choose NAMES and ENTER to paste the matrix name [A] on the home screen. Press ENTER again to see the matrix displayed as it is in Screen 3.

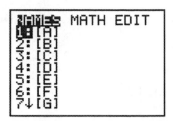

Screen 1

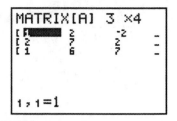

Screen 2

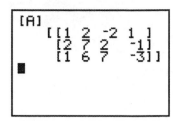

Screen 3

Now to access the row commands, return to the matrix commands and right arrow to MATH. Next, use the down arrow until the row operations are displayed as in Screen 4. To do the operation $R_2 - 2R_1 \rightarrow R_2$, choose the command F:*row+(and enter to return to the homescreen with the *row+(command displayed. The arguments for this command are the value to multiply by (here it is -2), the matrix to use (here it is [A], which is accessed via the MATRIX NAME command), the row number that will be multiplied (here it is row 1) and then the row this multiplied row is to be added to (here it is row 2). Press enter and the result is displayed in Screen 5. This matrix can be stored or simply used in the next operation. To store this result as matrix [B], press the ▓STO▓ and then MATRIX NAME and choose 2:[B].

Since we often carry out a series of row operations, we can use the Ans feature to access the last matrix used. In the next operation, $R_3 - R_1 \rightarrow R_3$, we will access the previous matrix by pressing ▓2ND▓ and then ▓(-)▓ to have Ans for our matrix name. See Screen 6.

Screen 4

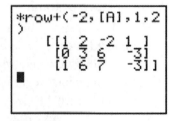

Screen 5

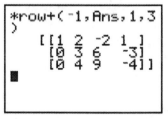

Screen 6

The next command is to do $\frac{1}{3}R_2 \rightarrow R_2$. The command *row(will do the row multiplication and it is found under the MATRIX MATH menu. The arguments for this command are the value to multiply the row by, the name of the matrix and the row to be multiplied. As before, we want to carry out this operation on the previous matrix, as shown in Screen 7. The last step, $R_3 - 4R_2 \rightarrow R_3$ is shown in Screen 8.

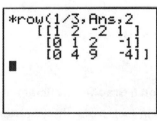

Screen 7

Screen 8

The use of these matrix commands are summarized in Table 1.2. It is assumed that matrix [A] is the augmented matrix to be operated on.

Elementary Row Operation	Calculator Command
$R_i \leftrightarrow R_j$	rowSwap([A], i, j)
$kR_i \rightarrow R_i$	*row(k, [A], i)
$R_i + kR_j \rightarrow R_i$	*row+(k, [A], i, j)

Table 1.2

⑨Technology Note 2 **Example 5 on a Graphing Calculator**

Begin by entering the augmented matrix into the calculator as above (see Screen 9). Then return to the MATRIX MATH menu and scroll to A:ref(and ENTER . Next use MATRIX NAME to enter the name of the matrix where the values were entered. Then ENTER to do the ref(operation, as shown in Screen 10. The matrix is now ready for backward substitution.

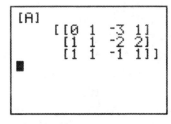

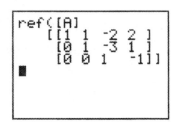

Screen 9 **Screen 10**

⑨Technology Note 3 **Example 6 on a Graphing Calculator**

The TI calculators are able to carry out the backward substitution within the augmented matrix. The explanation for this is detailed in the optional Gauss-Jordan subsection. However, the method is very straightforward to implement on the calculator. Begin by entering the augmented matrix into the calculator, as shown in Screen 11. Next go to the MATRIX MATH menu and scroll to B:rref(and ENTER . Next use MATRIX NAME to enter the name of the matrix where the values were entered. Then ENTER to do the rref(operation, as shown in Screen 12. The answer can be found by writing each row as an equation.

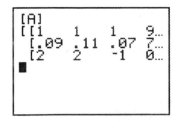

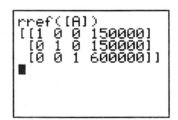

Screen 11 **Screen 12**

⑨Technology Note 4 **Example 3 on a Graphing Calculator** The rref(command outlined in Technology Note 3 is in fact, using the Gauss-Jordan method on the augmented matrix. As long as the number of rows in the augmented matrix is greater than or equal to 1+ the number of columns in the matrix, the calculator can perform all the row operations to obtain the solution to the system of linear equations. See Screens 13 and 14 for this example.

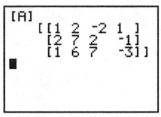

Screen 13

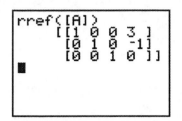

Screen 14

Self-Help Exercise 1.3

1. A store sells 30 sweaters on a certain day. The sweaters come in three styles: A, B, and C. Style A costs \$30, style B costs \$40, and style C costs \$50, If the store sold \$1340 worth of these sweaters on that day and the number of style C sold exceeded by 6 the sum of the other two styles sold, how many sweaters of each style were sold?

1.3 Exercises

Find the solution of each of the following systems using Gauss elimination.

1. $\quad x + 2y = 12$
   $\quad 2x + 3y = 19$

2. $\quad x + 3y = 2$
   $\quad 3x + 4y = 1$

3. $\quad 4x - 8y = 20$
   $\quad -x + 3y = -7$

4. $\quad 3x - 12y = 3$
   $\quad -2x + y = -9$

5. $\quad -2x + 8y = -6$
   $\quad -2x + 3y = -1$

6. $\quad -3x + 12y = -21$
   $\quad -10x + 2y = 6$

7. $\quad 3x + 6y = 0$
   $\quad x - y = -3$

8. $\quad 2x + 4y = 8$
   $\quad 2x - 4y = 0$

9. $\quad x + 2y = 5$
   $\quad 2x - 3y = -4$

10. $\quad 2x + 4y = 6$
    $\quad 4x - y = -6$

11. $\quad 3x - 3y + 6z = -3$
    $\quad 2x + y + 2z = 4$
    $\quad 2x - 2y + 5z = -2$

12. $\quad 2x - 4y + 2z = -6$
    $\quad 3x + 4y + 5z = 1$
    $\quad 2x - y + z = -3$

13. $\quad x + y + z = 10$
    $\quad x - y + z = 10$
    $\quad x + y - z = 0$

14. $\quad x + y + z = 1$
    $\quad 2x - y + z = 2$
    $\quad 3x + 2y + 5z = 3$

15. $\quad x + y + z = 6$
    $\quad 2x + y + 2z = 10$
    $\quad 3x + 2y + z = 10$

16. $\quad x + 2y + z = 6$
    $\quad -x + 3y - 2z = -4$
    $\quad 2x - y - 3z = -8$

17. $\quad x - y + 2z = -1$
    $\quad 2x + y - 3z = 6$
    $\quad y - z = 2$

18. $x - 2y + z = 9$
$3y - 2z = -11$
$x + y + 4z = 3$

19. $2x - 4y + 8z = 2$
$2x + 3y + 2z = 3$
$2x - 3y + 5z = 0$

20. $2x - y - 3z = 1$
$-x - 2y + z = -4$
$3x + y - 2z = 9$

21. $x + y + z + u = 6$
$y - z + 2u = 4$
$z + u = 3$
$x + 2y + 3z - u = 5$

22. $x - y - z + 2u = 1$
$x - y + z + 3u = 9$
$y + 2z - u = 5$
$3y + z + 2u = 8$

23. $x + 2y + z - u = -2$
$x + 2y + 2z + 2u = 9$
$y + z - u = -2$
$y - 2z + 3u = 4$

24. $x + y + z + u = 6$
$x + 2y - z + u = 5$
$x + y - z + 2u = 6$
$2x + 2y + 2z + u = 10$

25. A person has 25 coins, all of which are quarters and dimes. If the face value of the coins is $3.25, how many of each type of coin must this person have?

26. A person has three times as many dimes as quarters. If the total face value of these coins is $2.20, how many of each type of coin must this person have?

27. A person has 36 coins, all of which are nickels, dimes, and quarters. If there are twice as many dimes as nickels and if the face value of the coins is $4, how many of each type of coin must this person have?

28. A person has three times as many nickels as quarters and three more dimes than nickels. If the total face value of these coins is $2.40, how many of each type of coin must this person have?

Applications

29. Document Scheduling An insurance company has two types of documents to process: contracts and leases. The contracts need to be examined for 2 hours by the accountant and 3 hours by the attorney, while the leases needs to be examined for 4 hours by the accountant and 1 hour by the attorney. If the accountant has 40 hours and the attorney 30 hours each week to spend working on these documents, how many documents of each type can they process?

30. Tea Mixture A small store sells spearmint tea at $3.20 an ounce and peppermint tea at $4 an ounce. The store owner decides to make a batch of 100 ounces of tea that mixes both kinds and sell the mixture for $3.50 an ounce. How many ounces of each of the two varieties of tea should be mixed to obtain the same revenue as selling them unmixed?

31. Investments at Two Banks An individual has a total of $1000 in two banks. The first bank pays 8% a year and the second pays 10% a year. If the person receives $86 of interest in the first year, how much money must have been deposited in each bank?

32. Meal Planning A dietitian must plan a meal for a patient using two fruits, oranges and strawberries. Each orange contains 1 gram of fiber and 75 mg of vitamin C, while each cup of strawberries contains 2 grams of fiber and 60 mg of vitamin C. How much of each of these fruits needs to be eaten so that a total of 8 grams of fiber and 420 mg of vitamin C will be obtained?

33. Production Scheduling for Shirts A small plant with a cutting department and a sewing department produce their Pathfinder shirt and their Trekking shirt. It takes 0.5 work-hours to cut the Pathfinder shirt and 0.6 work-hours to sew it. It takes 0.4 work-hours to cut the Trekker shirt and 0.3 work-hours to sew it. If the cutting department has 200 work-hours available each day and the sewing department has 186 work-hours, how many of each shirt can be produced per day if both departments work at full capacity?

34. Boutique Sales A boutique sells blouses and purses. The blouses cost $30 each and the purses cost $40 each. On a certain day the store sells twice as many blouses as purses. If the store sold $400 worth of these two items on that day, how many of each were sold?

35. **Document Scheduling** An insurance company has three types of documents to process: appeals, claims, and enrollment forms. The appeal document needs to be examined for 2 hours by the accountant and 3 hours by the attorney. The claims document needs to be examined for 4 hours by the accountant and 2 hours by the attorney. Finally, the enrollment form document needs to be examined for 2 hours by the accountant and 4 hours by the attorney. The secretary needs 3 hours to type each document. If the accountant has 34 hours, the attorney 35 hours, and the secretary 36 hours available to spend working on these documents, how many documents of each type can they process?

36. **Production Scheduling for Sweaters** A small plant with a cutting department, a sewing department, and a packaging department produces three style of sweaters: crew, turtleneck, and V-neck. It takes 0.4 work-hours to cut a crew sweater and 0.2 work-hours to sew it. It takes 0.3 work-hours to cut a turtleneck sweater and the same to sew it. It takes 0.5 work-hours to cut a V-neck and 0.6 work-hours to sew it. It takes 0.1 work-hours to package each of the sweaters. If the cutting department has 110 work-hours available each day, the sewing department has 95 work-hours available each day, and the packaging department has 30 hours, how many sweaters of each styles can be produced if all departments work at full capacity?

37. **Investments** Jennifer has $4200 to invest. She decides to invest in three different companies. The MathOne company costs $20 per share and pays dividends of $1 per share each year. The NewModule company costs $60 per share and pays dividends of $2 per share each year. The JavaTime company costs $20 per share and pays $3 per share per year in dividends. Jennifer wants to have twice as much money in the MathOne company as in the JavaTime company. Jennifer also wants to earn $290 in dividends per year. How much should Jennifer invest in each company to meet her goals?

38. **Investments** Link has $14,800 to invest. He decides to invest in three different companies. The QX company costs $40 per share and pays dividends of $2 per share each year. The RY company costs $120 per share and pays dividends of $1 per share each year. The KZ company costs $80 per share and pays $2 per share per year in dividends. Link wants to have twice as much money in the RY company as in the KZ company. Link also wants to earn $300 in dividends per year. How much should Link invest in each company to meet his goals?

39. **Production of Picture Frames** A company makes three kinds of picture frames. The frames use wood, paint, and glass. The number of units of each material needed for each type of frame is given in the table. How many of each type of frame can be made if there are 180 units of wood, 150 units of glass, and 130 units of paint available?

	Wood	Paint	Glass
Frame A	2	3	3
Frame B	2	2	2
Frame C	4	1	2

40. **Production of Furniture** A furniture company makes loungers, chairs, and footstools made out of wood, fabric, and stuffing. The number of units of each of these materials needed for each of the products is given in the table below. How many of each product can be made if there are 54 units of wood, 63 units of fabric, and 43 units of stuffing available?

	Wood	Fabric	Stuffing
Lounger	1	2	2
Chair	2	2	1
Footstool	3	1	1

41. **Baked Goods** A bakery sells muffins, scones, and croissants. Each batch of 6 muffins uses 2 cups of sugar and 3 cups of flour. Each batch of 10 scones uses 2 cups of sugar and 5 cups of flour. Each batch of 12 croissants uses 1 cup of sugar and 4 cups of flour. The bakery has 17 cups of sugar and 37 cups of flour. Muffins sell for $2.50 each, scones sell for $2.00 each, and croissants sell for $1.50 each. How many of each item can be made if the revenue is $169?

42. **Diet Planning** A dietitian is preparing a meal of chicken, rice, and peas for a patient. The patient needs the meal to contain 87 grams of carbohydrate, 57 grams of protein, and 7 grams of fat. The table below shows the number of grams of carbohydrate, protein, and fat in 100 grams of each food. (Note, the total is not 100 grams due to the water and fiber content of the food.) How much of each food should be used so that the patient gets the needed nutri-

ents?

	Carbohydrate	Protein	Fat
Chicken	0	32	4
Rice	25	2	0
Peas	12	3	1

43. **Meal Planning** A dietitian wishes to design a meal for Sandy that will have her minimum daily requirements of iron, calcium, and folic acid. The dietitian will use Foods I, II, and III to make this meal. The table below shows how many units of each nutrient is found in each ounce of the foods. If Sandy needs 51 units of iron, 540 units of calcium, and 128 units of folic acid, how much of each food should she have in her meal?

	Iron	Calcium	Folic Acid
Food I	5	20	8
Food II	1	60	4
Food III	3	40	10

44. **Chinese Farm Problem** The ancient Chinese "way of calculating with arrays" can be found in Chapter 8 of the ancient text *Nine Chapters on Mathematical Art*. The following is the first problem listed in Chapter 8.

There are three grades of corn. After threshing, three bundles of top grade, two bundles of medium grade, and one bundle of low grade make 39 dou (a measure of volume). Two bundles of top grade, three bundles of medium grade, and one bundle of low grade make 34 dou. The yield of one bundle of top grade, two bundles of medium grade, and three bundles of low grade make 26 dou. How many dou are contained in each bundle of each grade?

45. **Nutrition** A dietitian must plan a meal for a patient using three fruits: oranges, strawberries, and blackberries. Each orange contains 1 gram of fiber, 75 mg of vitamin C, and 50 mg of phosphorus. Each cup of strawberries contains 2 grams of fiber, 60 mg of vitamin C, and 50 mg of phosphorus. Each cup of blackberries contains 6 grams of fiber, 30 mg of vitamin C, and 40 mg of phosphorus. How much of each of these fruits needs to be eaten so that a total of 13 grams of fiber, 375 mg of vitamin C, and 290 mg of phosphorus is obtained?

Extensions

46. **Four Investments** An individual wants to invest $100,000 in four investment vehicles: a money market fund, a bond fund, a conservative stock fund, and a speculative stock fund. These four investments are assumed to have annual returns of 6%, 8%, 10%, and 13% respectively. The investor wants the same amount in the money market as in the speculative stock fund and wants the same amount in the bond fund as in the conservative stock fund. Can the investor yield $8000 per year using the given restrictions? Why or why not?

47. **Diet** A dietitian will design a meal for Alice, who is in the hospital, that will have her minimum daily requirements of vitamin A, vitamin C, and copper. The dietitian wishes to use three foods readily available at the hospital: Food I, Food II, and Food III. The table below shows how many units of each nutrient is found in each ounce of the foods. Alice needs 37 units of vitamin A, 36 units of copper, and 177 units of vitamin C. Can the dietitian successfully find the amount of the three foods to satisfy Alice's needs?

	Vitamin A	Copper	Vitamin C
Food I	1	2	12
Food II	4	6	3
Food III	2	2	21

48. **Biological system** Suppose that in a biological system there are four species of animals with populations, x, y, z, and u, and four sources of food represented by the available daily supply. Let the system of linear equations be

$$
\begin{aligned}
x + 2y \quad\quad + 3u &= 3500 \quad \text{Food 1} \\
x \quad\quad + 2z + 2u &= 2700 \quad \text{Food 2} \\
z + \quad u &= 900 \quad \text{Food 3} \\
3z + 2u &= 3000 \quad \text{Food 4}
\end{aligned}
$$

Suppose $(x, y, z, u) = (1000, 500, 350, 400)$. Is there sufficient food to satisfy the average daily consumption?

49. **Biological system** Using the information in the question above, what is the maximum number of animals of the first species that could be individually added to the system with the supply of food still meeting the consumption?

50. **Biological system** Refer to the previous exercises. If the first species becomes extinct ($x = 0$), how much of an individual increase in the second species could be supported?

Solution to Self-Help Exercise 1.3

1. Define the variables first. Let

   x = the number of style A sweaters sold
   y = the number of style B sweaters sold
   z = the number of style C sweaters sold

   Since a total of 30 were sold, we have $x + y + z = 30$. The revenue in dollars from style A is $30x$, from style B is $40y$, and from style C is $50z$. Since \$1340 worth of sweaters were sold, we must have $30x + 40y + 50z = 1340$. Finally, since the number of style C exceeded by 6 the sum of the other two styles, we also have $z = x + y + 6$. Thus, we need to solve the system

$$
\begin{aligned}
x + y + z &= 30 \quad \text{total sweaters} \\
30x + 40y + 50z &= 1340 \quad \text{total revenue in \$} \\
-x - y + z &= 6 \quad \text{ratio of sweaters}
\end{aligned}
$$

Writing the augmented matrix and proceeding with Gauss elimination gives

$$
\begin{bmatrix}
1 & 1 & 1 & 30 \\
30 & 40 & 50 & 1340 \\
-1 & -1 & 1 & 6
\end{bmatrix}
\begin{aligned}
& \\
& R_2 - 30R_1 \to R_2 \\
& R_3 + R_1 \to R_3
\end{aligned}
$$

$$
\to
\begin{bmatrix}
1 & 1 & 1 & 30 \\
0 & 10 & 20 & 440 \\
0 & 0 & 2 & 36
\end{bmatrix}
\begin{aligned}
& \\
& \tfrac{1}{10}R_2 \to R_2 \\
& \tfrac{1}{2}R_3 \to R_3
\end{aligned}
$$

$$
\to
\begin{bmatrix}
1 & 1 & 1 & 30 \\
0 & 1 & 2 & 44 \\
0 & 0 & 1 & 18
\end{bmatrix}
$$

This corresponds to the system of equations

$$
\begin{aligned}
x + y + z &= 30 \\
y + 2z &= 44 \\
z &= 18
\end{aligned}
$$

Backward substituting gives

$$
\begin{aligned}
E_2: \quad y + 2z &= 44 \\
y + 2(18) &= 44 \\
y &= 8
\end{aligned}
$$

$$
\begin{aligned}
E_1: \quad x + y + z &= 30 \\
x + 8 + 18 &= 30 \\
x &= 4
\end{aligned}
$$

Thus, $(x, y, z) = (4, 8, 18)$, and the store sold 4 of style A, 8 of style B, and 18 of style C.

1.4   Systems of Linear Equations With Non-Unique Solutions

We now consider systems of linear equations that may have no solution or have infinitely many solutions. Nonetheless, we will see that Gauss elimination with backward substitution still provides the best and most efficient way to solve these systems.

✧ Systems of Equations With Two Variables

We begin by examining systems of linear equations with two variables. This will let us graph the equations and make connections to the geometrical meaning of non-unique solutions.

EXAMPLE 1   A System With No Solution   Solve the following system of linear equations using Gauss elimination and discuss geometrically.

$$E_1: \quad x - 2y = 3$$
$$E_2: -2x + 4y = 1$$

Solution   Now use Gauss elimination and the augmented matrix.

$$\begin{bmatrix} 1 & -2 & 4 \\ -2 & 4 & -1 \end{bmatrix} \quad R_2 + 2R_1 \to R_2 \quad \to \quad \begin{bmatrix} 1 & -2 & 3 \\ 0 & 0 & 7 \end{bmatrix}$$

This last matrix corresponds to the system of equations

$$x - 2y = 3$$
$$0 = 7$$

The last equation is $0 = 7$. Since this is not true, there is no solution.

Let us now see what has happened geometrically. The first equation can be written as $y = 0.5x - 1.5$ and the second as $y = 0.5x + 0.25$. Both are graphed in Figure 1.20. We can readily see that the two lines are parallel. This verifies that there is no solution to the system of equations as two different parallel lines do not intersect.   ◆

Next we examine systems of linear equations when the systems have infinitely many solutions.

EXAMPLE 2   Infinite Solutions   Find all solutions to the following system of linear equations and discuss geometrically.

$$E_1: \quad x - 2y = \quad 3$$
$$E_2: -2x + 4y = -6$$

Solution   Now use Gauss elimination and the augmented matrix.

$$\begin{bmatrix} 1 & -2 & 3 \\ -2 & 4 & -6 \end{bmatrix} \quad R_2 + 2R_1 \to R_2 \quad \to \quad \begin{bmatrix} 1 & -2 & 3 \\ 0 & 0 & 0 \end{bmatrix}$$

This last matrix corresponds to the system of equations

$$x - 2y = 3$$
$$0 = 0$$

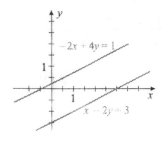

Figure 1.20

The second equation $(0 = 0)$ is clearly true. We then see that there is only one equation yielding information and this indicates there are an infinitely number of solutions. Since we did not find a value for y from our second equation, we can let y be any number, say t. Substituting this into the first equation gives $x - 2t = 3$ or $x = 3 + 2t$ and the solutions can be written as $(x, y) = (3 + 2t, t)$.

This type of solution is called a **parametric solution**. We call t the parameter and it can take on any real number as its value. We call $(x, y) = (3 + 2t, t)$ the **general solution** to this system of equations. Taking any particular value of t gives a **particular solution**. For example, taking $t = 0$, gives the particular solution $x = 3$, $y = 0$ and taking $t = 1$, gives the particular solution $x = 5$, $y = 1$.

Let us observe this situation geometrically. Note that both equations can be written as $y = 0.5x - 1.5$. They are graphed in Figure 1.21. This indeed implies that there are an infinite number of solutions to the system of equations because every point on one line is also on the other. ✦

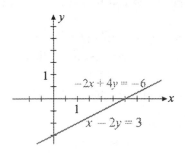

Figure 1.21

✧ Larger Systems

We now consider larger systems of linear equations. We continue to use Gauss elimination to ensure that we find *all* the solutions and not just some of them.

EXAMPLE 3   Infinite Number of Solutions   Solve the following system of linear equations.

$$\begin{aligned} E_1: && x + 2y + 3z &= 4 \\ E_2: && 2x + 5y + 7z &= 10 \\ E_3: && 2y + 2z &= 4 \end{aligned}$$

Solution   The augmented matrix is

$$\left[\begin{array}{ccc|c} 1 & 2 & 3 & 4 \\ 2 & 5 & 7 & 10 \\ 0 & 2 & 2 & 4 \end{array}\right]$$

When the first nonzero element in a row is 1, we call it a **leading one** and circle it. We then have

$$\left[\begin{array}{ccc|c} ① & 2 & 3 & 4 \\ 2 & 5 & 7 & 10 \\ 0 & 2 & 2 & 4 \end{array}\right]$$

As before we use elementary row operations to obtain zeros in the first column below the circled leading one. Indeed, we will always want zeros below the circled leading one. Proceed with Gauss elimination to find

$$\left[\begin{array}{ccc|c} ① & 2 & 3 & 4 \\ 2 & 5 & 7 & 10 \\ 0 & 2 & 2 & 4 \end{array}\right] \quad R_2 - 2R_1 \rightarrow R_2 \quad \rightarrow \quad \left[\begin{array}{ccc|c} ① & 2 & 3 & 4 \\ 0 & ① & 1 & 2 \\ 0 & 2 & 2 & 4 \end{array}\right] \quad R_3 - 2R_2 \rightarrow R_3$$

$$\rightarrow \quad \left[\begin{array}{ccc|c} ① & 2 & 3 & 4 \\ 0 & ① & 1 & 2 \\ 0 & 0 & 0 & 0 \end{array}\right]$$

or

$$\begin{cases} E_1 : x + 2y + 3z = 4 \\ E_2 : \quad\quad y + z = 2 \\ E_3 : \quad\quad\quad\quad\ 0 = 0 \end{cases}$$

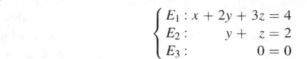

Technology Option

See Technology Note 1 on page 60 where Example 3 is solved using a graphing calculator

Notice that it is not possible to have a leading one in the last row since this row has all zeros.

We associate the basic variables with the columns with the leading ones. Thus, x and y are the basic variables. The remaining variables are called free variables. In this case, z is the free variable and we set z equal to the parameter t, $z = t$. Using $z = t$, we perform backward substitution to solve for the basic variables. We have

$$E_2 : \quad\quad\quad y + z = 2$$
$$y + t = 2$$
$$y = 2 - t$$

$$E_1 : \quad\quad\quad x + 2y + 3z = 4$$
$$x + 2(2 - t) + 3(t) = 4$$
$$x + 4 - 2t + 3t = 4$$
$$x = -t$$

Thus, the general solution can be written as $(x, y, z) = (-t, 2 - t, t)$, where t can be any real number. Particular solutions are found by choosing values for the parameter. Some particular solutions to this system are $(0, 2, 0)$, from using $t = 0$ and $(-1, 1, 1)$, from using the value $t = 1$.   ◆

EXAMPLE 4   **Systems With an Infinite Number Of Solutions**   Solve

$$E_1 : \ x + 2y + 3z + \ 4u = \ 5$$
$$E_2 : 2x + 4y + 8z + 14u = 14$$
$$E_3 : \quad\quad\quad\ 3z + 10u = \ 8$$

Solution   We first form the augmented matrix, then proceed.

$$\left[\begin{array}{cccc|c} ① & 2 & 3 & 4 & 5 \\ 2 & 4 & 8 & 14 & 14 \\ 0 & 0 & 3 & 10 & 8 \end{array}\right] \ R_2 - 2R_1 \rightarrow R_2 \quad \rightarrow \quad \left[\begin{array}{cccc|c} ① & 2 & 3 & 4 & 5 \\ 0 & 0 & 2 & 6 & 4 \\ 0 & 0 & 3 & 10 & 8 \end{array}\right]$$

Normally, our goal would be to get a 1 in the second row and second column. But we find a zero there. So we would normally switch the second row with a row below the second one. However, this will not help since the third row also has a zero in the second column. We then move over one element in the second row where we find a nonzero number. After dividing the second row by 2, this element will become our leading one. We do this and proceed as normal.

$$\left[\begin{array}{cccc|c} ① & 2 & 3 & 4 & 5 \\ 0 & 0 & 2 & 6 & 4 \\ 0 & 0 & 3 & 10 & 8 \end{array}\right] \ \tfrac{1}{2}R_2 \rightarrow R_2 \quad \rightarrow \quad \left[\begin{array}{cccc|c} ① & 2 & 3 & 4 & 5 \\ 0 & 0 & ① & 3 & 2 \\ 0 & 0 & 3 & 10 & 8 \end{array}\right] \ R_3 - 3R_2 \rightarrow R_3$$

$$\rightarrow \quad \left[\begin{array}{cccc|c} ① & 2 & 3 & 4 & 5 \\ 0 & 0 & ① & 3 & 2 \\ 0 & 0 & 0 & ① & 2 \end{array}\right]$$

The variables associated with the columns with the leading ones are the basic variables.

$$\begin{array}{cccc} \textcircled{x} & y & \textcircled{z} & \textcircled{u} \end{array}$$

$$\left[\begin{array}{cccc|c} \textcircled{1} & 2 & 3 & 4 & 5 \\ 0 & 0 & \textcircled{1} & 3 & 2 \\ 0 & 0 & 0 & \textcircled{1} & 2 \end{array}\right]$$

These are then x, z, and u, which have been circled. The remaining variable, y, is the free variable. We set $y = t$ and backward substitute.

$$E_3: \qquad\qquad u = 2$$

$$E_2: \qquad\qquad z + \ 3u = 2$$
$$z + 3(2) = 2$$
$$z = -4$$

$$E_1: x + \ 2y + \qquad 3z + \ 4u = 5$$
$$x + 2(t) + 3(-4) + 4(2) = 5$$
$$x = 9 - 2t$$

The general solution is $(x, y, z, u) = (9 - 2t, t, -4, 2)$, where t is any real number. ✦

Our goal is always to use elementary row operations to reduce the augmented matrix to a simple form where we can readily use backward substitution. When a matrix is in this form, we call it an **echelon matrix**. More precisely, we have the following definition:

> **Echelon Matrix**
> A matrix is in **echelon form** if
>
> 1. The first nonzero element in any row is 1, called the leading one.
>
> 2. The column containing the leading one has all elements below the leading one equal to 0.
>
> 3. The leading one in any row is to the left of the leading one in a lower row.
>
> 4. Any row consisting of all zeros must be below any row with at least one nonzero element.

A typical matrix in echelon form is shown to the left. Notice the "staircase pattern." For example, all of the following matrices are in echelon form.

$$\left[\begin{array}{ccccccc} \textcircled{1} & x & x & x & x & x & x \\ 0 & \textcircled{1} & x & x & x & x & x \\ 0 & 0 & 0 & \textcircled{1} & x & x & x \\ 0 & 0 & 0 & 0 & 0 & 0 & \textcircled{1} \\ 0 & 0 & 0 & 0 & 0 & 0 & 0 \end{array}\right]$$

$$\left[\begin{array}{cc|c} 1 & 2 & 2 \\ 0 & 1 & 3 \\ 0 & 0 & 0 \end{array}\right], \quad \left[\begin{array}{ccc|c} 1 & 4 & 2 & 3 \\ 0 & 0 & 1 & 2 \\ 0 & 0 & 0 & 0 \end{array}\right], \quad \left[\begin{array}{cccc|c} 1 & 2 & 3 & 2 & 3 \\ 0 & 1 & 2 & 3 & 2 \\ 0 & 0 & 0 & 1 & 4 \end{array}\right]$$

None of the following matrices are in echelon form

Technology Option

See Technology Note 2 on page 60 to see Example 4 worked on a graphing calculator.

$$\begin{bmatrix} 1 & 3 & | & 2 \\ 0 & 2 & | & 2 \end{bmatrix}, \quad \begin{bmatrix} 1 & 2 & 2 & | & 1 \\ 0 & 1 & 2 & | & 3 \\ 0 & 1 & 3 & | & 2 \end{bmatrix}, \quad \begin{bmatrix} 0 & 1 & | & 1 \\ 1 & 0 & | & 2 \end{bmatrix}, \quad \begin{bmatrix} 1 & 2 & 0 & | & 1 \\ 0 & 0 & 0 & | & 0 \\ 0 & 1 & 0 & | & 2 \end{bmatrix}$$

since the first matrix violates the first condition, the second matrix violates the second condition, the third matrix the third condition, and the fourth matrix the fourth condition.

REMARK: A matrix in echelon form may or may not have a solution.

EXAMPLE 5   A System With Many Parameters   Find the solution to the the following system.

$$\begin{cases} E_1 : x + 2y + 3z + u + v = 4 \\ E_2 : \qquad\qquad z + 2u + 2v = 1 \\ E_3 : \qquad\qquad\qquad\qquad v = 3 \end{cases}$$

Solution   The augmented matrix is

$$\begin{array}{ccccc} x & y & z & u & v \\ \end{array}$$
$$\begin{bmatrix} 1 & 2 & 3 & 1 & 1 & | & 4 \\ 0 & 0 & 1 & 2 & 2 & | & 1 \\ 0 & 0 & 0 & 0 & 1 & | & 3 \end{bmatrix}$$

We see that this is already in echelon form. We circle the leading ones.

$$\begin{array}{ccccc} ⓧ & y & ⓩ & u & ⓥ \\ \end{array}$$
$$\begin{bmatrix} ① & 2 & 3 & 1 & 1 & | & 4 \\ 0 & 0 & ① & 2 & 2 & | & 1 \\ 0 & 0 & 0 & 0 & ① & | & 3 \end{bmatrix}$$

We see that x, z, and v are basic variables. Thus, y and u are free variables. Set $y = s$ and $u = t$ and use backward substitution.

⑦ **Technology Option**

See Technology Note 3 on page 61 to see Example 5 worked on a graphing calculator.

$$E_3 : \qquad\qquad\qquad v = 3$$

$$E_2 : \qquad z + 2u + 2v = 1$$
$$z + 2(t) + 2(3) = 1$$
$$z = -5 - 2t$$

$$E_1 : \qquad x + 2y + 3z + u + v = 4$$
$$x + 2(s) + 3(-5 - 2t) + (t) + (3) = 4$$
$$x = 16 - 2s + 5t$$

So the solution is $(x, y, z, u, v) = (16 - 2s + 5t, s, -5 - 2t, t, 3)$ with s and t any real numbers. Particular solutions are found by choosing values for both s and t.   ◆

◈ Geometric Interpretations

Earlier we looked at geometric interpretations in the case with two equations and two unknowns. We now consider higher dimensions. It can be shown (but we do not do so here) that any equation of the form $ax + by + cz = d$, with not all of the constants a, b, and c being zero, is the equation of a plane in space. If there are three equations with three unknowns, Figure 1.22 indicates some of the possibilities. The three planes could intersect at a single point indicating that the corresponding linear system of three equations in three unknowns has precisely one solution. The three planes could intersect in one line or an entire plane, giving an infinite number of solutions to the corresponding system. Or there could be no point of intersection of the three planes, indicating that the corresponding system has no solution.

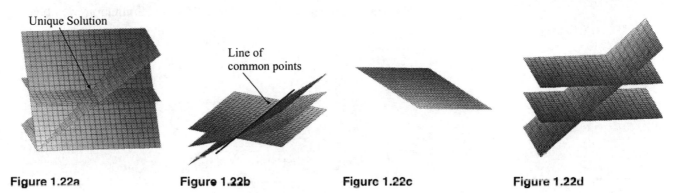

Unique Solution

Line of common points

Figure 1.22a   **Figure 1.22b**   **Figure 1.22c**   **Figure 1.22d**

The geometry can give us further insights. For example, from Figure 1.23 we can see that two linear equations in three unknowns cannot have precisely one solution. If two linear equations in three unknowns had precisely one solution, this would mean that the corresponding two planes intersected in precisely one point, but this is impossible. Thus, two linear equations in three unknowns has either no solution or an infinite number of solutions. This is true in general for any system with more variables than equations. A proof of this statement is outlined later under Enrichment (p. 57).

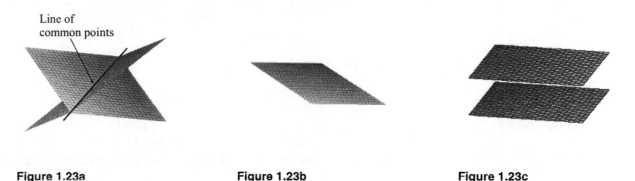

Line of common points

Figure 1.23a   **Figure 1.23b**   **Figure 1.23c**

✧ An Application

EXAMPLE 6   Purchasing Computers   A firm must purchase a total of 100 computers, some of small, some of medium, and some of large capacity. The small capacity computers cost $2000 each, the medium capacity computers cost $6000 each, and the large capacity computers cost $8000 each. If the firm plans to spend all of $400,000 on the total purchase, find the number of each type to be bought.

Solution   Let x, y, and z be the respective number of small, medium, and large capacity computers. Then the first sentence indicates that $x + y + z = 100$.

The cost of purchasing x small computers is $2000x$ dollars, of purchasing y medium computers is $6000y$ dollars, and of purchasing z large computers is $8000z$ dollars. Since the total cost is \$400,000, we have $2000x + 6000y + 8000z = 400,000$ or, in terms of thousands of dollars, $2x + 6y + 8z = 400$. We then have the system

$$\begin{array}{rcl} x + \ y + \ \ z &=& 100 \\ 2x + 6y + 8z &=& 400 \end{array}$$

Using the augmented matrix and using Gauss elimination, we obtain

$$\begin{bmatrix} 1 & 1 & 1 & \bigm| & 100 \\ 2 & 6 & 8 & \bigm| & 400 \end{bmatrix} \quad R_2 - 2R_1 \to R_2$$

$$\to \begin{bmatrix} 1 & 1 & 1 & \bigm| & 100 \\ 0 & 4 & 6 & \bigm| & 200 \end{bmatrix} \quad \tfrac{1}{4}R_2 \to R_2$$

$$\to \begin{bmatrix} 1 & 1 & 1 & \bigm| & 100 \\ 0 & 1 & 1.5 & \bigm| & 50 \end{bmatrix}$$

This corresponds to

$$\begin{array}{rrcl} E_1: & x + y + & z &=& 100 \\ E_2: & y + & 1.5z &=& 50 \end{array}$$

The free variable is z and we let z be the parameter t. We have

$$\begin{array}{rrcl} E_2: & y + 1.5z &=& 50 \\ & y + 1.5t &=& 50 \\ & y &=& 50 - 1.5t \\ E_1: & x + y + z &=& 100 \\ & x + (50 - 1.5t) + (t) &=& 100 \\ & x &=& 0.5t + 50 \end{array}$$

This gives

$$\begin{array}{rcl} x &=& 0.5t + 50 \\ y &=& 50 - 1.5t \\ z &=& t \end{array}$$

First notice that since $t = z$ and z has units in terms of integers, t must be a nonnegative integer. We also have the following clues about the possible solutions to this system

➤ Both x and y must be integers and therefore t must be an even integer. So far, then, t must be a nonnegative even integer.

➤ Since x must be nonnegative, we must have $0.5t + 50 \geq 0$. This gives $t \geq -100$. However, this gives no new information.

➤ Since y must be nonnegative, we must have $50 - 1.5t \geq 0$. This gives $t \leq 100/3$. But recall that t must be a nonnegative even integer. So we must take t to be the largest even integer less than $100/3$, which is $t = 32$. Therefore, $t \leq 32$.

We have the solutions $(x, y, z) = (0.5t + 50, 50 - 1.5t, t)$, where t is an even integer with $0 \leq t \leq 32$. For example, the firm can take $t = 30$ giving $x = 0.5(30) + 50 = 65$ small capacity computers, $y = 50 - 1.5(30) = 35$ medium capacity computers, and $t = 30$ large capacity computers, spending the entire \$400,000 and obtaining a total of 100 computers. ◆

REMARK: In general it is important in an application question to consider the domain of the variables when a parametric solution is found. Negative or fractional items are not realistic.

✧ Enrichment: A Proof

We mentioned earlier that when a system of equations has more variables than equations, then the system has no solution or an infinite number of solutions.

> **More Variables Than Equations**
> A system of linear equations that has more variables than equations has no solution or an infinite number of solutions.

By analyzing a typical reduced matrix, such as the one shown in Figure 1.24 we can see why this theorem must be true in general. Let us first assume the case in which there is no solution; that is, there is no row with all zeros except for the last entry. Then

$$\begin{aligned} \text{number of leading variables} \; &= \; \text{number of leading ones} \\ &\leq \; \text{number of equations} \\ &< \; \text{number of variables} \end{aligned}$$

Thus, there is one variable left to be free, and therefore, the system has an infinite number of solutions.

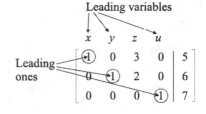

Figure 1.24

✧ Gauss-Jordan (Optional)

Recall in Example 4 that we ended with an echelon matrix that we then solved by backward substitution.

$$\begin{bmatrix} 1 & 2 & 3 & 4 & | & 5 \\ 0 & 0 & 1 & 3 & | & 2 \\ 0 & 0 & 0 & 1 & | & 2 \end{bmatrix}$$

It is possible, however, to continue to perform row operations to reduce this matrix to a simple form called reduced row echelon form (or RREF) that allows us to read off the solution. Keep in mind, however, that the amount of calculations that we will do is no more nor less than what we did in backward substitution.

We start with the leading one in the last row and perform row operations to obtain zeros in the column above this leading one. We use the row with the leading one to aid in this in an efficient way. We then move to the next-to-the-last row with a leading one and perform row operations to obtain zeros in the column above this leading one. We use the rows with the leading ones in an efficient way as shown below.

$$\begin{bmatrix} 1 & 2 & 3 & 4 & | & 5 \\ 0 & 0 & 1 & 3 & | & 2 \\ 0 & 0 & 0 & 1 & | & 2 \end{bmatrix} \begin{array}{l} R_1 - 4R_3 \rightarrow R_1 \\ R_2 - 3R_3 \rightarrow R_2 \end{array} \rightarrow \begin{bmatrix} 1 & 2 & 3 & 0 & | & -3 \\ 0 & 0 & 1 & 0 & | & -4 \\ 0 & 0 & 0 & 1 & | & 2 \end{bmatrix} R_1 - 3R_2 \rightarrow R_1$$

$$\rightarrow \begin{bmatrix} 1 & 2 & 0 & 0 & | & 9 \\ 0 & 0 & 1 & 0 & | & -4 \\ 0 & 0 & 0 & 1 & | & 2 \end{bmatrix}$$

This can then be written as the following system.

$$\begin{array}{rcl} x + 2y & = & 9 \\ z & = & -4 \\ u & = & 2 \end{array}$$

As before, we have $u = 2$. But now we see that we immediately have $z = -4$. From our previous discussion, we know that y is the free variable. So we let $y = t$, where t is any real number. Now from the first equation, we have

$$\begin{array}{rcl} x + 2y & = & 9 \\ x + 2(t) & = & 9 \\ x & = & 9 - 2t \end{array}$$

The general solution is then $(x, y, z, u) = (9 - 2t, t, -4, 2)$ as before.

REMARK: The Gauss-Jordan method consists of putting a matrix in row reduced echelon form using elementary row operations

---

Row Reduced Echelon Form

A matrix is in row reduced echelon form if the following are true about the matrix of coefficients found to the left of the vertical line in an augmented matrix.

1. The first nonzero element in any row is 1, called the leading one.

2. The column containing the leading one has all elements above and below the leading one equal to 0.

3. The leading one in any row is to the left of the leading one in a lower row.

4. Any row consisting of all zeros must be below any row with at least one nonzero element.

Consider a typical matrix that is already in echelon form as shown. We outline how the row operations would proceed.

$$\begin{bmatrix} \textcircled{1} & x & x & x & x & x & | & x \\ 0 & \textcircled{1} & x & x & x & x & | & x \\ 0 & 0 & 0 & \textcircled{1} & x & x & | & x \\ 0 & 0 & 0 & 0 & 0 & \textcircled{1} & | & x \\ 0 & 0 & 0 & 0 & 0 & 0 & | & 0 \end{bmatrix} \rightarrow \begin{bmatrix} \textcircled{1} & x & x & x & x & 0 & | & x \\ 0 & \textcircled{1} & x & x & x & 0 & | & x \\ 0 & 0 & 0 & \textcircled{1} & x & 0 & | & x \\ 0 & 0 & 0 & 0 & 0 & \textcircled{1} & | & x \\ 0 & 0 & 0 & 0 & 0 & 0 & | & 0 \end{bmatrix}$$

$$\rightarrow \begin{bmatrix} \textcircled{1} & x & x & 0 & x & 0 & | & x \\ 0 & \textcircled{1} & x & 0 & x & 0 & | & x \\ 0 & 0 & 0 & \textcircled{1} & x & 0 & | & x \\ 0 & 0 & 0 & 0 & 0 & \textcircled{1} & | & x \\ 0 & 0 & 0 & 0 & 0 & 0 & | & 0 \end{bmatrix}$$

$$\rightarrow \begin{bmatrix} \textcircled{1} & 0 & x & 0 & x & 0 & | & x \\ 0 & \textcircled{1} & x & 0 & x & 0 & | & x \\ 0 & 0 & 0 & \textcircled{1} & x & 0 & | & x \\ 0 & 0 & 0 & 0 & 0 & \textcircled{1} & | & x \\ 0 & 0 & 0 & 0 & 0 & 0 & | & 0 \end{bmatrix}$$

✧ Enrichment: Efficient Calculations

We will now consider the issue of the best way of doing the precise sequence of row operations that will result in the least number of calculations. Consider for convenience, that we have a system of three linear equations with the variables u, v, and w, and do not need to use row swaps. We outline the procedure.

1. Make sure that the coefficient of u in the first equation is 1.

2. Use row operations with the first equation to eliminate u from the second and third equations.

3. Make sure that the coefficient of v in the second equation is 1.

4. Use a row operation with the second equation to eliminate w from the third equation.

5. Make sure that the coefficient of w in the third equation is 1. Stopping at this point gives

$$\begin{bmatrix} x & x & x & | & x \\ x & x & x & | & x \\ x & x & x & | & x \end{bmatrix} \rightarrow \begin{bmatrix} 1 & x & x & | & x \\ 0 & x & x & | & x \\ 0 & x & x & | & x \end{bmatrix} \rightarrow \begin{bmatrix} 1 & x & x & | & x \\ 0 & 1 & x & | & x \\ 0 & 0 & x & | & x \end{bmatrix} \rightarrow \begin{bmatrix} 1 & x & x & | & x \\ 0 & 1 & x & | & x \\ 0 & 0 & 1 & | & x \end{bmatrix}$$

6. Now use row operations with the third equation to eliminate w from the first and second equations.

7. Use a row operation with the second equation to eliminate v from the first equation. Continuing we have

$$\begin{bmatrix} 1 & x & x & | & x \\ 0 & 1 & x & | & x \\ 0 & 0 & 1 & | & x \end{bmatrix} \rightarrow \begin{bmatrix} 1 & x & 0 & | & x \\ 0 & 1 & 0 & | & x \\ 0 & 0 & 1 & | & x \end{bmatrix} \rightarrow \begin{bmatrix} 1 & 0 & 0 & | & x \\ 0 & 1 & 0 & | & x \\ 0 & 0 & 1 & | & x \end{bmatrix}$$

In general, if you do row operations other than those outlined above, you will end up doing more calculations. You can actually prove this. Software created for solving systems always uses the procedure above to ensure that in general the process will use the least possible calculations. We therefore suggest that you follow this procedure in general so that you also can use the fewest possible calculations.

For example, doing the row operations in the following way will in general result in more calculations than that outlined above. See Exercises 66 and 67.

$$\left[\begin{array}{ccc|c} x & x & x & x \\ x & x & x & x \\ x & x & x & x \end{array}\right] \rightarrow \left[\begin{array}{ccc|c} 1 & x & x & x \\ 0 & x & x & x \\ 0 & x & x & x \end{array}\right] \rightarrow \left[\begin{array}{ccc|c} 1 & 0 & x & x \\ 0 & 1 & x & x \\ 0 & 0 & x & x \end{array}\right] \rightarrow \left[\begin{array}{ccc|c} 1 & 0 & 0 & x \\ 0 & 1 & 0 & x \\ 0 & 0 & 1 & x \end{array}\right]$$

✧ Technology Corner

⑦Technology Note 1   **Example 3 on a Graphing Calculator**

The calculator can do the Gauss elimination and backward substitution, but it cannot write the general solution. But, as before we can read the information off of the RREF form that is returned from the calculator. Screen 1 shows the initial augmented matrix and Screen 2 shows the final matrix.

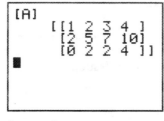
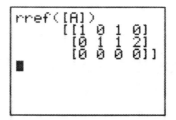

Screen 1   **Screen 2**

Note that the system of equations is slightly different in appearance (though, of course, the solution will be the same in the end) when the calculator puts the system in RREF form:

$$\begin{aligned} x \quad + z &= 0 \\ y + z &= 2 \\ 0 &= 0 \end{aligned}$$

The basic variables are still those with the leading ones, x and y in this system and z will be the parameter. Substitute $z = t$ into the system and simplify,

$$\begin{aligned} x \quad + t = 0 &\rightarrow x = -t \\ y + t = 2 &\rightarrow y = 2 - t \end{aligned}$$

The solution, as before, is $(x, y, z) = (-t, 2-t, t)$ where t can be any real number.

⑦ Technology Note 2   Example 4 on a Graphing Calculator

The initial and final matrices are shown in Screens 3 and 4.

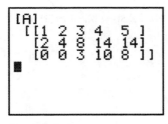

Screen 3

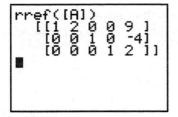

Screen 4

The system of equations in Screen 4 is

$$
\begin{aligned}
x + 2y &= 9 \\
z &= -4 \\
u &= 2
\end{aligned}
$$

The basic variables are x, z, and u. Set the free variable $y = t$ as above and find $x = 9 - 2z$. The solution is $(x, y, z, u) = (9 - 2t, t, -4, 2)$, where t is any real number.

⑦ Technology Note 3   Example 5 on a Graphing Calculator

The calculator will give the same solution, as shown in Screens 5 and 6.

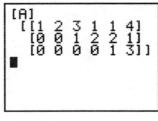

Screen 5

Screen 6

The system of equations from the RREF matrix is shown below. The columns without the leading ones have already been labeled as parameters. That is $y = s$ and $u = t$.

$$
\begin{array}{ccccc}
\textcircled{x} & s & \textcircled{z} & t & \textcircled{v} \\
\end{array}
$$

$$
\left[\begin{array}{ccccc|c}
1 & 2 & 0 & -5 & 0 & 16 \\
0 & 0 & 1 & 2 & 0 & -5 \\
0 & 0 & 0 & 0 & 1 & 3
\end{array}\right] \rightarrow
\begin{aligned}
x + 2s - 5t &= 16 \\
z + 2t &= -5 \\
v &= 3
\end{aligned}
$$

$$
\rightarrow
\begin{aligned}
x &= 16 - 2s + 5t \\
z &= -5 - 2t \\
v &= 3
\end{aligned}
$$

Putting this in the form $(x, y, z, u, v) = (16 - 2s + 5t, s, -5 - 2t, t, 3)$, with s and t any real number, we see the solution is the same.

Self-Help Exercises 1.4

1. Given the following augmented matrix, find the solution to the corresponding system.

$$\begin{array}{ccc} x & y & z \end{array}$$
$$\left[\begin{array}{ccc|c} 1 & 2 & 1 & 4 \\ 1 & 2 & 0 & 2 \\ 0 & 0 & 0 & 0 \end{array}\right]$$

2. Given the following augmented matrix, find the solution to the corresponding system.

$$\begin{array}{ccc} x & y & z \end{array}$$
$$\left[\begin{array}{ccc|c} 0 & 1 & 1 & 1 \\ 0 & 0 & 1 & 2 \\ 0 & 0 & 0 & 0 \end{array}\right]$$

3. A contractor has 2000 hours of labor available for three projects: a fence, a deck, and a porch. The cost per work-hour for each of the three projects is $10, $12, and $14, respectively, and the total labor cost is $25,000. Find the number of work-hours that should be allocated to each project if all the available work-hours are to be used and all $25,000 spent on labor.

1.4 Exercises

In Exercises 1 through 6, determine whether or not each matrix is in echelon form.

1. $\left[\begin{array}{ccc|c} 1 & 2 & 2 & 1 \\ 0 & 1 & 3 & 2 \end{array}\right]$

2. $\left[\begin{array}{ccc|c} 1 & 0 & 1 & 2 \\ 0 & 0 & 1 & 3 \end{array}\right]$

3. $\left[\begin{array}{ccccc|c} 1 & 2 & 4 & 2 & 3 & 1 \\ 0 & 0 & 0 & 1 & 2 & 2 \end{array}\right]$

4. $\left[\begin{array}{ccc|c} 0 & 1 & 2 & 1 \\ 0 & 0 & 1 & 1 \\ 0 & 0 & 0 & 0 \end{array}\right]$

5. $\left[\begin{array}{ccc|c} 1 & 0 & 0 & 3 \\ 0 & 0 & 0 & 0 \\ 0 & 0 & 1 & 2 \end{array}\right]$

6. $\left[\begin{array}{ccccccc|c} 0 & 0 & 1 & 2 & 2 & 4 & 2 & 1 \\ 0 & 0 & 0 & 0 & 1 & 2 & 3 & 2 \\ 0 & 0 & 0 & 0 & 0 & 0 & 0 & 0 \end{array}\right]$

In Exercises 7 through 16, each of the matrices is in echelon form. Write the corresponding linear system and solve.

7. $\begin{array}{cc} x & y \end{array}$
$\left[\begin{array}{cc|c} 1 & 0 & 2 \\ 0 & 1 & 3 \end{array}\right]$

8. $\begin{array}{cc} x & y \end{array}$
$\left[\begin{array}{cc|c} 1 & 3 & 0 \\ 0 & 0 & 0 \end{array}\right]$

9. $\begin{array}{cc} x & y \end{array}$
$\left[\begin{array}{cc|c} 1 & 2 & 4 \\ 0 & 0 & 0 \end{array}\right]$

10. $\begin{array}{ccc} x & y & z \end{array}$
$\left[\begin{array}{ccc|c} 1 & 0 & 2 & 1 \\ 0 & 1 & 0 & 0 \end{array}\right]$

11. $\begin{array}{cccc} x & y & z & u \end{array}$
$\left[\begin{array}{cccc|c} 1 & 0 & 2 & 3 & 4 \\ 0 & 1 & 2 & 3 & 5 \end{array}\right]$

12. $\begin{array}{cccc} x & y & z & u \end{array}$
$\left[\begin{array}{cccc|c} 1 & 0 & 0 & 0 & 3 \\ 0 & 1 & 2 & 3 & 4 \end{array}\right]$

13. $\begin{array}{cccc} x & y & z & u \end{array}$
$\left[\begin{array}{cccc|c} 1 & 0 & 2 & 4 & 6 \\ 0 & 1 & 2 & 3 & 1 \\ 0 & 0 & 0 & 0 & 0 \end{array}\right]$

14. $\begin{array}{ccc} x & y & z \end{array}$
$\left[\begin{array}{ccc|c} 0 & 1 & 0 & 1 \\ 0 & 0 & 1 & 2 \\ 0 & 0 & 0 & 0 \end{array}\right]$

15.
$$\begin{array}{cccccc} x & y & z & u & v & w \end{array}$$
$$\left[\begin{array}{cccccc|c} 0 & 1 & 2 & 0 & 2 & 0 & 1 \\ 0 & 0 & 0 & 1 & 1 & 0 & 2 \\ 0 & 0 & 0 & 0 & 0 & 1 & 3 \end{array}\right]$$

16.
$$\begin{array}{cccc} x & y & z & u \end{array}$$
$$\left[\begin{array}{cccc|c} 0 & 0 & 1 & 0 & 2 \\ 0 & 0 & 0 & 1 & 0 \\ 0 & 0 & 0 & 0 & 0 \end{array}\right]$$

In Exercises 17 through 42, solve. You will find systems with an infinite number of solutions, with no solution, or with a unique solution.

17. $2x - 4y = 8$
$\quad\ -x + 2y = 4$

18. $-3x + 6y = 12$
$\quad\quad\ x - 2y = \ \ 4$

19. $3x - 6y = \ \ 12$
$\quad\ -x + 2y = -4$

20. $-2x + 4y = \ \ 12$
$\quad\quad\ x - 2y = -6$

21. $-x + 3y = \quad 7$
$\quad\ 2x - 6y = -14$

22. $\quad x - 3y = -8$
$\quad -2x + 6y = \ \ 16$

23. $0.1x - 0.3y = 0.4$
$\quad -2x + \ \ 6y = \ \ 4$

24. $-0.1x + 0.3y = 0.5$
$\quad\quad\ 2x - \ \ 6y = \ \ 1$

25. $-x + 2y + 3z = 14$
$\quad\ 2x - \ y + 2z = \ \ 2$

26. $2x - 2y + 2z = -2$
$\quad 3x + \ y - \ z = \ \ 5$

27. $-2x + 6y + 4z = \quad 12$
$\quad\ 3x - 9y - 6z = -18$

28. $\quad 3x - 3y + 6z = \quad 15$
$\quad -2x + 2y - 4z = -10$

29. $-x + \ \ 5y + 3z = \quad\ 7$
$\quad\ 2x - 10y + 6z = -14$

30. $\quad x - \ y + 3z = \quad 4$
$\quad -2x + 2y - 6z = -8$

31. $x + y + z = 1$
$\quad x - y - z = 2$
$\quad 3x + y + z = 4$

32. $x - y - z = 2$
$\quad 2x + y + z = 1$
$\quad 4x - y - z = 5$

33. $2x + \ y - \ z = 0$
$\quad 3x - \ y + 2z = 1$
$\quad\ x - 2y + 3z = 2$

34. $x - \ y + \ z = 1$
$\quad 2x + 3y - 2z = 1$
$\quad 3x + 2y - \ z = 1$

35. $x - 2y + 2z = 1$
$\quad 2x + \ y - \ z = 2$
$\quad 3x - \ y + \ z = 3$

36. $\quad x + \ y - 2z = 2$
$\quad -x + 2y + \ z = 3$
$\quad\ x + 4y - 3z = 7$

37. $x + \ y = \quad 4$
$\quad 2x - 3y = -7$
$\quad 3x - 4y = -9$

38. $x - 3y = -7$
$\quad 3x + 4y = \quad 5$
$\quad 2x - \ y = -4$

39. $x + 2y = 4$
$\quad 2x - 3y = 5$
$\quad\ x - 5y = 2$

40. $x - 3y = 2$
$\quad 3x + 2y = 1$
$\quad 2x + 5y = 1$

41. $x + y + \ z = 1$
$\quad x - y + \ z = 2$
$\quad 3x + y + 3z = 1$

42. $x + \ y + \ z = 1$
$\quad\ x - \ y - \ z = 1$
$\quad 4x + 4y + 2z = 2$

Perform the elementary row operations to find the solution to the systems in Exercises 43 and 44.

43. $1.2x + 2.1y + 3.4z = 54.2$
$\quad 2.1x + 5.1y + 1.4z = 72.7$
$\quad 3.7x + 1.4y + 3.8z = 62.9$

44. $\quad 2.3x + 1.04y + 3.65z = 44.554$
$\quad 1.32x + 2.87y + 5.21z = 59.923$
$\quad 1.66x + 1.92y + 3.41z = 42.617$

For Exercises 45 through 47, graph the equations to see if there is a solution.

45. $x + 2y = 4$
$2x - 3y = 5$
$x - 5y = 3$

46. $x - 3y = 2$
$3x + 2y = 1$
$2x + 5y = 2$

47. $x - 3y = 2$
$3x + 2y = 1$
$4x - y = 3$

48. A person has three more dimes than nickels. If the total value of these coins is $2.40, how many of each type of coin must this person have?

49. A person has 36 coins, all of which are nickels, dimes, and quarters. If the total value of the coins is $4, how many of each type of coin must this person have?

Applications

50. Investments A pension fund manager has been given a total of $900,000 by a corporate client to invest in certain types of stocks and bonds over the next year. Stocks must be restricted to a certain class of low-risk stocks and another class of medium-risk stocks. Furthermore, the client demands an annual return of 8%. The pension fund manager assumes from historical data that the low-risk stocks should return 9% annually, the medium-risk stocks 11% annually, and bonds 7%. If the client demands an annual return of 9%, what should the pension fund manager do?

51. Cake Baking A bakery makes three kinds of special cakes. The Moon cake uses 2 cups of butter and 2 cups of sugar. The Spoon cake uses 1 cup of butter and 2 cups of sugar. The Loon cake uses 7 cups of butter and 4 cups of sugar. The bakery has 30 cups of butter and 30 cups of sugar available to make cakes today. How many of each type of cake can be made to use all the sugar and butter available?

52. Production Scheduling A small plant with a cutting department, a sewing department, and a packaging department produces three styles of sweaters: crew, turtleneck, and V-neck. It takes 0.4 work-hours to cut a crew sweater and 0.2 work-hours to sew it. It takes 0.3 work-hours to cut a turtleneck and the same to sew it. It takes 0.5 work-hours to cut a V-neck and 0.6 work-hours to sew it. If every day the cutting department has 110 work-hours available, the sewing department has 95 work-hours available, and the packaging department has 30 work-hours available, how many sweaters of each style can be produced eachday if all departments work at full capacity?

53. Sales of Sandals A store sells a total of 300 sandals in a certain month. The sandals come in three styles: Tiderunner, Sport, and Stone Harbor. The sales of the Sport sandal equaled the sum of the other two. The Tiderunner sandal costs $30, the Sport costs $40, and the Stone Harbor costs $50. If the store sold $11,500 worth of these sandals in that month, how many sandals of each style were sold?

54. Production Each day a firm produces 100 units of a perishable ingredient I and 200 units of another perishable ingredient II, both of which are used to manufacture four products, X, Y, Z, and U. The following table indicates how many units of each of the two perishable ingredients are used to manufacture each unit of the four products.

	I	II
X	0.1	0.4
Y	0.3	0.2
Z	0.6	0.4
U	0.2	0.3

Let x, y, z, and u be respectively the number of units of X, Y, Z, and U that are manufactured each day. If the manufacturer wishes to use the perishable ingredient that day, what are the options for the amounts of the four products to be manufactured?

55. Production Refer to the previous exercise. Just before production for the day is to begin, an order for 500 units of product U is received. The production manager is told to fill this order this very same day (while still using all the perishable ingredients) or be fired. Will the production manager be fired? Why or why not?

56. Production A woodworking company makes footstools, coffee tables, and rocking chairs. Each spends time in a fabrication shop, a gluing shop, and a painting shop. The following table shows the number of hours each item spends in each shop. If there are 42 hours available in the fabrication shop, 30 hours in the gluing shop, and 24 hours in the painting shop, how many of each item can be made if all the available hours are to be used?

	Fabrication shop hours	Gluing shop hours	Painting shop hours
Foot – stool	1	0.5	1
Coffee table	2	1.5	1
Rocking chair	8	7	2

57. **Scheduling Documents** An insurance company has three types of documents to process: appeals, claims, and enrollment forms. The appeals document needs to be examined for 2 hours by the accountant and 3 hours by the attorney. The claims document needs to be examined for 4 hours by the accountant and 2 hours by the attorney. Finally, the enrollment forms document needs to be examined for 2 hours by the accountant and 4 hours by the attorney. If the accountant has 34 hours and the attorney 35 hours, how many documents of each type can they process?

Extensions

58. What condition must a, b, and c satisfy so that the following system has a solution?

$$x + 2y = a$$
$$3x + 4y = b$$
$$2x + 3y = c$$

59. Show that the system of equations

$$x + 2y + az = b$$
$$2x + 5y + cz = d$$

has a solution no matter what a, b, c, and d are.

60. **Traffic Flow** The accompanying flow diagram indicates the traffic flow into and out of three intersections during rush hour. Traffic lights placed at each intersection can be timed to control the flow of traffic. Find all possible meaningful flow patterns.

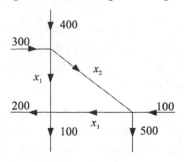

61. **Traffic Flow** The accompanying flow diagram indicates the traffic flow in numbers of vehicles per hour into and out of four intersections during rush hour. Traffic lights placed at each intersection can be timed to control the flow of traffic. Find all possible meaningful flow patterns.

Hint: For each intersection write an equation that states that the total flow into the intersection must equal the total flow out. For example, the diagram indicates that

$$x_1 + x_4 = 300 + 400 = 700$$

Now, using the diagram, find the other three equations. Solve.

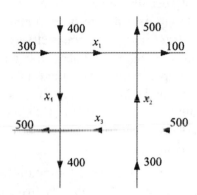

62. **Demand and Supply** Cotterill and Haller estimated the costs and prices in the cereal-manufacturing industry and developed a mathematical model for demand curves for Shredded Wheat and Grape Nuts. They found that when the price p of Shredded Wheat went up, not only did the demand x for Shredded Wheat go down, but the demand for Grape Nuts went up. In the same way, when the price of q of Grape Nuts went up, not only did the demand y for Grape Nuts go down, but the demand for Shredded Wheat went up. They found the demand equations approximated by

$$x = 1.00 - 0.43p + 0.18q$$
$$y = 1.34 + 0.17p - 0.56q$$

Let the supply equations be given as

$$p = 1 + 0.5x + y$$
$$q = 1 + x + y$$

Find the point of equilibrium, that is, the point at which all four equations are satisfied.

Source: Cotterill and Haller 1997

63. **Demand and Supply** When the price p of pork goes up, not only does the demand x for pork go down, but the demand for beef goes up. In the same way, when the price of q of beef goes up, not only does

the demand y for beef go down, but the demand for pork goes up. Let the demand equations be given by

$$x = 6 - 2p + q \qquad y = 16 + p - 3q$$

and let the supply equations be given as

$$p = 1 + 0.5x + y \qquad q = 1 + x + y$$

Find the point of equilibrium, that is, the point at which all four equations are satisfied.

64. **Four Investments** An individual wants to invest $100,000 in four investment vehicles: a money market fund, a bond fund, a conservative stock fund, and a speculative stock fund. These four investments are assumed to have annual returns of 6%, 8%, 10%, and 13%, respectively. The investor wants the same amount in the money market as in the speculative stock fund and wants the same amount in the bond fund as the sum of the amounts in the two stock funds. Can the investor yield $9,000 per year using the given restrictions? Why or why not?

65. **Investments** Use the information found in the previous exercise, except that the investor wants a yield of $10,000 per year. How can the investor do this?

66. **Efficient Calculations** Consider the following system of linear equations.

$$
\begin{aligned}
2x + 4y + 4z &= 10 \\
3x + 2y + z &= 7 \\
2x - y - z &= 4
\end{aligned}
$$

First solve this system carefully counting the number of multiplications and divisions needed by exactly following the method shown in the text. Now solve this system carefully counting the number of multiplications and divisions needed by exactly following the alternative method shown in the text in the Enrichment subsection (p. 59). Which method required the least number of multiplications plus divisions?

67. **Efficient Calculations** Consider the following system of linear equations.

$$
\begin{aligned}
x + 2y - 3z &= 4 \\
2x - y + z &= 0 \\
5x - 3y + 2z &= -2
\end{aligned}
$$

First solve this system carefully counting the number of multiplications and divisions needed by exactly following the method shown in the text. Now solve this system carefully counting the number of multiplications and divisions needed by exactly following the alternative method shown in the text in the Enrichment subsection (p. 59). Which method required the least number of multiplications plus divisions?

Solutions to Self-Help Exercises 1.4

1. We have

$$
\begin{bmatrix}
1 & 2 & 1 & 4 \\
1 & 2 & 0 & 2 \\
0 & 0 & 0 & 0
\end{bmatrix}
\quad R_1 - R_2 \to R_2 \quad \to \quad
\begin{bmatrix}
1 & 2 & 1 & 4 \\
0 & 0 & 1 & 2 \\
0 & 0 & 0 & 0
\end{bmatrix}
$$

This can be written as

$$
\begin{aligned}
x + 2y + z &= 4 \\
z &= 2
\end{aligned}
$$

The leading variables are x and z, while y is the free variable. Since y is taken to be arbitrary, we set $y = t$, where t is any real number. Then $x + 2y + z = 4$ becomes $x + 2(t) + (2) = 4$ or $x = 2 - 2t$. The general solution is then $(2 - 2t, t, 2)$, where t is any real number.

2. The matrix is already in echelon form. The leading variables are y and z. The free variable is x. We have $z = 2$. Setting x equal to the parameter t yields $y + z = 1$ or $y = 1 - 2 = -1$. The general solution is then $(t, -1, 2)$.

3. Let x, y, and z be the amount of work-hours allocated to, respectively, the first, second, and third projects. Since the total number of work-hours is 2000, then $x + y + z = 2000$. The labor cost for the first project is $\$10x$, for the second is $\$14z$. Since the total labor funds is $\$25,000$, we then have $10x + 12y + 14z = 25,000$. These two equations are then written as

$$x + y + z = \quad 2000 \text{ work hours}$$
$$10x + 12y + 14z = 25,000 \text{ labor hours}$$

We then have

$$\begin{bmatrix} 1 & 1 & 1 & 2000 \\ 10 & 12 & 14 & 25,000 \end{bmatrix} \quad R_2 - 10R_1 \rightarrow R_2$$

$$\rightarrow \begin{bmatrix} 1 & 1 & 1 & 2000 \\ 0 & 2 & 4 & 5000 \end{bmatrix} \quad 0.5R_2 \rightarrow R_2$$

$$\rightarrow \begin{bmatrix} 1 & 1 & 1 & 2000 \\ 0 & 1 & 2 & 2500 \end{bmatrix}$$

Since the free variable is z, we set $z = t$ where t is any nonnegative number. (Work-hours are nonnegative.) Using backward substitution we have

$$y + 2(t) = 2500$$
$$y = 2500 - 2t$$

$$x + y + z = 2000$$
$$x + (2500 - 2t) + (t) = 2000$$
$$x = t - 500$$

Then the general solution is $(t - 500, 2500 - 2t, t)$. To obtain a reasonable answer we must also have $t - 500 \geq 0$ and $2500 - 2t \geq 0$. This requires $500 \leq t \leq 1250$. Thus, the contractor can allocate $t - 500$ work-hours to the first project, $2500 - 2t$ to the second, and t to the third. For example, taking $t = 800$, means the contractor can allocate 300 work-hours to the first project, 900 work-hours to the first project, and 800 to the third and use all of the available work-hours with all of the $\$25,000$ spent on labor.

1.5   Method of Least Squares

> In 1995 Cohen published a study correlating corporate spending on communications and computers (as a percent of all spending on equipment) with annual productivity growth. He collected data on 11 companies for the period from 1985-1989. This data is found in the following table.
>
> | x | 0.06 | 0.11 | 0.16 | 0.20 | 0.22 | 0.25 | 0.33 | 0.33 | 0.47 | 0.62 | 0.78 |
> |---|---|---|---|---|---|---|---|---|---|---|---|
> | y | −1.0 | 4.5 | −0.6 | 4.2 | 0.4 | 0.1 | 0.4 | 1.4 | 1.1 | 3.4 | 5.5 |
>
> x is the spending on communications and computers as a percent of all spending on equipment, and y is the annual productivity growth as a percent.
>
> What is the equation of a line that best approximates this data? What can you conclude about the relationship between spending on communications and computers and annual productivity growth? See Example 3 for the answer.
>
> *Source:* Cohen 1995

APPLICATION
Technology and Productivity

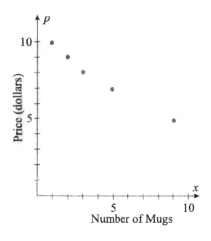

Figure 1.25

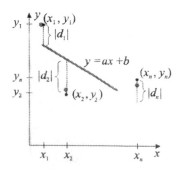

Figure 1.26

✧ The Method of Least Squares

Let x be the number of insulated mugs produced and sold, and let p be the price of each mug. Suppose x_1 mugs were sold at a price of p_1 and x_2 mugs were sold at a price of p_2. If we then *assume* that the demand equation is linear, then of course there is only one straight line through these two points, and we can easily calculate the equation $y = ax + b$ of this line.

What if we have more than two data points? Suppose, as shown in Table 1.3, that we have five points available. Here, p_i are the prices in dollars for insulated mugs, and x_i is the corresponding demand for these insulated mugs in thousands of mugs sold per day.

x_i	1	2	3	5	9
p_i	10	9	8	7	5

Table 1.3

These are plotted in Figure 1.25, which is called a scatter diagram.

If we examine the scatter diagram, we see clearly that the points do not lie on any single straight line but seem to be scattered in a more or less linear fashion. Under such circumstances we might be justified in assuming that the demand equation was more or less a straight line. But what straight line? Any line that we draw will miss most of the points. We might then think to draw a line that is somehow closest to the data points. To actually follow such a procedure, we need to state exactly how we are to measure this closeness. We will measure this closeness in a manner that will lead us to the method of least squares.

First notice that to be given a non-vertical straight line is the same as to be given two numbers a and b with the equation of the straight line given as $y = ax + b$. Suppose now we are given n data points (x_1, y_1), (x_2, y_2), ..., (x_n, y_n) and a line $y = ax + b$. We then define $d_1 = y_1 - (ax_1 + b)$, and note from the figure that $|d_1|$ is just the vertical distance from the first data point (x_1, y_1) to the line $y = ax + b$. Doing the same for all the data points, we then have

$$d_1 = y_1 - (ax_1 + b)$$
$$d_2 = y_2 - (ax_2 + b)$$
$$\vdots$$
$$d_n = y_n - (ax_n + b)$$

where $|d_2|$ is the vertical distance from the second data point (x_2, y_2) to the line $y = ax + b$, and so on. Refer to Figure 1.26.

Now if all the data points were on the line $y = ax + b$, then all the distances $|d_1|, |d_2|, \ldots, |d_n|$ would be zero. Unfortunately, this will rarely be the case. We then use the sum of the squares of these distances

$$d = d_1^2 + d_2^2 + \cdots + d_n^2$$

as a measure of how close the set of data points is to the line $y = ax + b$. Notice that this number d will be different for different straight lines: large if the straight line is far removed from the data points and small if the straight line passes close to all the data points. We then seek this line; that is, we need to find the two numbers a and b that will make this sum of squares the least. Thus the name *least squares*.

EXAMPLE 1 A Demand Function Find the best-fitting line through the data points in Table 1.3 and thus find a linear demand function. Then use the linear demand function to estimate the price if the demand is 6000 mugs. Finally, if the price is $8.00 per mug, use the linear demand function to estimate the number of mugs that will be sold.

Solution Find the best-fitting line using the linear regression operation on a spreadsheet or graphing calculator. The steps are detailed in Technology Notes 1 and 2. You will find that $a = -0.6$ and $b = 10.2$. Thus, the equation of the best-fitting straight line that we are seeking is

$$y = p(x) = -0.6x + 10.2$$

The graph is shown in Figure 1.27. If technology is unavailable, the best-fitting line can be found by hand.

In general, the line $y = ax + b$ closest to the data points (x_1, y_1), (x_2, y_2), ..., (x_n, y_n) can be found by solving the following two linear equations for a and b:

$$(x_1^2 + \cdots + x_n^2)a + (x_1 + \cdots + x_n)b = x_1y_1 + \cdots + x_ny_n$$
$$(x_1 + \cdots + x_n)a + nb = y_1 + \cdots + y_n$$

For our example we indicate these calculations by the following table.

x_i	y_i	x_i^2	x_iy_i
1	10	1	10
2	9	4	18
3	8	9	24
5	7	25	35
9	5	81	45
Sum 20	39	120	132

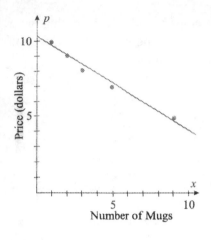

Figure 1.27

Technology Option

Finding the correlation coefficient using a graphing calculator or Microsoft Excel is discussed in Technology Note 3 on page 74.

We then have the system of two equations in the two unknowns a and b.

$$120a + 20b = 132$$
$$20a + 5b = 39$$

These equations can be readily solved using the techniques we used in the last several sections.

To find the price for 6000 mugs, we will use $x = 6$ in the demand equation.

$$p(6) = (-0.6)(6) + 10.2 = 6.6$$

That is, if 6000 mugs are to be sold, then the price should be $6.60 each.

For a price of $8.00 we set $p = 8$ and solve for x,

$$8 = -0.6x + 10.2$$
$$0.6x = 2.2$$
$$x = \frac{2.2}{0.6} = \frac{11}{3} \approx 3.6667$$

Next note that since x represents thousands of mugs, we will expect to sell 3667 mugs at a price of $8.00 each. ◆

✧ Correlation

We have just seen how to determine a functional relationship between two variables. This is called regression analysis. We now wish to determine the strength or degree of association between two variables. This is referred to as correlation analysis. The strength of association is measured by the correlation coefficient which is defined as

$$r = \frac{n \sum x_i y_i - \sum x_i \sum y_i}{\sqrt{[n \sum x_i^2 - (\sum x_i)^2][n \sum y_i^2 - (\sum y_i)^2]}}$$

where $\sum y_i$, for example, is $y_1 + y_2 + \cdots + y_n$. The value of this correlation coefficient ranges from $+1$ for two variables with perfect positive correlation to -1 for two variables with perfect negative correlation. See Figure 1.28 for examples.

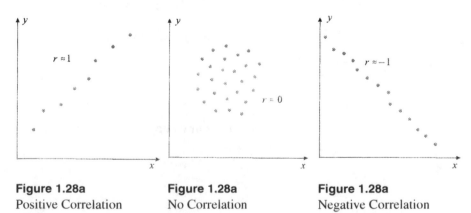

| Figure 1.28a | Figure 1.28a | Figure 1.28a |
| Positive Correlation | No Correlation | Negative Correlation |

EXAMPLE 2 Correlation Find the correlation coefficient for the data in Table 1.3.

Solution We can use the above formula or let our computers or graphing calculators do the work. In doing Example 1 you will find that $r \approx -0.99$. This indicates a high negative correlation, which can easily be seen by observing the original data in Figure 1.25. We conclude that there is a strong negative correlation between price and demand in this instance. Thus, we expect increases in prices to lead to decreases in demand. ◆

✧ Additional Examples

There has been a debate recently as to whether corporate investment in computers has a positive effect on productivity. Some suggest that worker difficulties in adjusting to using computers might actually hinder productivity. The paper mentioned in the following example explores this question.

EXAMPLE 3 Technology and Productivity In 1995 Cohen published a study correlating corporate spending on communications and computers (as a percent of all spending on equipment) with annual productivity growth. He collected data on 11 companies for the period from 1985-1989. This data is found in the following table.

x	0.06	0.11	0.16	0.20	0.22	0.25	0.33	0.33	0.47	0.62	0.78
y	−1.0	4.5	−0.6	4.2	0.4	0.1	0.4	1.4	1.1	3.4	5.5

x is the spending on communications and computers as a percent of all spending on equipment, and y is the annual productivity growth as a percent.

Determine the best-fitting line using least squares and find the correlation coefficient. Discuss the results.

Source: Cohen 1995

Solution Using a spreadsheet or a graphing calculator, we find that $a \approx 5.246$, $b \approx 0.080$, and $r \approx 0.518$. Thus, the best-fitting straight line is

$$y = ax + b = 5.246x + 0.080$$

The correlation coefficient is $r = 0.518$. This is somewhat significant and we say, on the basis of this study, that investment in communications and computers increases the productivity of corporations. See Figure 1.29 ◆

EXAMPLE 4 Plant Costs In 1997 Fuller and coworkers at Texas A&M University estimated the operating costs of cotton gin plants of various sizes. The operating costs of the smallest plant is shown in the following table.

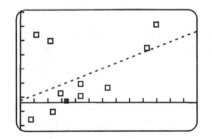

Figure 1.29

x	2	4	6	8
y	109.40	187.24	273.36	367.60

x is annual number of thousands of bales produced, and y is the total cost in thousands of dollars

a. Determine the best-fitting line using least squares and the correlation coefficient.

b. The study noted that revenue was \$55.45 per bale. At what level of production will this plant break even?

c. What are the profits or losses when production is 1000 bales? 2000 bales?

Source: Fuller, Gillis, Parnell, Ramaiyer, and Childers 1997

Solution   **a.** Using a spreadsheet or graphing calculator, we find that linear regression gives the cost equation as $y = C(x) = 43.036x + 19.22$ and $r = 0.9991$. This is certainly significant, as can be seen in Figure 1.30.

b. We set revenue equal to cost and obtain

$$R = C$$
$$55.45x = 43.036x + 19.22$$
$$12.414x = 19.22$$
$$x = 1.548$$

Thus, this plant will break even when production is set at approximately 1548 bales.

We can also solve this problem by finding profits, P, and set this equal to zero. We have profit is revenue less cost. Doing this we obtain

$$P = R - C$$
$$= 55.45x - (43.036x + 19.22)$$
$$= 12.414x - 19.22$$

Setting $P = 0$, gives $12.414x = 19.22$ and $x = 1.548$ as before.

c. Since $P(x) = 12.414x - 19.22$, $P(1) = -6.806$ and $P(2) = 5.608$. Thus, there is a loss of \$6806 when production is at 1000 bales and a profit of \$5608 when production is set at 2000 bales.   ◆

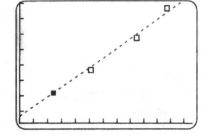

Figure 1.30

Technology Option

Example 4 is solved using a graphing calculator in Technology Note 4 on page 74

✧ Technology Corner

Technology Note 1   **Example 1 on a Graphing Calculator**

We can plot scatter diagrams on our calculator. To graph a scatter plot on your calculator, begin by entering the data into two lists as shown in Screen 1. The lists are accessed via the **STAT** button and choosing the 1:EDIT option. After all pairs of data have been entered, QUIT to the homescreen.

Set up the the STAT PLOT options by pressing **2ND** and then **Y=** button. Press **ENTER** to edit the options for Plot1. The correct settings are shown in Screen 2. Note that the Xlist and Ylist names match the names of the lists that were edited. L1 and L2 are found above the keypad numbers **1** and **2**, respectively. The command 9:ZoomStat found under the **ZOOM** menu will find a window that fits the data to be displayed. The result is shown in Screen 3.

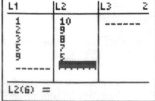

Screen 1

Screen 2

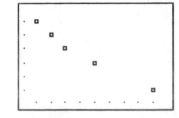

Screen 3

To find the best-fitting line, press [STAT] and right arrow to CALC and choose 4:LinReg(ax+b) as shown in Screen 4. Press [ENTER] to paste this on the home-screen. When LinReg(ax+b) is displayed on the homescreen, enter [VARS], then arrow over to Y-VARS, then 1:Function and press [ENTER] to paste Y_1 next to the LinReg(ax+b) command. The results are displayed in Screen 5 and are also found under Y_1. See Technology Note 4 if your screen lacks the display of r^2 and r.

```
EDIT CALC TESTS
1:1-Var Stats
2:2-Var Stats
3:Med-Med
4:LinReg(ax+b)
5:QuadReg
6:CubicReg
7↓QuartReg
```

Screen 4

```
LinReg
  y=ax+b
  a=-.6
  b=10.2
  r²=.972972973
  r=-.9863939238
■
```

Screen 5

```
Y1=-.6X+10.2


X=6        Y=6.6
```

Screen 6

$[.2,9.8] \times [4.15,10.85]$

To evaluate the regression equation with 6000 mugs, we need to evaluate the function at $x = 6$ (since it is in thousands of mugs). To do this, go to the CALC menu (above [TRACE]) and choose 1:value, as shown in Screen 7. You will be sent back to the graph and enter 6 for X and [ENTER]. The result is shown in Screen 8. To find the number of mugs sold at a price of $8.00, enter 8 for Y2= and then [GRAPH]. Use CALC and 5:intersect to find the number of mugs in thousands.

```
Plot1 Plot2 Plot3
\Y1=-.6X+10.2
\Y2=8
\Y3=■
\Y4=
\Y5=
\Y6=
\Y7=
```

Screen 7

```




Intersection
X=3.6666667  Y=8
```

Screen 8

⑨ **Technology Note 2   Example 1 with Microsoft Excel**

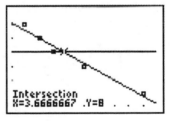

Worksheet 1

Begin by opening a new worksheet. Label Column A with an x and Column B with a p. Enter the data from Table 1.3 as shown in Worksheet 1.1. Highlight the data and choose Chart Wizard from the tool bar or Insert and then Chart, if the Chart Wizard is not on the toolbar. Then pick the XY (Scatter) graph and choose the first chart type, Scatter. Compares pairs of values. Continue clicking Next until the chart is complete, adding titles and labels as needed. When the scatter plot is complete, click on the graph and then on Chart in the tool bar. Choose Add Trendline.... Pick the linear trend line and under the options menu, choose Display equation on chart and Display R-squared value on chart. The completed graph is shown below:

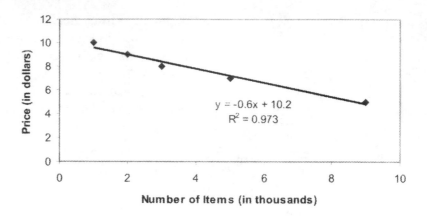

Screen 9

⑨ Technology Note 3 Correlation Coefficient

If your calculator does not display the correlation coefficient, r, it can be enabled by going to the CATALOG menu (above the 0) and scroll down to DiagnosticOn (see Screen 9) and press ENTER . Press ENTER again on the homescreen to enable the diagnostic. Next time a regression is done, the correlation coefficient, r, and the square of the correlation coefficient, r^2, will automatically be displayed. The correlation coefficient will be displayed on the Excel chart when this option is enabled. See Worksheet 1.

⑨ Technology Note 4 Example 4 on a Graphing Calculator

Enter the data into lists L1 and L2. Then, as in Technology Note 2, find the regression equation and enter it into $Y_1 =$ for our cost equation. In $Y_2 =$ enter the revenue equation, 55.45X, as shown in Screen 10. Screen 11 has the graph.

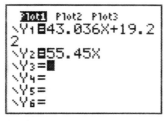

Screen 10

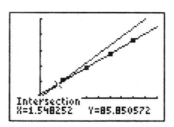

Screen 11

$[-2, 10] \times [-100, 500]$

Self-Help Exercises 1.5

1. Using the method of least squares, find the best-fitting line through the three points $(0,0)$, $(2,2)$, and $(3,2)$. Find the correlation coefficient.

2. The table below shows x, the number of boxes of cereal in thousands that will be supplied at a price y, in dollars. Use the method of least squares and

the supply information in the table to determine how many boxes of cereal will be supplied at a price of $3.75.

x	9	7	6	4	3
y	4.49	3.05	2.49	2.10	1.92

1.5 Exercises

In Exercises 1 through 8, find the best-fitting straight line to the given set of data, using the method of least squares. Graph this straight line on a scatter diagram. Find the correlation coefficient.

1. $(0,0), (1,2), (2,1)$

2. $(0,1), (1,2), (2,2)$

3. $(0,0), (1,1), (2,3), (3,3)$

4. $(0,0), (1,2), (2,2), (3,0)$

5. $(1,4), (2,2), (3,2), (4,1)$

6. $(0,0), (1,1), (2,2), (3,4)$

7. $(0,4), (1,2), (2,2), (3,1), (4,1)$

Applications

8. Selling Strawberries The table below shows x, the number cartons of strawberries, that a fruit stand can sell at different prices y in dollars. Find the demand equation for strawberries using linear regression. Using the demand equation, find the price the stand should charge if they wish to sell 35 cartons of strawberries.

x	12	15	20	27	44	60
y	5.00	4.00	3.50	3.00	2.50	2.00

9. Selling Puzzles The table below shows x, the number of puzzles (in thousands), that the A-Mart company can sell at different prices, y in dollars. Find the demand equation for these puzzles using linear regression. Using that demand equation, find the price that A-Mart should charge if they wish to sell 10,000 puzzles.

x	8	5	12	3	15
y	5.00	6.00	3.50	8.00	3.00

10. Supply of Mugs The table below shows x, the number of mugs in thousands supplied by the Big Mug company for different prices in euros (y). Using linear regression find the supply equation and use it to determine the number of mugs that the Big Mug company will supply when the price is 3 euros.

x	3	5	6	13	18
y	1.50	1.80	2.00	3.20	4.75

11. Purchase Price of a Car The value of a 1998 car is given in the table below (value is in thousands of dollars). Find the depreciation equation using linear regression and use it to estimate to the nearest dollar the purchase price of this car.

Year	2000	2001	2002	2003	2004
Value	19	15	12	9	7

12. Purchase Price of a Machine The data in the table below is the value of a milling machine in thousands of dollars and the number of years since the item was purchased. Use linear regression to estimate the purchase price of this milling machine to the nearest dollar.

years since purchase	1	2	4	6	7
value in dollars	3.9	3.2	2.5	2	1.8

Referenced Applications

13. Deer Population and Deer-Vehicle Accidents Rondeau and Conrad studied the relationship of deer population in urban areas to accidents with vehicles on roads. Below is the data where x is the deer population in Irondequoit, NY, and y is the number of collisions with deer in the same city.

x	340	350	480	510	515	600	650
y	150	60	90	130	120	110	140

x	700	760	765	820	850
y	120	210	170	180	230

a. Determine the best-fitting line using least squares and the correlation coefficient.

b. Explain what the linear model is saying about the deer population and collisions.

Source: Rondeau and Conrad 2003

14. Economies of Scale in Plant Size *Strategic Management* relates a study in economies of scale in the machine-tool industry. The data is found in the following table,

x	70	115	130	190	195	400	450
y	1.1	1.0	0.85	0.75	0.85	0.67	0.50

where x is the plant capacity in thousands of units, and y is the employee-hours per unit.

a. Determine the best-fitting line using least squares and the correlation coefficient.

b. Is there an advantage in having a large plant? Explain.

c. What does this model predict the employee-hours per unit will be when the plant capacity is 300,000 units?

d. What does this model predict the plant capacity will be if the employee-hours per unit is 0.90?

Source: Rowe, Mason, Dickel, Mann, and Mockler 1994

15. **Cost Curve** Dean made a statistical estimation of the cost-output relationship in a hosiery mill. The data is given in the following table,

x	16	31	48	57	63	103	110
y	30	60	100	130	135	230	230

x	114	116	117	118	123	126
y	235	245	250	235	250	260

where x is the output in thousands of dozens and y is the total cost in thousands of dollars.

a. Determine the best-fitting line using least squares and find the correlation coefficient. Graph.

b. What does this model predict the total cost will be when the output is 100,000 dozen?

c. What does this model predict the output will be if the total cost is $125,000?

Source: Dean 1976

16. **Cost Curve** Johnston estimated the cost-output relationship for 40 firms. The data for the fifth firm is given in the following table where x is the output in millions of units and y is the total cost in thousands of pounds sterling

x	180	210	215	230	260	290	340	400
y	130	180	205	190	215	220	250	300

x	405	430	430	450	470	490	510
y	285	305	325	330	330	340	375

a. Determine the best-fitting line using least squares and find the correlation coefficient. Graph.

b. What does this model predict the total cost will be when the output is 300 million units?

c. What does this model predict the output will be if the total cost is 200,000 of pounds sterling?

Source: Johnston 1960

17. **Productivity** Bernstein studied the correlation between productivity growth and gross national product (GNP) growth of six countries. The countries were France (F), Germany (G), Italy (I), Japan (J), the United Kingdom (UK), and the United States (US). Productivity is given as output per employee-hour in manufacturing. The data they collected for the years 1950–1977 is given in the following table where x is the productivity growth (%) and y is the GNP growth (%).

	US	UK	F	I	G	J
x	2.5	2.7	5.2	5.6	5.7	9.0
y	3.5	2.3	4.9	4.9	5.7	8.5

a. Determine the best-fitting line using least squares and the correlation coefficient.

b. What does this model predict the GNP growth will be when the productivity growth is 7 percent?

c. What does this model predict the productivity growth will be if the GNP growth is 7%?

Source: Berstein 1980

18. **Productivity** Recall from Example 3 that Cohen studied the correlation between corporate spending on communications and computers (as a percent of all spending on equipment) and annual productivity growth. In Example 3 we looked at his data on 11 companies for the period from 1985 to 1989. The data found in the following table is for the years 1977–1984 where x is the spending on communications and computers as a percent of all spending on equipment and y is the annual productivity growth.

x	0.03	0.07	0.10	0.13	0.14	0.17
y	−2.0	−1.5	1.7	−0.6	2.2	0.3

x	0.24	0.29	0.39	0.62	0.83
y	1.3	4.2	3.4	4.0	−0.5

Determine the best-fitting line using least squares and the correlation coefficient.

Source: Cohen 1995

19. **Environmental Entomology** The fall armyworm has historically been a severe agricultural pest. How the age at first mating of the female of this pest affected its fecundity as measured by the number of viable larvae resulting from the eggs laid has been studied. The data is shown in following table, where x is the age of first mating of the female in days and y is the total number of viable larvae per female.

x	1	1	3	4	4	6
y	1650	1450	550	1150	650	850

x	6	8	10	10	12	13	15
y	800	450	900	500	100	100	200

Determine the best-fitting line using least squares. Also determine the correlation coefficient.

Source: Rogers and O. G. Marti 1994

20. **Plant Resistance** Talekar and Lin collected the data shown in the table that relates the pod diameter (seed size) of soybeans to the percentage of pods damaged by the limabean pod borer.

x	3.1	3.4	3.9	4.1	4.2	4.5
y	12	28	38	37	44	48

x is the pod diameter in mm and y is the percentage of damaged pods.

   a. Use linear regression to find the best-fitting line that relates the pod diameter to the percentage of pods damaged.
   b. Find the correlation coefficient.
   c. Interpret what the slope of the line means.

Source: Talekar and Lin 1994

21. **Horticultural Entomology** The brown citrus aphid and the melon aphid both spread the citrus tristeza virus to fruit, and thus, have become important pests. Yokomi and coworkers collected the data found in the following table.

x	1	5	10	20
y	25	22	50	85
z	10	5	18	45

x is the number of aphids per plant, y and z are the percentage of times the virus is transmitted to the fruit for the brown and melon aphid, respectively.

   a. Use linear regression for each aphid to find the best-fitting line that relates the number of aphids per plant to the percentage of times the virus is transmitted to the fruit.
   b. Find the correlation coefficients.
   c. Interpret what the slope of the line means in each case.
   d. Which aphid is more destructive? Why?

Source: Yokomi, Lastra, Stoetzel, Damsteegt, Lee, Garnsey, Gottwald, Rocha-Pena, and Niblett 1994

22. **Biological Control** Briano and colleagues studied the host-pathogen relationship between the black imported fire ant and a microsporidium (*T. solenopsae*) that infects them. The fire ant represents a serious medical and agricultural pest. The study was to determine whether *T. solenopae* could be used as a biological control of the imported fire ants. The table includes data that they collected and relates the number of colonies per hectare of the ants with the percentage that are infected with *T. Solenopsae*.

x	23	30	32	50	72	74	79	81	98	110
y	27	35	50	34	14	25	15	33	23	26

x	116	122	132	138	140	150	150	152	162
y	18	28	19	23	22	18	24	21	22

x is the colonies of ants per hectare, and y is the percentage of infected colonies.

   a. Use linear regression to find the best-fitting line that relates the number of colonies of ants per hectare to the percentage of infected colonies.
   b. Find the correlation coefficient.
   c. Interpret what the slope of the line means.

Source: Briano, Patterson, and Cordo 1995

23. **Federal Government Outlays** The federal government budget outlays for recent years is given in the table.

x	2000	2001	2002	203	2004	2005
y	1.789	1.863	2.011	2.160	2.292	2.479

x is the year and y is budget outlays in billions of dollars.

   a. Use linear regression to find the best-fitting line that relates the budget outlays in billions of dollars to the year.
   b. Use this line to estimate the budget outlays for the year 2006.
   c. Find the correlation coefficient.

Source: Office of Management and Budget

24. **Death Rate** The table gives the death rate for the total population of the United States for recent years.

x	2000	2001	2002	2003	2004
y	8.7	8.5	8.5	8.3	8.1

x is the year and y is the death rate per 1000 total population in the United States.

a. Use linear regression to find the best-fitting line that relates the death rate to the year.

b. Use this line to estimated the death rate for the year 2006.

c. Find the correlation coefficient.

Source: U.S. National Center for Health Statistics

25. **Homeownership Rate** The table gives the rate of homeownership in the United States for recent years.

x	1999	2000	2001	2002	2003
y	66.8	67.4	67.8	67.9	68.3

x is the year and y is the percent of family units who own houses.

a. Use linear regression to find the best-fitting line that relates the percent of homeownership to the year.

b. Use this line to estimate the homeownership rate for the year 2006.

c. Find the correlation coefficient.

26. **Corn Production.** The table gives the U.S. production in millions of metric tons of corn.

x	1995	1999	2000	2004
y	188.0	240.0	251.9	300.0

x is the year and y is the U.S. production of corn in metric tons.

a. Use linear regression to find the best-fitting line that relates the U.S. production of corn to the year.

b. Use this line to estimate the U.S. production of corn for the year 2006.

c. Find the correlation coefficient.

Source: U.S. Dept. of Agriculture

27. **Gross Domestic Product** The table gives the U.S. gross domestic product (GDP) in billions of dollars for recent years.

x	1990	2000	2003	2004
y	5803	9817	10,971	11,734

x is the year and y is the U.S. gross domestic product in billions of dollars.

a. Use linear regression to find the best-fitting line that relates the U.S. GDP to the year.

b. Use this line to estimate the U.S. GDB for the year 2006.

c. Find the correlation coefficient.

d. Interpret what the slope of the line means.

Source: U.S. Bureau of Economic Analysis

28. **Consumer Price Index** The table gives the consumer price index(CPI) for recent years.

x	2000	2001	2002	2003	2004
y	172.2	177.1	179.9	184.0	188.9

x is the year and y is the CPI.

a. Use linear regression to find the best-fitting line that relates the U.S. CPI to the year.

b. Use this line to estimate the U.S. CPI for the year 2006.

c. Find the correlation coefficient.

Source: U.S. Bureau of the Census

29. **Consumer Credit** The table gives the consumer credit outstanding in billions of dollars for some recent years.

x	2000	2002	2003	2004
y	1704	1923	2014	2105

x is the year and y is the consumer credit outstanding in billions of dollars.

a. Use linear regression to find the best-fitting line that relates the U.S. consumer credit outstanding to the year.

b. Use this line to estimate the U.S. consumer credit outstanding for the year 2006.

c. Find the correlation coefficient.

Source: Board of Governors of the Federal Reserve System

30. **Advertising** The table shows the advertising expenditures in the U.S. (in billions of dollars) for recent years.

x	2000	2001	2002	2003	2004
y	244	231	236	245	264

x is the year and y the advertising expenditures in the U.S. in billions of dollars

a. Use linear regression to find the best-fitting line that relates the U.S. advertising expenditures to the year.

b. Use this line to estimate the U.S. advertising expenditures for the year 2006.

c. Find the correlation coefficient.

Source: Advertising Age

31. **World Crude Oil Production** The table shows the world crude oil production (in million of barrels per day) in recent years.

x	1990	2000	2002	2003
y	60.57	68.34	66.84	69.32

x is the year and y the world crude oil production in million of barrels per day

a. Use linear regression to find the best-fitting line that relates the world crude oil production in millions of barrels per day to the year.

b. Use this line to estimate the world crude oil production in millions of barrels per day for the year 2006.

c. Find the correlation coefficient.

Source: U.S. Dept. of Energy

32. **Personal Computer Sales Average Price** The table shows the average price of a personal computer in dollars for each year.

x	1999	2000	2001	2002
y	1100	1000	900	855

x is the year and y the average price of a personal computer.

a. Use linear regression to find the best-fitting line that relates the average price of a personal computer to the year.

b. Use this line to estimate the price of a personal computer for the year 2006.

c. Find the correlation coefficient.

d. Interpret what the slope of the line means.

Source: Consumer Electronics Association

Solutions to Self-Help Exercises 1.5

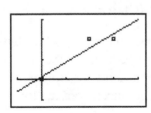

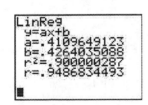

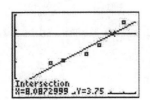

1. Input the data into a spreadsheet or graphing calculator. Using the linear regression operation, we find that $a \approx 0.714$, $b \approx 0.143$, and $r \approx 0.9449$. Thus, the best-fitting straight line is

$$y = ax + b = 0.714x + 0.143$$

The correlation coefficient is $r = 0.9449$. This is significant. See the screen on the left.

2. Input the data into a spreadsheet or graphing calculator. Using the linear regression operation we find that $a \approx 0.41096$ and $b \approx 0.42640$. The correlation is quite significant at $r \approx 0.94868$, see the screen below. To find the number of boxes of cereal demanded at a price of $3.75, either solve the equation

$$3.75 = 0.41096x + 0.42640 \rightarrow x \approx 8.0873$$

Or graph the regression equation and the line $p = 3.75$ and find the intersection, as shown in the screen on the left. The value $x \approx 8.0873$ means that 8087 boxes of cereal will be demanded.

Review

✧ Summary Outline

- A function f from the set D to the set R is a rule that assigns to each element x in D one and only one element $y = f(x)$ in R.

- The set D above is called the domain.

- One thinks of the domain as the set of inputs and the values $y = f(x)$ as the outputs.

- The set of all possible outputs is called the range.

- The letter representing the elements in the domain is called the independent variable.

- The letter representing the elements in the range is called the dependent variable.

- The graph of the function f consists of all points (x, y) such that x is in the domain of f and $y = f(x)$.

- Linear Cost, Revenue, and Profit Equations. Let x be the number of items made and sold.

   variable cost = (cost per item) × (number of items produced) = mx.

   C = cost = (variable cost) + (fixed cost) = $mx + b$.

   R = revenue = (price per item) × (number sold) = px.

   P = profit = (revenue) − (cost) = $R - C$.

- The quantity at which the profit is zero is called the break-even quantity.

- Let x be the number of items made and sold and p the price of each item. A linear demand equation, which governs the behavior of the consumer, is of the form $p = mx + b$, where m must be negative. A linear supply equation, which governs the behavior of the producer, is of the form $p = mx + b$, where m must be positive.

- The point at which supply equals demand is called the equilibrium point. The x-coordinate of the equilibrium point is called the equilibrium quantity, and the p-coordinate is called the equilibrium price.

- A system of linear equations is a set of linear equations.

- The set of all solutions to a system of linear equations is called the solution set.

- Two systems of equations with the same solution set are said to be equivalent.

- A matrix is a rectangular array of numbers.

- There are three elementary operations performed on a system of equations (matrix). Interchange two equations (rows). Replace an equation (row) with a constant times the equation (row). Replace an equation (row) plus a constant times another equation (row).

- Elementary operations yield an equivalent system of equations.

- Gauss elimination is a procedure for a systematically using elementary operations to reduce a system of linear equations to an equivalent system whose solution set can be immediately determined by backward substitution.

- There are three possibilities in solving a system of linear equations: There can be precisely one solution. There can be no solution. There can be infinitely many solutions.

- A matrix is in echelon form if:

  1. The first nonzero element in any row is 1, called the leading one.

  2. The column containing the leading one has all elements below the leading one equal to 0.

  3. The leading one in any row is to the left of the leading one in a lower row.

  4. Any row consisting of all zeros must be below any row with at least one nonzero element.

- The leftmost nonzero element in a nonzero row of a matrix in echelon form is called a leading one.

- The variable in the column of a matrix in echelon form containing the leading one is called a leading variable. The remaining variables are called free variables.

- A parameter is any real number. Free variables are set equal to a parameter and are thus free to be any number.

Review Exercises

1. Assuming a linear cost model, find the equation for the cost C, where x is the number produced, the cost per item is $6, and the fixed cost is $2000.

2. Assuming a linear revenue equation, find the revenue equation for R, where x is the number sold and the price per item is $10.

3. Assuming the cost and revenue equations in the previous two exercises, find the profit equations. Also find the break-even quantity.

4. Given that the cost equation is $C = 5x + 3000$ and the revenue equation is $R = 25x$, find the break-even quantity.

5. Given the demand curve $p = -2x + 4000$ and the supply curve $p = x + 1000$, find the equilibrium point.

6. **Demand for Pens** A company notes from experience that it can sell 100,000 pens at $1 each and 120,000 of the same pens at $.90 each. Find the demand equation, assuming it is linear.

7. **Profit from Magazines** It costs a publisher $2 to

produce a copy of a weekly magazine. The magazine sells for $2.50 a copy, and the publisher obtains advertising revenue equal to 30% of the revenue from sales. How many copies must be sold to obtain a profit of $15,000?

8. **Oil Wildcatter** An oil wildcatter has drilled an oil well at a cost of $70,000. We will assume there are no variable costs. The revenue for this well is $12,000 per year. Determine a profit equation $P(t)$, where t is given in years.

9. **Oil Secondary Recovery** After drilling, striking oil, and extracting an optimal amount of oil, a wildcatter decides to introduce secondary recovery techniques at a fixed cost of $20,000. The revenue using this recovery technique should yield an additional $2000 per year. Write a profit function $P(t)$ as a function of the years t, assuming no variable costs.

10. **Rent or Buy Decision Analysis** A forester wants to split many logs for sale for firewood. On the one hand he could, when needed, rent a log splitter for $150 a day. Since he has a large amount of work to do, he is considering purchasing a log splitter for $1400. He estimates that he will need to spend $10 per day on maintenance.

   a. Let x be the number of days he will use a log splitter. Write a formula that gives him the total cost of renting for x days.

   b. Write a formula that gives him the total cost of buying and maintaining the log splitter for x days of use.

   c. If the forester estimates he will need to use the splitter for 12 days, should he buy or rent?

   d. Determine the number of days of use before the forester can save as much money by buying the splitter as opposed to renting.

In Exercises 11 through 18, find all the solutions, if any exist, of the given system.

11. $x + 3y = 7$
    $3x + 4y = 11$

12. $x + 3y = 1$
    $3x + 9y = 2$

13. $x + 3y = 1$
    $3x + 9y = 3$

14. $2x + 3y = 18$
    $3x - y = 5$

15. $x + 3y - z = 4$
    $3x - y + z = 4$

16. $\quad\quad x + y = 10$
    $2x + 2y + 2z = 20$

17. $x + 2y - 3z = 4$
    $2x - y + z = 0$
    $5x - 3y + 2z = -2$

18. $x + y + z = 5$
    $2x + y - z = 3$
    $y + 3z = 7$

19. **Golf Course** A certain 9-hole golf course has the number of par 3 holes equal to one plus the number of par 5 holes. If par at this course for 9 holes is 35, how many par 3, 4, and 5 holes are there?

20. **Sales of Sweepers** A wholesaler receives an order for a total of a dozen standard and deluxe electric sweepers. The standard sweepers cost $200 and the deluxe $300. With the order is a check for $2900, but the order neglects to specify the number of each type of sweeper. Determine how to fill the order.

21. **Sales of Condominiums** A developer sells two sizes of condominiums. One sells for $75,000 and the other $100,000. One year the developer sold 14 condominiums for a total of $12 million. How many of each size of condominium did the developer sell?

22. **Sales of Specials** A small restaurant sold 50 specials one day. The ham special went for $10 and the beef special for $12. The revenue from these specials is $560. The cook was too busy to keep track of how many of each were served. Find the answer for her.

23. **Acid Mixture** Three acid solutions are available. The first has 20% acid, the second 30%, and the third 40%. The three solutions need to be mixed to form 300 liters of a solution with 32% acid. If the amount of the third solution must be equal to the sum of the amounts of the first two, find the amount of each solution.

24. **Distribution** A firm has three manufacturing plants located in different parts of the country. Three major wholesalers obtain the percentages of the product from the three plants according to the following table. Also included is the demand (in numbers) from each of the wholesalers. What should be the

number produced by each of the plants to meet this demand with the given percentage distributions?

	Plant 1	Plant 2	Plant 3	Demand
Wholesaler A	20%	30%	50%	105
Wholesaler B	40%	20%	40%	100
Wholesaler C	10%	30%	60%	100

25. Using the method of least squares, find the best-fitting line through the four points $(0,0)$, $(2,2)$, $(3,2)$, and $(4,3)$.

26. **Percent of U.S. Homes with Home Computer** The table gives the percentage of U.S. homes with a personal computer for recent years.

x	1999	2000	2001	2002
y	48	54	58	60

x is the year and y the percentage of U.S. homes with a personal computer.

a. Use linear regression to find the best-fitting line that relates the percentage of U.S. homes with a personal computer to the year.

b. Use this line to estimate the percentage of U.S. homes with a personal computer for the year 2006.

c. Find the correlation coefficient.

Source: Telecommunications Association

✧ Project: Supply and Demand Dynamics

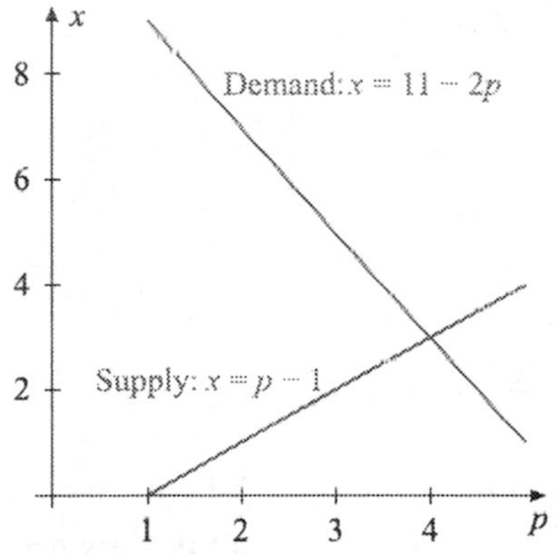

Figure 1.31
Supply and Demand for Corn

Let us consider some commodity, corn, to be specific. For this discussion we will find it convenient to have demand as a function of price. Thus, the price p will be on the horizontal axis, and the demand x will be on the vertical axis. Let us now suppose that the supply equation is $x = p - 1$ and the demand equation is $x = 11 - 2p$, where x is bushels and p is in dollars per bushel.

The graphs are shown in Figure 1.31. Notice from the supply curve that as the price decreases, the supply does also until a point is reached at which there will be no supply. Normally, there is a price at which suppliers refuse to produce anything (sometimes called the "choke" price). We can readily find the equilibrium price for our model:

$$p - 1 = 11 - 2p$$
$$3p = 12$$
$$p = 4$$

We noted that in equilibrium, demand must equal supply, which corresponds to the point where the demand curve and the supply curve intersect. This rarely happens. What actually happens is the farmer bases production on the price p_n of corn that prevails at planting time. The supply equation will then determine the supply of corn. Owing to the time lag in the growing process, the resulting supply of corn is not available until the next period, that is, the fall. At that time the price will be determined by the demand equation. The price will adjust so that all the corn is sold. The farmer notes the new price p_{n+1} at planting time, and a new cycle begins.

The supply s_{n+1} is determined by the equation $s_{n+1} = p_n - 1$, and the demand is determined by the equation $d_{n+1} = 11 - 2p_{n+1}$ according to the discussion in the previous paragraph. We impose the realistic condition that the price (at the time the corn is brought to market) is adjusted so that demand equals supply, that is, so that all the corn is sold. Imposing the condition that supply must equal demand gives the equation

$$p_n - 1 = s_{n+1} = d_{n+1} = 11 - 2p_{n+1}$$

This gives

$$p_{n+1} = 6 - 0.5p_n$$

That is, the price next year, p_{n+1}, will be 6 less one-half times this year's price.

Now let's suppose that the price starts out at $p_0 = 2$. Then rounding off to the nearest cent we have

$$p_1 = 6 - 0.5(2) \quad = 5$$

$$p_2 = 6 - 0.5(5) \quad = 3.5$$

$$p_3 = 6 - 0.5(3.5) \quad = 4.25$$

$$p_4 = 6 - 0.5(4.25) = 3.88$$

$$p_5 = 6 - 0.5(3.88) = 4.06$$

$$p_6 = 6 - 0.5(4.06) = 3.97$$

$$p_7 = 6 - 0.5(3.97) = 4.02$$

$$p_8 = 6 - 0.5(4.02) = 3.99$$

$$p_9 = 6 - 0.5(3.99) = 4.01$$

$$p_{10} = 6 - 0.5(4.01) = 4.00$$

So the price in this case moves steadily toward the equilibrium price.

There is a dramatic graphical way of determining and seeing the price movements. This graphical technique is called a cobweb. The cobweb is shown in Figure 1.32. We start at the point labeled A. The price is $2. With such a low price, far below the equilibrium, farmers plant a small crop and bring the crop to market in the fall of that year. Fortunately for the farmer, the small supply results from the demand equation with a high price of $5.00 (point B). This is obtained by drawing the horizontal line seen in Figure 1.32. Now proceed to the spring of the next year by drawing a vertical line until we hit the supply curve at point C. Now the farmer sees a high price of $5 for corn, so the supply curve determines the supply to be produced, which is relatively large. When the corn is brought to market in the fall (follow the horizontal to the demand curve), the price is set by the demand curve at point D. The large amount of corn results in a poor price (for the farmer) of $3.50. So the farmer produces little corn the following year, resulting in a higher price of $4.25, point E, and so on. As the cobweb indicates, the price gets closer and closer to the equilibrium price.

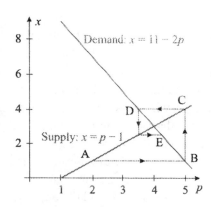

Figure 1.32

CHAPTER 2

Matrices

CONNECTION

Japanese Economy

The Japanese Ministry of Economy, Trade and Industry (METI) has prepared input–output models for the Japanese economy since 1955. For example, in 2000 the Japanese economy was broken down into as many as 104 sectors such as mining, construction, and manufacturing. This allows the Japanese government to accurately track the performance and needs of different parts of its economy.

METI now also studies how the United States and Japanese economies interact. The Japan–U.S. input–output table lists how 27 sectors of the economies depend on each other. These sectors include agriculture, forestry, fishing, textiles, steel, precision instruments, and services. This has led to greater understanding of how the two countries can work together on economic issues. Indeed as the economy becomes more global, this type of information is increasingly important.

Source: http://www.stat.go.jp/english/

2.1 Introduction to Matrices

A firm makes bulldozers (B), cranes (C), and tractors (T) at two locations, New York and Los Angeles, and the number of each produced at each site during January and February is given in tabulated form on the left. Find the total number of each product produced at each site for the January through February period in tabulated form. See Example 4 for the answer.

January	B	C	T
NYC	120	240	360
LA	310	0	240

February	B	C	T
NYC	200	10	0
LA	150	200	300

✧ Basic Properties and Definitions

Matrices were introduced in the previous chapter to allow systems of linear equations to be solved with less writing (or on the calculator). We will now see that matrices are a natural way of presenting tabulated data. Certain calculations with this data correspond to certain matrix operations. These operations will be considered in this and the next section, and some applications will be given.

As mentioned previously, a matrix is a rectangular array of numbers. The matrix A below is a matrix with 2 rows and 3 columns.

$$\begin{array}{c} \text{column 1} \quad \text{column 2} \quad \text{column 3} \end{array}$$

$$\begin{array}{c} \text{row 1} \\ \text{row 2} \end{array} \begin{bmatrix} 2 & 3 & 5 \\ 0 & -2 & 4 \end{bmatrix}$$

The order of a matrix is $m \times n$ where m is the number of rows and n is the number of columns. Thus, the order of the above matrix A is 2×3.

Given a matrix such as A above, the entry in the ith row and jth column is denoted by a_{ij}. For matrix A, $a_{11} = 2$, $a_{12} = 3$, $a_{13} = 5$, $a_{21} = 0$, $a_{22} = -2$, $a_{23} = 4$.

Some Matrix Terminology
A matrix A, also denoted by $(a_{ij})_{m \times n}$ or simply (a_{ij}), is a rectangular array of numbers. The order of A is denoted by $m \times n$, where m is the number of rows and n is the number of columns. The element in the ith row and jth column is denoted by a_{ij}.

If $A = (a_{ij})_{m \times n}$, then we have

$$
A = \begin{array}{c} \\ \text{row 1} \\ \text{row 2} \\ \\ \text{row } i \\ \\ \text{row } n \end{array}
\begin{array}{c} \overset{\text{column 1}}{} \quad \overset{\text{column 2}}{} \qquad \overset{\text{column } j}{} \qquad \overset{\text{column } n}{} \end{array}
\left[\begin{array}{cccccc}
a_{11} & a_{12} & \cdots & a_{1j} & \cdots & a_{1n} \\
a_{21} & a_{22} & \cdots & a_{2j} & \cdots & a_{2n} \\
\vdots & & \cdots & & \cdots & \\
a_{i1} & a_{i2} & \cdots & a_{ij} & \cdots & a_{in} \\
\vdots & & \cdots & & \cdots & \\
a_{m1} & a_{m2} & \cdots & a_{mj} & \cdots & a_{mn}
\end{array} \right]
$$

EXAMPLE 1   Order of Matrices   Determine the order of B, C, and D. Find b_{22}, b_{32}, c_{12}, and d_{31}.

$$
B = \begin{bmatrix} 1 & 2 \\ -1 & 0 \\ 4 & 8 \end{bmatrix} \qquad C = \begin{bmatrix} 1 & 2 & 5 & 0 \end{bmatrix} \qquad D = \begin{bmatrix} 1 \\ 3 \\ 4 \end{bmatrix}
$$

Solution
The matrix B has 3 rows and 2 columns, and so the order of B is 3×2.
The matrix C has 1 row and 4 columns, and so the order of C is 1×4.
The matrix D has 3 rows and 1 column, and so the order of D is 3×1.
$b_{22} = 0$ as it is in the second row, and second column of the matrix B.
$b_{32} = 8$ as it is in the third row and second column of the matrix B.
$c_{12} = 2$ as it is in the first row and second column of the matrix C.
$d_{31} = 4$ as it is in the third row and first column of the matrix D.   ◆

There are three special types of matrices that arise often: column matrices, row matrices, and square matrices.

Row and Column Matrices
A matrix of order $1 \times n$ (1 row and n columns) is called a row matrix or a row matrix of dimension n.

A matrix of order $m \times 1$ (m rows and 1 column) is called a column matrix or a column matrix of dimension m.

In Example 1 the matrix C is a row matrix of dimension 4 and matrix D is a column matrix of dimension 3. Square matrices have the natural definition of a matrix that is square.

Square Matrices
A matrix is called a square matrix if the number of rows equals the number of columns.

Naturally we need to know when two matrices are equal. Two matrices are equal when they are absolutely identical. The following definition says just that.

> **Equality of Matrices**
> Two matrices are equal if they have the same order and all corresponding entries are equal.

For example, none of the matrices below are equal. Remember, first the matrices must be the same order and then all corresponding entries must be equal.

$$\begin{bmatrix} 1 & 2 \\ 3 & 4 \end{bmatrix} \quad \begin{bmatrix} 1 & 3 \\ 2 & 4 \end{bmatrix} \quad \begin{bmatrix} 1 & 2 & 0 \\ 3 & 4 & 0 \end{bmatrix} \quad \begin{bmatrix} 1 & 2 \\ 3 & 4 \\ 0 & 0 \end{bmatrix}$$

EXAMPLE 2   Equal Matrices Find x, y, and z, such that

$$\begin{bmatrix} 1 & 2 & x \\ 3 & 0 & 5 \end{bmatrix} = \begin{bmatrix} 1 & 2 & 4 \\ y & 0 & z \end{bmatrix}$$

Solution Since both matrices have order 2×3, equality is possible. Setting the corresponding entries equal gives $x = 4$, $y = 3$, and $z = 5$.   ◆

We now state three fundamental operations on matrices.

> **Multiplication of a Matrix by a Number**
> If c is a number and A is a matrix, then the matrix cA is the matrix obtained by multiplying every entry in A by c.

REMARK: The number c can be referred to as a scalar to distinguish it from a 1×1 matrix. Then the operation defined above would be referred to as scalar multiplication

> **Addition and Subtraction of Matrices**
> Two matrices of the same order can be added (or subtracted) to obtain another matrix of the same order by adding (or subtracting) corresponding entries.

> **The Transpose of a Matrix**
> If A is an $m \times n$ matrix with elements a_{ij}, then the transpose of A is the $n \times m$ matrix A^T with elements a_{ji}.

EXAMPLE 3   Elementary Matrix Operations Let

$$A = \begin{bmatrix} 6 & -2 \\ 5 & -3 \\ -5 & 7 \end{bmatrix}, \quad B = \begin{bmatrix} 1 & 2 \\ -1 & 0 \\ 4 & 8 \end{bmatrix}, \quad C = \begin{bmatrix} 1 & 5 & 0 \end{bmatrix}, \quad D = \begin{bmatrix} -2 \\ 3 \\ 4 \end{bmatrix}$$

Find

a. $2A$ **b.** B^T **c.** $A+B$ **d.** $A+C$ **e.** $C+D^T$ **f.** $A-2B$

Solution

a. $2A = 2\begin{bmatrix} 6 & -2 \\ 5 & -3 \\ -5 & 7 \end{bmatrix} = \begin{bmatrix} 2(6) & 2(-2) \\ 2(5) & 2(-3) \\ 2(-5) & 2(7) \end{bmatrix} = \begin{bmatrix} 12 & -4 \\ 10 & -6 \\ -10 & 14 \end{bmatrix}$

b. $B^T = \begin{bmatrix} 1 & 2 \\ -1 & 0 \\ 4 & 8 \end{bmatrix}^T = \begin{bmatrix} 1 & -1 & 4 \\ 2 & 0 & 8 \end{bmatrix}$

c. $A+B = \begin{bmatrix} 6 & -2 \\ 5 & -3 \\ -5 & 7 \end{bmatrix} + \begin{bmatrix} 1 & 2 \\ -1 & 0 \\ 4 & 8 \end{bmatrix} = \begin{bmatrix} 6+1 & -2+2 \\ 5-1 & -3+0 \\ -5+4 & 7+8 \end{bmatrix}$

$= \begin{bmatrix} 7 & 0 \\ 4 & -3 \\ -1 & 15 \end{bmatrix}$

d. $A+C$ is not defined.

e. $C+D^T = \begin{bmatrix} 1 & 5 & 0 \end{bmatrix} + \begin{bmatrix} -2 \\ 3 \\ 4 \end{bmatrix}^T = \begin{bmatrix} 1 & 5 & 0 \end{bmatrix} + \begin{bmatrix} -2 & 3 & 4 \end{bmatrix}$

$= \begin{bmatrix} 1+(-2) & 5+3 & 0+4 \end{bmatrix} = \begin{bmatrix} -1 & 8 & 4 \end{bmatrix}$

f. $A-2B = \begin{bmatrix} 6 & -2 \\ 5 & -3 \\ -5 & 7 \end{bmatrix} - 2\begin{bmatrix} 1 & 2 \\ -1 & 0 \\ 4 & 8 \end{bmatrix}$

$= \begin{bmatrix} 6-2(1) & -2-2(2) \\ 5-2(-1) & -3-2(0) \\ -5-2(4) & 7-2(8) \end{bmatrix}$

$= \begin{bmatrix} 4 & -6 \\ 7 & -3 \\ -13 & -9 \end{bmatrix}$ ◆

Technology Option

Example 3 is solved with a graphing calculator in Technology Note 1 on page 92. Note that the transpose command is found under the MATRIX MATH menu.

```
NAMES MATH EDIT
1:det(
2:ᵀ
3:dim(
4:Fill(
5:identity(
6:randM(
7↓augment(
```

The number 0 has the property that $x+0=0+x=x$ for any number x. There is a matrix, called the zero matrix, with an analogous property.

> **The Zero Matrix**
> The zero matrix of order $m \times n$ is the matrix O with m rows and n columns, all of whose entries are zero.

Thus, the zero matrix of order 2×3 is

$$O = \begin{bmatrix} 0 & 0 & 0 \\ 0 & 0 & 0 \end{bmatrix}$$

Notice that we have the following.

Properties of the Zero Matrix
If A is any matrix of order $m \times n$ and O is the zero matrix of the same order, then

$$A + O = O + A = A$$
$$A - A = O$$

The following properties of matrices can also be shown to be true. The proofs are left as exercises.

Further Properties of Matrices
If A, B, and C are three matrices all of the same order, then

$$A + B = B + A$$
$$A + (B + C) = (A + B) + C$$

✧ Applications

Data are often presented in matrix form. Suppose a firm makes bulldozers (B), cranes (C), and tractors (T) at two locations, New York and Los Angeles, and the number of each produced at each location during January is given by the following table:

	B	C	T
NYC	120	240	360
LA	310	0	240

A **production matrix** for January can be given as

$$
J = \begin{bmatrix} 120 & 240 & 360 \\ 310 & 0 & 249 \end{bmatrix} = \begin{array}{c} \\ \text{NYC} \\ \text{LA} \end{array} \begin{array}{ccc} \text{B} & \text{C} & \text{T} \\ \end{array} \begin{bmatrix} 120 & 240 & 360 \\ 310 & 0 & 249 \end{bmatrix}
$$

where it is understood that in the first matrix, the first row refers to NYC, the second row to LA, the first column to the number of bulldozers, etc. In the second matrix, the rows and columns are explicitly labeled. The importance of labels on applications matrices cannot be over-emphasized. It is critically important to avoid things such as adding apples to oranges!

EXAMPLE 4   Adding Production Matrices   Now suppose that the same firm as above has a February production matrix given by

$$
F = \begin{bmatrix} 200 & 100 & 0 \\ 150 & 200 & 300 \end{bmatrix}
$$

a. Find the production matrix for the January to February period.

b. Find the number of cranes produced in NYC during the period.

Technology Option

Example 4a is solved using Microsoft Excel in Technology Note 2 on page 93.

Solution

a. The matrix $J + F$ is the production matrix for the two-month period.

$$J + F = \begin{bmatrix} 120 & 240 & 360 \\ 310 & 0 & 240 \end{bmatrix} + \begin{bmatrix} 200 & 100 & 0 \\ 150 & 200 & 300 \end{bmatrix}$$

$$= \begin{bmatrix} 320 & 340 & 360 \\ 460 & 200 & 540 \end{bmatrix} = \begin{matrix} \\ NYC \\ LA \end{matrix} \begin{matrix} B & C & T \\ \begin{bmatrix} 320 & 340 & 360 \\ 460 & 200 & 540 \end{bmatrix} \end{matrix}$$

b. This is the element in the first row and second column of $J + F$, which is 340 cranes. ◆

EXAMPLE 5 **Multiplying a Number With a Production Matrix** Suppose the production of the above firm in March increases by 10% from that of February for all products at all locations. Find

a. the production M for March, and

b. how many tractors were produced in LA during March.

Technology Option

Example 5a is solved using Microsoft Excel in Technology Note 3 on page 93.

Solution

a. The production matrix M for March is $1.1F$ or

$$M = 1.1F = \begin{bmatrix} 1.1(200) & 1.1(100) & 1.1(0) \\ 1.1(150) & 1.1(200) & 1.1(300) \end{bmatrix} = \begin{bmatrix} 220 & 110 & 0 \\ 165 & 220 & 330 \end{bmatrix}$$

$$= \begin{matrix} \\ NYC \\ LA \end{matrix} \begin{matrix} B & C & T \\ \begin{bmatrix} 220 & 110 & 0 \\ 165 & 220 & 330 \end{bmatrix} \end{matrix}$$

b. $M = (m_{ij})$, then m_{23} is the number of tractors produced in LA in March. We see that $m_{23} = 330$ tractors. ◆

✧ Technology Corner

Technology Note 1 **Example 3 on a Graphing Calculator**

As in the last chapter, we will use the MATRIX EDIT commands to enter the matrix in the calculator and MATRIX NAMES to access the matrices. The matrix operations are carried out in the home screen as shown below in Screens 1–6.

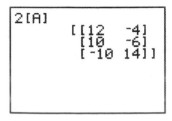

Screen 1

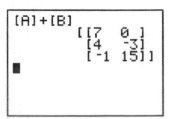

Screen 2

```
[A]+[B]
         [[7   0 ]
          [4  -3]
          [-1  15]]
■
```

Screen 3

```
ERR:DIM MISMATCH
1:Quit
2:Goto
```

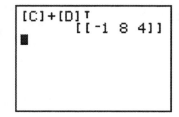

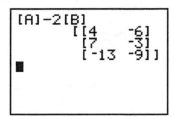

Screen 4   **Screen 5**   **Screen 6**

⑦Technology Note 2   Example 4a Using Microsoft Excel

Open a new spreadsheet and enter the matrices J and F as shown in Worksheet 1. Note how the columns and rows are labeled. Label the destination location. Then select with the mouse the destination cells, B7 to D8. Now type = and select with your mouse the cells of Matrix J then + and the cells of Matrix F, also shown in Worksheet 1. Finally, press Ctrl-Shift-Enter to find the sum, as shown in Worksheet 2. The sequence Ctrl-Shift-Enter is needed to evaluate any operation in Excel that involves more than one cell. Since our matrix has 6 cells, a simple Enter will not work.

	A	B	C	D	E	F	G	H	I
1	J	D	C	T		F	D	C	T
2	NYC	120	240	360		NYC	200	100	0
3	LA	310	0	240		LA	150	200	300
4									
5	J+F	D	C	T					
6	NYC	=B2.D3+G2.I3							
7	LA								

Worksheet 1

	A	B	C	D	E	F	G	H	I
1	J	D	C	T		F	D	C	T
2	NYC	120	240	360		NYC	200	100	0
3	LA	310	0	240		LA	150	200	300
4									
5	J+F	D	C	T					
6	NYC	320	340	360					
7	LA	460	200	540					

Worksheet 2

⑦Technology Note 3   Example 5a Using Microsoft Excel

Begin by putting the necessary labels for our March matrix in the spreadsheet. Then highlight the destination cells, G7 to I8. Then press =, enter 1.1* and highlight the cells for February, G3 to I4, as shown in Worksheet 3. Press the sequence Ctrl-Shift-Enter and the result is shown in Worksheet 4.

	A	B	C	D	E	F	G	H	I
1	J	D	C	T		F	D	C	T
2	NYC	120	240	360		NYC	200	100	0
3	LA	310	0	240		LA	150	200	300
4									
5	J+F	D	C	T		M	D	C	T
6	NYC	320	340	360		NYC	=1.1*G2.I3		
7	LA	460	200	540		LA			

Worksheet 3

	A	B	C	D	E	F	G	H	I
1	J	D	C	T		F	D	C	T
2	NYC	120	240	360		NYC	200	100	0
3	LA	310	0	240		LA	150	200	300
4									
5	J+F	D	C	T		M	D	C	T
6	NYC	320	340	360		NYC	220	110	0
7	LA	460	200	540		LA	165	220	330

Worksheet 4

Self-Help Exercises 2.1

1. $A = (a_{ij})$ is a matrix of order 2×3 and $a_{ij} = i + 2j$ for all i and j. Write down the matrix, A.

2. Find

$$3 \begin{bmatrix} 3 & 2 \\ -2 & 0 \\ 5 & 1 \end{bmatrix} - 2 \begin{bmatrix} 1 & -3 \\ 0 & 2 \\ -3 & 2 \end{bmatrix}$$

3. A person owns two furniture stores. The first store shows the following number of sales for the indi-

cated two months:

Store 1	Sofas	Love Seats	Chairs
April	30	20	40
May	30	30	50

The second store shows sales exactly 20% higher for all three types of furniture for each of the months. Use matrix operations to find the total sales in both stores.

2.1 Exercises

In Exercise 1 through 14, let

$$A = \begin{bmatrix} 3 & 1 \\ -2 & 4 \\ 0 & 3 \\ 2 & 8 \end{bmatrix}, \quad B = \begin{bmatrix} -1 & 0 & 2 & 6 \\ 3 & 1 & -2 & 4 \\ 5 & 3 & 0 & -5 \end{bmatrix},$$

$$C = \begin{bmatrix} -1 & 2 \end{bmatrix}, \quad D = \begin{bmatrix} 0 \\ 1 \\ -3 \\ 4 \end{bmatrix}$$

Find the order of the following matrices.

1. A **2.** B **3.** C **4.** D

Find the following matrix elements.

5. a_{12} **6.** a_{21} **7.** a_{42} **8.** a_{41} **9.** b_{23}

10. b_{34} **11.** b_{14} **12.** b_{33} **13.** c_{12} **14.** d_{31}

15. Find A if A is a matrix of order 2×3 and $a_{ij} = 5$ for all i and j.

16. If $A = (a_{ij})$ is a matrix of order 2×3 and $a_{ij} = i + j$ for all i and j, write down A.

17. If $A = (a_{ij})$ is a matrix of order 3×3 and $a_{ij} = 1$ if $i = j$, and $a_{ij} = 0$ if $i \neq j$, write down A.

18. If $A = (a_{ij})$ is a matrix of order 3×2 and $a_{ij} = 1$ for all i and j, write down A.

19. If $A = (a_{ij})$ is a matrix of order 3×3 and $a_{ij} = 0$ for all i and j, write down A.

20. If $A = (a_{ij})$ is a matrix of order 4×3 and $a_{ij} = 2i + j$ for all i and j, write down A.

21. Find x, y, and z, such that

$$\begin{bmatrix} 3 & 2 \\ 4 & x \end{bmatrix} = \begin{bmatrix} 3+y & z-2 \\ 4 & 3 \end{bmatrix}$$

22. Find x, y, and z, such that

$$\begin{bmatrix} x & 3 \\ -1 & 0 \\ 4 & 5 \end{bmatrix} = \begin{bmatrix} 1 & 3 \\ y-1 & 0 \\ 3 & z+x \end{bmatrix}$$

In Exercises 23 through 40, let

$$E = \begin{bmatrix} 1 & 4 \\ 3 & 6 \\ -3 & 7 \\ 3 & -2 \end{bmatrix}, \quad F = \begin{bmatrix} 4 & 3 & -1 & -6 \\ 5 & 0 & -2 & 7 \\ 8 & 1 & -3 & 0 \end{bmatrix}$$

$$G = \begin{bmatrix} 1 & 4 \end{bmatrix}, \quad H = \begin{bmatrix} 3 \\ -1 \\ 5 \\ 1 \end{bmatrix}$$

and let A, B, C, and D be the matrices given before Exercise 1. Find the indicated quantities.

23. $A + E$ **24.** $B + F$ **25.** $C + G$

26. $D + H$ **27.** $A - E$ **28.** F^T

29. $C - G$ **30.** $D - H$ **31.** $2E^T$

32. $-3F$ **33.** $4G$ **34.** $\dfrac{1}{2}H$

35. $2A + E$ **36.** $B - 2F$ **37.** $2C + 3G$

38. H^T **39.** $A - F$ **40.** $H - H$

41. Matrix F is a 3×3 matrix, matrix H is a 3×2 matrix, matrix J is a 2×3 matrix, and matrix K is a 2×2 matrix. Find the dimensions sums below, if they exist.
   a. $H + K$ **b.** $H + J^T$ **c.** $F + K$ **d.** $J + J$

42. Matrix L is a 5×4 matrix, matrix M is a 4×4 matrix, matrix N is a 5×5 matrix, and matrix P is a 4×5 matrix. Find the dimensions sums below, if they exist.
   a. $L + M$ **b.** $L + P^T$ **c.** $M + N$ **d.** $N + N$

43. Find the values for a, b, c, and d for the matrix equation below:

$$2\begin{bmatrix} a & 4 \\ 0 & -1 \end{bmatrix} + \begin{bmatrix} 6 & b \\ -2 & 0 \end{bmatrix}^T = \begin{bmatrix} 8 & c \\ 2 & d \end{bmatrix}$$

44. Find the values for a, b, c, and d for the matrix equation below:

$$\begin{bmatrix} a & b \\ c & d \end{bmatrix} + 3\begin{bmatrix} -2 & 1 \\ 4 & x \end{bmatrix}^T = \begin{bmatrix} 6 & 4 \\ 0 & 7 \end{bmatrix}$$

Applications

For Exercises 45 to 48, use the following production matrices from Examples 4 and 5 along with a production matrix A from April.

$$J = \begin{array}{c} \\ \text{NYC} \\ \text{LA} \end{array} \begin{array}{ccc} \text{B} & \text{C} & \text{T} \\ \left[\begin{array}{ccc} 120 & 240 & 360 \\ 310 & 0 & 249 \end{array}\right] \end{array} \qquad F = \begin{array}{c} \\ \text{NYC} \\ \text{LA} \end{array} \begin{array}{ccc} \text{B} & \text{C} & \text{T} \\ \left[\begin{array}{ccc} 200 & 100 & 0 \\ 150 & 200 & 300 \end{array}\right] \end{array}$$

$$M = \begin{array}{c} \\ \text{NYC} \\ \text{LA} \end{array} \begin{array}{ccc} \text{B} & \text{C} & \text{T} \\ \left[\begin{array}{ccc} 220 & 110 & 0 \\ 165 & 220 & 330 \end{array}\right] \end{array} \qquad A = \begin{array}{c} \\ \text{NYC} \\ \text{LA} \end{array} \begin{array}{ccc} \text{B} & \text{C} & \text{T} \\ \left[\begin{array}{ccc} 300 & 200 & 100 \\ 200 & 200 & 400 \end{array}\right] \end{array}$$

45. **Production** Write a production matrix for the period from March to April as a sum of two matrices and then carry out the calculation.

46. **Production** Find $A - M$. What does $A - M$ stand for?

47. **Production** Suppose that production of all products at all locations was reduced by 10% in May from what it was in April. Write the production matrix for May as a scalar times a matrix. Then carry out the calculations to obtain the production for May.

48. **Production** Suppose the production for June of all products at all locations was the average of the January and February production. Write an expression using the matrices J and F for the June production matrix and then carry out the indicated calculation to obtain this matrix.

49. **Reserve Forces**

    a. In the U.S. Army Selected Reserve there were 37,615 officers, 2682 warrant officers, and 171,593 enlisted in the year 2003. In the U.S. Navy Selected Reserve there were 18,596 officers, 190 warrant officers, and 69,369 enlisted in the year 2003 as of September 30. Organize this information as a 3×2 matrix.

    b. In the U.S. Army Individual Ready Reserve there were 19,211 officers, 1774 warrant officers, and 96,420 enlisted in the year 2003. In the U.S. Navy Individual Ready Reserve there were 13,617 officers, 6 warrant officers, and 51,074 enlisted in the year 2003 as of September 30. Organize this information as a 3×2 matrix.

    c. The Total Ready Reserve is defined as the sum of Select Reserve and the Individual Ready Reserve for each of the Army and the Navy. Write the Total Ready Reserve as the sum of two matrices and calculate it.
    Source: U.S. Department of Defense, Selected Manpower Statistics

50. **Composition of State Legislatures** In 2005 the state legislatures were surveyed.

    a. In the state senates of Alabama, Alaska, Arizona, and Arkansas there were, respectively, 25, 8, 12, and 27 Democrats, and there were, respectively, 10, 12, 18, and 8 Republicans. Organize this information using a 4×2 matrix.

    b. In the state houses of Alabama, Alaska, Arizona, and Arkansas there were, respectively, 63, 14, 22, and 72 Democrats, and there were, respectively, 42, 26, 38, and 28 Republicans. Organize this information using a 4×2 matrix.

    c. Organize the total number of Democrats and Republicans in the four given state legislatures as a sum of two matrices. How many Democrats were there in the Alabama Legislature? How many Republicans were there in the Alaska Legislature?
    Source: National Conference of State Legislatures

In Exercises 51 through 54, we have a cost matrix C and two revenue matrices R and Q for a firm that produces blouses, skirts, and dresses at plants located at Atlanta and Chicago. The numbers are given in thousands of dollars per week.

$$C = \begin{array}{c} \\ \text{Blouses} \\ \text{Skirts} \\ \text{Dresses} \end{array} \begin{array}{cc} \text{Atlanta} & \text{Chicago} \\ \left[\begin{array}{cc} 11 & 9 \\ 5 & 4 \\ 7 & 13 \end{array}\right] \end{array}$$

$$R = \begin{array}{c} \\ \text{Blouses} \\ \text{Skirts} \\ \text{Dresses} \end{array} \begin{array}{cc} \text{Atlanta} & \text{Chicago} \\ \left[\begin{array}{cc} 15 & 14 \\ 8 & 7 \\ 11 & 12 \end{array}\right] \end{array}$$

$$Q = \begin{array}{c} \\ \text{Blouses} \\ \text{Skirts} \\ \text{Dresses} \end{array} \begin{array}{cc} \text{Atlanta} & \text{Chicago} \\ \left[\begin{array}{cc} 17 & 17 \\ 9 & 5 \\ 14 & 14 \end{array}\right] \end{array}$$

51. **Revenue, Cost, Profit** Write a profit matrix using the revenue from matrix R. What was the profit (loss) for skirts in Atlanta? Of dresses in Chicago?

52. **Revenue** Revenue matrix Q is for 10 weeks after revenue matrix R. Write a matrix giving the increase (or decrease) of revenue at the two plants for

the three items. What was the revenue increase (decrease) for skirts in Atlanta?

53. **Revenue** The firm estimates that all items at both plants will generate a 10% gain in revenue in 52 weeks. Write a new revenue matrix using the matrix Q as the starting point. What was the revenue for blouses in Chicago?

54. **Revenue** Consider the revenue matrices R and Q. Find a matrix that gives the average revenue for each item at both plants. What was the average revenue for skirts in Atlanta?

For Exercises 55 through 60, consider the information below. A firm has a plant in NYC that has produced the following numbers of items of three products during the four quarters of the last year.

	First Quarter	Second Quarter	Third Quarter	Fourth Quarter
Product A	250	300	350	300
Product B	300	200	250	150
Product C	200	240	320	220

The following table gives the firm's production for the same period for its other production plant located in LA.

	First Quarter	Second Quarter	Third Quarter	Fourth Quarter
Product A	300	350	450	400
Product B	320	240	280	250
Product C	250	260	420	280

55. Write a production matrix N for the NYC plant.

56. Write a production matrix L for the LA plant.

57. Write an expression involving the matrices N and L that gives the production matrix for the firm for the last year. Carry out the indicated calculations.

58. Calculate $L - N$ and indicate what this matrix stands for.

59. Next year the firm is predicting production to increase by 20% at NYC. Write the production matrix for next year for NYC as a scalar times a matrix and then carry out the indicated calculations.

60. Write a matrix expression that gives the production matrix that represents the average production of its two plants and carry out the indicated calculation.

Extensions

In Exercises 61 through 65, let A, B, and C be 2×2 matrices and let O be the 2×2 zero matrix.

61. Prove that $A + B = B + A$.

62. Prove that $A + (B + C) = (A + B) + C$.

63. Prove that $A + O = O + A = A$.

64. Prove that $(c + d)A = cA + dA$, where c and d are numbers.

65. Prove that $A - A = O$.

66. A matrix $D = (d_{ij})$ is a diagonal matrix if $d_{ij} = 0$ when $i \neq j$, that is, all entries of the "main diagonal" are zero. Suppose $A = (a_{ij})$ and $B = (b_{ij})$ are both diagonal matrices of order 4×4. Show that

    a. $A + B$ is diagonal.

    b. cA is diagonal where c is a real number.

67. Show that the matrix $X + A = B$ has the solution $X = B - A$ and show that the matrix $A - X = B$ has the solution $X = A - B$.

68. A matrix $U = (u_{ij})$ is upper triangular if $u_{ij} = 0$ when $i > j$, that is, when all entries below the main diagonal are zero. Suppose $A = (a_{ij})$ and $B = (b_{ij})$ are both upper triangular matrices of order 4×4. Show that

    a. $A + B$ is upper triangular.

    b. cA is upper triangular where c is a real number.

Solutions to Self-Help Exercises 2.1

1. $a_{11} = 1 + 2(1) = 3, \quad a_{12} = 1 + 2(2) = 5, \quad a_{13} = 1 + 2(3) = 7,$
$a_{21} = 2 + 2(1) = 4, \quad a_{22} = 2 + 2(2) = 6, \quad a_{23} = 2 + 2(3) = 8.$

Thus,

$$A = \begin{bmatrix} 3 & 5 & 7 \\ 4 & 6 & 8 \end{bmatrix}$$

2. $3 \begin{bmatrix} 3 & 2 \\ -2 & 0 \\ 5 & 1 \end{bmatrix} - 2 \begin{bmatrix} 1 & -3 \\ 0 & 2 \\ -3 & 2 \end{bmatrix} = \begin{bmatrix} 9 & 6 \\ -6 & 0 \\ 15 & 3 \end{bmatrix} - \begin{bmatrix} 2 & -6 \\ 0 & 4 \\ -6 & 4 \end{bmatrix}$

$$= \begin{bmatrix} 9-2 & 6-(-6) \\ -6-0 & 0-4 \\ 15-(-6) & 3-4 \end{bmatrix}$$

$$= \begin{bmatrix} 7 & 12 \\ -6 & -4 \\ 21 & -1 \end{bmatrix}$$

3. The indicated matrix operations are

$$\begin{bmatrix} 30 & 20 & 40 \\ 30 & 30 & 50 \end{bmatrix} + 1.2 \begin{bmatrix} 30 & 20 & 40 \\ 30 & 30 & 50 \end{bmatrix}$$

$$= \begin{bmatrix} 30 & 20 & 40 \\ 30 & 30 & 50 \end{bmatrix} + \begin{bmatrix} 36 & 24 & 48 \\ 36 & 36 & 60 \end{bmatrix}$$

$$= \begin{bmatrix} 66 & 44 & 88 \\ 66 & 66 & 110 \end{bmatrix}$$

$$= \begin{array}{c} \\ \text{April} \\ \text{May} \end{array} \begin{array}{ccc} \text{Sofa} & \text{Love seat} & \text{Chair} \\ \begin{bmatrix} 66 & 44 & 88 \\ 66 & 66 & 110 \end{bmatrix} \end{array}$$

2.2   Matrix Multiplication

The definition of multiplication of two matrices may at first seem strange. But, in doing applications we will see how this definition becomes natural. Furthermore, this definition of multiplication plays a central role in writing systems of equations in matrix form. In the next section we will see how systems of equations with the same number of equations as unknowns can be solved using matrix operations and this definition of multiplication.

✧ A Row Matrix Times a Column Matrix

To understand how to multiply two general matrices, we first need to know how to multiply a row matrix with a column matrix with the same number of entries. We therefore begin by defining such a multiplication.

> **Row Matrix Times Column Matrix**
> Let R be the row matrix $R = \begin{bmatrix} r_1 & r_2 & \cdots & r_n \end{bmatrix}$
>
> and let C be the column matrix $C = \begin{bmatrix} c_1 \\ c_2 \\ \vdots \\ c_n \end{bmatrix}$
>
> with the number of elements of R equal to the number of elements of C. Then the product matrix RC is defined to be
>
> $$RC = \begin{bmatrix} r_1 & r_2 & \cdots & r_n \end{bmatrix} \begin{bmatrix} c_1 \\ c_2 \\ \vdots \\ c_n \end{bmatrix} = [r_1 c_1 + r_2 c_2 + \cdots + r_n c_n]$$

REMARK: Notice that the answer, RC, is a 1×1 matrix (a real number).

EXAMPLE 1   Multiplying Row Matrices With Column Matrices   Perform the indicated operations.

a. $\begin{bmatrix} 5 & 2 \end{bmatrix} \begin{bmatrix} 1 \\ 6 \end{bmatrix}$ **b.** $\begin{bmatrix} 3 & 0 & -2 \end{bmatrix} \begin{bmatrix} 3 \\ 2 \\ 1 \end{bmatrix}$ **c.** $\begin{bmatrix} 3 & 2 & 0 \end{bmatrix} \begin{bmatrix} 3 \\ 5 \end{bmatrix}$

Solution

a. $\begin{bmatrix} 5 & 2 \end{bmatrix} \begin{bmatrix} 1 \\ 6 \end{bmatrix} = [(5)(1) + (2)(6)] = [17]$

b. $\begin{bmatrix} 3 & 0 & -2 \end{bmatrix} \begin{bmatrix} 3 \\ 2 \\ 1 \end{bmatrix} = [(3)(3) + (0)(2) + (-2)(1)] = [7]$

c. $\begin{bmatrix} 3 & 2 & 0 \end{bmatrix} \begin{bmatrix} 3 \\ 5 \end{bmatrix} = $ undefined

Notice from **c.** that if the number of elements in the row is not equal to the number of elements in the column, then the product is not defined   ◆

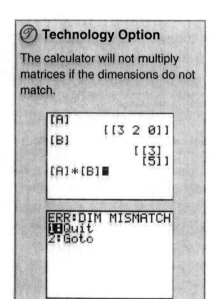
EXAMPLE 2   Cost of Cookies   Suppose a baker makes sugar cookies out of flour, sugar, butter, and eggs. Each batch of cookies requires 10 units of flour, 5 units of sugar, 7 units of butter, and 15 units of eggs. The cost per unit of each of the items is, respectively, $2, $3, $7, $4.

a. Write a row matrix that expresses how much of each ingredient is used in a batch of sugar cookies.

b. Write a column matrix that expresses the cost of each unit of each ingredient.

c. Express the total cost for a batch of sugar cookies using the four ingredients by a product of a row matrix and a column matrix.

Solution

a. There are four different ingredients, and therefore this will be a 1×4 matrix as shown below.

$$R = \text{\# of units} \begin{array}{cccc} F & S & B & E \\ [10 & 5 & 7 & 15] \end{array}$$

b. Each of the four ingredients has a cost, so this will be a 4×1 matrix,

$$C = \begin{array}{c} \\ F \\ S \\ B \\ E \end{array} \overset{\$/\text{unit}}{\begin{bmatrix} 2 \\ 3 \\ 7 \\ 4 \end{bmatrix}}$$

c. The cost of one batch of sugar cookies is then

$$RC = \begin{array}{c} \\ \text{\# of units} \end{array} \begin{array}{cccc} F & S & B & E \\ [10 & 5 & 7 & 15] \end{array} \times \begin{array}{c} \\ F \\ S \\ B \\ E \end{array} \overset{\$/\text{unit}}{\begin{bmatrix} 2 \\ 3 \\ 7 \\ 4 \end{bmatrix}}$$

$$= [10 \text{ units flour} \times \$2/\text{unit flour}$$
$$+ 5 \text{ units sugar} \times \$3/\text{unit sugar}$$
$$+ 7 \text{ units butter} \times \$7/\text{unit butter}$$
$$+ 15 \text{ units eggs} \times \$4/\text{unit eggs}]$$

$$= [(10)(2) + (5)(3) + (7)(7) + (15)(4)] = [144]$$

giving a total cost of \$144. ✦

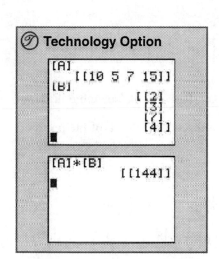

Technology Option

[A]
[[10 5 7 15]]
[B]
[[2]
[3]
[7]
[4]]

[A]*[B]
[[144]]

REMARK: Note that the labels of the columns of matrix R matched the labels of the rows of matrix C. This is generally true for application problems. Care must be taken to avoid situations such as multiplying the number of units of sugar by the unit price of flour!

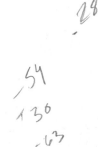

◆ Multiplication in General

We now turn to multiplying two general matrices and the condition that two matrices must satisfy before they can be multiplied. We show how to multiply general matrices by working out the specific example.

$$AB = \begin{bmatrix} 3 & 1 \\ 2 & 4 \\ 5 & 0 \end{bmatrix} \begin{bmatrix} 2 & 3 \\ 4 & 6 \end{bmatrix}$$

We obtain the product by the following rule: multiply the *i*th row of A times the *j*th column of B and place the resulting number in the *i*th row and *j*th column of the product matrix.

Technology Option

Matrix multiplication using Microsoft Excel is discussed in Technology Note 3 on page 107.

Notice for this process to work we must have the dimension of the ith row of A equal to the jth column of B. In other words, the number of columns of A must equal the number of rows of B. The result of the multiplication will have the same number of rows as A and the same number of columns as B.

We start by taking the product of the first row of A, $\begin{bmatrix} 3 & 1 \end{bmatrix}$, and the first column of B, $\begin{bmatrix} 2 \\ 4 \end{bmatrix}$, that is,

$$\begin{bmatrix} 3 & 1 \end{bmatrix} \begin{bmatrix} 2 \\ 4 \end{bmatrix} = (3)(2) + (1)(4) = 10$$

and place the result in the first row and first column of the product. The product will have 3 rows (just like A) and 2 columns (just like B). We draw an empty 3×2 matrix and place the 10 in its proper place.

$$\begin{bmatrix} 3 & 1 \\ 2 & 4 \\ 5 & 0 \end{bmatrix} \begin{bmatrix} 2 & 3 \\ 4 & 6 \end{bmatrix} = \begin{bmatrix} 10 & \_\_ \\ \_\_ & \_\_ \\ \_\_ & \_\_ \end{bmatrix}$$

Now take the product of the first row of A, $\begin{bmatrix} 3 & 1 \end{bmatrix}$, and the second column of B, $\begin{bmatrix} 3 \\ 6 \end{bmatrix}$, and place the result in the first row and second column of the product:

$$\begin{bmatrix} 3 & 1 \\ 2 & 4 \\ 5 & 0 \end{bmatrix} \begin{bmatrix} 2 & 3 \\ 4 & 6 \end{bmatrix} = \begin{bmatrix} 10 & 15 \\ \_\_ & \_\_ \\ \_\_ & \_\_ \end{bmatrix}$$

Since there are no more columns of B, we move on to the second row of A. Take the product of the second row of A, $\begin{bmatrix} 2 & 4 \end{bmatrix}$, and the first column of B, $\begin{bmatrix} 2 \\ 4 \end{bmatrix}$, and place the result in the second row and first column of the product:

$$\begin{bmatrix} 3 & 1 \\ 2 & 4 \\ 5 & 0 \end{bmatrix} \begin{bmatrix} 2 & 3 \\ 4 & 6 \end{bmatrix} = \begin{bmatrix} 10 & 15 \\ 20 & \_\_ \\ \_\_ & \_\_ \end{bmatrix}$$

Take the product of the second row of A, $\begin{bmatrix} 2 & 4 \end{bmatrix}$, and the second column of B, $\begin{bmatrix} 3 \\ 6 \end{bmatrix}$, and place the result in the second row and second column of the product:

$$\begin{bmatrix} 3 & 1 \\ 2 & 4 \\ 5 & 0 \end{bmatrix} \begin{bmatrix} 2 & 3 \\ 4 & 6 \end{bmatrix} = \begin{bmatrix} 10 & 15 \\ 20 & 30 \\ \_\_ & \_\_ \end{bmatrix}$$

Since there are no more columns of B, we move on to the third row of A. Take the product of the third row of A, $\begin{bmatrix} 5 & 0 \end{bmatrix}$, and the first column of B, $\begin{bmatrix} 2 \\ 4 \end{bmatrix}$, and place the result in the third row and first column of the product:

$$\begin{bmatrix} 3 & 1 \\ 2 & 4 \\ 5 & 0 \end{bmatrix} \begin{bmatrix} 2 & 3 \\ 4 & 6 \end{bmatrix} = \begin{bmatrix} 10 & 15 \\ 20 & 30 \\ 10 & \_\_ \end{bmatrix}$$

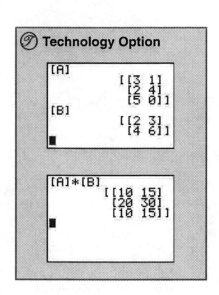

Take the product of the third row of A, $\begin{bmatrix} 5 & 0 \end{bmatrix}$, and the second column of B, $\begin{bmatrix} 3 \\ 6 \end{bmatrix}$, and place the result in the third row and second column of the product:

$$\begin{bmatrix} 3 & 1 \\ 2 & 4 \\ 5 & 0 \end{bmatrix} \begin{bmatrix} 2 & 3 \\ 4 & 6 \end{bmatrix} = \begin{bmatrix} 10 & 15 \\ 20 & 30 \\ 10 & 15 \end{bmatrix}$$

Since there are no more columns of B, we move on to the next row of A. Since there are no more rows of A, we are done.

Multiplication of Matrices

Given two matrices $A = (a_{ij})_{m \times p}$ and $B = (b_{ij})_{q \times n}$, the product $AB = C = (c_{ij})$ is defined if $p = q$, that is, if the number of columns of A equals the number of rows of B. In such a case, the element in the ith row and jth column, c_{ij}, of the product matrix C is obtained by taking the product of the ith row of A and the jth column of B.

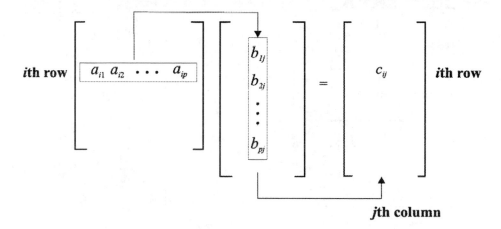

jth column

Notice that to obtain the first row of the product $C = AB$, we take the product of the first row of A and the successive columns of B until we exhaust the columns of B. This indicates that the number of columns of the product AB must equal the number of columns of B. Also notice that a row of B is obtained for each row of A. This indicates that the number of rows of the product AB must equal the number of rows of A. Thus

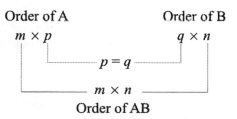

Order of AB

Given the two matrices $A = (a_{ij})_{m \times p}$ and $B = (b_{ij})_{p \times n}$, the product matrix AB has order $m \times n$.

Applying this to the previous example we have

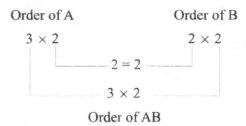

Order of A   Order of B

3×2 2×2

$2 = 2$

3×2

Order of AB

EXAMPLE 3   Multiplying Matrices Given matrices A and B below, find the products AB and BA

$$A = \begin{bmatrix} 1 & 2 \\ 3 & 4 \end{bmatrix} \quad B = \begin{bmatrix} 5 & 6 \\ 7 & 8 \end{bmatrix}$$

Solution

$$AB = \begin{bmatrix} 1 & 2 \\ 3 & 4 \end{bmatrix} \begin{bmatrix} 5 & 6 \\ 7 & 8 \end{bmatrix} = \begin{bmatrix} (1)(5)+(2)(7) & (1)(6)+(2)(8) \\ (3)(5)+(4)(7) & (3)(6)+(4)(8) \end{bmatrix}$$

$$= \begin{bmatrix} 19 & 22 \\ 43 & 50 \end{bmatrix}$$

$$BA = \begin{bmatrix} 5 & 6 \\ 7 & 8 \end{bmatrix} \begin{bmatrix} 1 & 2 \\ 3 & 4 \end{bmatrix} = \begin{bmatrix} (5)(1)+(6)(3) & (5)(2)+(6)(4) \\ (7)(1)+(8)(3) & (7)(2)+(8)(4) \end{bmatrix}$$

$$= \begin{bmatrix} 23 & 34 \\ 31 & 46 \end{bmatrix}$$

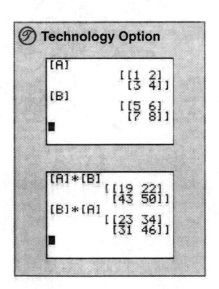

Technology Option

```
[A]
            [[1 2]
             [3 4]]
[B]
            [[5 6]
             [7 8]]
■
```

```
[A]*[B]
            [[19 22]
             [43 50]]
[B]*[A]
            [[23 34]
             [31 46]]
■
```

Notice that this example illustrates that in general AB need not equal BA even when they are both defined and of the same order.   ◆

Earlier we saw that

$$AB = \begin{bmatrix} 3 & 1 \\ 2 & 4 \\ 5 & 0 \end{bmatrix} \begin{bmatrix} 2 & 3 \\ 4 & 6 \end{bmatrix} = \begin{bmatrix} 10 & 15 \\ 20 & 30 \\ 10 & 15 \end{bmatrix}$$

But notice that for this A and B, the product BA is not even defined, since the number of columns of B does not equal the number of rows of A.

Order of B   Order of A

2×2 3×2

$2 \neq 3$

BA undefined

$$BA = \begin{bmatrix} 2 & 3 \\ 4 & 6 \end{bmatrix} \begin{bmatrix} 3 & 1 \\ 2 & 4 \\ 5 & 0 \end{bmatrix} = \text{undefined}$$

At the beginning of this section we defined the product RC where R was a row matrix and C a column matrix of the same order n. The answer we obtained was a 1×1 matrix (a single number). What happens if we reverse the order of the multiplication? Checking the orders we have for CR,

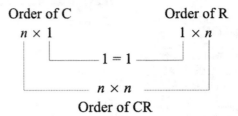

Order of CR

We obtain a square matrix of order $n \times n$. Note however that this product is meaningless in the context of our application.

EXAMPLE 4   Multiplying Matrices   Find the following products

a. $\begin{bmatrix} 1 \\ 2 \end{bmatrix} \begin{bmatrix} 3 & 4 \end{bmatrix}$ **b.** $\begin{bmatrix} 3 & 4 \end{bmatrix} \begin{bmatrix} 1 \\ 2 \end{bmatrix}$

Solution

a. $\begin{bmatrix} 1 \\ 2 \end{bmatrix} \begin{bmatrix} 3 & 4 \end{bmatrix} = \begin{bmatrix} (1)(3) & (1)(4) \\ (2)(3) & (2)(4) \end{bmatrix} = \begin{bmatrix} 3 & 4 \\ 6 & 8 \end{bmatrix}$

b. $\begin{bmatrix} 3 & 4 \end{bmatrix} \begin{bmatrix} 1 \\ 2 \end{bmatrix} = [(3)(1) + (4)(2)] = [11]$ ◆

We now have several examples that indicate that, in general, matrix multiplication is NOT commutative,

$$AB \neq BA$$

even if both matrices A and B are square. However, matrix multiplication is associative and distributive as listed in the box.

Properties of Matrix Multiplication
For any matrices A, B, and C,

$$A(BC) = (AB)C$$

$$A(B+C) = AB + AC$$

whenever the indicated products are defined.

If a is any number, then the number 1 has the property that

$$a \cdot 1 = 1 \cdot a = a$$

There is a matrix analog to the number 1. This matrix, which must be a square matrix, is called the identity matrix.

> **The Identity Matrix**
> The $n \times n$ identity matrix, I_n, is the square matrix of order $n \times n$ with ones down the main diagonal and zeros elsewhere.

Technology Option

An identity matrix can be generated on the calculator via the MATRIX button and choosing 5:identity(in the MATH menu. A 2×2 and a 3×3 identity matrix are shown.

```
identity(2)
          [[1 0]
           [0 1]]
identity(3)
          [[1 0 0]
           [0 1 0]
           [0 0 1]]
```

Thus,

$$I_n = \begin{bmatrix} 1 & 0 & 0 & \cdots & 0 \\ 0 & 1 & 0 & \cdots & 0 \\ \vdots & & & \cdots & \\ 0 & 0 & 0 & \cdots & 1 \end{bmatrix}$$

with n rows and n columns. The identity matrix then has the following property:

> **Multiplication Property of the Identity Matrix**
> If A is a square matrix of order $n \times n$, then
>
> $$AI_n = I_nA = A$$

For example,

$$\begin{aligned} AI_2 &= \begin{bmatrix} a & b \\ c & d \end{bmatrix} \begin{bmatrix} 1 & 0 \\ 0 & 1 \end{bmatrix} = \begin{bmatrix} a \cdot 1 + b \cdot 0 & a \cdot 0 + b \cdot 1 \\ c \cdot 1 + d \cdot 0 & c \cdot 0 + d \cdot 1 \end{bmatrix} \\ &= \begin{bmatrix} a & b \\ c & d \end{bmatrix} = A \end{aligned}$$

✧ Applications

Matrix techniques are regularly used in business applications. Here we show how production planning can be done using matrices and matrix multiplication.

A microbrewer makes four products called Light (L), Dark (D), Ale (A), and Stout (S). A facility is located in St. Louis, where three ingredients, malt, hops, and yeast, are purchased and then available to produce the four products. (We will assume that the microbrewer has a free supply of water.) The following matrix P gives the number of units of each ingredient needed to produce 1000 gallons of each product.

$$P = \begin{array}{c} \\ L \\ D \\ A \\ S \end{array} \begin{array}{ccc} \text{Malt} & \text{Hops} & \text{Yeast} \end{array} \\ \begin{bmatrix} 1 & 2 & 1 \\ 2 & 1 & 1 \\ 0 & 2 & 1 \\ 3 & 1 & 4 \end{bmatrix}$$

Suppose the cost of each unit of the ingredients malt (M), hops (H), and yeast (Y) is, respectively, \$10, \$30, and \$20. Let us summarize this in the following cost (column) matrix:

$$\text{$/unit}$$

$$C = \begin{array}{c} M \\ H \\ Y \end{array} \left[\begin{array}{c} 10 \\ 30 \\ 20 \end{array} \right]$$

The microbrewery might naturally wish to know the total cost of the ingredients that go into each product. This is given by the product of P and C:

$$PC = \begin{array}{c} \\ L \\ D \\ A \\ S \end{array} \overset{\displaystyle M \ H \ Y}{\left[\begin{array}{ccc} 1 & 2 & 1 \\ 2 & 1 & 1 \\ 0 & 2 & 1 \\ 3 & 1 & 4 \end{array} \right]} \times \begin{array}{c} \\ \text{Malt} \\ \text{Hops} \\ \text{Yeast} \end{array} \overset{\displaystyle \text{$/unit}}{\left[\begin{array}{c} 10 \\ 30 \\ 20 \end{array} \right]} = \left[\begin{array}{c} 10+60+20 \\ 20+30+20 \\ 0+60+20 \\ 30+30+80 \end{array} \right] = \begin{array}{c} \\ L \\ D \\ A \\ S \end{array} \overset{\displaystyle \$}{\left[\begin{array}{c} 90 \\ 70 \\ 80 \\ 140 \end{array} \right]}$$

where the four numbers in the last column matrix represent the total cost of ingredients to make 1000 gallons of Light, Dark, Ale, and Stout.

Suppose the microbrewery has an order for 9000 gallons of Light, 6000 gallons of Dark, 7000 gallons of Ale, and 5000 gallons of Stout and then wanted to know the total number of units of each of the ingredients needed. If we expressed the amounts ordered (in thousands) as a row matrix

$$R = \# \overset{\displaystyle L \ \ D \ \ A \ \ S}{\left[\begin{array}{cccc} 9 & 6 & 7 & 5 \end{array} \right]}$$

then the product matrix

$$RP = \# \overset{\displaystyle L \ \ D \ \ A \ \ S}{\left[\begin{array}{cccc} 9 & 6 & 7 & 5 \end{array} \right]} \times \begin{array}{c} \\ L \\ D \\ A \\ S \end{array} \overset{\displaystyle M \ \ H \ \ Y}{\left[\begin{array}{ccc} 1 & 2 & 1 \\ 2 & 1 & 1 \\ 0 & 2 & 1 \\ 3 & 1 & 4 \end{array} \right]} = \# \overset{\displaystyle M \ \ H \ \ Y}{\left[\begin{array}{ccc} 36 & 43 & 42 \end{array} \right]}$$

represents, respectively, the number of units of the ingredients malt, hops, and yeast to fill the order.

Now suppose, after the ingredients are purchased and stored in the St. Louis facility, they are shipped out to the two manufacturing plants, one in LA and one in NYC, where the four products are actually produced. The following table and matrix A give the number in thousands of products manufactured at each of the two plants.

	Light	Dark	Ale	Stout
LA	2	1	1	2
NYC	3	1	0	1

Suppose the microbrewer wishes to keep track of how many units of each ingredient is going to LA and to NYC. The matrix

$$AP = \left[\begin{array}{cccc} 2 & 1 & 1 & 2 \\ 3 & 1 & 0 & 1 \end{array} \right] \left[\begin{array}{ccc} 1 & 2 & 1 \\ 2 & 1 & 1 \\ 0 & 2 & 1 \\ 3 & 1 & 4 \end{array} \right] = \begin{array}{c} \\ \text{LA} \\ \text{NYC} \end{array} \overset{\displaystyle \text{Malt} \ \ \text{Hops} \ \ \text{Yeast}}{\left[\begin{array}{ccc} 10 & 9 & 12 \\ 8 & 8 & 8 \end{array} \right]}$$

summarizes this information. Thus, the element in the first row and first column, 10, is the number of thousands of units of malt that are used in the LA plant.

✧ Systems of Equations

We shall now see how to use matrices to represent systems of equations. Consider the following system of equations.

$$2x_1 + 3x_2 + 5x_3 = 2$$
$$5x_1 - 4x_2 + 3x_3 = 4$$
$$3x_1 + 2x_2 - 2x_3 = 1$$

Define the following three matrices:

$$A = \begin{bmatrix} 2 & 3 & 5 \\ 5 & -4 & 3 \\ 3 & 2 & -2 \end{bmatrix}, \quad X = \begin{bmatrix} x_1 \\ x_2 \\ x_3 \end{bmatrix}, \quad B = \begin{bmatrix} 2 \\ 4 \\ 1 \end{bmatrix}$$

The matrix A is called the coefficient matrix, the matrix X is the variable matrix, and matrix B is the constant matrix. Then notice that

$$AX = \begin{bmatrix} 2 & 3 & 5 \\ 5 & -4 & 3 \\ 3 & 2 & -2 \end{bmatrix} \begin{bmatrix} x_1 \\ x_2 \\ x_3 \end{bmatrix} = \begin{bmatrix} 2x_1 + 3x_2 + 5x_3 \\ 5x_1 - 4x_2 + 3x_3 \\ 3x_1 + 2x_2 - 2x_3 \end{bmatrix} = \begin{bmatrix} 2 \\ 4 \\ 1 \end{bmatrix} = B$$

That is, our system of equations can be represented by a matrix equation. More generally, the system of equations

$$a_{11}x_1 + a_{12}x_2 + \cdots a_{1n}x_n = b_1$$
$$a_{21}x_1 + a_{22}x_2 + \cdots a_{2n}x_n = b_2$$
$$\cdots$$
$$a_{m1}x_1 + a_{m2}x_2 + \cdots a_{mn}x_n = b_m$$

can be written as $AX = B$ if we define

$$A = \begin{bmatrix} a_{11} & a_{12} & \cdots & a_{1n} \\ a_{21} & a_{22} & \cdots & a_{2n} \\ & \cdots & & \\ a_{m1} & a_{m2} & \cdots & a_{mn} \end{bmatrix}, \quad X = \begin{bmatrix} x_1 \\ x_2 \\ \vdots \\ x_n \end{bmatrix}, \quad B = \begin{bmatrix} b_1 \\ b_2 \\ \vdots \\ b_m \end{bmatrix}$$

✧ Enrichment: Matrices in Least Squares

In Section 1.5 we found the closest straight line $y = ax + b$ to a set of data points $(x_1, y_1), (x_2, y_2), \ldots, (x_n, y_n)$. We give the following method.

Method of Least Squares

The line $y = ax + b$ closest to the data points (x_1, y_1), (x_2, y_2), ..., (x_n, y_n) can be found by solving the following two linear equations for a and b:

$$(x_1^2 + \cdots + x_n^2)a + (x_1 + \cdots + x_n)b = x_1 y_1 + \cdots + x_n y_n$$
$$(x_1 + \cdots + x_n)a + \qquad\qquad nb = y_1 + \cdots + y_n$$

Furthermore, the augmented matrix A for this system is given by

$$A = \begin{bmatrix} x_1 & x_2 & \cdots & x_n \\ 1 & 1 & \cdots & 1 \end{bmatrix} \begin{bmatrix} x_1 & 1 & y_1 \\ x_2 & 1 & y_2 \\ \vdots & \vdots & \vdots \\ x_n & 1 & y_n \end{bmatrix}$$

As an example, consider again the first example we looked at in Section 1.5. We had five data points on a demand curve (x_i, p_i) given. They were $(1, 10)$, $(2, 9)$, $(3, 8)$, $(5, 7)$, and $(9, 5)$. We can find the augmented matrix by the following method:

$$A = \begin{bmatrix} x_1 & x_2 & \cdots & x_n \\ 1 & 1 & \cdots & 1 \end{bmatrix} \begin{bmatrix} x_1 & 1 & y_1 \\ x_2 & 1 & y_2 \\ \vdots & \vdots & \vdots \\ x_n & 1 & y_n \end{bmatrix} = \begin{bmatrix} 1 & 2 & 3 & 5 & 9 \\ 1 & 1 & 1 & 1 & 1 \end{bmatrix} \begin{bmatrix} 1 & 1 & 10 \\ 2 & 1 & 9 \\ 3 & 1 & 8 \\ 5 & 1 & 7 \\ 9 & 1 & 5 \end{bmatrix}$$

$$= \begin{bmatrix} 120 & 20 & 132 \\ 20 & 5 & 39 \end{bmatrix}$$

We can then readily solve for a and b using techniques found in Chapter 1 for systems of linear equations.

✧ Technology Corner

⑨Technology Note 1   **Matrix Multiplication in Microsoft Excel**

To multiply using a spreadsheet, begin by entering the matrices as shown in Worksheet 1 and highlighting a 3x2 block of cells for the product. Then enter =MMULT(and highlight the cells of matrix A. Then, a comma and highlight the cells in matrix B. Click Ctrl-Shift-Enter to evaluate the product as shown in Worksheet 2.

	A	B	C	D	E
1	A			B	
2	3	1		2	3
3	2	4		4	6
4	5	0			
5					
6	AB				
7	=MMULT(A2:B4,D2:E3)				
8					
9					

Worksheet 1

	A	B	C	D	E
1	A			B	
2	3	1		2	3
3	2	4		4	6
4	5	0			
5					
6	AB				
7	10	15			
8	20	30			
9	10	15			

Worksheet 2

Self-Help Exercises 2.2

1. Perform the indicated operation.

$$\begin{bmatrix} 1 & 2 \\ -1 & 3 \end{bmatrix} \begin{bmatrix} 3 & 0 & 4 \\ 1 & -2 & 5 \end{bmatrix}$$

2. A firm makes two types of a product and uses three parts according to the following table.

	Part A	Part B	Part C
$P =$ Type I	3	2	1
Type II	1	2	4

Both types of this product are manufactured at two different factories: Factory X and Factory Y. The time in work-hours that is required to install each part is given as follows:

	Factory X	Factory Y
Part A	3	2
$Q =$ Part B	4	4
Part C	5	3

Compute PQ and explain what each entry in this product matrix means.

3. Put the following system in matrix form $AX = B$, where X is a column matrix with the unknowns:

$$\begin{aligned} 10x + 2y + 8z &= 7 \\ -3x + 5y - 7z &= 5 \\ -4x - 3y + 5z &= 3 \end{aligned}$$

2.2 Exercises

In Exercises 1 through 6, perform the indicated multiplication if possible.

1. $\begin{bmatrix} 2 & 3 \end{bmatrix} \begin{bmatrix} 5 \\ 2 \end{bmatrix}$

2. $\begin{bmatrix} 1 & 4 & -2 \end{bmatrix} \begin{bmatrix} 3 \\ 2 \\ 5 \end{bmatrix}$

3. $\begin{bmatrix} -2 & 3 & 4 & 2 \end{bmatrix} \begin{bmatrix} -2 \\ -1 \\ 3 \\ 5 \end{bmatrix}$

4. $\begin{bmatrix} 2 & -3 & 0 & 4 & 2 \end{bmatrix} \begin{bmatrix} 3 \\ 4 \\ 3 \\ -3 \\ b \end{bmatrix}$

5. $\begin{bmatrix} 2 & 3 \end{bmatrix} \begin{bmatrix} 5 \\ 2 \\ 0 \end{bmatrix}$

6. $\begin{bmatrix} 0 & 0 & 0 \end{bmatrix} \begin{bmatrix} 0 \\ 0 \end{bmatrix}$

In Exercises 7 through 16, find the order of AB and BA when either one exists.

7. A is order 2×3 and B is order 3×4.

8. A is order 3×5 and B is order 5×7.

9. A is order 3×4 and B is order 5×3.

10. A is order 5×7 and B is order 8×5.

11. A is order 3×3 and B is order 3×5.

12. A is order 5×4 and B is order 4×4.

13. A is order 6×6 and B is order 6×6.

14. A is order 8×8 and B is order 8×8.

15. A is order 3×40 and B is order 2×20.

16. A is order 3×40 and B is order 50×3.

In Exercises 17 through 42, perform the indicated multiplications if possible.

17. $\begin{bmatrix} 2 & 5 \\ 4 & 3 \end{bmatrix} \begin{bmatrix} 2 \\ 5 \end{bmatrix}$

18. $\begin{bmatrix} 5 & -3 \\ -2 & 4 \end{bmatrix} \begin{bmatrix} -3 \\ 4 \end{bmatrix}$

19. $\begin{bmatrix} 3 & 7 \end{bmatrix} \begin{bmatrix} -2 & 5 \\ 7 & 2 \end{bmatrix}$

20. $\begin{bmatrix} 2 & 1 \end{bmatrix} \begin{bmatrix} 3 & 20 \\ -3 & 5 \end{bmatrix}$

21. $\begin{bmatrix} 0.2 & 0.1 \\ 0.4 & 0.5 \end{bmatrix} \begin{bmatrix} 2 & 3 \\ 5 & 2 \end{bmatrix}$

22. $\begin{bmatrix} -1 & -3 \\ -2 & -4 \end{bmatrix} \begin{bmatrix} 0 & 2 \\ 2 & 5 \end{bmatrix}$

23. $\begin{bmatrix} 2 & 8 & 4 \\ 3 & 0 & 2 \end{bmatrix} \begin{bmatrix} 4 \\ 2 \\ 3 \end{bmatrix}$

24. $\begin{bmatrix} 4 & 2 \end{bmatrix} \begin{bmatrix} 2 & -3 & 4 \\ -1 & 3 & 5 \end{bmatrix}$

25. $\begin{bmatrix} 0.1 & 0.4 & 0.2 \\ 0.5 & 0.2 & 0.1 \end{bmatrix} \begin{bmatrix} 2 & 4 \\ -1 & 5 \\ 5 & -2 \end{bmatrix}$

26. $\begin{bmatrix} 10 & 20 \\ 30 & 40 \end{bmatrix} \begin{bmatrix} 3 & 2 & 0 \\ 1 & 3 & 2 \end{bmatrix}$

27. $\begin{bmatrix} 3 & 5 \\ 8 & 2 \end{bmatrix} \begin{bmatrix} 1 & 5 & 2 & 3 \\ 0 & 3 & 5 & 1 \end{bmatrix}$

28. $\begin{bmatrix} 4 & 2 \\ -1 & 6 \\ 3 & -2 \end{bmatrix} \begin{bmatrix} 2 \\ 3 \end{bmatrix}$

29. $\begin{bmatrix} 0.01 & 0.03 \end{bmatrix} \begin{bmatrix} 1 & 3 & 2 \\ 2 & 5 & 1 \end{bmatrix}$

30. $\begin{bmatrix} -1 & -2 & -5 & -2 \\ 3 & 5 & 1 & 0 \end{bmatrix} \begin{bmatrix} 0 & 3 \\ 2 & 0 \end{bmatrix}$

31. $\begin{bmatrix} 3 & 2 & 5 \\ 1 & 3 & 2 \\ 4 & 2 & 1 \end{bmatrix} \begin{bmatrix} 2 \\ 0 \\ 4 \end{bmatrix}$

32. $\begin{bmatrix} 4 & 0 & 1 \\ 2 & -2 & 2 \\ 1 & -1 & 0 \end{bmatrix} \begin{bmatrix} 2 \\ 4 \\ 1 \end{bmatrix}$

33. $\begin{bmatrix} 3 & -2 & 1 \end{bmatrix} \begin{bmatrix} 2 & 1 & 5 \\ 5 & 0 & -2 \\ 0 & 1 & 2 \end{bmatrix}$

34. $\begin{bmatrix} -1 & 0 & 1 \end{bmatrix} \begin{bmatrix} 2 & 1 & 2 \\ 1 & -1 & -1 \\ 2 & 1 & 1 \end{bmatrix}$

35. $\begin{bmatrix} 1 & 4 & 2 \\ 0 & 2 & 0 \\ 5 & 2 & 1 \end{bmatrix} \begin{bmatrix} 3 & 0 & 1 \\ 0 & 2 & 4 \\ 1 & 1 & 2 \end{bmatrix}$

36. $\begin{bmatrix} 0 & -1 & 2 \\ -1 & 0 & 2 \\ 2 & -2 & 0 \end{bmatrix} \begin{bmatrix} 1 & 4 & 2 \\ 0 & 1 & 1 \\ 2 & 4 & 2 \end{bmatrix}$

37. $\begin{bmatrix} 1 & 2 \\ 0 & 0 \\ 1 & 0 \end{bmatrix} \begin{bmatrix} 2 & 3 \\ 1 & 1 \\ 0 & 0 \end{bmatrix}$

38. $\begin{bmatrix} 0 & 0 \\ 0 & 0 \end{bmatrix} \begin{bmatrix} 1 & 1 \\ 1 & 1 \\ 1 & 1 \end{bmatrix}$

39. $\begin{bmatrix} 2 \\ 5 \end{bmatrix} \begin{bmatrix} 3 & 5 \end{bmatrix}$

40. $\begin{bmatrix} y \\ 0 \\ -1 \end{bmatrix} \begin{bmatrix} 2 & 0 & -1 \end{bmatrix}$

41. $\begin{bmatrix} 0 & 0 & 0 \\ 0 & 0 & 0 \end{bmatrix} \begin{bmatrix} 0 & 0 \\ 0 & 0 \end{bmatrix}$

42. $\begin{bmatrix} 1 & 1 & 1 \\ 1 & 1 & 1 \end{bmatrix} \begin{bmatrix} 1 & 1 & 1 \\ 1 & 1 & 1 \end{bmatrix}$

43. Let

$$A = \begin{bmatrix} 1 & 1 \\ 1 & 1 \end{bmatrix} \quad \text{and} \quad B = \begin{bmatrix} 1 & 1 \\ -1 & -1 \end{bmatrix}$$

Show that $AB = O$. Thus, a product of two matrices may be the zero matrix without either matrix being the zero matrix.

44. Consider the four matrices

$$\begin{bmatrix} 1 & 0 \\ 0 & 1 \end{bmatrix}, \begin{bmatrix} 1 & 0 \\ 0 & -1 \end{bmatrix}, \begin{bmatrix} -1 & 0 \\ 0 & 1 \end{bmatrix}, \begin{bmatrix} -1 & 0 \\ 0 & -1 \end{bmatrix}$$

Show that the square of each of them is I_2. Thus, the identity matrix has many square roots.

45. Let

$$A = \begin{bmatrix} 1 & 1 \\ -1 & -1 \end{bmatrix}$$

Show that $A^2 = AA = O$.

46. Let

$$A = \begin{bmatrix} a_{11} & a_{12} & a_{13} \\ a_{21} & a_{22} & a_{33} \\ a_{31} & a_{32} & a_{33} \end{bmatrix}$$

Show that $AI_3 = I_3A = A$.

47. Let

$$A = \begin{bmatrix} 1 & 2 \\ 3 & 4 \end{bmatrix}, \quad B = \begin{bmatrix} 1 & -1 \\ 1 & 2 \end{bmatrix}$$

Show that $(A + B)^2 \neq A^2 + 2AB + B^2$.

48. Let

$$A = \begin{bmatrix} 1 & 1 \\ 2 & 1 \end{bmatrix}, B = \begin{bmatrix} 2 & 2 \\ 5 & 4 \end{bmatrix}, C = \begin{bmatrix} 1 & 1 \\ -1 & -1 \end{bmatrix}$$

Show $AC = BC$, but $A \neq B$.

49. Let A, B, and C be the matrices in Exercise 48. Show that

$$A(B+C) = AB + AC$$

$$A(BC) = (AB)C$$

50. A matrix $U = (u_{ij})$ is upper triangular if $u_{ij} = 0$ when $i > j$, that is, when all entries below the main diagonal are zero. Suppose $A = (a_{ij})$ and $B = (b_{ij})$ are both upper triangular matrices of order (3×3). Show that

a. A^2 is upper triangular.

b. AB is upper triangular.

51. Let

$$A = \begin{bmatrix} 0 & 1 & 2 \\ 0 & 0 & 3 \\ 0 & 0 & 0 \end{bmatrix}$$

Show $A^3 = AAA = O$, the zero matrix.

52. A matrix $U = (u_{ij})$ is strictly upper triangular if $u_{ij} = 0$ when $i \geq j$, that is, when all entries below and on the main diagonal are zero. If $U = (u_{ij})$ is a strictly upper triangular matrix of order (3×3), show that $U^3 = O$, the zero matrix.

In Exercises 53 through 60, find matrices A, X, and B so that the given system of equations can be written as $AX = B$.

53.
$$2x_1 + 3x_2 = 5$$
$$3x_1 - 5x_2 = 7$$

54.
$$4x_1 - 5x_2 = 6$$
$$2x_1 + 7x_2 = 9$$

55.
$$2x_1 + 5x_2 + 3x_3 = 16$$
$$4x_1 - 7x_2 - 2x_3 = 12$$
$$5x_1 - 2x_2 + 6x_3 = 24$$

56.
$$-3x_1 + 7x_2 + 2x_3 = 0$$
$$-7x_2 + 5x_3 = 2$$
$$4x_1 + 3x_2 - 7x_3 = 4$$

57.
$$2x_1 - 3x_2 + 3x_3 = 3$$
$$5x_1 + 6x_2 - 2x_3 = 1$$

58.
$$2x_1 - 7x_2 = 3$$
$$x_1 + 8x_2 = 2$$
$$3x_1 + 4x_2 = 5$$

59. $2x_1 + 3x_2 = 7$

60. $3x_1 + 5x_2 - 6x_3 = 2$

Applications

61. Matrix G shows the number of burritos sold at three local restaurants at lunch. The veggie burritos sell for $3.00, the beef for $4.50 and the chicken for $4.00. Find a matrix H such that the product of matrix G and matrix H will show the revenue, R, from selling burritos at each restaurant.

$$G = \begin{array}{c} \text{store } 1 \\ \text{store } 2 \\ \text{store } 3 \end{array} \begin{bmatrix} \overset{\text{veggie}}{15} & \overset{\text{beef}}{12} & \overset{\text{chicken}}{22} \\ 21 & 14 & 19 \\ 23 & 25 & 17 \end{bmatrix}$$

62. Matrix A shows the number of calories from fat, protein, and carbohydrates per unit of each food. Matrix B shows the number of units of each food eaten by each person. Find the product AB. What does the product matrix AB represent?

$$\begin{array}{c} \text{Food A} \\ \text{Food B} \\ \text{Food C} \end{array} \begin{bmatrix} \overset{\text{fat}}{25} & \overset{\text{carbs}}{8} & \overset{\text{protein}}{12} \\ 31 & 24 & 19 \\ 30 & 12 & 22 \end{bmatrix}$$

$$\begin{array}{c} \text{fat} \\ \text{carbs} \\ \text{protein} \end{array} \begin{bmatrix} \overset{\text{Tom}}{3} & \overset{\text{Susan}}{1} & \overset{\text{Bob}}{2} \\ 0 & 5 & 6 \\ 2 & 2 & 0 \end{bmatrix}$$

63. Matrix M shows the number of each type of flower used in each type of centerpiece (type F, type G, and type H). Given that mums cost $3.00 each, lilies cost $2.00 each, and carnations cost $1.00 each, find a matrix N such that the product of the two matrices shows the cost to make each type of arrangement.

$$M = \begin{array}{c} \text{mums} \\ \text{lilies} \\ \text{carnations} \end{array} \begin{bmatrix} \overset{F}{3} & \overset{G}{2} & \overset{H}{6} \\ 4 & 5 & 8 \\ 5 & 3 & 5 \end{bmatrix}$$

64. Matrix F shows the investment portfolio of three employees, Bill, Sue, and Tom. There are three funds the employees have invested in, Fund I, Fund II, and Fund III. The entries in the matrix represent how much money each employee has invested in each fund. Fund I has an average return of 6%, Fund II has an average rate of return of 9%, and Fund III has an average rate of return of 4%. Find a matrix G such that the product of matrix G and matrix F will show H, how much each employee earns on their portfolio.

$$
\begin{array}{c}
 & \text{I} & \text{II} & \text{III} \\
\begin{matrix} \text{Bill} \\ \text{Sue} \\ \text{Tom} \end{matrix}
\begin{bmatrix} 1500 & 1020 & 2200 \\ 2100 & 1400 & 1090 \\ 2030 & 2500 & 1070 \end{bmatrix}
\end{array}
$$

65. Matrix M shows the nutritional contents of three different kinds of dog food. Each entry represents the number of units of the vitamin per gram of food. Matrix N shows the number of grams of each type of food that is fed to a dog. Find the product MN. What does the product matrix MN mean?

$$
M = \begin{array}{c}
 & \text{kibble} & \text{bits} & \text{chunks} \\
\begin{matrix} \text{Vitamin X} \\ \text{Vitamin Y} \\ \text{Vitamin Z} \end{matrix}
\begin{bmatrix} 3 & 2 & 4 \\ 2 & 4 & 5 \\ 2 & 5 & 1 \end{bmatrix}
\end{array}
$$

$$
N = \begin{array}{c}
 & \text{grams} \\
\begin{matrix} \text{kibble} \\ \text{bits} \\ \text{chunks} \end{matrix}
\begin{bmatrix} 27 \\ 55 \\ 68 \end{bmatrix}
\end{array}
$$

66. Matthew has started a new business selling rocks. He sells two different kinds of rocks, skipping stones (SS) and pet rocks (PR). Matthew collects his rocks around Mertzon or Eden. The number of each type of rock collected in each location during June is found in matrix J. Matrix C gives Matthew's cost for collecting the rocks and matrix S gives the selling price for the rocks. If all the rocks collected in June are sold, what does the matrix $J(S-C)$ represent?

$$
J = \begin{array}{c}
 & SS \ PR \\
\begin{matrix} \text{Mertzon} \\ \text{Eden} \end{matrix}
\begin{bmatrix} 40 & 50 \\ 30 & 20 \end{bmatrix}
\end{array}
$$

$$
C = \begin{array}{c}
 & \$ \\
\begin{matrix} SS \\ PR \end{matrix}
\begin{bmatrix} 1 \\ 3 \end{bmatrix}
\end{array}
\qquad
S = \begin{array}{c}
 & \$ \\
\begin{matrix} SS \\ PR \end{matrix}
\begin{bmatrix} 2 \\ 12 \end{bmatrix}
\end{array}
$$

67. Spare Parts Planning A car rental firm is planning a maintenance program involving certain parts of various makes of compact automobiles. The following matrix indicates the number of hundreds of automobiles available for rent in the three cities in which the firm operates.

$$
N = \begin{array}{c}
 & \text{GM} & \text{Ford} & \text{Chrysler} & \text{Toyota} \\
\begin{matrix} \text{LA} \\ \text{NYC} \\ \text{SL} \end{matrix}
\begin{bmatrix} 1 & 2 & 2 & 3 \\ 3 & 1 & 1 & 2 \\ 2 & 2 & 1 & 1 \end{bmatrix}
\end{array}
$$

Past repair records for the three cities indicate the number of each part needed per car per year. This is given in the following:

$$
R = \begin{array}{c}
 & \text{Tires} & \text{Batteries} & \text{Plugs} \\
\begin{matrix} \text{GM} \\ \text{Ford} \\ \text{Chrysler} \\ \text{Toyota} \end{matrix}
\begin{bmatrix} 4 & 0.5 & 6 \\ 3 & 0.5 & 7 \\ 4 & 0.4 & 5 \\ 3 & 1.0 & 4 \end{bmatrix}
\end{array}
$$

a. Show that the quantity of each part needed in each city is given by $Q = NR$. Indicate for what each column and each row of Q stands.

b. Let the elements in the column matrix

$$
C = \begin{array}{c}
 & \$ \\
\begin{matrix} \text{Tires} \\ \text{Batteries} \\ \text{Plugs} \end{matrix}
\begin{bmatrix} 100 \\ 40 \\ 1 \end{bmatrix}
\end{array}
$$

be, respectively, the cost per each for tires, batteries, and plugs. Determine QC and interpret what the elements stand for.

Extensions

68. Networks The following application is a very scaled-down version of a technique used by the major airlines. The actual calculations are carried out by computers. The diagram indicates the nonstop service between four cities, LA, Chicago, NYC, and Miami. For example, the arrows indicate that there is nonstop service in both directions between LA and NYC but only one-way service from Chicago to NYC. The network in the diagram can be summarized by an adjacency matrix $A = (a_{ij})$, as follows. We set $a_{ij} = 1$ if there is nonstop service from city i to city j, otherwise a_{ij} is zero. We then have

$$A = \text{From} \quad \begin{array}{c} \\ L \\ C \\ N \\ M \end{array} \begin{array}{cccc} L & \text{toC} & N & M \\ \left[\begin{array}{cccc} 0 & 1 & 1 & 0 \\ 0 & 0 & 1 & 0 \\ 1 & 0 & 0 & 1 \\ 0 & 0 & 1 & 0 \end{array}\right] \end{array}$$

a. Compute A^2 and verify from the diagram that the element in the ith row and jth column of A^2 represents the number of one-stop routes between the city in the ith row and the city in the jth column.

b. Compute $A + A^2$ and interpret what this matrix means.

c. Compute A^3 and verify from the diagram that the element in the ith row and jth column of A^3 represents the number of two-stop routes between the city in the ith row and the city in the jth column.

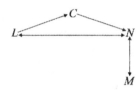

69. **Traffic Flow** The figure shows the traffic flow through nine intersections. Traffic enters from two roads from the left and exits on four roads to the right. All roads are one-way. Given the number of cars x_1 and x_2, that enter the intersections I_1 and I_2, respectively, we wish to determine the number of cars exiting each of the four roads on the right. Notice, for example, according to the figure that 40% of the traffic that enters intersection I_1 exits due east. Thus, $y_1 = 0.4x_1$. We also see that $y_2 = (0.6)(0.3)x_1 = 0.18x_1$ and $y_3 = (0.6)(0.7)x_1 + x_2$. Thus,

$$y_1 = 0.4x_1$$
$$y_2 = 0.18x_1$$
$$y_3 = 0.42x_1 + x_2$$

If

$$X = \begin{bmatrix} x_1 \\ x_2 \end{bmatrix}, A = \begin{bmatrix} 0.40 & 0 \\ 0.18 & 0 \\ 0.42 & 1 \end{bmatrix}, Y = \begin{bmatrix} y_1 \\ y_2 \\ y_3 \end{bmatrix}$$

then $Y = AX$.

a. Now by considering intersections I_4, I_5, and I_6, find a 3×3 matrix B such that $Z = BY$, where

$$Z = \begin{bmatrix} z_1 \\ z_2 \\ z_3 \end{bmatrix}$$

b. Now by considering intersections I_7, I_8, and I_9, find a 4×3 matrix C such that $W = CZ$, where

$$W = \begin{bmatrix} w_1 \\ w_2 \\ w_3 \\ w_4 \end{bmatrix}$$

c. Show that $W = (CBA)X$.

d. If $x_1 = 5000$ and $x_2 = 5000$, find W.

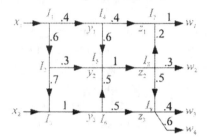

70. **Social Interaction** The digraph indicates the influence in decision making that one individual has over another. For example, according to the digraph, A has influence over B and D has influence over A, B, and C.

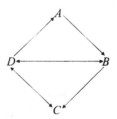

The following matrix T is then formed to represent this information:

$$T = \begin{array}{c} \\ A \\ B \\ C \\ D \end{array} \begin{array}{cccc} A & B & C & D \\ \left[\begin{array}{cccc} 0 & 1 & 0 & 0 \\ 0 & 0 & 1 & 1 \\ 0 & 0 & 0 & 1 \\ 1 & 1 & 1 & 0 \end{array}\right] \end{array}$$

A number one in the ith row and jth column indicates that the person in the ith row has direct influence over the person in the jth column, while a zero indicates no direct influence.

a. Calculate T^2 and show that a number 1 indicates that the individual in the row containing the 1 has influence over the individual in the column containing the 1 through one intermediary and that a number 2 indicates that the individual in the row containing the 2 has influence over the individual in the column containing the 2 through two different intermediaries.

b. Calculate $T + T^2$ and interpret what this matrix means.

71. **Least Squares** Redo Exercise 7 from Section 1.5 using the matrix formula found in the Enrichment subsection.

x	0	1	2	3	4
y	4	2	2	1	1

72. **Least Squares** Find the least square equation using the matrix formula found in the Enrichment subsection.

x	0	1	2	3	4
y	0	2	1	2	4

Solutions to Self-Help Exercises 2.2

1. $\begin{bmatrix} 1 & 2 \\ -1 & 3 \end{bmatrix}\begin{bmatrix} 3 & 0 & 4 \\ 1 & -2 & 5 \end{bmatrix}$

$= \begin{bmatrix} (1)(3)+(2)(1) & (1)(0)+(2)(-2) & (1)(4)+(2)(5) \\ (-1)(3)+(3)(1) & (-1)(0)+(3)(-2) & (-1)(4)+(3)(5) \end{bmatrix}$

$= \begin{bmatrix} 5 & -4 & 14 \\ 0 & -6 & 11 \end{bmatrix}$

2. $PQ = \begin{bmatrix} 3 & 2 & 1 \\ 1 & 2 & 4 \end{bmatrix}\begin{bmatrix} 3 & 2 \\ 4 & 4 \\ 5 & 3 \end{bmatrix}$

$= \begin{bmatrix} (3)(3)+(2)(4)+(1)(5) & (3)(2)+(2)(4)+(1)(3) \\ (1)(3)+(2)(4)+(4)(5) & (1)(2)+(2)(4)+(4)(3) \end{bmatrix}$

$= \begin{array}{c} \text{Type 1} \\ \text{Type 2} \end{array}\begin{matrix} \overset{\text{Factory X}}{} & \overset{\text{Factory Y}}{} \\ \begin{bmatrix} 22 & 17 \\ 31 & 22 \end{bmatrix} \end{matrix}$

3. The system is in the form $AX = B$ if

$$A = \begin{bmatrix} 10 & 2 & 8 \\ -3 & 5 & -7 \\ -4 & -3 & 5 \end{bmatrix}, \quad X = \begin{bmatrix} x \\ y \\ z \end{bmatrix}, \quad B = \begin{bmatrix} 7 \\ 5 \\ 3 \end{bmatrix}$$

2.3   Inverse of a Square Matrix

APPLICATION
Allocation of Funds

An investment adviser has two mutual funds that she is recommending: a conservative bond fund with an assumed return of 7% a year and a stock fund with a projected return of 12% a year. One client has $100,000 to invest and wishes a return of 9% a year, and a second client has $50,000 and wants a 10% annual return. How should she allocate the money of each client between the bond fund and the stock fund? The answer is found in Example 4.

✧ Definition of the Inverse of a Matrix

In this section we will define the inverse of a square matrix and will see that the inverse matrix is an extremely powerful tool in solving systems of equations where the number of unknowns is the same as the number of equations. We will develop a technique to find the inverse of a square matrix. We will also explore other applications of matrix inverses such as decoding messages (cryptography).

The equation $ax = 1$ has the solution $x = 1/a = a^{-1}$ if $a \neq 0$. The number a^{-1} is the reciprocal, or inverse, of the real number a and it has the property that $aa^{-1} = a^{-1}a = 1$. All real numbers except 0 have an inverse. We wish to find the matrix equivalent of this relationship. That is, given a square $n \times n$ matrix A, we wish to find a matrix A^{-1} called the inverse of A with the property that

$$AA^{-1} = A^{-1}A = I_n$$

where I_n is the $n \times n$ identity matrix.

Inverse Matrix
The $n \times n$ matrix B is said to be the inverse to the $n \times n$ matrix A if

$$AB = BA = I_n$$

If the inverse matrix B exists, we write $B = A^{-1}$.

REMARK: Do not think that the inverse matrix A^{-1} can be written as $1/A$. We never divide matrices.

EXAMPLE 1   Showing a Matrix Is the Inverse Matrix   Let

$$A = \begin{bmatrix} 3 & 1 \\ 5 & 2 \end{bmatrix}$$

Then show that the inverse of A is

$$A^{-1} = \begin{bmatrix} 2 & -1 \\ -5 & 3 \end{bmatrix}$$

Solution Find AA^{-1} and $A^{-1}A$,

$$AA^{-1} = \begin{bmatrix} 3 & 1 \\ 5 & 2 \end{bmatrix} \begin{bmatrix} 2 & -1 \\ -5 & 3 \end{bmatrix} = \begin{bmatrix} 1 & 0 \\ 0 & 1 \end{bmatrix} = I_2$$

and

$$AA^{-1} = \begin{bmatrix} 2 & -1 \\ -5 & 3 \end{bmatrix} \begin{bmatrix} 3 & 1 \\ 5 & 2 \end{bmatrix} = \begin{bmatrix} 1 & 0 \\ 0 & 1 \end{bmatrix} = I_2$$

Since $AA^{-1} = I = A^{-1}A$, A^{-1} is the inverse of A.   ◆

Not every matrix has an inverse. Consider $B = \begin{bmatrix} 2 & 1 \\ 4 & 2 \end{bmatrix}$. Let us try to find a 2×2 matrix X such that $BX = I_2$,

$$\begin{bmatrix} 1 & 0 \\ 0 & 1 \end{bmatrix} = I_2 = BX = \begin{bmatrix} 2 & 1 \\ 4 & 2 \end{bmatrix} \begin{bmatrix} a & b \\ c & d \end{bmatrix} = \begin{bmatrix} 2a+c & 2b+d \\ 4a+2c & 4b+2d \end{bmatrix}$$

Using the property of matrix equality gives the following two of the four equations.

$$\begin{array}{rcl} 2a+c &=& 1 \\ 4a+2c &=& 0 \end{array}$$

But 2 times the first of these two equations yields $4a+2c = 2$. This is inconsistent with the second equation, and thus no solution can exist. This shows that B^{-1} does not exist. If the inverse does not exist, the matrix is called singular.

✧ Finding the Inverse

We shall now develop a technique that will find the inverse of a square matrix, if it exists, or indicate that the inverse does not exist. Consider

$$A = \begin{bmatrix} 1 & 2 \\ 3 & 7 \end{bmatrix}$$

To find

$$A^{-1} = X = \begin{bmatrix} x_1 & y_1 \\ x_2 & y_2 \end{bmatrix}$$

we must solve the equation $AX = I_2$ or

$$AX = \begin{bmatrix} 1 & 2 \\ 3 & 7 \end{bmatrix} \begin{bmatrix} x_1 & y_1 \\ x_2 & y_2 \end{bmatrix} = \begin{bmatrix} x_1+2x_2 & y_1+2y_2 \\ 3x_1+7x_2 & 3y_1+7y_2 \end{bmatrix} = \begin{bmatrix} 1 & 0 \\ 0 & 1 \end{bmatrix}$$

This gives the four equations

$$\begin{array}{ll} x_1+2x_2 = 1 & y_1+2y_2 = 0 \\ 3x_1+7x_2 = 0 & 3y_1+7y_2 = 1 \end{array}$$

which have been written as two systems. We can then solve each system by first forming the augmented matrices

$$\begin{bmatrix} 1 & 2 & | & 1 \\ 3 & 7 & | & 0 \end{bmatrix} \qquad \begin{bmatrix} 1 & 2 & | & 0 \\ 3 & 7 & | & 1 \end{bmatrix}$$

But since both of these systems have the same coefficient matrix, they both will be solved by precisely the same row operations. Thus, we may as well solve them together. We do this by forming the augmented matrix

$$\left[\begin{array}{cc|cc} 1 & 2 & 1 & 0 \\ 3 & 7 & 0 & 1 \end{array}\right]$$

Now perform the usual row operations and obtain

$$\left[\begin{array}{cc|cc} 1 & 2 & 1 & 0 \\ 3 & 7 & 0 & 1 \end{array}\right] \quad R_2 - 3R_1 \to R_2 \quad \to \quad \left[\begin{array}{cc|cc} 1 & 2 & 1 & 0 \\ 0 & 1 & -3 & 1 \end{array}\right]$$

We could solve using backward substitution. Instead we will use another row operation to obtain a zero in the first row and second column. We then continue.

$$\left[\begin{array}{cc|cc} 1 & 2 & 1 & 0 \\ 0 & 1 & -3 & 1 \end{array}\right] \quad R_1 - 2R_2 \to R_1 \quad \to \quad \left[\begin{array}{cc|cc} 1 & 0 & 7 & -2 \\ 0 & 1 & -3 & 1 \end{array}\right]$$

This means that the solutions to the two systems are

$$\begin{array}{ll} x_1 = 7 & y_1 = -2 \\ x_2 = -3 & y_2 = 1 \end{array}$$

Thus

$$A^{-1} = \left[\begin{array}{cc} 7 & -2 \\ -3 & 1 \end{array}\right]$$

Notice that we started with $[A|I]$ and used row operations to end with $[I|B]$ where $B = A^{-1}$. This can be generalized to the following technique.

To Find A^{-1}

1. Form the augmented matrix $[A|I]$.

2. Use row operations to reduce $[A|I]$ to $[I|B]$ if possible.

3. $A^{-1} = B$

In the next example, we see again how to use row operations to go from $[A|I]$ to $[I|A^{-1}]$.

EXAMPLE 2   Finding the Inverse of a Matrix   Find A^{-1} if

$$A = \left[\begin{array}{ccc} 1 & 1 & 2 \\ 2 & 3 & 2 \\ 1 & 1 & 3 \end{array}\right]$$

Solution   Following the above technique, we have

$$[A|I] = \left[\begin{array}{ccc|ccc} 1 & 1 & 2 & 1 & 0 & 0 \\ 2 & 3 & 2 & 0 & 1 & 0 \\ 1 & 1 & 3 & 0 & 0 & 1 \end{array}\right] \quad \begin{array}{c} R_2 - 2R_1 \to R_2 \\ R_3 - R_1 \to R_3 \end{array} \quad \to \quad \left[\begin{array}{ccc|ccc} 1 & 1 & 2 & 1 & 0 & 0 \\ 0 & 1 & -2 & -2 & 1 & 0 \\ 0 & 0 & 1 & -1 & 0 & 1 \end{array}\right]$$

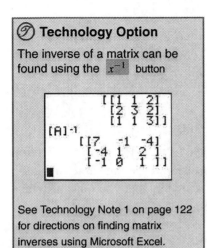

Technology Option

The inverse of a matrix can be found using the x^{-1} button

See Technology Note 1 on page 122 for directions on finding matrix inverses using Microsoft Excel.

Notice we have ones down the diagonal and zeros below the diagonal. If we wish, we could solve using backward substitution. Instead, we continue to use row operations to end with $[I|A^{-1}]$. The efficient way to proceed is to obtain all zeros in the elements in the last column above the lowest one. After that we obtain zeros in the next to the last column above the one. In other words we always move from the last column to the left column until finished. We actually refer to this as the Gauss-Jordan method.

$$\begin{bmatrix} 1 & 1 & 2 & 1 & 0 & 0 \\ 0 & 1 & -2 & -2 & 1 & 0 \\ 0 & 0 & 1 & -1 & 0 & 1 \end{bmatrix} \begin{matrix} R_1 - 2R_3 \to R_1 \\ R_2 + 2R_3 \to R_2 \\ \\ \end{matrix}$$

$$\to \begin{bmatrix} 1 & 1 & 0 & 3 & 0 & -2 \\ 0 & 1 & 0 & -4 & 1 & 2 \\ 0 & 0 & 1 & -1 & 0 & 1 \end{bmatrix} R_1 - R_2 \to R_1 \to \begin{bmatrix} 1 & 0 & 0 & 7 & -1 & -4 \\ 0 & 1 & 0 & -4 & 1 & 2 \\ 0 & 0 & 1 & -1 & 0 & 1 \end{bmatrix}$$

We have now found $A^{-1} = \begin{bmatrix} 7 & -1 & -4 \\ -4 & 1 & 2 \\ -1 & 0 & 1 \end{bmatrix}$ ✦

If a matrix does not have an inverse (it is a singular matrix), the above technique will so indicate, as in the following example.

EXAMPLE 3 Singular Matrix Find A^{-1} if

$$A = \begin{bmatrix} 1 & 2 & 3 \\ 2 & 5 & 7 \\ 2 & 4 & 6 \end{bmatrix}$$

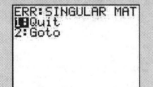

Technology Option

If a matrix is singular, the calculator will give the following message

Solution   Forming the augmented matrix and proceeding yields

$$[A|I] = \begin{bmatrix} 1 & 2 & 3 & 1 & 0 & 0 \\ 2 & 5 & 7 & 0 & 1 & 0 \\ 2 & 4 & 6 & 0 & 0 & 1 \end{bmatrix} \begin{matrix} \\ R_2 - 2R_1 \to R_2 \\ R_3 - 2R_1 \to R_3 \end{matrix} \to \begin{bmatrix} 1 & 2 & 3 & 1 & 0 & 0 \\ 0 & 1 & 1 & -2 & 1 & 0 \\ 0 & 0 & 0 & -2 & 0 & 1 \end{bmatrix}$$

The last row indicates that there can be no solution. Thus, A^{-1} does not exist and A is a singular matrix. ✦

✧ Systems of Equations

We shall now see how the inverse matrix can be used to solve systems of equations with the number of unknowns equal to the number of equations. Consider the system

$$a_{11}x_1 + a_{12}x_2 + \cdots a_{1n}x_n = b_1$$
$$a_{21}x_1 + a_{22}x_2 + \cdots a_{2n}x_n = b_2$$
$$\cdots$$
$$a_{n1}x_1 + a_{n2}x_2 + \cdots a_{nn}x_n = b_n$$

If $A = \begin{bmatrix} a_{11} & a_{12} & \cdots & a_{1n} \\ a_{21} & a_{22} & \cdots & a_{2n} \\ & & \cdots & \\ a_{n1} & a_{n2} & \cdots & a_{nn} \end{bmatrix}$, $X = \begin{bmatrix} x_1 \\ x_2 \\ \vdots \\ x_n \end{bmatrix}$, $B = \begin{bmatrix} b_1 \\ b_2 \\ \vdots \\ b_n \end{bmatrix}$

then the system can be written as

$$AX = B$$

If this was the numerical equation $ax = b$ with $a \neq 0$, you would divide both sides by a to obtain the solution for x as $x = b/a$. However, this is a matrix equation, so we must multiply by the inverse, rather than dividing. Now if A^{-1} exists (that is, A is nonsingular), multiply both sides of $AX = B$ on the left by A^{-1}, obtaining

$$A^{-1}(AX) = A^{-1}B$$

Note that we left-multiplied both sides by A^{-1}. The fact that matrix multiplication is non-commutative means that not only do you need to do the same operation on both sides of the matrix equation as in regular algebra, but you must also take care to do it on the same side. Now the left side is

$$A^{-1}(AX) = (A^{-1}A)X = I_nX = X$$

Thus, $X = A^{-1}B$ is the solution of the system.

Solution of $AX = B$

Let A be a square matrix of order n and B a column matrix of order n. If A^{-1} exists, then the linear system of equations

$$AX = B$$

has the unique solution

$$X = A^{-1}B$$

REMARK: If A^{-1} *does not exist*, then the system of equations does not have a single, unique solution. The system must have a parametric solution or no solution in this case.

EXAMPLE 4   Solving Systems of Equations Using Matrices   Solve the following systems of linear equations using matrix inverses.

$$\begin{array}{ccc} x + y + 2z = 1 & \quad & x + y + 2z = 2 \\ 2x + 3y + 2z = 2 & \quad & 2x + 3y + 2z = 0 \\ x + y + 3z = 0 & \quad & x + y + 3z = 1 \end{array}$$

Solution   First notice that the two systems can be written as $AX = B$ and $AX = C$ with

$$A = \begin{bmatrix} 1 & 1 & 2 \\ 2 & 3 & 2 \\ 1 & 1 & 3 \end{bmatrix}, \qquad X = \begin{bmatrix} x \\ y \\ z \end{bmatrix}, \qquad B = \begin{bmatrix} 1 \\ 2 \\ 0 \end{bmatrix}, \qquad C = \begin{bmatrix} 2 \\ 0 \\ 1 \end{bmatrix}$$

The solutions are, respectively,

$$X = A^{-1}B \qquad X = A^{-1}C$$

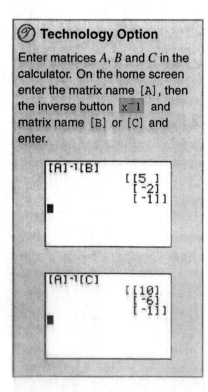

⑨ Technology Option

Enter matrices A, B and C in the calculator. On the home screen enter the matrix name [A], then the inverse button x⁻1 and matrix name [B] or [C] and enter.

[A]⁻1[B]
      [[5]
       [-2]
       [-1]]

[A]⁻1[C]
      [[10]
       [-6]
       [-1]]

We already found A^{-1} in Example 2. Thus, the first system has the solution

$$A^{-1}B = \begin{bmatrix} 7 & -1 & -4 \\ -4 & 1 & 2 \\ -1 & 0 & 1 \end{bmatrix} \begin{bmatrix} 1 \\ 2 \\ 0 \end{bmatrix} = \begin{bmatrix} 5 \\ -2 \\ -1 \end{bmatrix}$$

or $x = 5$, $y = -2$, and $z = -1$. The second system has the solution

$$A^{-1}B = \begin{bmatrix} 7 & -1 & -4 \\ -4 & 1 & 2 \\ -1 & 0 & 1 \end{bmatrix} \begin{bmatrix} 2 \\ 0 \\ 1 \end{bmatrix} = \begin{bmatrix} 10 \\ -6 \\ -1 \end{bmatrix}$$

or $x = 10$, $y = -6$, and $z = -1$. ✦

✧ Applications

There are many applications of matrix inverses. Some are simply related to the fact that a system of linear equations can be solved using $X = A^{-1}B$. Other applications, such as input–output analysis use more complex matrix equations to solve business and economic models. In this section we cover the applications that are systems of linear equations and cryptography (as an enrichment). Section 2.4 covers the total cost model and input–output analysis.

EXAMPLE 5   Investments An investment adviser has two mutual funds that she is recommending: a conservative bond fund with an assumed return of 7% a year and a stock fund with a projected return of 12% a year. One client has $100,000 to invest and wishes a return of 9% a year, and a second client has $50,000 and wants a 10% annual return. How should she allocate the money of each client between the bond fund and the stock fund?

Solution   Begin by defining the variables. Let

$x =$ amount of money in dollars invested in the bond fund

$y =$ amount of money in dollars invested in the stock fund

If T is the total amount invested, then $x + y = T$. The return on the bond fund will be $0.07x$, and the return on the stock fund will be $0.12y$, for a total return of $0.07x + 0.12y$. If R is the return desired, then $0.07x + 0.15y = R$. We then have

$$\begin{aligned} x + y &= T \quad \text{total investment in dollars} \\ 0.07x + 0.12y &= R \quad \text{total return in dollars} \end{aligned}$$

Define the matrices A, X, and B as

$$A = \begin{bmatrix} 1 & 1 \\ 0.07 & 0.12 \end{bmatrix}, \quad X = \begin{bmatrix} x \\ y \end{bmatrix}, \quad B = \begin{bmatrix} T \\ R \end{bmatrix}.$$

Now the system can be written as $AX = B$ and the solution is $X = A^{-1}B$. To find A^{-1} we use the Gauss-Jordan method.

$$[A|I] = \begin{bmatrix} 1 & 1 & | & 1 & 0 \\ 0.07 & 0.12 & | & 0 & 1 \end{bmatrix} \quad R_2 - 0.07R_1 \rightarrow R_2$$

$$\rightarrow \begin{bmatrix} 1 & 1 & | & 1 & 0 \\ 0 & 0.05 & | & -0.07 & 1 \end{bmatrix} \quad 20R_2 \rightarrow R_2$$

$$\rightarrow \begin{bmatrix} 1 & 1 & | & 1 & 0 \\ 0 & 1 & | & -1.4 & 20 \end{bmatrix} \quad R_1 - R_2 \rightarrow R_1$$

$$\rightarrow \begin{bmatrix} 1 & 0 & | & 2.4 & -20 \\ 0 & 1 & | & -1.4 & 20 \end{bmatrix}$$

$$A^{-1} = \begin{bmatrix} 2.4 & -20 \\ -1.4 & 20 \end{bmatrix}$$

The first client has \$100,000 to invest and wishes a return of 9% which is $(0.09)(\$100,000) = \$9000$. Thus,

$$X = A^{-1}B = \begin{bmatrix} 2.4 & -20 \\ -1.4 & 20 \end{bmatrix} \begin{bmatrix} 100,000 \\ 9000 \end{bmatrix} = \begin{bmatrix} 60,000 \\ 40,000 \end{bmatrix}$$

The first client should invest \$60,000 in the bond fund and \$40,000 in the stock fund.

The second client has \$50,000 to invest and wishes a return of 10% which is $(0.10)(\$50,000) = \$5000$. Thus,

$$X = A^{-1}B = \begin{bmatrix} 2.4 & -20 \\ -1.4 & 20 \end{bmatrix} \begin{bmatrix} 50,000 \\ 5000 \end{bmatrix} = \begin{bmatrix} 20,000 \\ 30,000 \end{bmatrix}$$

The second client should invest \$20,000 in the bond fund and \$30,000 in the stock fund. ◆

✧ Enrichment: Cryptography

It can be important to send information in a way that an interceptor can't read. Sophisticated ways of coding and decoding information have recently been developed. One way is to use matrices. First let us assign the number 1 to a, 2 to b, and so forth, with the number 27 assigned to a space between two words. Then the word encode would then be represented by the message

$$4\ 5\ 3\ 15\ 4\ 5$$

This message would be rather easy to decode, so we will introduce an encoding matrix. This is any square matrix with positive integers and with an inverse. For example,

$$E = \begin{bmatrix} 2 & 1 & 3 \\ 3 & 1 & 3 \\ 2 & 1 & 4 \end{bmatrix}$$

a = 1	b = 2	c = 3
d = 4	e = 5	f = 6
g = 7	h = 8	i = 9
j = 19	k = 11	l = 12
m = 13	n = 14	o = 15
p = 16	q = 17	r = 18
s = 19	t = 20	u = 21
v = 22	w = 23	x = 24
y = 25	z = 26	⊔ = 27

We now convert our message into a matrix M with three rows, the same as the encoding matrix E. We then have

$$M = \begin{bmatrix} 4 & 15 \\ 5 & 4 \\ 3 & 5 \end{bmatrix}$$

We now code our message by creating $C = EM$. We get

$$C = EM = \begin{bmatrix} 2 & 1 & 3 \\ 3 & 1 & 3 \\ 2 & 1 & 4 \end{bmatrix} \begin{bmatrix} 4 & 15 \\ 5 & 4 \\ 3 & 5 \end{bmatrix} = \begin{bmatrix} 22 & 49 \\ 26 & 64 \\ 25 & 54 \end{bmatrix}$$

So, we send this off as

$$22 \ 26 \ 25 \ 49 \ 64 \ 54$$

Our receiver knows what the encoding matrix E is and so rewrites our message as the matrix C and obtains the matrix M as $E^{-1}C$. They now write the numbers from the matrix M as

$$4 \ 5 \ 3 \ 15 \ 4 \ 5$$

They now convert these numbers to known letters and finally obtain the message "encode".

EXAMPLE 6   **Decoding**   You have just received a coded message as

$$87 \ 100 \ 107 \ 70 \ 78 \ 79 \ 83 \ 102 \ 89 \ 137 \ 158 \ 164$$

Decode the message with the encoding matrix E given before.

Solution   We first write the sequence of numbers as the matrix

$$C = \begin{bmatrix} 87 & 70 & 83 & 137 \\ 100 & 78 & 102 & 158 \\ 107 & 79 & 89 & 164 \end{bmatrix}$$

Now we use the encode matrix E, known only to us and the message sender, to find the original message M as

$$M = E^{-1}C = \begin{bmatrix} 13 & 8 & 19 & 21 \\ 1 & 27 & 27 & 14 \\ 20 & 9 & 6 & 27 \end{bmatrix}$$

We write this as the string of numbers

$$13 \ 1 \ 20 \ 8 \ 27 \ 9 \ 19 \ 27 \ 6 \ 21 \ 14 \ 27$$

We now convert these numbers to the agreed-to-letters and obtain

math is fun   ◆

Since both the sender and receiver of the coded message know the encoded matrix, it is very difficult for any code breaker to determine the message. When large matrices are used, a code is very unlikely to be broken.

✧ Technology Corner

⑨Technology Note 1   **Finding the Inverse Matrix Using Microsoft Excel**

Open a spreadsheet and enter the values into the cells A1:B2. Highlight the destination cells D1:E2. Type = and then enter MINVERSE and select the matrix cells A1:B2, as shown in Worksheet 1. Then Ctrl-Shift-Enter to evaluate the inverse, Worksheet 2. In Worksheets 3 and 4 you see that a singular matrix will produce an error.

	A	B	C	D	E	F	G
1	1	2		=MINVERSE(A1:B2)			
2	3	7					

Worksheet 1

	A	B	C	D	E
1	1	2		7	-2
2	3	7		-3	1

Worksheet 2

	A	B	C	D	E	F	G
1	1	2	3		=MINVERSE(A1:C3)		
2	2	5	7				
3	2	4	6				

Worksheet 3

	A	B	C	D	E	F	G
1	1	2	3	#NUM!	#NUM!	#NUM!	
2	2	5	7	#NUM!	#NUM!	#NUM!	
3	2	4	6	#NUM!	#NUM!	#NUM!	

Worksheet 4

Self-Help Exercises 2.3

1. Find A^{-1} if

$$A = \begin{bmatrix} 1 & 0 & 0 & 1 \\ 0 & 0 & 1 & 0 \\ 0 & 0 & 0 & 1 \\ 0 & 1 & 0 & 2 \end{bmatrix}$$

2. Solve the following system of equations using the inverse of the coefficient matrix:

$$x - 2z = 1$$
$$y + z = 2$$
$$x + y = 4$$

3. Solution A is 3% alcohol, and solution B is 7% alcohol. A lab technician needs to mix the two solutions to obtain 50 liters of a solution that is 4.2% alcohol. How many liters of each solution must be used? Use the inverse matrix to find the answer.

4. Solve the matrix equation $XA + B = C$ for X.

2.3 Exercises

In Exercises 1 through 10, determine if the given pairs of matrices are inverses to each other by showing if their product is the identity matrix.

1. $\begin{bmatrix} 1 & 2 \\ 3 & 5 \end{bmatrix}$ and $\begin{bmatrix} -5 & 2 \\ 3 & -1 \end{bmatrix}$

2. $\begin{bmatrix} 10 & 3 \\ 3 & 1 \end{bmatrix}$ and $\begin{bmatrix} 1 & -3 \\ -3 & 10 \end{bmatrix}$

3. $\begin{bmatrix} 4 & 7 \\ 1 & 2 \end{bmatrix}$ and $\begin{bmatrix} 2 & -7 \\ -1 & 4 \end{bmatrix}$

4. $\begin{bmatrix} 13 & 4 \\ 3 & 1 \end{bmatrix}$ and $\begin{bmatrix} 1 & 4 \\ -3 & 13 \end{bmatrix}$

5. $\begin{bmatrix} 1 & 2 & 0 \\ 2 & 1 & -1 \\ 3 & 1 & 1 \end{bmatrix}$ and $\dfrac{1}{8}\begin{bmatrix} -2 & 2 & 2 \\ 5 & -1 & -1 \\ 1 & -5 & 3 \end{bmatrix}$

6. $\begin{bmatrix} 2 & 1 & 3 \\ 3 & 1 & 3 \\ 2 & 1 & 4 \end{bmatrix}$ and $\begin{bmatrix} -1 & 1 & 0 \\ 0 & -2 & -3 \\ 1 & 0 & 1 \end{bmatrix}$

7. $\begin{bmatrix} 1 & 1 & 0 \\ 0 & 1 & 1 \\ 0 & 0 & 1 \end{bmatrix}$ and $\begin{bmatrix} 1 & -1 & 1 \\ 0 & 1 & -1 \\ 0 & 0 & 1 \end{bmatrix}$

8. $\begin{bmatrix} 1 & 2 & 3 \\ 0 & 1 & 3 \\ 0 & 0 & 1 \end{bmatrix}$ and $\begin{bmatrix} 1 & -2 & 3 \\ 0 & 1 & -3 \\ 0 & 0 & 1 \end{bmatrix}$

9. $\begin{bmatrix} 2 & 0 & 1 & 2 \\ 1 & 1 & 0 & 2 \\ 2 & -1 & 3 & 1 \\ 3 & -1 & 4 & 3 \end{bmatrix}$ and $\dfrac{1}{3}\begin{bmatrix} 3 & 0 & 3 & -3 \\ -3 & 5 & 5 & -3 \\ -3 & 2 & 2 & 0 \\ 0 & -1 & -4 & 3 \end{bmatrix}$

10. $\begin{bmatrix} 1 & 0 & 0 & 0 \\ 0 & 1 & 0 & 0 \\ 0 & 0 & 5 & 2 \\ 0 & 0 & 1 & 1 \end{bmatrix}$ and $\begin{bmatrix} 1 & 0 & 0 & 0 \\ 0 & 1 & 0 & 0 \\ 0 & 0 & 1 & -2 \\ 0 & 0 & 1 & 5 \end{bmatrix}$

In Exercises 11 through 26, find the inverses of the given matrices, if they exist.

11. $\begin{bmatrix} 1 & 3 \\ 3 & 10 \end{bmatrix}$ 12. $\begin{bmatrix} 1 & 3 \\ 1 & 4 \end{bmatrix}$

13. $\begin{bmatrix} 5 & -1 \\ -3 & 2 \end{bmatrix}$ 14. $\begin{bmatrix} 5 & -1 \\ 4 & 2 \end{bmatrix}$

15. $\begin{bmatrix} 4 & 2 \\ 2 & 1 \end{bmatrix}$ 16. $\begin{bmatrix} 1 & 1 \\ 1 & 1 \end{bmatrix}$

17. $\begin{bmatrix} 1 & 2 & 1 \\ 1 & 2 & 1 \\ 2 & 0 & 1 \end{bmatrix}$ 18. $\begin{bmatrix} 1 & 0 & 1 \\ 0 & 2 & 1 \\ 1 & 0 & 2 \end{bmatrix}$

19. $\begin{bmatrix} 1 & 1 & 1 \\ 0 & 2 & 2 \\ -1 & 0 & 1 \end{bmatrix}$ 20. $\begin{bmatrix} 1 & 0 & 1 \\ 0 & 1 & 1 \\ 1 & 1 & 1 \end{bmatrix}$

21. $\begin{bmatrix} 1 & 2 & 0 \\ 1 & 1 & 2 \\ 0 & -1 & -1 \end{bmatrix}$ 22. $\begin{bmatrix} 2 & 4 & 4 \\ 1 & 2 & 1 \\ 1 & 0 & -1 \end{bmatrix}$

23. $\begin{bmatrix} 1 & 1 & 1 \\ 1 & 2 & 4 \\ 2 & 1 & 1 \end{bmatrix}$ 24. $\begin{bmatrix} 0 & 1 & 1 \\ 1 & 1 & 0 \\ 1 & 0 & 1 \end{bmatrix}$

25. $\begin{bmatrix} 1 & 1 & 1 & 1 \\ 0 & 2 & 1 & 1 \\ 1 & 0 & 2 & 1 \\ 0 & 1 & 0 & 1 \end{bmatrix}$ 26. $\begin{bmatrix} 0 & 1 & 1 & 0 \\ 1 & 0 & 0 & 2 \\ 2 & 0 & 1 & 0 \\ 2 & 0 & 0 & 1 \end{bmatrix}$

In Exercises 27 through 32, solve by using the inverse of the coefficient matrix.

27. $2x - 4y = 10$
    $x - y = -2$

28. $2x - y = 7$
    $x + 3y = 7$

29. $x + y = 6$
    $2x + 3y = 9$

30. $x + y = 5$
    $2x - 3y = -5$

31. $2x + 4y = 6$
    $3x + 5y = 4$

32. $3x - 6y = 6$
    $x - y = 9$

In Exercises 33 through 36, solve by using your answers to Exercises 11 through 14.

33. $x + 3y = 2$
    $3x + 10y = 3$

34. $x + 3y = 1$
    $x + 4y = 6$

35. $5x - y = 4$
    $-3x + 2y = 3$

36. $5x - y = -3$
    $4x + 2y = 5$

In Exercises 37 through 42, solve by using your answers to Exercises 21 through 26.

37. $x + 2y = 1$
    $x + y + 2z = 0$
    $-y - z = 2$

38. $2x + 4y + 4z = 1$
    $x + 2y + z = 1$
    $x - z = 3$

39. $x + y + z = 0$
    $x + 2y + 4z = 1$
    $2x + y + z = 2$

40. $y + z = -2$
    $x + y = 2$
    $x + z = 4$

41. $x_1 + x_2 + x_3 + x_4 = 1$
    $2x_1 + x_2 + x_3 + x_4 = 1$
    $x_1 + 2x_3 + x_4 = 2$
    $x_2 + x_4 = 2$

42. $x_2 + x_3 = 2$
    $x_1 + x_4 = -3$
    $2x_1 + x_3 = 4$
    $2x_1 + x_4 = 6$

43. Let $A = \begin{bmatrix} a & b \\ c & d \end{bmatrix}$ and assume that $D = ad - bc \neq 0$.
    Show that $A^{-1} = \dfrac{1}{D}\begin{bmatrix} d & -b \\ -c & a \end{bmatrix}$

44. If A^{-1} and B^{-1} exist, show that $(AB)^{-1} = B^{-1}A^{-1}$

Applications

45. **Investment** Redo Example 5 with a bond fund return of 8%.

46. **Investment** Redo Example 5 with a bond fund return of 8% and a stock fund return of 13%.

47. **Scheduling** The material and labor costs of manufacturing two styles of chair are given as follows:

	Material	Labor
Style A	40	50
Style B	30	40

If $10,000 is allocated for both material and labor, how many of each style of chair should be manufactured to exactly use the $10,000 if

a. $4400 is allocated for material and $5600 for labor.

b. $4300 is allocated for material and $5700 for labor.

48. **Mixture** A small store sells spearmint tea at $3.20 an ounce and peppermint tea at $4 an ounce. The store owner decides to make a batch of 100 ounces of tea that mixes both kinds and to sell the mixture for $3.50 an ounce. How many ounces of each of the two varieties of tea should be mixed to obtain the same revenue as selling them unmixed?

In Exercises 49 through 56, use matrices A and B below. A graphing calculator is suggested for this problem set.

$$A = \begin{bmatrix} 1 & 4 & 5 & -3 & 6 \\ -11 & 6 & 4 & -2 & 3 \\ 4 & 16 & -1 & 8 & 1 \\ 2 & -8 & 1 & 4 & -1 \\ 1 & 9 & 10 & 4 & 8 \end{bmatrix}$$

$$B = \begin{bmatrix} 1 & -4 & 3 & 2 & 1 \\ 6 & 1 & -8 & 5 & 1 \\ -2 & 8 & -5 & 7 & 3 \\ 4 & -5 & -16 & 2 & 4 \\ 1 & 3 & 1 & -5 & 1 \end{bmatrix}$$

49. Does $AB = BA$?

50. Does A^{-1} exist?

51. Does B^{-1} exist?

52. Does $(AB)^{-1}$ exist?

53. Does $(AB)^{-1} = A^{-1}B^{-1}$?

54. Does $(AB)^{-1} = B^{-1}A^{-1}$?

55. Is it possible to solve $AX = C$ where

$$C = \begin{bmatrix} 10 \\ 8 \\ 20 \\ 22 \\ 37 \end{bmatrix}$$

56. Is it possible to solve $BX = C$ where C is given in the previous exercise.

Extensions

In Exercises 57 through 60, assume the matrices A, B, and X are all square matrices. Solve for X in terms of the matrices A and B. Determine under what conditions this is possible.

57. $AX + X = B$

58. $XA + X = B$

59. $AX - A = B$

60. $AX + A = B$

61. **Cryptography** Use the given encoding matrix to send the message "work hard".

$$\begin{bmatrix} 1 & 1 & 2 \\ 2 & 3 & 2 \\ 1 & 1 & 3 \end{bmatrix}$$

62. **Cryptography** You are sent the message

    61 73 88 64 100 82 55 76 75 106 185 133

    Decode this message using the encoding matrix found in the previous exercise.

Solutions to Self-Help Exercises 2.3

1. We have

$$[A|I] = \left[\begin{array}{cccc|cccc} 1 & 0 & 0 & 1 & 1 & 0 & 0 & 0 \\ 0 & 0 & 1 & 0 & 0 & 1 & 0 & 0 \\ 0 & 0 & 0 & 1 & 0 & 0 & 1 & 0 \\ 0 & 1 & 0 & 2 & 0 & 0 & 0 & 1 \end{array}\right] \begin{array}{c} R_2 \leftrightarrow R_4 \\ \rightarrow \end{array} \left[\begin{array}{cccc|cccc} 1 & 0 & 0 & 1 & 1 & 0 & 0 & 0 \\ 0 & 1 & 0 & 2 & 0 & 0 & 0 & 1 \\ 0 & 0 & 0 & 1 & 0 & 0 & 1 & 0 \\ 0 & 0 & 1 & 0 & 0 & 1 & 0 & 0 \end{array}\right] \begin{array}{c} R_3 \leftrightarrow R_4 \\ \end{array}$$

$$\rightarrow \left[\begin{array}{cccc|cccc} 1 & 0 & 0 & 1 & 1 & 0 & 0 & 0 \\ 0 & 1 & 0 & 2 & 0 & 0 & 0 & 1 \\ 0 & 0 & 1 & 0 & 0 & 1 & 0 & 0 \\ 0 & 0 & 0 & 1 & 0 & 0 & 1 & 0 \end{array}\right] \begin{array}{c} R_1 - R_4 \rightarrow R_1 \\ R_2 - 2R_4 \rightarrow R_2 \\ \rightarrow \end{array} \left[\begin{array}{cccc|cccc} 1 & 0 & 0 & 0 & 1 & 0 & -1 & 0 \\ 0 & 1 & 0 & 0 & 0 & 0 & -2 & 1 \\ 0 & 0 & 1 & 0 & 0 & 1 & 0 & 0 \\ 0 & 0 & 0 & 1 & 0 & 0 & 1 & 0 \end{array}\right]$$

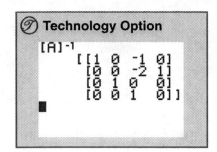

Thus

$$A^{-1} = \begin{bmatrix} 1 & 0 & -1 & 0 \\ 0 & 0 & -2 & 1 \\ 0 & 1 & 0 & 0 \\ 0 & 0 & 1 & 0 \end{bmatrix}$$

2. Let

$$A = \begin{bmatrix} 1 & 0 & -2 \\ 0 & 1 & 1 \\ 1 & 1 & 0 \end{bmatrix}, \qquad X = \begin{bmatrix} x \\ y \\ z \end{bmatrix}, \qquad B = \begin{bmatrix} 1 \\ 2 \\ 4 \end{bmatrix}$$

Then the system of equations can be written as $AX = B$. The solution is $X = A^{-1}B$. To find A^{-1}, we use the Gauss-Jordan method and obtain

$$[A|I] = \begin{bmatrix} 1 & 0 & -2 & 1 & 0 & 0 \\ 0 & 1 & 1 & 0 & 1 & 0 \\ 1 & 1 & 0 & 0 & 0 & 1 \end{bmatrix} \quad R_3 - R_1 \rightarrow R_3$$

$$\rightarrow \begin{bmatrix} 1 & 0 & -2 & 1 & 0 & 0 \\ 0 & 1 & 1 & 0 & 1 & 0 \\ 0 & 1 & 2 & -1 & 0 & 1 \end{bmatrix} \quad R_3 - R_2 \rightarrow R_3$$

$$\rightarrow \begin{bmatrix} 1 & 0 & -2 & 1 & 0 & 0 \\ 0 & 1 & 1 & 0 & 1 & 0 \\ 0 & 0 & 1 & -1 & -1 & 1 \end{bmatrix} \begin{matrix} R_1 + 2R_3 \rightarrow R_1 \\ R_2 - R_3 \rightarrow R_2 \end{matrix}$$

$$\rightarrow \begin{bmatrix} 1 & 0 & 0 & -1 & -2 & 2 \\ 0 & 1 & 0 & 1 & 2 & -1 \\ 0 & 0 & 1 & -1 & -1 & 1 \end{bmatrix}$$

Thus

$$A^{-1} = \begin{bmatrix} -1 & -2 & 2 \\ 1 & 2 & -1 \\ -1 & -1 & 1 \end{bmatrix}$$

and

$$\begin{aligned} X &= A^{-1}B \\ &= \begin{bmatrix} -1 & -2 & 2 \\ 1 & 2 & -1 \\ -1 & -1 & 1 \end{bmatrix} \begin{bmatrix} 1 \\ 2 \\ 4 \end{bmatrix} \\ &= \begin{bmatrix} (-1)(1) + (-2)(2) + (2)(4) \\ (1)(1) + (2)(2) + (-1)(4) \\ (-1)(1) + (-1)(2) + (1)(4) \end{bmatrix} = \begin{bmatrix} 3 \\ 1 \\ 1 \end{bmatrix} \end{aligned}$$

3. Let x and y denote, respectively, the number of liters of solution A and B to be used. Then since there must be 50 liters, we have $x + y = 50$. The amount of alcohol in liters in solution A is $0.03x$, in solution B is $0.07y$, and in the mixture is $0.042(50) = 2.1$. Thus, $0.03x + 0.07y = 2.1$. We then have the system of equations

$$x + y = 50$$
$$0.03x + 0.07y = 2.1$$

This can be written in matrix form as $AX = B$ if

$$A = \begin{bmatrix} 1 & 1 \\ 0.03 & 0.07 \end{bmatrix}, \quad X = \begin{bmatrix} x \\ y \end{bmatrix}, \quad B = \begin{bmatrix} 50 \\ 2.1 \end{bmatrix}$$

The solution is $X = A^{-1}B$. To find A^{-1} we use the Gauss-Jordan method and obtain

$$[A|I] = \begin{bmatrix} 1 & 1 & | & 1 & 0 \\ 0.03 & 0.07 & | & 0 & 1 \end{bmatrix} \quad R_2 - 0.03R_1 \to R_2$$

$$\to \begin{bmatrix} 1 & 1 & | & 1 & 0 \\ 0 & 0.04 & | & -0.03 & 1 \end{bmatrix} \quad 25R_2 \to R_2$$

$$\to \begin{bmatrix} 1 & 1 & | & 1 & 0 \\ 0 & 1 & | & -0.75 & 25 \end{bmatrix} \quad R_1 - R_2 \to R_1$$

$$\to \begin{bmatrix} 1 & 0 & | & 1.75 & -25 \\ 0 & 1 & | & -0.75 & 25 \end{bmatrix}$$

$$A^{-1} = \begin{bmatrix} 1.75 & -25 \\ -0.75 & 25 \end{bmatrix}$$

Then

$$X = A^{-1}B = \begin{bmatrix} 1.75 & -25 \\ -0.75 & 25 \end{bmatrix} \begin{bmatrix} 50 \\ 2.1 \end{bmatrix} = \begin{bmatrix} 35 \\ 15 \end{bmatrix}$$

The technician should use 35 liters of solution A and 15 liters of solution B.

4. Begin by subtracting matrix B from both sides to have $XA = (C - B)$. Since division by A is not allowed, right-multiply both sides of the equation by A^{-1} and simplify,

$$\begin{aligned} (C - B)A^{-1} &= XA \cdot A^{-1} \\ &= XI \\ &= X \end{aligned}$$

So the solution is $X = (C - B)A^{-1}$

2.4   Additional Matrix Applications

✧ Open Leontief Input–Output Models

There are three branches of economics that rely heavily on linear systems and matrix theory: game theory, input–output analysis, and linear programming. Game theory arrived on the scene first with the publication of a fundamental result by John von Neumann in 1928. The impact of game theory on economics, however, was considerably delayed. While game theory uses matrices extensively, it will be taken up in a later chapter in this text as it also uses probability. Linear programming, which will be considered in another chapter, appeared immediately after World War II. Input–output analysis was the second of these three branches of economics to appear. Input–output analysis was initiated by Wassily Leontief with the publication of a paper in 1936. In 1941 he published a full exposition of this method. For this work, he was awarded a Nobel Prize in economics in 1973. Leontief divided the American economy into hundreds of sectors, such as automobiles, glass, copper, and so on, and then studied how these sectors interact with each other.

In order to effectively handle the hundreds of linear equations in the input–output analysis, one naturally needs to use computers. We will obtain a flavor for the method by working with economies with only a few sectors. We will use all the basic principles of input–output analysis including the premise that everything produced by the economy is consumed. Supply will always equal the demand. In an open model, some of the demand is external to the economy and in the closed model the consumption is purely internal. We begin with an open model as described in the example below.

Consider the economy of a small village consisting of two industries, farming and weaving. The farmers produce food for themselves and the weavers along with extra food to export to a nearby city. The weavers produce cloth for themselves and the farmers along with extra cloth to export to the city.

EXAMPLE 1 **Open Village Economy** The villagers have found that to produce $1.00 worth of food, $.40 worth of food, and $.10 worth of cloth is needed locally to feed and clothe the farmers. To produce $1.00 worth of cloth, $.30 worth of food, and $.20 worth of cloth is needed locally to feed and clothe the weavers. The additional food and cloth produced is then available to export to the city. If the city demands $7200 worth of food and $2700 worth of cloth each month, how much food and cloth should be produced by the village to meet its own needs and to supply the city?

Solution Begin by defining our variables

$$x_1 = \text{total supply of food from the farming industry}$$
$$x_2 = \text{total supply of cloth from the weaving industry}$$

Next calculate the total demand for food and cloth.

Food demanded $= x_1 = \quad 0.40x_1 \quad + \quad 0.30x_2 \quad + \quad 7200$
food for   food for   food for
the farmers   the weavers   the city

Cloth demanded $= x_2 = \quad 0.10x_1 \quad + \quad 0.20x_2 \quad + \quad 2700$
cloth for   cloth for   cloth for
the farmers   the weavers   the city

That is, we have the following system of linear equations to solve:

$$x_1 = 0.40x_1 + 0.30x_2 + 7200$$
$$x_2 = 0.10x_1 + 0.20x_2 + 2700$$

The system can be written as a matrix equation,

$$\begin{bmatrix} x_1 \\ x_2 \end{bmatrix} = \begin{bmatrix} 0.4 & 0.3 \\ 0.1 & 0.2 \end{bmatrix} \begin{bmatrix} x_1 \\ x_2 \end{bmatrix} + \begin{bmatrix} 7200 \\ 2700 \end{bmatrix} \rightarrow X = AX + D$$

where

$X = \begin{bmatrix} x_1 \\ x_2 \end{bmatrix}$ is the production matrix

$A = \begin{bmatrix} 0.4 & 0.3 \\ 0.1 & 0.2 \end{bmatrix}$ is the input–output (IO) matrix, and

$D = \begin{bmatrix} 7200 \\ 2700 \end{bmatrix}$ is the demand matrix.

The matrix equation can then be solved using the techniques from the previous section.

$$X = AX + D$$
$$D = X - AX$$
$$D = (I - A)X$$
$$X = (I - A)^{-1}D$$

$(I - A)^{-1}$ is called the multiplier matrix and when it exists (that is, when it is non-singular), we can find how much of each item must be produced. In this example, the inverse does exist and we find

$$X = \left(\begin{bmatrix} 1 & 0 \\ 0 & 1 \end{bmatrix} - \begin{bmatrix} 0.4 & 0.3 \\ 0.1 & 0.2 \end{bmatrix} \right)^{-1} \begin{bmatrix} 7200 \\ 2700 \end{bmatrix}$$

$$= \begin{bmatrix} 1 - 0.4 & 0 - 0.3 \\ 0 - 0.1 & 1 - 0.2 \end{bmatrix}^{-1} \begin{bmatrix} 7200 \\ 2700 \end{bmatrix}$$

$$= \begin{bmatrix} 16/9 & 2/3 \\ 2/9 & 4/3 \end{bmatrix} \begin{bmatrix} 7200 \\ 2700 \end{bmatrix} = \begin{bmatrix} 14600 \\ 5200 \end{bmatrix}$$

If the village produces $14,600 worth of food and $5200 worth of cloth, they will have enough food and cloth for their own needs and have the required surplus to export to the city.   ◆

The matrix $(I - A)^{-1}$ is called the multiplier matrix because the entries can predict the effects of changing the demand. If $1 worth more of food is demanded by the city, the village will need to produce more than $1 worth of food because of the village demand for food. The entries in column 1 of $(I - A)^{-1}$ tell us that to produce $1 worth more of food for the city the village will need to produce $16/9 \approx \$1.78$ worth more food and $2/9 \approx \$.22$ worth more cloth. For the village to produce $1 worth more of cloth for the city, a total of $2/3 \approx \$.67$ worth more food and $4/3 \approx \$1.33$ worth more of cloth.

If A is an input–output matrix and $(I - A)^{-1}$ has only nonnegative elements, then for any demand matrix D with nonnegative elements, $X = (I - A)^{-1}D$ will also have all nonnegative elements and thus a meaningful solution. This means that, in this situation, any outside (nonindustry) demand can be met. The following theorem can be proven.

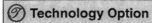

Technology Option

Entering the IO matrix as matrix [A] and demand matrix as matrix [B]. The multiplier matrix is

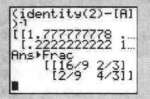

To find the production matrix, X, multiply the multiplier matrix by matrix [B] or simply enter the sequence of commands below

Example 1 is solved using Microsoft Excel in Technology Note 1 on page 135.

> **When Outside Demand can be Met**
> If A is an input–output matrix and the sum of the elements in each row of A is less than one, then any outside demand can be met.

If the multiplier matrix $(I - A)^{-1}$ has all non-negative entries it is called productive. In our village, the multiplier matrix was productive and we were able to find a solution to the production problem.

As shown in the previous discussion, in an input–output analysis we seek to determine the amount each industry must produce so that both the interindustry (internal) demands and the nonindustry (external) demands are both met exactly. That is, the supply and demand are exactly balanced. We will model the interindustry demand with an input–output matrix $A = (a_{ij})$. The IO matrix can be determined directly from the known demands of each industry without writing the system of linear equations first. Examine the columns in matrix A above. In column 1 the entry a_{11} is the amount of food needed to produce a unit ($1) of food and the entry a_{21} the amount of cloth needed to produce a unit of food. In column 2, the entry a_{21} is the amount of food needed to produce a unit of cloth and a_{22} is the amount of cloth needed to produce a unit of cloth. We can generalize this to say in an economy with n sectors or industries that the IO matrix will be a $n \times n$ matrix where the entries in each column show the amount needed from each sector to produce one unit of that column's sector. This is illustrated in the next example.

EXAMPLE 2   A Three–Sector Economy   Assume a very simple model of three industries: auto (A), energy (E), and transportation (T). Each of these industries acts as a supplier and a user of their products. The IO matrix for this economy is given by

$$
A = \text{Input} \quad
\begin{array}{c}
\\ A \\ E \\ T
\end{array}
\begin{array}{c}
\text{Output} \\
\begin{array}{ccc}
A & E & T
\end{array} \\
\begin{bmatrix}
0.2 & 0.4 & 0.1 \\
0.1 & 0.2 & 0.2 \\
0.2 & 0.2 & 0.1
\end{bmatrix}
\end{array}
$$

a. Explain the entries in the IO matrix.

b. Find the production matrix X if the external demand for automobiles is $474 million, the demand for energy is $948 million, and the demand for transportation is $474 million.

c. If the demand for automobiles increases by $1 million, how much more will need to be produced by the energy sector?

Solution

a. Column 1 represents the output of the automobile industry. Element $a_{11} = 0.20$ indicates that every dollar of output from the automobile industry has 20% of its input contributed by the auto industry. Element $a_{21} = 0.10$ indicates that of every dollar of output from the auto industry, 10% of this value is input by the energy industry. The element $a_{31} = 0.20$ indicates that of every dollar of output, the automobile industry, 20% of this value is input by the transportation industry. Column 2 shows that to produce $1 of energy, $.40 of automobile, $.20 of energy, and $.20 of transportation is needed. Column 3 shows that the production of $1.00 of transportation requires $.10 of automobile, $.20 of energy, and $.10 of transportation.

b. Begin by writing the demand matrix in millions of dollars as

$$D = \begin{bmatrix} 474 \\ 948 \\ 474 \end{bmatrix}$$

Then let x_1, x_2, and x_3 represent, respectively, the output in dollars of auto, energy, and transportation produced. Therefore the production matrix is

$$X = \begin{bmatrix} x_1 \\ x_2 \\ x_3 \end{bmatrix}$$

and we need to solve the matrix equation $X = (I - A)^{-1}D$ to find our production matrix. The matrix $(I - A)$ is

$$I - A = \begin{bmatrix} 1 & 0 & 0 \\ 0 & 1 & 0 \\ 0 & 0 & 1 \end{bmatrix} - \begin{bmatrix} 0.2 & 0.4 & 0.1 \\ 0.1 & 0.2 & 0.2 \\ 0.2 & 0.2 & 0.1 \end{bmatrix} = \begin{bmatrix} 0.8 & -0.4 & -0.1 \\ -0.1 & 0.8 & -0.2 \\ -0.2 & -0.2 & 0.9 \end{bmatrix}$$

Using the Gauss-Jordan method, one obtains

$$(I - A)^{-1} = \frac{1}{237} \begin{bmatrix} 340 & 190 & 80 \\ 65 & 350 & 85 \\ 90 & 120 & 300 \end{bmatrix}$$

Thus

$$X = (I - A)^{-1}D = \frac{1}{237} \begin{bmatrix} 340 & 190 & 80 \\ 65 & 350 & 85 \\ 90 & 120 & 300 \end{bmatrix} \begin{bmatrix} 474 \\ 948 \\ 474 \end{bmatrix} = \begin{bmatrix} 1600 \\ 1700 \\ 1260 \end{bmatrix}$$

Reading from the matrix, we find that the automobile industry needs to produce $1600 million ($1,600,000,000) of automobiles, the energy industry needs to produce $1700 million ($1,700,000,000) worth of energy, and the transportation industry needs to provide $1260 million ($1,260,000,000) of transportation.

c. The entry in row 2, column 1 of the multiplier matrix $(I - A)^{-1}$ is $130/474 \approx$ 0.27, so about $270,000 worth of energy is needed to produce $1 million more of automobiles. ◆

Technology Option
Example 2 is solved using a graphing calculator and with Microsoft Excel in Technology Note 2 on page 135.

✧ Accounting

Just as an economy has sectors that depend on each other, a company has different departments that depend on each other. Some of the departments make a product to be sold outside the company and other departments support themselves and the production departments. To calculate the total costs, both the direct costs for producing the items and the indirect cost from the support departments must all be accounted for. This important accounting method is developed in the following example.

EXAMPLE 3 Making Candles The Acme Candle Company produces 30,000 jar candles per week. The production of these candles is done in three departments: blending, filling, and packaging. These production departments are supported by two service departments: custodial and maintenance. In determining the total cost to produce the candles, there are both direct costs from the production departments along with the indirect costs from the supporting service departments. The direct costs are known. These are the costs for the employees' salaries and for materials. The direct costs for the custodial are $1500, for maintenance $2000, for blending $11,000, for filling $12,000, and for packaging $6400. The custodial staff spends 10% of its time servicing its own areas, 5% on servicing the maintenance areas, and 25% of the time on each of the production areas. The maintenance department spends 10% of its time maintaining the custodial equipment, 15% maintaining their own equipment and then 35%, 25%, and 20% in the blending, filling, and packaging deparments, respectively. Determine the total cost of each department.

Solution Begin by defining the variables. Let $x_i =$ total cost of each department as shown in the table below. Then list the direct and indirect costs for each department.

Department	total costs	direct costs	Indirect costs	
			custodial	maintenance
Custodial	x_1	$1500	$0.10\,x_1$	$0.15\,x_2$
Maintenance	x_2	$2000	$0.15\,x_1$	$0.05\,x_2$
Blending	x_3	$11,000	$0.25\,x_1$	$0.35\,x_2$
Filling	x_4	$12,000	$0.25\,x_1$	$0.25\,x_2$
Packaging	x_5	$6400	$0.25\,x_1$	$0.20\,x_2$
Totals		$32,900	x_1	x_2

We now have the following system of linear equations:

$$\begin{aligned}
x_1 &= 1500 + 0.10x_1 + 0.15x_2 \quad \text{custodial cost} \\
x_2 &= 2000 + 0.15x_1 + 0.05x_2 \quad \text{maintenance cost} \\
x_3 &= 11000 + 0.25x_1 + 0.35x_2 \quad \text{blending cost} \\
x_4 &= 12000 + 0.25x_1 + 0.25x_2 \quad \text{filling cost} \\
x_5 &= 6400 + 0.25x_1 + 0.20x_2 \quad \text{packing cost}
\end{aligned}$$

However, the last three equations can be solved by simple substitution once the values for x_1 and x_2 are determined. So the system to be solved is

$$\begin{aligned}
x_1 &= 1500 + 0.10x_1 + 0.15x_2 \\
x_2 &= 2000 + 0.15x_1 + 0.05x_2
\end{aligned}$$

This can be written as a matrix equation

$$\begin{bmatrix} x_1 \\ x_2 \end{bmatrix} = \begin{bmatrix} 1500 \\ 2000 \end{bmatrix} + \begin{bmatrix} 0.10 & 0.15 \\ 0.15 & 0.05 \end{bmatrix} \begin{bmatrix} x_1 \\ x_2 \end{bmatrix}$$

Now define the following matrices

$$X = \begin{bmatrix} x_1 \\ x_2 \end{bmatrix} \quad D = \begin{bmatrix} 1500 \\ 2000 \end{bmatrix} \quad C = \begin{bmatrix} 0.10 & 0.15 \\ 0.15 & 0.05 \end{bmatrix}$$

and our system can be written as $X = D + CX$. Solve this matrix equation for X as follows:

$$X = D + CX$$
$$X - CX = D$$
$$I_2 X - CX = D$$
$$(I_2 - C)X = D$$
$$(I_2 - C)^{-1}(I_2 - C)X = (I_2 - C)^{-1}D$$
$$X = (I_2 - C)^{-1}D$$

Using the values given we have

$$X = \begin{bmatrix} x_1 \\ x_2 \end{bmatrix} = \left(\begin{bmatrix} 1 & 0 \\ 0 & 1 \end{bmatrix} - \begin{bmatrix} 0.10 & 0.15 \\ 0.15 & 0.05 \end{bmatrix} \right)^{-1} \begin{bmatrix} 1500 \\ 2000 \end{bmatrix} \approx \begin{bmatrix} 2072.07 \\ 2432.43 \end{bmatrix}$$

Now the total costs for each department can be found as

$$x_1 = 2072.07$$
$$x_2 = 2432.43$$
$$x_3 = 11000 + 0.25(2072.07) + 0.35(2432.43) = 12,369.37$$
$$x_4 = 12000 + 0.25(2072.07) + 0.25(2432.43) = 13,126.13$$
$$x_5 = 6400 + 0.25(2072.07) + 0.20(2432.43) = 7404.50$$

The total cost for the custodial department is $2072.07, the maintenance department is $2432.43, the blending cost is $12,369.37, the filling cost is $13,126.13 and the packing cost is $7404.50. ◆

✧ Manufacturing

As another example of matrix applications, we look at a manufacturing process where some items are built from other items. Once again, these concepts will be developed through an example.

EXAMPLE 4 Sprinkler Kits The RainMan Company makes sprinklers. Each sprinkler head is made from 4 straight connectors, 1 elbow connector, and 1 T-connector. The elbow connectors are made from two straight connectors. The T-connectors are made from 3 straight connectors. If the company has a demand for 20 sprinkler heads, 15 T-connectors, 10 elbow connectors, and 25 straight connectors, how many of each part should be made to meet the demand?

Solution Begin by defining the variables
x_1 = the number of straight connectors to be made
x_2 = the number of elbow connectors to be made
x_3 = the number of T-connectors to be made
x_4 = the number of heads to be made
We can organize the manufacturing process in a parts diagram shown on the left. Then we write this as a system of equations $X = AX + D$ where A is the matrix of internal part usage and D is the parts needed to meet demand. Note that

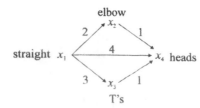

each column shows the number of other parts needed to make that column's part and p_1 is straight connectors, p_2 is elbow connectors, p_3 is T-connectors and p_4 is heads.

$$A = \begin{array}{c} \\ p_1 \\ p_2 \\ p_3 \\ p_4 \end{array} \begin{array}{cccc} p_1 & p_2 & p_3 & p_4 \\ \begin{bmatrix} 0 & 2 & 3 & 4 \\ 0 & 0 & 0 & 1 \\ 0 & 0 & 0 & 1 \\ 0 & 0 & 0 & 0 \end{bmatrix} \end{array} \qquad D = \begin{array}{c} \\ p_1 \\ p_2 \\ p_3 \\ p_4 \end{array} \begin{array}{c} \text{number} \\ \begin{bmatrix} 25 \\ 10 \\ 15 \\ 20 \end{bmatrix} \end{array}$$

As before, the solution to the system $X = AX + D$ is $X = (I - A)^{-1}D$, so we have

$$X = \left(\begin{bmatrix} 1 & 0 & 0 & 0 \\ 0 & 1 & 0 & 0 \\ 0 & 0 & 1 & 0 \\ 0 & 0 & 0 & 1 \end{bmatrix} - \begin{bmatrix} 0 & 2 & 3 & 4 \\ 0 & 0 & 0 & 1 \\ 0 & 0 & 0 & 1 \\ 0 & 0 & 0 & 0 \end{bmatrix} \right)^{-1} \begin{bmatrix} 25 \\ 10 \\ 15 \\ 25 \end{bmatrix} = \begin{bmatrix} 270 \\ 30 \\ 35 \\ 20 \end{bmatrix}$$

If the company makes 270 straight connectors, 30 elbow connectors, 35 T-connectors, and 20 heads, then the demand for these parts will be met. ✦

✧ Closed Leontief Input–Output Model

In the closed input–output model, we assume that there is no demand from outside the n industries under consideration. Therefore the sum of the values in each column will be one, so that everything produced is consumed with no external demand. If we look at our matrix equation for the open economy, $X = AX + D$, in a closed economy we have $D = O$, so the matrix equation will be $X = AX$ or $(I - A)X = O$. Unfortunately, the matrix $(I - A)$ is singular for closed IO systems and we will need to find the equilibrium using the Gauss-Jordan method.

Since the amount consumed is equal to the amount produced, the problem then is to find suitable prices for each of the n outputs so that the total expenditure of each industry equals its total income. Any such price structure represents equilibrium for the economy. We will develop this concept looking at an isolated village economy.

EXAMPLE 5 **Closed Village Economy** Consider an isolated village. The economy of this village is closed so the residents will need to find the prices to charge for the local goods and services. The economy has three sectors: farming, building, and services (such as the doctor and barber). To produce 1 unit from the farming sector, it takes $1/2$ unit of farming, $1/3$ unit of building, and $1/6$ unit of services. To produce 1 unit from the building sector, it takes $1/3$ unit of farming, $1/3$ unit of building, and $1/3$ unit of services. To produce 1 unit from the service sector, it takes $1/4$ unit of farming, $1/4$ unit of building, and $1/2$ unit of services. What are the equilibrium prices for these three sectors?

Solution First find the matrix A to represent this economy.

$$A = \begin{array}{c} \\ F \\ B \\ S \end{array} \begin{array}{ccc} F & B & S \\ \begin{bmatrix} 1/2 & 1/3 & 1/4 \\ 1/3 & 1/3 & 1/4 \\ 1/6 & 1/3 & 1/2 \end{bmatrix} \end{array}$$

Next define the variables. Let

p_1 = price charged by the farming industry for its total output
p_2 = price charged by the building industry for its total output
p_3 = price charged by the service industry for its total output

Finally, set the price charged to the price gained from selling each output.

$$p_1 = \tfrac{1}{2}p_1 + \tfrac{1}{3}p_2 + \tfrac{1}{4}p_3$$

$$p_2 = \tfrac{1}{3}p_1 + \tfrac{1}{3}p_2 + \tfrac{1}{4}p_3$$

$$p_3 = \tfrac{1}{6}p_1 + \tfrac{1}{3}p_2 + \tfrac{1}{2}p_3$$

Let the price matrix be

$$X = \begin{bmatrix} p_1 \\ p_2 \\ p_3 \end{bmatrix}$$

and then these last three equations can be written in matrix form as

$$X = AX$$

This can be rewritten as

$$X - AX = O$$
$$IX - AX = O$$
$$(I - A)X = O$$

It turns out that $(I - A)$ does not have an inverse. The solutions can be found using the Gauss-Jordan method. Now solve the linear system $(I - A)X = O$. The augmented matrix $[I - A|O]$ is below.

$$\left[\begin{array}{ccc|c} 1/2 & -1/3 & -1/4 & 0 \\ -1/3 & 2/3 & -1/4 & 0 \\ -1/6 & -1/3 & 1/2 & 0 \end{array}\right] \begin{array}{l} R_1 \to 2R_1 \\ \\ \\ \end{array} \to \left[\begin{array}{ccc|c} 1 & -2/3 & -1/2 & 0 \\ -1/3 & 2/3 & -1/4 & 0 \\ -1/6 & -1/3 & 1/2 & 0 \end{array}\right] \begin{array}{l} \\ R_2 + \tfrac{1}{3}R_1 \to R_2 \\ R_3 + \tfrac{1}{6}R_1 \to R_3 \end{array}$$

$$\to \left[\begin{array}{ccc|c} 1 & -2/3 & -1/2 & 0 \\ 0 & 4/9 & -5/12 & 0 \\ 0 & -4/9 & 5/12 & 0 \end{array}\right] \begin{array}{l} \\ \tfrac{9}{4}R_2 \to R_2 \\ R_3 + R_2 \to R_3 \end{array}$$

$$\to \left[\begin{array}{ccc|c} 1 & -2/3 & -1/2 & 0 \\ 0 & 1 & -15/16 & 0 \\ 0 & 0 & 0 & 0 \end{array}\right]$$

The third variable, p_3, is free. So we let $p_3 = t$, where t is any real number. Backward substitution then gives

$$p_2 = \frac{15}{16}p_1 = \frac{15}{16}t = 0.9375t$$

and

$$p_1 - \frac{2}{3}p_2 - \frac{1}{2}p_3 = 0$$

$$p_1 - \frac{2}{3}\left(\frac{15}{16}\right)t - \frac{1}{2}(t) = 0$$

$$p_1 = \frac{9}{8}t = 1.125t$$

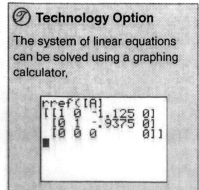

These are the suitable prices for each of the three outputs, that is, prices such that the total expenditure of each industry equals its total income. So, if the villagers use simoleons for the local money and each unit of services costs 1 simoleon, then a unit of farming would cost $9/8$ simoleons and a unit of building would cost $15/16$ simoleon. If a unit of services costs 2 simoleons, the cost of farming and building would also double. ◆

✧ Technology Corner

⑨ Technology Note 1   **Example 1 Using Microsoft Excel**

Using a spreadsheet for input–output modeling has several advantages over the calculator. Very large economies can be handled by the spreadsheet and the labels can be kept with the matrices. Additionally, once a template spreadsheet has been created, it can be modified when the data needs to be updated or a new model used.

Begin by entering a 2×2 identity matrix, a 2×2 production matrix, and a 2×1 demand matrix. Then highlight a 2×2 block of cells to hold the multiplier matrix, $(I - A)^{-1}$. Type in MINVERSE(B2:C3-F2:G3) as shown in Worksheet 1.

	A	B	C	D	E	F	G	H	I	J	K	L	M	N	O
1	Identity				IO	food	cloth		Demand		Multiplier			Production	
2		1	0		food	0.4	0.3		7200		=MINVERSE(B2:C3-F2:G3)				
3		0	1		cloth	0.1	0.2		2700						

Worksheet 1

Do a Ctrl-Shift-Enter. The result is shown in Worksheet 2.

	A	B	C	D	E	F	G	H	I	J	K	L	M	N	O	P
1	Identity				IO	food	cloth		Demand		Multiplier			Production		
2		1	0		food	0.4	0.3		7200		1.7778	0.6667		=MMULT(K2:L3,I2:I3)		
3		0	1		cloth	0.1	0.2		2700		0.2222	1.3333				

Worksheet 2

To find the production matrix, highlight a 2×1 block of cells and type =MMULT(L2:M3,I2:I3) and then Ctrl-Shift-Enter to see the results shown in Worksheet 3.

	A	B	C	D	E	F	G	H	I	J	K	L	M	N	O	P
1	Identity				IO	food	cloth		Demand		Multiplier			Production		
2		1	0		food	0.4	0.3		7200		1.7778	0.6667		14600		
3		0	1		cloth	0.1	0.2		2700		0.2222	1.3333		5200		

Worksheet 3

⑨ Technology Note 2   **Example 2 Using a Graphing Calculator and Microsoft Excel**

Enter the IO matrix as a 3×3 matrix [A] and the demand matrix as a 3×1 matrix [B]. The multiplier matrix is then found with $(\text{identity}(3) - [A])^{-1}$ as shown in Screen 1. Since there are repeating decimals, use the Frac command to convert to a fraction as shown in Screen 2. To clear the fractions, multiply by the greatest common denominator, 237, to get the multiplier matrix as shown in Screen 3. Or, if the multiplier matrix is not needed, the answer can be found directly. This is shown in Screen 4.

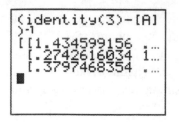

Screen 1

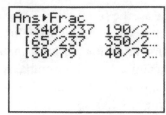

Screen 2

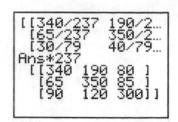

Screen 3

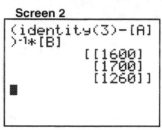

Screen 4

To use a spreadsheet, enter the 3×3 identity matrix, the IO matrix and the demand matrix. Then highlight a 3×3 block of cells for the multiplier matrix. Use the command =MINVERSE((B2:D4)-(G2:I4)) and then Ctrl-Shift-Enter. Then multiply the multiplier matrix and the demand matrix by highlighting a 3×1 block of cells and typing the command =MMULT(N2:P4,K2:K4) followed by Ctrl-Shift-Enter. This is shown in Worksheet 4.

	A	B	C	D	E	F	G	H	I	J	K	L	M	N	O	P	Q
1	Identity					IO	A	E	T		Demand	Multiplier					Production
2		1	0	0		A	0.2	0.4	0.1		474	1.4346	0.8017	0.3376			1600
3		0	1	0		E	0.1	0.2	0.2		948	0.2743	1.4768	0.3586			1700
4		0	0	1		T	0.2	0.2	0.1		474	0.3797	0.5063	1.2658			1260

Worksheet 4

Self-Help Exercise 2.4

1. Find the production matrix when the input–output matrix and the demand matrix are

$$A = \begin{bmatrix} 0.6 & 0.2 \\ 0.2 & 0.4 \end{bmatrix} \qquad D = \begin{bmatrix} 50,000,000 \\ 30,000,000 \end{bmatrix}$$

2.4 Exercises

In Exercises 1 through 6, you are given an input–output matrix A and a demand matrix D. Assuming a Leontief open input–output model, find the production matrix.

1. $A = \begin{bmatrix} 0.3 & 0.2 \\ 0.4 & 0.3 \end{bmatrix}$, $D = \begin{bmatrix} 10,000,000 \\ 20,000,000 \end{bmatrix}$

2. $A = \begin{bmatrix} 0.1 & 0.2 \\ 0.4 & 0.3 \end{bmatrix}$, $D = \begin{bmatrix} 30,000,000 \\ 40,000,000 \end{bmatrix}$

3. $A = \begin{bmatrix} 0.5 & 0.2 \\ 0.4 & 0.2 \end{bmatrix}$, $D = \begin{bmatrix} 100,000,000 \\ 200,000,000 \end{bmatrix}$

4. $A = \begin{bmatrix} 0.2 & 0.3 \\ 0.4 & 0.3 \end{bmatrix}$, $D = \begin{bmatrix} 30,000,000 \\ 50,000,000 \end{bmatrix}$

5. $A = \begin{bmatrix} 0.5 & 0.1 \\ 0.4 & 0.1 \end{bmatrix}$, $D = \begin{bmatrix} 200,000,000 \\ 300,000,000 \end{bmatrix}$

6. $A = \begin{bmatrix} 0.1 & 0.3 \\ 0.5 & 0.3 \end{bmatrix}$, $D = \begin{bmatrix} 5,000,000 \\ 6,000,000 \end{bmatrix}$

7. **Village Economy** The villagers have found that to produce $1.00 worth of food, $.10 worth of food, $.40 worth of cloth, and $.20 worth of wood is needed locally to feed, clothe, and shelter the farmers. To produce $1.00 worth of cloth, $.10 worth of food, $.10 worth of cloth, and $.30 worth of wood is needed locally to feed, clothe, and shelter the weavers. To produce $1.00 worth of wood, $.20 worth of food, $.10 worth of cloth, and $.10 worth of wood is needed locally to feed, clothe, and shelter the builders. The additional food, cloth, and wood produced is then available to export to the city. If the city demands $1000 worth of food, $2600 worth of cloth, and $200 worth of wood each week, how much food, cloth, and wood should be produced by the village to meet its own needs and to supply the city?

8. **Village Economy** The villagers have found that to produce $1.00 worth of food, $.20 worth of food, $.10 worth of cloth, and $.10 worth of wood is needed locally to feed, clothe, and shelter the farmers. To produce $1.00 worth of cloth, $.10 worth of food, $.10 worth of cloth, and $.30 worth of wood is needed locally to feed, clothe, and shelter the weavers. To produce $1.00 worth of wood, $.10 worth of food, $.30 worth of cloth, and $.10 worth of wood is needed locally to feed, clothe, and shelter the builders. The additional food, cloth, and wood produced is then available to export to the city. If the city demands $3200 worth of food, $400 worth of cloth, and $800 worth of wood each week, how much food, cloth, and wood should be produced by the village to meet its own needs and to supply the city?

9. **Three–Sector Economy** This economy has three sectors: agriculture, manufacturing, and transportation. To produce $1.00 worth of agriculture, $0.10 worth of agriculture, $.30 worth of manufacturing, and $.10 worth of transportation is needed internally. To produce $1.00 worth of manufacturing, $.20 worth of agriculture, $.30 worth of manufacturing, and $.20 worth of transportation is needed internally. To produce $1.00 worth of transportation, $.40 worth of agriculture, $.10 worth of manufacturing, and $.20 worth of services is needed internally. If the external demand is for $2,000,000 worth of agriculture, $1,000,000 worth of manufacturing, and $1,000,000 worth of transportation, determine the production matrix.

10. **Three–Sector Economy** This economy has three sectors: agriculture, manufacturing, and services. To produce $1.00 worth of agriculture, $.10 worth of agriculture, $.30 worth of manufacturing, and $.20 worth of services is needed internally. To produce $1.00 worth of manufacturing, $.10 worth of agriculture, $.20 worth of manufacturing, and $.20 worth of services is needed internally. To produce $1.00 worth of services, $.20 worth of agriculture, $.10 worth of manufacturing, and $.30 worth of services is needed internally. If the external demand is for $1,000,000 worth of agriculture, $2,000,000 worth of manufacturing, and $1,000,000 worth of services, determine the production matrix.

In Exercises 11 through 16, you are given an input–output matrix F for a closed Leontief input–output model. Find the equilibrium prices.

11. $F = \begin{bmatrix} 0.3 & 0.2 \\ 0.7 & 0.8 \end{bmatrix}$

12. $F = \begin{bmatrix} 0.5 & 0.4 \\ 0.5 & 0.6 \end{bmatrix}$

13. $F = \begin{bmatrix} 0.4 & 0.1 \\ 0.6 & 0.9 \end{bmatrix}$

14. $F = \begin{bmatrix} 0.2 & 0.1 \\ 0.8 & 0.9 \end{bmatrix}$

15. $F = \begin{bmatrix} 0.1 & 0.1 & 0.2 \\ 0.5 & 0 & 0.8 \\ 0.4 & 0.9 & 0 \end{bmatrix}$

16. $F = \begin{bmatrix} 0.2 & 0.1 & 0.3 \\ 0.4 & 0.3 & 0.4 \\ 0.4 & 0.6 & 0.3 \end{bmatrix}$

17. **Three–Sector Economy** This economy has three sectors: auto, energy, and transportation. To produce $1.00 worth of auto, $.30 worth of auto, $.30 worth of energy, and $.40 worth of transportation is needed internally. To produce $1.00 worth of energy, $.10 worth of auto, $.40 worth of energy, and $.50 worth of transportation is needed internally. To produce $1.00 worth of transportation, $.20 worth of auto, $.20 worth of energy, and $.60 worth of transportation is needed internally. Find the equilibrium prices.

18. **Closed Leontief Input–Output Model** Suppose in the closed Leontief input–output model for a three industry system, the input–output matrix is given by $A = (a_{ij})$. We then wish to solve $(I - A)X = O$. To solve we form the augmented matrix $[I - A | O]$. In

the closed model we must have

$$a_{11} + a_{21} + a_{31} = 1$$
$$a_{12} + a_{22} + a_{32} = 1$$
$$a_{13} + a_{23} + a_{33} = 1$$

Using these three equations and the operations $R_3 + R_1 \rightarrow R_3$ and $R_3 + R_2 \rightarrow R_3$ on the augmented matrix, show that the augmented matrix becomes

$$\begin{bmatrix} 1-a_{11} & -a_{12} & a_{13} & 0 \\ -a_{21} & 1-a_{22} & -a_{23} & 0 \\ 0 & 0 & 0 & 0 \end{bmatrix}$$

19. **State of Washington Input–Output** The following aggregate 1997 State of Washington Input–Output table is shown. R is for resources, M for manufacturing, and TS for trade and services. The numbers are in millions of dollars.

	R	M	TS	External Demand	Total Output
R	728	3114	350	2793	6985
M	409	7624	6737	66,784	81,554
TS	1008	9159	43,949	131,749	185,865

a. Convert this data to an input–output matrix A.
Hint: $a_{11} = 728/6985$, $a_{21} = 409/6985$, $a_{12} = 3114/81554$.

b. Use the column in the table under External Demand as the matrix D. Solve for $X = (I - A)^{-1}D$.

c. Where is X in the table?

d. Check your answers by finding $(I - A)X = D$.

20. **Input–Output for Four–Sector Economy** An economy has four sectors: energy, textiles, transportation, and chemicals. Energy requires 0.1 unit of itself, 0.2 unit of transportation, and 0.4 unit of chemicals. Textiles requires 0.4 unit of energy, 0.1 unit of itself, 0.15 unit of transportation, and 0.25 unit of chemicals. Transportation requires 0.6 unit of energy, 0.1 unit of itself, and 0.25 unit of chemicals. Chemicals requires 0.2 unit of energy, 0.1 unit of textiles, 0.3 unit of transportation, and 0.2 unit of itself.

a. Determine the input–output matrix.

b. Suppose the external demand for energy for $253.5 million, textiles $16.75 million, transportation $55.75 million, and chemicals $135.5 million. Find the production matrix.

21. Given the following input–output matrix A and demand matrix D and assuming a Leontief open input–output model, find the production matrix.

$$A = \begin{bmatrix} 0.20 & 0.20 & 0.15 & 0.10 \\ 0.40 & 0.10 & 0.20 & 0.15 \\ 0.02 & 0.03 & 0.01 & 0.12 \\ 0.25 & 0.04 & 0.01 & 0.10 \end{bmatrix}, \quad D = \begin{bmatrix} 800 \\ 450 \\ 1760 \\ 300 \end{bmatrix}$$

22. In the matrix in Exercise 21, replace $a_{11} = 0.20$ with 1. Now find the production matrix. What happened?

Solution to Self-Help Exercise 2.4

1. $I - A = \begin{bmatrix} 0.4 & -0.2 \\ -0.2 & 0.6 \end{bmatrix}$. Now find the inverse matrix.

$$\begin{bmatrix} 0.4 & -0.2 & 1 & 0 \\ -0.2 & 0.6 & 0 & 1 \end{bmatrix} \xrightarrow{\frac{1}{0.4}R_1 \rightarrow R_1} \begin{bmatrix} 1 & -0.5 & 2.5 & 0 \\ -0.2 & 0.6 & 0 & 1 \end{bmatrix} R_2 + 0.2R_1 \rightarrow R_2$$

$$\rightarrow \begin{bmatrix} 1 & -0.5 & 2.5 & 0 \\ 0 & 0.5 & 0.5 & 1 \end{bmatrix} 2R_2 \rightarrow R_2 \quad \rightarrow \begin{bmatrix} 1 & -0.5 & 2.5 & 0 \\ 0 & 1 & 1 & 2 \end{bmatrix} R_1 + 0.5R_2 \rightarrow R_1$$

$$\rightarrow \begin{bmatrix} 1 & 0 & 3 & 1 \\ 0 & 1 & 1 & 2 \end{bmatrix}$$

Thus $(I - A)^{-1} = \begin{bmatrix} 3 & 1 \\ 1 & 2 \end{bmatrix}$

and $X = (I - A)^{-1}D = \begin{bmatrix} 3 & 1 \\ 1 & 2 \end{bmatrix} \begin{bmatrix} 50,000,000 \\ 30,000,000 \end{bmatrix} = \begin{bmatrix} 180,000,000 \\ 100,000,000 \end{bmatrix}$

Review

♢ **Summary Outline**

- The order of a matrix A is denoted by $m \times n$ where m is the number of rows and n is the number of columns.

- The element in the ith row and jth column of a matrix A is denoted by a_{ij}.

- A row matrix is a matrix with one row. A column matrix is a matrix with one column. A square matrix is a matrix with equal numbers of rows and columns.

- Two matrices are equal if and only if they have the same order and all corresponding entries are equal.

- Multiplying a matrix by a real number. If c is a real number and A is a matrix, then the matrix cA is the matrix obtained by multiplying every entry in A by c.

- Adding and subtracting matrices. Two matrices of the same order can be added (or subtracted) to obtain another matrix of the same order by adding (or subtracting) corresponding entries.

- The zero matrix of order $m \times n$ is the matrix with m rows and n columns, all of whose entries are zero.

- Some matrix properties. Let A, B, C, and O be four matrices, all of the same order with O the zero matrix. Then

$$A + O = O + A = A$$
$$A - A = O$$
$$A + B = B + A$$
$$A + (B + C) = (A + B) + C$$

- Multiplying a row matrix times a column matrix. Let R be the row matrix $R = \begin{bmatrix} r_1 & r_2 & \cdots & r_n \end{bmatrix}$ and let C be the column matrix $C^T = \begin{bmatrix} c_1 & c_2 & \cdots & c_n \end{bmatrix}$ with the number of elements of R equal to the number of elements of C. Then the product matrix RC is defined to be

$$RC = \begin{bmatrix} r_1 & r_2 & \cdots & r_n \end{bmatrix} \begin{bmatrix} c_1 \\ c_2 \\ \vdots \\ c_n \end{bmatrix} = [r_1 c_1 + r_2 c_2 + \cdots + r_n c_n]$$

- Multiplication of Matrices Given two matrices $A = (a_{ij})_{m \times p}$ and $B = (b_{ij})_{q \times n}$, the product $AB = C = (c_{ij})$ is defined if $p = q$, that is, if the number of columns of A equals the number of rows of B. In such a case, the element in the ith row and jth column, c_{ij}, of the product matrix C is obtained by taking the product of the ith row of A and the jth column of B.

- Order of a product Given the two matrices $A = (a_{ij})_{m \times p}$ and $B = (b_{ij})_{p \times n}$, the matrix AB has order $m \times n$.

- The $n \times n$ **identity matrix**, I_n, is the square matrix of order $n \times n$ with ones down the main diagonal and zeros elsewhere.

- **Matrix multiplication properties.** For any matrices A, B, and C:

$$A(BC) = (AB)C$$
$$A(B+C) = AB+AC$$
$$AI_n = I_nA = A$$

whenever the indicated products are defined.

- Given a square $n \times n$ matrix A, the matrix A^{-1} is called the **inverse** of A if $AA^{-1} = A^{-1}A = I_n$

- To find A^{-1}. (1) Form the augmented matrix $[A|I]$. (2) Use row operations to reduce $[A|I]$ to $[I|B]$, if possible. (3) $A^{-1} = B$

- The system of equations

$$a_{11}x_1 + a_{12}x_2 + \cdots a_{1n}x_n = b_1$$
$$a_{21}x_1 + a_{22}x_2 + \cdots a_{2n}x_n = b_2$$
$$\cdots$$
$$a_{m1}x_1 + a_{m2}x_2 + \cdots a_{mn}x_n = b_m$$

can be put into **matrix form** $AX = B$ by letting

$$A = \begin{bmatrix} a_{11} & a_{12} & \cdots & a_{1n} \\ a_{21} & a_{22} & \cdots & a_{2n} \\ & \cdots & & \\ a_{m1} & a_{m2} & \cdots & a_{mn} \end{bmatrix}, \quad X = \begin{bmatrix} x_1 \\ x_2 \\ \vdots \\ x_n \end{bmatrix}, \quad B = \begin{bmatrix} b_1 \\ b_2 \\ \vdots \\ b_m \end{bmatrix}$$

The matrix A is called the **coefficient matrix**.

- **Solution of** $AX = B$. Let A be a square matrix of order $n \times n$ and B a column matrix of order n. If A^{-1} exists, then the linear system of equations $AX = B$ has the unique solution $X = A^{-1}B$.

- The **input–output** matrix $A = (a_{ij})$ represents the dollar amount of the output of industry i required in producing one dollar of output in industry j.

- If x_1, x_2, and x_3 represent the respective outputs in dollars of a three-industry economy and d_1, d_2, and d_3 the respective nonindustry demand in dollars for the three products produced by the three industries, then we define the **production column matrix** X and the **demand column matrix** D, respectively, by

$$X = \begin{bmatrix} x_1 \\ x_2 \\ x_3 \end{bmatrix}, \quad D = \begin{bmatrix} d_1 \\ d_2 \\ d_3 \end{bmatrix}$$

- The **production matrix** X is given by $X = (I - A)^{-1}D$.

• In the closed Leontief input–output model no demand is assumed from outside the industries being considered. If f_{ij} is the fraction of the total output of the jth industry purchased by the ith industry, and p_i the price charged by the ith industry for its total output, then the matrix P must satisfy the equation $(I - F)P = 0$, where $F = (f_{ij})$ is the price matrix and

$$P = \begin{bmatrix} p_1 \\ p_2 \\ p_3 \end{bmatrix}$$

is the equilibrium price matrix.

Review Exercises

In Exercises 1 through 12, let

$$A = \begin{bmatrix} 1 & 3 \\ 2 & 1 \\ -1 & 3 \end{bmatrix}, \quad B = \begin{bmatrix} 2 & 5 \\ 1 & 0 \\ 3 & -2 \end{bmatrix}, \quad C = \begin{bmatrix} 1 & 3 \end{bmatrix}$$

$$D = \begin{bmatrix} 2 \\ 4 \end{bmatrix}, \quad E = \begin{bmatrix} 2 & 0 & -1 \\ 3 & 1 & 2 \end{bmatrix},$$

$$F = \begin{bmatrix} 2 & 4 & 1 \end{bmatrix}, \quad G = \begin{bmatrix} 1 \\ 3 \\ -2 \end{bmatrix}$$

and find the requested quantity if defined.

1. $3A$ **2.** $-2B^T$ **3.** $3A - 2B$ **4.** CD

5. DG **6.** AC **7.** EG **8.** AF

9. AE **10.** EA **11.** AB **12.** FG

13. A matrix $D = (d_{ij})$ is a diagonal matrix if $d_{ij} = 0$ if $i \neq j$, that is, all entries off the main diagonal are zero. Suppose $A = (a_{ij})$ and $B = (b_{ij})$ are both diagonal matrices of order 3×3. Show that

    a. A^2 is diagonal

    b. AB is diagonal.

In Exercises 14 through 19, find the inverse of the given matrix, if it exists.

14. $\begin{bmatrix} 5 & 1 \\ 2 & 1 \end{bmatrix}$ **15.** $\begin{bmatrix} 4 & 2 \\ 2 & 1 \end{bmatrix}$

16. $\begin{bmatrix} 2 & -3 \\ -3 & 1 \end{bmatrix}$ **17.** $\begin{bmatrix} 1 & 3 & 0 \\ 2 & 5 & 1 \\ -1 & -2 & 2 \end{bmatrix}$

18. $\begin{bmatrix} 1 & 4 & 0 \\ 2 & 9 & 1 \\ 5 & 22 & 2 \end{bmatrix}$ **19.** $\begin{bmatrix} 1 & 1 & 1 \\ -1 & 2 & 2 \\ 2 & 1 & 2 \end{bmatrix}$

In Exercises 20 through 23, solve the system using the inverses found in the previous exercises.

20. $5x + y = 1$
    $2x + y = -2$

21. $2x - 3y = 14$
    $-3x + y = 35$

22. $\quad x + 3y = -1$
    $2x + 5y + z = 3$
    $-x - 2y + 2z = 2$

23. $\quad x + y + z = 30$
    $-x + 2y + 2z = -9$
    $2x + y + 2z = 0$

In Exercises 24 and 25, you are given an input–input matrix A and a demand matrix D. Assuming a Leontief open input–output model, find the production matrix.

24. $\begin{bmatrix} 0.2 & 0.2 \\ 0.7 & 0.3 \end{bmatrix}, \quad \begin{bmatrix} 10{,}000{,}000 \\ 20{,}000{,}000 \end{bmatrix}$

25. $\begin{bmatrix} 0 & 0.10 & 0.25 \\ 0.50 & 0 & 0.20 \\ 0.20 & 0.30 & 0 \end{bmatrix}, \quad \begin{bmatrix} 10{,}000{,}000 \\ 20{,}000{,}000 \\ 30{,}000{,}000 \end{bmatrix}$

In Exercises 26 and 27, you are given an input–input matrix F for a closed Leontief input–output model. Find the equilibrium price matrix.

26. $\begin{bmatrix} 0.2 & 0.3 \\ 0.8 & 0.7 \end{bmatrix}$ **27.** $\begin{bmatrix} 0.1 & 0.1 & 0.3 \\ 0.5 & 0 & 0.7 \\ 0.4 & 0.3 & 0 \end{bmatrix}$

CHAPTER 3

Linear Programming:
The Graphical Method

CONNECTION

Jan de Wit Company

The Jan de Wit company implemented a decision-support system based on linear programming as a production-planning and trade tool for the management of its lily flower business. The linear programming maximizes the farm's total contribution margin, subject to such constraints as market-defined sales limits, market requirements, characteristics of the production cycle duration, technical requirements, bulb inventory, and greenhouse limitations. The main decision variable to be calculated is the number of flower beds in a specific greenhouse, from a specific bulb patch, of a specific variety, for a specific purpose, taking into consideration planting and expected harvesting weeks.

Source: Caixeta-Filho, van Swaay-Neto, and de Pádua Wagemaker 2002

3.1 Linear Programming Problems

APPLICATION
Manufacture of Wooden Boats

A small company manufactures two types of wooden boats: dinghies and skiffs. The manufacture of each boat must go through three operations: cutting of the wood, assembly of the pieces, and painting of the completed boat. Each dinghy requires 2 hours of cutting, 4 hours of assembling, and 2 hours of painting. Each skiff requires 4 hours of cutting, 2 hours of assembling, and 2 hours of painting. The total time available per week in the cutting section is 80 hours, in the assembly section 50 hours, and in the painting section 50 hours. There is a profit of $60 for every dinghy and $80 for every skiff. Write a system of inequalities that expresses this information, determine the objective function, and write all this as a linear programming problem. See Example 2 for the answer.

✧ Introduction

Business, economics, finance, and many other areas are replete with complex decision or allocation problems that involve the selection of specific values of many interrelated variables. Often one can focus attention on one specific objective that is to be maximized or minimized. Examples of such objectives are profit, revenue, cost, expected return on an investment, or perhaps some measure of social welfare for a government program. The variables are normally subject to constraints that take the form of a set of inequalities. These inequalities limit the possible selection of the values of the variables under consideration.

In this chapter we will optimize (maximize or minimize) a linear function of several variables. The function to be optimized is called the objective function. The variables will satisfy a system of linear inequalities called constraints that will give a solution set of points, called the feasible region. In the applications the variables will be nonnegative. This will give us the nonnegative constraints. The other constraints are called problem constraints. We will then attempt to optimize the objective function subject to the constraints that the variables satisfy. This is called linear programming.

In this section we will concentrate on translating a question into a linear programming problem, but not solving it. In Section 3.2 we will see how to graph the feasible region for the system of linear inequalities associated with the linear programming problem, and in Section 3.3 we will see how to solve the linear programming problem by a geometric method. The full power of linear programming will be taken up in another chapter.

✧ Linear Programming Applications

EXAMPLE 1 Maximizing Profits From Benches A shop manufactures two styles of aluminum park benches, fancy and plain. The fancy style requires 4 kilograms of aluminum and 6 hours of labor, while the plain style requires 4 kilograms of aluminum and 3 hours of labor. There are 32 kilograms of aluminum and 36 hours of labor available for the day. The fancy style bench earns a profit of $24 and the plain one $18. Naturally, the shop's objective is to maximize its profits. Write a system of inequalities that expresses this information, determine the objective function, and write all this as a linear programming problem.

Solution   Begin by defining the variables. Let

x = the number of fancy benches made

y = the number of plain benches made

The information given in the problem is summarized in the table below.

	Fancy	Plain	Available
Kilograms of Aluminum	4	4	32
Hours of Labor	6	3	36
Profit	$24	$18	

Since each fancy bench requires 4 kilograms of aluminum, there is a total of $4x$ kilograms of aluminum for these benches. Since each plain bench requires 4 kilograms of aluminum, there are a total of $4y$ kilograms of aluminum for these benches. Then $4x + 4y$ is the total number of kilograms of aluminum needed to make both of the benches, while the total amount available is 32 kilograms. Thus, $4x + 4y \leq 32$.

Since each fancy bench requires 6 hours of labor, there are a total of $6x$ hours of labor needed for these benches. Since each plain bench requires 3 hours of labor, there are a total of $3y$ hours of labor needed for these benches. Then $6x + 3y$ is the total number of hours of labor needed to make both types of the benches, while the total labor available is 36 hours. Thus, $6x + 3y \leq 36$.

Naturally, we must have $x \geq 0$ and $y \geq 0$, which we refer to as the nonnegativity constraint. We then have the system of inequalities (constraints):

$$4x + 4y \leq 32 \quad \text{kilograms of aluminum constraint}$$
$$6x + 3y \leq 36 \quad \text{hours of labor constraint}$$
$$x, y \geq \quad 0 \quad \text{nonnegativity constraint}$$

The profit function in dollars is $P = 24x + 18y$. Our objective is to maximize this function.

$$\text{Maximize} \quad P = 24x + 18y \quad \text{objective function}$$
$$\text{Subject to} \quad 4x + 4y \leq 32 \quad \text{kilograms of aluminum}$$
$$6x + 3y \leq 36 \quad \text{hours of labor}$$
$$x, y \geq 0 \quad \text{nonnegativity}$$

◆

Notice that we now have several possibilities for the number of benches produced. For example, the shop could make one fancy bench and one plain bench. A total of $4(1) + 4(1) = 8$ kilograms of aluminum would be used (less than the 32 kilograms that are available) and $6(1) + 3(1) = 9$ hours of labor (less than the 36 hours that are available). However, the profit would be only $P = 24(1) + 18(1) = 42$, or $42. It is likely that they could make more money by making more benches with the remaining resources. That is the job of linear programming.

In some linear programming problems we have a limit on our resources and an objective function to maximize with our available materials. In other cases we need to minimize our objective function while ensuring certain requirements are met. Both of these kinds of application problems are quite different than the problems that were solved in Chapter 2 where all of the resources would be used.

When stating a linear programming problem, certain forms are followed. If it is an application, begin by defining the variables. Next list the objective function and state if it is to be minimized or maximized. On the next line write "subject to" and list the problem constraints. If it is an application problem, state what the constraint means.

CONNECTION
Sears, Roebuck and Co. Cost Savings

Sears, Roebuck and Co. is one of the largest procurers of trucking services in the world. It controls elements of the supply chain that connect the vendor (manufacturer), distribution centers, retail stores, and cross-dock facilities (similar to airline hubs for redistributing cargo). A major portion of Sears operations is contracting for truck and carrier services; Sears has sought to consolidate its use of these services to reduce its costs. Using linear programming resulted in reducing Sears trucking services from $190 million to $165 million per year.

Source: Ledyard, Olsen, Porter, Swanson, and Torma 2002

EXAMPLE 2   Manufacture of Wooden Boats   A small company manufactures two types of wooden boats: dinghies and skiffs. The manufacture of each boat must go through three operations: cutting of the wood, assembly of the pieces, and painting of the completed boat. Each dinghy requires 2 hours of cutting, 4 hours of assembling, and 2 hours of painting. Each skiff requires 4 hours of cutting, 2 hours of assembling, and 2 hours of painting. The total time available per week in the cutting section is 80 hours, in the assembly section 50 hours, and in the painting section 50 hours. There is a profit of $60 for every dinghy and $80 for every skiff. Write a system of inequalities that expresses this information, determine the objective function, and write all this as a linear programming problem.

Solution   Define the variables. Let
x = the number of dinghies manufactured each week
y = the number of skiffs manufactured each week
The information given in the problem is summarized in the table below.

	Dinghies	Skiffs	Hours Available
Cutting hours	2	4	80
Assembly hours	4	2	84
Painting hours	2	2	50
Profit	$60	$80	

Each of the dinghies requires 2 hours of cutting and each of the skiffs requires 4 hours of cutting. Thus, the cutting section will be occupied $2x$ hours with the dinghies and $4y$ hours with the skiffs, for a total of $2x + 4y$ hours. Since this must be at most 80 hours, we have $2x + 4y \leq 80$.

Since each of the dinghies requires 4 hours to assemble and each of the skiffs requires 2 hours, the assembly section will be occupied $4x + 2y$ hours and therefore $4x + 2y \leq 84$.

Finally since each of the dinghies and skiffs requires 2 hours to paint, the painting section will be occupied $2x + 2y$ hours and therefore $2x + 2y \leq 50$.

Naturally, x and y must be nonnegative. We then have a system of inequalities:

$$2x + 4y \leq 80 \quad \text{cutting hours constraint}$$
$$4x + 2y \leq 84 \quad \text{assembly hours constraint}$$
$$2x + 2y \leq 50 \quad \text{painting hours constraint}$$
$$x, y \geq 0 \quad \text{nonnegativity constraint}$$

The profit function, $P = 60x + 80y$, is to be maximized. Our linear programming problem is then

$$
\begin{array}{lll}
\text{Maximize} & P = 60x + 80y & \text{objective function} \\
\text{Subject to} & 2x + 4y \leq 80 & \text{cutting hours} \\
 & 4x + 2y \leq 84 & \text{assembly hours} \\
 & 2x + 2y \leq 50 & \text{painting hours} \\
 & x, y \geq 0 & \text{nonnegativity}
\end{array}
$$

◆

CONNECTION
Overhauling IBM's
Supply-chain Management
Applications

In the early 1990s, the IBM Corporation decided that its microelectronics division should expand from producing parts exclusively for other IBM locations to producing a range of products for diverse customers. To overhaul its supply-chain management applications to handle the new business, it developed mathematical models, including linear programming, to match assets with demand to determine which demands it could meet when and to provide manufacturing guidelines. This work has improved manufacturing utilization and customer-order response time, saving about $80 million per year.

Source: Lyon, Milne, Orzell, and Rice 2001

EXAMPLE 3   Buying Fertilizer   A farmer can buy two types of 100-pound bags of fertilizer, type A and type B. Each 100-pound bag of type A fertilizer costs $20 and contains 50 pounds of nitrogen, 30 pounds of phosphoric acid, and 20 pounds of potash, whereas each 100-pound bag of type B fertilizer costs $30 and contains 10 pounds of nitrogen, 30 pounds of phosphoric acid, and 60 pounds of potash. The farmer requires at least 1000 pounds of nitrogen, 1800 pounds of phosphoric acid, and 2800 pounds of potash. He wishes to get these nutrients at a minimum cost. Write a system of inequalities that expresses this information, determine the objective function, and write all this as a linear programming problem.

Solution   Begin by defining the variables. Let
   $x =$ the number of bags of type A fertilizer purchased
   $y =$ the number of bags of type B fertilizer purchased
We organize the information in the table below.

	Pounds per Bag		
	Type A	Type B	Pounds Needed
Nitrogen	50	10	1000
Phosphoric acid	30	30	1800
Potash	20	60	2800
Cost	$20	$30	

There are x bags of type A each containing 50 pounds of nitrogen and y bags of type B each containing 10 pounds of nitrogen for a total of $50x + 10y$ pounds of nitrogen. Since this must be at least 1000 pounds, we have $50x + 10y \geq 1000$. In a similar fashion we obtain the other two constraints together with the nonnegative constraints and have the following system of linear inequalities:

$$50x + 10y \geq 1000 \quad \text{pounds of nitrogen constraint}$$
$$30x + 30y \geq 1800 \quad \text{pounds of phosphoric acid constraint}$$
$$20x + 60y \geq 2800 \quad \text{pounds of potash constraint}$$
$$x, y \geq \quad 0 \quad \text{nonnegativity constraint}$$

The cost function, $C = 20x + 30y$, is to be minimized. Our linear programming problem is then

$$\text{Minimize} \quad C = 20x + 30y \quad \text{objective function}$$
$$\text{Subject to} \quad 50x + 10y \geq 1000 \quad \text{pounds of nitrogen}$$
$$30x + 30y \geq 1800 \quad \text{pounds of phosphoric acid}$$
$$20x + 60y \geq 2800 \quad \text{pounds of potash}$$
$$x, y \geq 0 \quad \text{nonnegativity} \qquad \blacklozenge$$

CONNECTION
Kellogg Company Optimizes Production, Inventory, and Distribution

The Kellogg Company has been using a large-scale linear program for more than a decade to guide its weekly operational, production, inventory, and distribution decisions for breakfast cereal and other foods. Using this linear program has resulted in savings of about $40 million per year.
Source: Brown, Keegan, Vigus, and Wood 2001

EXAMPLE 4 **Allocation of Funds** An individual wishes to distribute at most $100,000 among a money market mutual fund, 30-year U.S. Treasury bonds, and a stock index fund that mimics the Standard and Poor's 500. This individual is conservative and so she wants at all times at least 30% of her investment in treasury bonds and the amount of money in stocks less than or equal to the total in the money market and in treasury bonds. On the other hand, some exposure to equities is desired and at least 20% of the total invested should be in stocks. Based on historical data, this individual assumes the money market, bonds, and stocks will earn returns of 6%, 8%, and 10%, respectively. How should this person allocate the funds among these three investments to maximize the return? Write down the linear programming problem associated with this question.

Solution Begin by defining the variables. Let
$x =$ the amount in thousands of dollars invested in the money market
$y =$ the amount in thousands of dollars invested in bonds
$z =$ the amount in thousands of dollars invested in stocks
Since the total must be at most $100,000, $x + y + z \leq 100$. At least 30% must be in bonds and so we have $y \geq 0.30(x + y + z)$ and since at least 20% must be in

stocks, $z \geq 0.20(x + y + z)$. We also have the amount in stocks less than or equal to the totals in the money market and bonds. Thus, $z \leq x + y$. We then have the following system of inequalities or constraints.

$$
\begin{aligned}
x + y + z &\leq 100 && \text{total money in thousands of dollars} \\
z &\leq x + y && \text{ratio of money market and bonds to stocks} \\
y &\geq 0.3(x + y + z) && \text{minimum invested in bonds} \\
z &\geq 0.2(x + y + z) && \text{minimum invested in stocks} \\
x, y, z &\geq 0 && \text{nonnegativity constraint}
\end{aligned}
$$

We always prefer to have all variables on the left of the inequalities. The first inequality is already in that form. The second inequality is rewritten as

$$
\begin{aligned}
z &\leq x + y && \text{subtract } x \text{ and } y \text{ from both sides} \\
-x - y + z &\leq 0
\end{aligned}
$$

The third inequality as

$$
\begin{aligned}
y &\geq 0.3(x + y + z) && \text{multiply out and rearrange} \\
0.3x + 0.3y + 0.3z &\leq y && \text{subtract } y \text{ from both sides} \\
0.3x - 0.7y + 0.3z &\leq 0
\end{aligned}
$$

The fourth inequality as

$$
\begin{aligned}
z &\geq 0.2(x + y + z) && \text{multiply out and rearrange} \\
0.2x + 0.2y - 0.8z &\leq 0
\end{aligned}
$$

The objective function is the return in dollars, $R = 60x + 80y + 100z$, since we defined our variables in thousands of dollars. The linear programming problem is then

$$
\begin{aligned}
\text{Maximize} \quad R &= 60x + 80y + 100z && \text{objective function} \\
\text{Subject to} \quad x + y + z &\leq 100 && \text{available funds} \\
-x - y + z &\leq 0 && \text{ratio} \\
0.3x - 0.7y + 0.3z &\leq 0 && \text{minimum invested in bonds} \\
0.2x + 0.2y - 0.8z &\leq 0 && \text{minimum invested in stocks} \\
x, y, z &\geq 0 && \text{nonnegativity}
\end{aligned}
$$
◆

CONNECTION
Optimization-Based Planning System for UPS

UPS is the world's largest package delivery company, serving over 200 countries and territories, including every address in the United States. To provide overnight service, UPS relies on the efficient design and operation of its domestic hub-and-spoke air network, with seven hubs located throughout the continental United States. Nearly 100 additional airports serve as originating and terminating locations for packages, and more than 160 jet aircraft move nearly one million packages each night.

Through a joint research and development effort, the United Parcel Service and the Massachusetts Institute of Technology have produced a new linear programming–based planning system for designing the UPS aircraft network. The system enables UPS planners to rapidly determine aircraft routes, fleet assignments, and package flows for its time-critical overnight delivery network. The system has yielded significant cost savings, and internal studies indicate future savings in the millions of dollars.

Source: Keefer 2001

EXAMPLE 5 **Transportation of Flat Screen Monitors** A firm has two stockpiles of large flat screen monitors in warehouses at two different locations, Denver (D) and Santa Fe (SF). The monitors must be shipped to two plants, located in Des Moines (DM) and Fort Wayne (FW), for assembly into home entertainment centers. At the beginning of a week the stockpile at Denver has 150 flat screens and the stockpile at Santa Fe has 180. The Des Moines plant needs at least 100 flat screens, and the Fort Wayne plant needs at least 120 that week.

The cost of sending each screen from the stockpile at Denver to the plants in Des Moines and Fort Wayne is, respectively, $20 and $30, while the cost of sending each item from the stockpile at Santa Fe to the plants in Des Moines and Fort Wayne is, respectively, $30 and $50. Find the number of screens that should be shipped from each stockpile to each plant in order to minimize cost. Determine the associated linear programming problem. Refer to Figure 3.1.

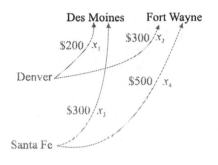

Figure 3.1

Solution   Begin by defining the variables. Let

x_1 = the number of screens shipped from Denver to Des Moines
x_2 = the number of screens shipped from Denver to Fort Wayne
x_3 = the number of screens shipped from Santa Fe to Des Moines
x_4 = the number of screens shipped from Santa Fe to Fort Wayne

	Des Moines Plant	Fort Wayne Plant	Supply
Stockpile at Denver	$20	$30	150
Stockpile at Santa Fe	$30	$50	180
Demand	100	120	

Since the stockpile at Denver has 150 screens and the total number of screens they ship is $x_1 + x_2$, we then have the constraint $x_1 + x_2 \leq 150$. Since the stockpile at Santa Fe has 180 screens and the total they ship is $x_3 + x_4$, we then have the constraint $x_3 + x_4 \leq 180$. The Des Moines plant is demanding at least 100 screens with x_1 coming from the stockpile at Denver and x_3 coming from the stockpile at Santa Fe. Thus, $x_1 + x_3 \geq 100$. We also see that the Fort Wayne plant is demanding at least 120 screens with x_2 coming from the stockpile at Denver and x_4 coming from the stockpile at Santa Fe. Thus, $x_2 + x_4 \geq 120$. We then have the following system of inequalities:

$$x_1 + x_2 \leq 150 \quad \text{screens available at Denver stockpile}$$
$$x_3 + x_4 \leq 180 \quad \text{screens available at Santa Fe stockpile}$$
$$x_1 + x_3 \geq 100 \quad \text{screens needed at Des Moines plant}$$
$$x_2 + x_4 \geq 120 \quad \text{screens needed at Fort Wayne plant}$$
$$x_1, x_2, x_3, x_4 \geq 0 \quad \text{nonnegativity constraint}$$

The cost, according to the table, is $C = 20x_1 + 30x_2 + 30x_3 + 50x_4$. The linear programming problem can now be stated as follows.

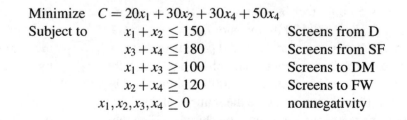

Self-Help Exercises 3.1

1. Two types of metal connectors require for their manufacture spending a certain number of minutes on a stamping machine and also a grinding machine. A DVI connector requires 4 minutes on the stamping machine and 3 minutes on the grinding machine, while an HDMI connector requires 5 minutes on the stamping machine and 1 minute on the grinding machine. The stamping machine is available at most 50 minutes each hour, and the grinding machine is available at most 21 minutes each hour. Furthermore, each hour a total of at least two of the connectors must be produced. If each of the DVI connectors brings a profit of $.50 and each of the HDMI connectors a profit of $.60, find the number of each of these products that should be manufactured to maximize profits. Determine the associated linear programming problem.

2. A dietitian has three foods, baby carrots, canned (in water) tuna, and orange juice, to use to prepare a meal for a patient. The table indicates the minimum required amounts of three important nutrients. Formulate a linear programming problem that will determine the number of ounces of each of the foods to use in order to minimize the cost.

| | Units per Ounce | | | |
	Carrots	Tuna	OJ	Constraints
Vit. C	2 mg	0 mg	13 mg	at least 120 mg
Vit. E	0 mcg	90 mcg	0 mcg	at least 500 mcg
Vit. A	3900 IU	16 IU	45 IU	at most 25,000 IU
Calories	10	33	14	at most 500
Cost/oz.	$.30	$.70	$.20	

3.1 Exercises

In the following exercises formulate a linear programming problem that can be used to solve the question. Many of these questions will be graphed in Section 3.2 and solved in Section 3.3.

1. Shipping Tractors Kubota Corporation supplies its tractor CA35 to distributors located in St. Louis and Minneapolis. The St. Louis distributor needs at least 100 of the CA35 tractors next month, while the Minneapolis distributor needs at least 50. At most 200 of the CA35 tractors can be manufactured and delivered to the distributors. If it costs $30 to ship each tractor to the St. Louis distributor and $40 to the Minneapolis distributor, find the number to be shipped to each distributor which minimizes cost.

2. Transporting Cargo A plane delivers cargo in two types of crates between two destinations. The light crate is 5 cubic feet in volume and 100 pounds in weight, and earns $20 in revenue. Each heavy crate is 5 cubic feet in volume and 200 pounds in weight, and earns $30 in revenue. The plane has available at most 400 cubic feet and 10,000 pounds for the crates. Finally, at least twice the number of the light crates as the heavy ones must be shipped. Find the number of crates of each type of cargo to ship in order to maximize revenue.

3. Manufacturing Pen Tips Old-fashioned pen tips require for their manufacture time on a stamping machine, a grinding machine, and a polishing machine. The plain tips require 1 minute on the stamping machine, 2 minutes on the grinding machine, and 2 minutes on the polishing machine. The fancy tips require 2 minutes on the stamping machine, 2 minutes on the grinding machine, and 1 minute on the polishing machine. The stamping machine can operate a maximum of 20 minutes, the grinding machine a maximum of 22 minutes, and the polishing machine a maximum of 15 minutes each hour. The profit on each of the plain tips is $4 and the profit on each of the fancy tips is $5. How many of each type of tip should be made to maximize profits?

4. Diet Planning An individual needs a daily supplement of at least 500 units of vitamin C and 200 units of vitamin E and agrees to obtain this supplement by eating two foods, I and II. Each ounce of food I contains 40 units of vitamin C and 10 units of vitamin E, while each ounce of food II contains 20 units of vitamin C and also 20 units of vitamin E.

The total supplement of these two foods must be at most 30 ounces. Unfortunately, food I contains 30 units of cholesterol per ounce, and food II contains 20 units of cholesterol per ounce. Find the appropriate amounts of the two food supplements so that cholesterol is minimized.

5. **Manufacturing Furniture** A firm manufactures tables and desks. To produce each table requires 1 hour of labor, 10 square feet of wood, and 2 quarts of finish. To produce each desk requires 3 hours of labor, 20 square feet of wood, and 1 quart of finish. Available are at most 45 hours of labor, at most 350 square feet of wood, and at most 55 quarts of finish. The tables and desks yield profits of $4 and $3 respectively. Find the number of each product to be made in order to maximize profits.

6. **Mixed Nuts** A dealer has 7600 pounds of peanuts, 5800 pounds of almonds, and 3000 pounds of cashews to be used to make two mixtures. The first mixture wholesales for $2 per pound and consists of 60% peanuts, 30% almonds, and 10% cashews. The second mixture wholesales for $3 per pound and consists of 20% peanuts, 50% almonds, and 30% cashews. How many pounds of each mixture should the dealer make in order to maximize revenue?

7. **Fish Food** A certain lake has smallmouth and largemouth bass and also three types of food for these fish: minnows, insects, and worms. Each month the lake can supply 800 pounds of minnows, 500 pounds of insects, and 700 pounds of worms. Each month each smallmouth bass requires 1 pound of minnows, 1 pound of insects, and 2 pounds of worms, and each largemouth bass requires 4 pounds of minnows, 2 pounds of insects, and 1 pound of worms. What is the maximum number of these fish that the lake can support?

8. **Scheduling Hot Tubs** A firm has plants in Boston and Baltimore that manufacture three models of hot tubs: regular, fancy, and super. In one day the Boston plant can manufacture 30 of the regular model, 30 of the fancy model, and 10 of the super model, and costs $3000 a day to operate, whereas the Baltimore plant can manufacture 10 of the regular model, 20 of the fancy model, and 30 of the super model, and costs $4000 a day to operate. At least 240 of the regular model, 390 of the fancy model, and 410 of the super model are needed. How many days must each plant operate in order to minimize cost?

9. **Planting Corn** Farmer Blue has 100 acres available to plant white and yellow corn. Each acre of white corn will yield 95 bushels of corn and each acre of yellow corn will yield 120 bushels of corn. He wants to have at least three times as many bushels of white corn as he does of yellow corn. The white corn will sell for $4.00 per bushel and the yellow corn will sell for $3.50 per bushel. How many acres of each type of corn should Farmer Blue plant to maximize his revenue?

10. **Planting Carrots** Farmer Green has 10 acres available to plant maroon and orange carrots. Each acre of maroon carrots will yield 2 tons of carrots and each acre of orange carrots will yield 4 tons of carrots. He wants to have at least three times as many tons of maroon carrots as he does of orange carrots. The profit for maroon carrots is $200 per ton and the profit for orange carrots is $100 per ton. How many acres of each type of carrots should Farmer Green plant to maximize his profit?

11. **Baking Cookies** A baker has 50 pounds of oatmeal to make oatmeal cookies and oatmeal bars. Oatmeal cookies sell for $1.00 each and oatmeal bars sell for $1.50 each. A batch of 36 oatmeal cookies requires 2 pounds of oatmeal and a batch of 24 oatmeal bars requires 1.5 pounds of oatmeal. Additionally she wants to have twice as many cookies as bars. How many of each item should she make to maximize revenue?

12. **Fried Treats** A baker has 23 pounds of sugar to make donuts and fritters. Donuts sell for $.50 each and fritters sell for $1.50 each. A batch of 24 donuts requires 1.5 pounds of sugar and a batch of 15 fritters requires 2 pounds of sugar. The baker wants to have four times as many donuts as fritters. How many of each item should the baker make to maximize revenue?

13. **Investments** An individual has at most $100,000 to invest in four funds: a money market fund, a bond fund, a conservative stock fund, and a speculative stock fund. These four investments are assumed to have annual returns of 6%, 8%, 10%, and 13%, respectively. The investor wants at least $10,000 in the conservative stock fund, at least $10,000 and at most $40,000 in the money market fund, the amount in speculative stocks less than or equal to the amount in the money market, and finally the amount in conservative stocks less or equal to the amount in bonds. Find the appropriate allocations

of funds among these four investments to maximize the return.

14. **Investments** Redo Example 4 of the text if the investor wants at least 40% invested in stocks with everything else remaining the same.

15. **Transportation** Redo Example 5 of the text using the following table:

	DM Plant	FW Plant	Supply
Denver Stockpile	$20	$40	500
SF Stockpile	$50	$20	100
Demand	150	250	

16. **Transportation** A firm has warehouses with bookshelf speakers in Long Island (LI) and in Miami (M). These speakers need to be shipped in various quantities to plants in Austin, Phoenix, and Boston. The following table gives the transportation cost of sending each speaker from the two warehouses to the three plants (in dollars), the number of speakers in each warehouse, and the demanded number of speakers for each of the plants.

	Austin Plant	Phoenix Plant	Boston Plant	Supply
LI Warehouse	$2	$1	$3	600
M Warehouse	$1	$3	$2	650
Demand	150	300	350	

Find the number of items to be shipped from each of the warehouses to each of the plants in order to minimize transportation cost.

17. **Diet** Three foods, A, B, and C, are being used by a dietitian at a hospital to obtain certain minimum supplements of three vitamins, I, II, and III. The following table gives the number of units of each vitamin in each ounce of each food, the daily minimum requirement of each vitamin, and the cost in dollars per ounce of each of the foods.

	Food A	Food B	Food C	Required
Vitamin I	30	30	10	500
Vitamin II	20	20	10	329
Vitamin III	35	50	20	425
Cost/oz	$4	$3	$1	

At most 20 ounces of the three foods are to be given. How many of each of the foods should be given if the cost is to be minimized?

18. **Investments** Suppose for an investment no more than $10,000 is placed in three mutual funds with annual returns of 8%, 9%, and 10%, respectively.

The investor requires an annual return of at least $900 on the investment and wishes to minimize the risk. The second mutual fund is twice as risky as the first, and the third is 4 times as risky as the first. How should the money be allocated to minimize the risk? Let risk $= x_1 + 2x_2 + 4x_3$.

19. **Plant Nutrition** A farmer can buy three types of 100-pound bags of fertilizer, type A, type B, and type C. Each 100-pound bag of type A fertilizer costs $20 and contains 40 pounds of nitrogen, 30 pounds of phosphoric acid, and 10 pounds of potash. Each 100-pound bag of type B fertilizer costs $30 and contains 20 pounds of nitrogen, 20 pounds of phosphoric acid, and 60 pounds of potash. Each 100-pound bag of type C fertilizer costs $20 and contains no nitrogen, 30 pounds of phosphoric acid, and 40 pounds of potash. The farmer requires 4400 pounds of nitrogen, 1800 pounds of phosphoric acid, and 2800 pounds of potash. How many bags of each type of fertilizer should she buy in order to minimize cost?

20. **Tour Cost** An airline has three types of airplanes and has contracted with a tour group to provide accommodations for a minimum of 80 first-class, 50 tourist, and 60 economy-class passengers. The first plane costs $4000 for the trip and can accommodate 40 first-class, 10 tourist, and 10 economy-class passengers; the second plane costs $5000 for the trip and can accommodate 10 first-class, 10 tourist, and 20 economy-class passengers; the third plane costs $6000 for the trip and can accommodate 10 first-class, 12 tourist, and 24 economy-class passengers. How many of each type of airplane should be used to minimize the operating cost?

21. **Oil Costs** An oil company has three refineries and must refine and deliver at least 40,000 gallons of medium-grade gasoline and 24,000 gallons of high-grade gasoline to its stations. The first plant can refine 8000 gallons of medium-grade gasoline and 3000 gallons of high-grade gasoline and costs $40,000 a day to operate. The second plant can refine 4000 gallons of medium-grade gasoline and 6000 gallons of high-grade gasoline and costs $30,000 a day to operate. The third plant can refine 4500 gallons of medium-grade gasoline and 6500 gallons of high-grade gasoline and costs $45,000 a day to operate. How many days should each plant operate to minimize the cost?

22. **Production Scheduling** A company has three plants that produce three different sizes of their product. The North plant can produce 2000 items in the small size, 1000 in the medium size, and 1000 in the large size. The Center plant can produce 1000 items in the small size, 1000 in the medium size, and 2000 in the large size. The South plant can produce 2000 items in the small size, 2000 in the medium size, and 1000 in the large size. The company needs to produce at least 9000 of the small items, 8000 of the medium items, and 9000 of the large items on a given day. The cost of producing the small item is $2, the medium item $3, and the large item $2. Find the number of items each plant should produce in order to minimize the cost.

23. **Mine Production** A mining company has three mines that produce three grades of ore. The North mine can produce 2 tons of low-grade ore, 1 ton of medium-grade ore, and 1 ton of high-grade ore each day. The Center mine can produce 1 ton of low-grade ore, 1 ton of medium-grade ore, and 4 tons of high-grade ore each day. The South mine can produce 1 ton of low-grade ore, 3 tons of medium-grade ore, and 3 tons of high-grade ore each day. At a particular time the company needs at least 21 tons of low-grade ore, 19 tons of medium-grade ore, and at least 25 tons of high-grade ore. It costs $2000 per day to operate the North mine for a day, $3000 per day for the Center mine, and $4000 for the Center mine. Find the number of days each mine should be operated to minimize cost.

24. **Ordering Plants** A store decides to have a sale on pink and red azaleas. Two nurseries, East and West, will supply these plants. East nursery charges $4 for a pink azalea and $6 for a red one. West nursery charges $7 for a pink azalea and $5 for a red one. East nursery can supply at most 200 azaleas of either color, while West nursery can supply at most 400 of these azaleas. The store needs at least 250 pink azaleas and at least 300 red azaleas. How many azaleas of each color should the store order from each nursery in order to minimize the cost?

25. **School Rezoning** A small city has two high schools, NW school and NE school, located in predominantly white districts and two high schools, SW school and SE school, located in two predominantly minority districts. A decision is made to bus at least 400 minority students from SW and at least 300 minority students from SE to the two high schools in the predominantly white districts. NW can accommodate at most an additional 200 students and NE at most 600. The weekly cost per student of busing from SW to NW is $4, from SE to NW $2, from SW to NE $2, and from SE to NE $4. Determine the numbers of students that should be bused from each of the schools in the southern districts to each of the schools in the northern districts in order to minimize the cost.

Source: Hickman 1970

26. **Farming** A farmer has two fields in which he grows wheat and corn. Because of different conditions, there are differences in the yield of growing these crops in these two fields. The yields and cost are shown in the table. Each field has 100 acres available for cultivation; 15,000 bushels of wheat and 9000 bushels of corn are to be grown. Determine a planting plan that will minimize the cost.

	Field 1	Field 2
Corn yield/acre	150 bushels	200 bushels
Cost/acre of corn	$180	$210
Wheat yield/acre	40 bushels	50 bushels
Cost/acre of wheat	$140	$120

27. **Diet Planning** A dietitian has four foods, A, B, C, and D, to use to prepare a meal. The table indicates the constraints and the costs. If the total number of ounces must be at most 18, determine the number of ounces of each of the foods to use in order to minimize the cost.

| | Units per Ounce | | | | Constraints in Units |
	A	B	C	D	
Iron	1	2	0	0	at least 10
Calcium	100	50	0	10	at least 800
Vitamin C	100	0	200	20	at least 500
Vitamin E	0	0	50	70	at least 200
Vitamin A	0	2000	0	5000	at most 25,000
Calories	200	150	75	250	at most 3000
Cholesterol	5	20	30	70	at most 130
Cost/ounce	$.50	$.40	$.60	$.75	

28. **Diet Planning** Redo the exercise above if the cholesterol is to be minimized and the cost is to be at most $10.

Extensions

29. **Candy Mixtures** A shop is going to produce two types of candy, both of which consist solely of sugar, nuts, and chocolate. In stock are 200 ounces

of sugar, 30 ounces of nuts, and 60 ounces of chocolate. The mixture used to make the first candy must contain at least 25% nuts. The mixture used to make the second candy must contain at least 15% nuts and at least 10% chocolate. Each ounce of the first candy can be sold for 50 cents, and each ounce of the second candy for 65 cents. Determine the ounces of each ingredient necessary to make each candy in order to maximize revenue.

30. **Oil Refinery** An oil refinery blends three types of crude oil, crude A, crude B, and crude C, to make regular, premium, and super gasoline. Crude A has an octane rating of 90, costs $20 a barrel, and 50,000 barrels are on hand. Crude B has an octane rating of 96, costs $24 a barrel, and 30,000 barrels are on hand. Crude C has an octane rating of 98, costs $26 a barrel, and 20,000 barrels are on hand. The octane rating for regular gasoline must be at least 92, for premium at least 96, and for super at least 97. Regular gasoline sells for $26 a barrel, premium for $30, and super for $32. If the refinery has an order for 30,000 barrels of regular gasoline, 20,000 barrels of premium, and 28,000 barrels of super, how much of each type of crude should be used in each type of gasoline to maximize the profit?

31. **Work Schedule** A chemical plant must operate every day of the week and requires different numbers of employees on different days of the week. Each employee must work five consecutive days and then receive two days off. For example, an employee who works Tuesday to Saturday must be off on Sunday and Monday. The table indicates the required number of employees on each day. What are the minimum number of employees that must be used?

Day	Employees Required
Monday	82
Tuesday	87
Wednesday	77
Thursday	73
Friday	75
Saturday	42
Sunday	23

32. **Land Allocation** A corporation owns three farms. The following table gives the size, usable land, and water allocation (in acre-feet) for each:

Farm	Usable Land	Water Allocation
1	1200	18,000
2	1500	2000
3	1000	1300

The farms can grow corn, wheat, or sorghum. The following table gives the maximum area (in acres) that can be planted with each crop, water used (in acre-feet/acre), and net return (in dollars/acre):

Crop	Maximum Area	Water Used	Net Return
Corn	1400	3	500
Wheat	1500	2	400
Sorghum	1700	1	100

How many acres of each crop should be planted on each farm to maximize net return.

33. **Investment Planning** Mazie has at most $12,000 to invest in three different stocks. The KO company costs $42.00 per share and pays dividends of $1.25 per share. The INTC company costs $21.00 per share and pays dividends of $.40 per share. The MCD company costs $35.00 per share and pays $.67 per share in dividends. Mazie has given her broker the following instructions: Invest at least twice as much money in INTC as in KO. Also, no more than 25% of the total invested should be in MCD. How should Mazie invest her money to maximize the dividends?

34. **Investment Planning** Pyxie has at most $20,000 to invest in three different stocks. The TWX company costs $17.00 per share and pays dividends of $.20 per share. The GE company costs $34.00 per share and pays dividends of $1.00 per share. The WMT company costs $45.00 per share and pays $.67 per share in dividends. Pyxie has given her broker the following instructions: Invest at least twice as much money in GE as in WMT. Also, no more than 25% of the total money invested should be in TWX. How should Pyxie invest her money to maximize the dividends?

Solutions to Self-Help Exercises 3.1

1. Begin by defining the variables. Let

x = the number of DVI connectors manufactured each hour

y = the number of HDMI connectors manufactured each hour.

Then most of the information can be summarized in the following table:

	DVI Connector	HDMI Connector	Minutes Available
Stamping Machine	4	5	50
Grinding Machine	3	1	21
Profit	$.50	$.60	

Each of the DVI connectors requires 4 minutes on the stamping machine, and each of the HDMI connectors requires 5 minutes on this machine. Thus, the stamping machine will be occupied $4x$ minutes with the DVI connectors and $5y$ minutes with the HDMI connectors, for a total $4x + 5y$ minutes. Since this must be at most 50, we have the constraint $4x + 5y \leq 50$.

Each of the DVI connectors requires 3 minutes on the grinding machine, and each of the HDMI connectors requires 1 minute on this machine. Thus, the grinding machine will be occupied $3x + y$ minutes and the constraint will be $3x + y \leq 21$. Since at least two connectors must be produced, we have $x + y \geq 2$. Naturally, we must have the nonnegativity constraint. Therefore we have four inequalities,

$$4x + 5y \leq 50 \quad \text{stamping machine minutes}$$
$$3x + y \leq 21 \quad \text{grinding machine minutes}$$
$$x + y \geq 2 \quad \text{minimum production}$$
$$x, y \geq 0 \quad \text{nonnegativity}$$

The profit is $P = 0.50x + 0.60y$. We then have the following linear programming problem:

$$\text{Maximize} \quad P = 0.50x + 0.60y \quad \text{objective function}$$
$$\text{Subject to} \quad 4x + 5y \leq 50 \quad \quad \text{stamping machine minutes}$$
$$3x + y \leq 21 \quad \quad \text{grinding machine minutes}$$
$$x + y \geq 2 \quad \quad \text{minimum production}$$
$$x, y \geq 0 \quad \quad \text{nonnegativity}$$

2. Let x_1, x_2, and x_3 be the respective number of ounces of carrots, tuna, and orange juice. Then

$$\text{Maximize} \quad P = 0.30x + 0.70y + 0.20z \quad \text{objective function}$$
$$\text{Subject to} \quad 2x_1 + 13x_3 \geq 120 \quad \text{mg vitamin C}$$
$$90x_2 \geq 500 \quad \text{mcg vitamin E}$$
$$3900x_1 + 16x_2 + 45x_3 \leq 25,000 \quad \text{IU vitamin A}$$
$$10x_1 + 33x_2 + 14x_3 \leq 500 \quad \text{calories}$$
$$x_1, x_2, x_3 \geq 0 \quad \text{nonnegativity}$$

3.2 Graphing Linear Inequalities

APPLICATION
Park Benches

A shop manufactures two styles of aluminum park benches, fancy and plain. The fancy style requires 4 kilograms of aluminum and 6 hours of labor, while the plain style requires 4 kilograms of aluminum and 3 hours of labor. If there are 32 kilograms of aluminum and 36 hours of labor available for the day, write a system of inequalities that expresses this information and find the feasible region. List four possible ways that these benches can be made. See Example 4 for the answer.

In the last section we introduced linear programming. We saw that every linear programming problem has a system of linear inequalities associated with it. In this section we will learn how to graph a system of linear inequalities. The graph of the system of linear inequalities is the feasible region or solution to the system. The feasible region is needed to find the solution to the linear programming problem. In the next section we will develop the geometric method to solve linear programming problems in two dimensions by graphing the system of linear inequalities.

✦ Graphing One Linear Inequality

We know that if a and b are not both zero, then the graph of the linear equation

$$ax + by = c$$

is a straight line in the xy-plane. We are now interested in the graph of linear inequalities such as

$$ax + by < c, \quad ax + by \leq c, \quad ax + by > c, \quad ax + by \geq c$$

As we found in the previous section, these are the forms of constraints in application problems.

EXAMPLE 1 **Graphing Linear Inequalities** Graph

a. $x + y = 4$ **b.** $x + y > 4$ **c.** $x + y \leq 4$

Solution

a. This can be written as $y = -x + 4$. The graph is in Figure 3.2 as the line L.

b. Rewrite $x + y > 4$ as $y > -x + 4$. Now consider the point $(1, 3)$ that lies on the straight line $y = -x + 4$ as shown in Figure 3.3a. Next, take a point directly above $(1, 3)$ which is $(1, y)$ with $y > 3$. The inequality $x + y > 4$ will be true at this point $(1, y)$ as x is equal to 1 and y is greater than 3.

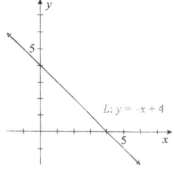

Figure 3.2

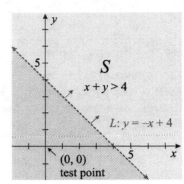

Figure 3.3a   **Figure 3.3b**

In general, we can pick any value for x on the line $y = -x + 4$ and find that if we choose values for y that lie above the line that the inequality $x + y > 4$ will be true. We can then conclude that the graph of $y > -x + 4$ or $x + y > 4$ is the half-plane above the line L. See Figure 3.3b where arrows have been drawn to indicate that the solution to the inequality lies above the line L. The letter S is written in the half-plane that is the solution of the inequality. Note that the line L has been drawn using a dotted line to indicate that the line is not on part of the solution when the inequality is strict.

c. Rewrite $x + y \leq 4$ as $y \leq -x + 4$ and consider the point $(1, y)$ with $y < 3$. As Figure 3.4a indicates, the point $(1, y)$ must lie below the line. We conclude that the graph of $x + y \leq 4$ is the half-plane below the line L along with the line L as $\leq$ includes equality. See Figure 3.4b. Note the line is solid to indicate it is part of the solution.

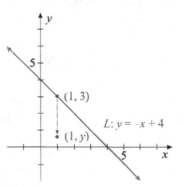

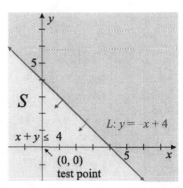

Figure 3.4a   **Figure 3.4b**   ◆

There is a simpler way to graph linear inequalities. For example, since we know that the graph of $x + y < 4$ must be a half-plane, we only need to decide which half-plane. A practical way of deciding is to choose a convenient test point (x_0, y_0) which is not on the line and test to see if this point satisfies the inequality. If it does, then the half-plane containing this point must be the solution. If the test point does not satisfy the inequality, then the half-plane containing this point is not the region being sought. Thus, the solution being sought is the other half-plane. Always pick the point $(0, 0)$ as a test point, if possible, since this is the easiest point to evaluate.

For example, in order to decide in which half-plane the graph of $x + y \leq 4$

Technology Option

See Technology Note 1 for instructions on graphing an inequality on a graphing calculator.

lies, pick $(0,0)$ as a test point. Since

$$0+0 = 0 \leq 4$$

the point $(0,0)$ satisfies the inequality, and thus the solution of the inequality is the half-plane containing $(0,0)$. As Figure 3.4b indicates, $(0,0)$ is below the line L, and thus the solution is the half-plane below the line L along with the line L.

In order to decide in which half-plane the solution of $x+y > 4$ lies, pick $(0,0)$ as a test point. Since

$$0+0 = 0 \not< 4$$

we find that $(0,0)$ does not satisfy the inequality, the solution of the inequality is the half-plane not containing $(0,0)$. Since $(0,0)$ is below the line L, the graph is the half-plane above the line L. See Figure 3.3b.

EXAMPLE 2   Graphing a Constraint   Graph $4x + 2y \leq 84$, which is the assembly constraint given Example 2 in Section 3.1, the wood boat example.

Solution   We first graph $4x + 2y = 84$. This graph is the line L shown in Figure 3.5. The graph of the linear inequality $4x + 2y \leq 84$ is either the half-plane above and including L, or the half-plane below and including L. We select the test point $(0,0)$ and evaluate the inequality at this point and obtain

$$4(0) + 2(0) = 0 \leq 84$$

Since $(0,0)$ does satisfy the inequality and is below the line L, the graph we are seeking is the half-plane below L and including L. This is indicated in Figure 3.5 using a solid line. Not that this solution to our constraint is reasonable as there is enough wood to make no dinghies and no skiffs.   ◆

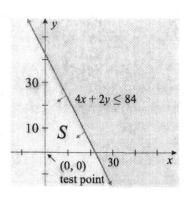

Figure 3.5

EXAMPLE 3   Graphing a Linear Inequality   Graph $x < -2$.

Solution   The boundary of the half-plane will be a dashed line at $x = -2$. The solution will be the half-plane to the left of the line $x = -2$ as this is where $x < -2$, as shown in Figure 3.6. Alternately, we can pick the test point $(0,0)$ that is to the right of the line $x = -2$ and notice that $0 \not< -2$. This implies that $(0,0)$ is not in the half-plane we are seeking. Thus, the half-plane we are seeking is to the left of $x = -2$.   ◆

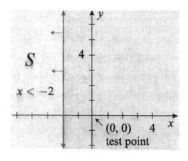

Figure 3.6

We shall now summarize how to graph linear inequalities. In the remaining graphs in this section, the arrows indicating which half-plane contains the solution will not be shown. However, the feasible region will always be labeled with an S.

> **Graphing a Linear Inequality**
> Following are the steps required to graph the linear inequality
>
> $$ax + by < c \qquad (\text{or} \leq c, \text{ or} > c, \text{ or} \geq c)$$
>
> 1. First graph the straight line L given by $ax + by = c$, using a dotted line if the inequalities "$<$" or "$>$" are given and a solid line if the inequalities "$\leq$" or "$\geq$" are given. The dotted line indicates the straight line L is not part of the solution graph, while the solid line indicates that the line L is part of the solution graph.
>
> 2. Pick any convenient test point not on line L and evaluate the inequality at that test point. If the inequality is true, then the solution graph is the half-plane on the same side of the line L as the test point. If the inequality is not satisfied, then the solution graph is the half-plane on that side of L that does not include the test point.

✧ Graphing System of Linear Inequalities

If we are given several linear inequalities, as in the park bench example in Section 3.1, then we find the solution set of each of the linear inequalities individually just as previously indicated. The solution set of the system is then the region common to all the solution sets of the individual inequalities. This common region is also called the feasible region. In other words, any point (x, y) that satisfies all of the inequalities is in the feasible region. The feasible region is the set of all such points. The first step in solving a linear programming problem by the graphical method is to determine the feasible region for the problem.

CONNECTION
Pfizer's Plan for its Operations

> To manage a large-scale distribution network effectively, Pfizer has had a well-constructed and well-maintained decision-support system since 1998. Such a system facilitates effective short-term and long-term decision making. Pfizer uses basic tools such as optimization and simulation, coupled with large-scale databases, spreadsheet tools, and linear programming. The system is designed to support activities ranging from long-term strategic network design to short-run day-to-day operations and customer service.
>
> *Source:* Gupta, Peters, and Miller 2002

EXAMPLE 4   Feasible Region for Park Benches A shop manufactures two styles of aluminum park benches, fancy and plain. The fancy style requires 4 kilograms of aluminum and 6 hours of labor, while the plain style requires 4 kilograms of aluminum and 3 hours of labor. If there are 32 kilograms of aluminum and 36 hours of labor available for the day, write a system of inequalities that expresses this information and find the feasible region. What are the corners of the feasible region? List four possible ways that these benches can be made.

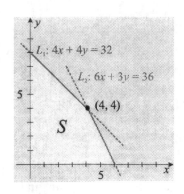

Figure 3.7

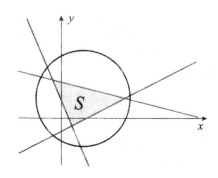

Figure 3.8

Solution   In the last section we found the following constraints:

$$4x + 4y \leq 32 \text{ kilograms of aluminum}$$
$$6x + 3y \leq 36 \text{ hours of labor}$$
$$x, y \geq 0 \text{ nonnegativity}$$

where x was the number of fancy benches and y was the number of plain benches. To determine the feasible region, first notice that since x and y are both nonnegative, the feasible region must be in the first quadrant. Now graph the line $4x + 4y = 32$, denoted by L_1, and take $(0,0)$ as a test point. Since $4(0) + 4(0) \leq 32$, the point $(0,0)$ satisfies this inequality and is below the line L_1. Therefore, the feasible region for this inequality is the half-plane below the line L_1.

Now graph the line $6x + 3y = 36$, denoted by L_2, and take $(0,0)$ as a test point. Since $6(0) + 3(0) \leq 36$, the point $(0,0)$ satisfies this inequality and is below the line L_2. Therefore, the feasible region for this inequality is the half-plane below the line L_2. The feasible region for the system of two inequalities, must then be common to the regions below both of the lines L_1 and L_2. This is shown in Figure 3.7. The corner point $(4,4)$ is determined by solving the system

$$4x + 4y = 32$$
$$6x + 3y = 36$$

Any pair of integers in the feasible region will represent a possible number of benches that can be made. The obvious possibilities are the corner points $(0,0)$, $(0,8)$, $(6,0)$, $(4,4)$. That is, you have enough aluminum and labor time to make 0 fancy and 0 plain benches or 0 fancy and 8 plain benches or 6 fancy and 0 plain benches or 4 fancy and 4 plain benches.   ◆

When solving a linear programming problem we often need to know if the feasible region is bounded. For example, the region shown in Figure 3.7 is bounded, but the region shown in Figure 3.6 is not bounded. The precise mathematical definition of a bounded feasible region is not needed for our purposes. It suffices to say that if the feasible region can be enclosed by a circle, then it is bounded. Figure 3.8 shows a typical bounded region.

Bounded Feasible Regions
A feasible region is bounded if it can be enclosed in a circle with a finite diameter.

The goal of a linear programming problem is to find the optimal values (maximum or minimum) of the objective function subject to the problem constraints, as discussed in Section 3.1. In this section we now see that those constraints will produce a feasible region and the feasible region can be graphed if the problem has only two dimensions. There will often be many possible values of x and y that will satisfy the constraints, as we noted in Example 4 for park benches. In the next section we will see how to find which of the possible x and y values will give the optimal value of the objective function.

CONNECTION
Operating Room Time at
Mount Sinai Hospital

A linear programming model allocates operating room time to the five surgical divisions at Toronto's Mount Sinai Hospital. The hospital has used this approach for several years and credits it with both administrative savings and the ability to produce quickly an equitable master surgical schedule.

Source: Blake and Donald 2002

EXAMPLE 5   Feasible Region for Making Boats   Find the feasible region for the system of inequalities that arose in the wooden boat manufacturing problem discussed on page 145 in the last section. List all the corners of this feasible region.

Solution   Recall that we have the system inequalities (constraints)

$$2x + 4y \leq 80 \;\; \text{cutting hours}$$
$$4x + 2y \leq 84 \;\; \text{assembly hours}$$
$$2x + 2y \leq 50 \;\; \text{painting hours}$$
$$x, y \geq \;\; 0 \;\; \text{nonnegativity}$$

where x is the number of dinghies and y is the number of skiffs. Since the point $(0, 0)$ satisfies each of the first three inequalities and lies below the three lines $2x + 4y = 80$, $4x + 2y = 84$, and $2x + 2y = 50$, the solution set for each of these inequalities is the half-plane below and including each of the lines $2x + 4y = 80$, $4x + 2y = 84$, and $2x + 2y = 50$. This is indicated in Figure 3.9.   The two inequalities $x \geq 0$ and $y \geq 0$ indicate that the solution set is in the first quadrant. The corner point $(10, 15)$ shown in Figure 3.9 can be found by solving the system

$$2x + 4y = 80$$
$$2x + 2y = 50$$

while the corner point $(17, 8)$ shown in Figure 3.9 can be found by solving the system

$$4x + 2y = 84$$
$$2x + 2y = 50$$

Finding the y-intercept for $2x + 4y = 80$ leads to the corner point $(0, 20)$, while finding the x-intercept $4x + 2y = 84$ leads to the corner $(21, 0)$.   ◆

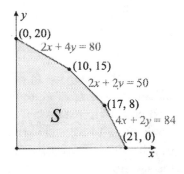

Figure 3.9

EXAMPLE 6   Feasible Region for Purchasing Fertilizer   Find the feasible region for the system of inequalities that arose in the purchasing fertilizer problem discussed on page 146 in the last section. List all the corners of this feasible region.

Solution   Recall that we have the system of inequalities (constraints)

$$50x + 10y \geq 1000 \;\; \text{pounds of nitrogen}$$
$$30x + 30y \geq 1800 \;\; \text{pounds of phosphoric acid}$$
$$20x + 60y \geq 2800 \;\; \text{pounds of potash}$$
$$x, y \geq \;\;\;\; 0 \;\; \text{nonnegativity}$$

where x is the number of bags of type A fertilizer and y is the number of type

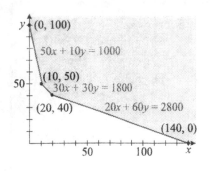

Figure 3.10

B bags. Notice that the test point $(0,0)$ does not satisfy any of the linear inequalities. Thus, the feasible region is above the lines $50x + 10y = 1000$, $30x + 30y = 1800$, and $20x + 60y = 2800$. These are then graphed in Figure 3.10. The corner point $(10, 15)$ is found by solving the system

$$50x + 10y = 1000$$
$$30x + 30y = 1800$$

while the corner point $(20, 40)$ is found by solving the system

$$30x + 30y = 1800$$
$$20x + 60y = 2800$$

The corner point $(0, 100)$ is the y-intercept of $5x + 10y = 1000$, while the corner point $(140, 0)$ is the x-intercept of $20x + 60y = 2800$. ◆

✧ Technology Corner

⑦Technology Note 1 **Graphing Inequalities on the Calculator**

Screen 1

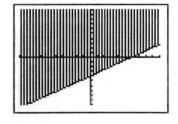

Screen 2

[-10, 10] × [-10, 10]

The calculator is able to shade above or below a line. If the true side of each of the n inequalities in a system is shaded on the calculator, the feasible region will be that part of the graph shaded n times. This can be hard to read when n is greater than 2. So, when shading on the calculator, only the FALSE side will be shaded. Then at the end of graphing the n inequalities the region left unshaded is the region true for the entire system and therefore the solution.

To plot an inequality on the calculator, start by graphing the line in a suitable window. In the Y= screen place the cursor on the line with the equation you have graphed. Then use the left arrow button to move to the left of Y$_1$. In this spot, there is an icon you can use to control the type of line and any shading. Initially, there is a regular line, \. As you hit **ENTER** successively you can set it to shade above the line (▜) or below the line (▙). Continue to hit **ENTER** to return to graphing a regular line, \.

To graph the inequality $2x - 3y \geq 12$ on the calculator, begin by writing the equation of the bounding line in slope-intercept form,

$$2x - 3y \geq 12 \rightarrow 2x - 3y = 12 \rightarrow y = (2/3)x - 4$$

Take the test point $(0, 0)$ and try it in the ORIGINAL inequality, to see if the origin is part of the solution half-plane, S, or not. We have

$$2x - 3y \rightarrow 2(0) - 3(0) \not\geq 12$$

so the inequality is FALSE at the origin. This means that all points in the upper half-plane are false. Choose the shade above option to cross out this region, as shown in Screen 1. The graph is shown in Screen 2.

⑦Technology Note 2 **Solution to Example 2**

Begin by rewriting the inequality $4x + 2y \leq 18$ as an equation in slope-intercept form. Enter this for Y$_1$

$$4x + 2y = 84 \rightarrow y = -2x + 32$$

Next the origin is tested on the original inequality, $4x + 2y \leq 84$ and find that the point $(0,0)$ is true. Therefore the lower half-plane is true, and we choose the shade above option to cross out the false upper half-plane as shown in Screen 3. The graph is shown in Screen 4.

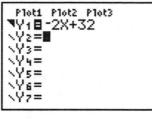

Screen 3

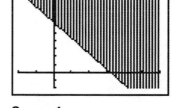

Screen 4

$[-10, \ 30] \times [-10, \ 50]$

⑨Technology Note 3 Vertical Lines on the Calculator

It is not possible to write the vertical line $x = a$ in $y =$ form. Therefore, a true vertical line cannot be graphed on the calculator[1]. However, you can draw an apparently vertical line by having a line the passes through the point $(a, 0)$ with a very steep slope. This can be done with the line $y = -10^9(x - a)$. This is a line with a large negative slope that passes through the point $(a, 0)$. In this example we want to graph the line $x = -2$ which corresponds to $Y_1 = -10^9(x + 2)$. To shade to the right of this line, use the shade above option on the calculator. See Screens 5 and 6.

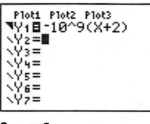

Screen 5

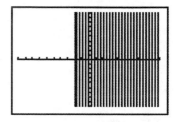

Screen 6

$[-10, \ 10] \times [-10, \ 10]$

⑨Technology Note 4 Systems of Linear Inequalities on a Graphing Calculator

Here are the steps to finding the feasible region for a system of linear inequalities on a graphing calculator:

1. Graph the first linear inequality. Note the intercepts of the bounding line since they may be a corner of the feasible region at the end of the process. Be sure to shade the false half-plane.

2. Graph the next inequality as in step 1. Continue until all inequalities have been graphed.

3. The feasible region is the area on the plane that is clear (that is, not shaded one or more times).

---

[1] A vertical line can be drawn, but it is not usable for shading or intersecting.

4. Find all corners (exact x and y coordinates) of the feasible region. Some corners may be an x- or y-intercept. Other corners will be the intersection of two of the bounding lines.

The system from Example 4 is

$$4x + 4y \leq 32 \rightarrow y = -x + 8$$
$$6x + 3y \leq 36 \rightarrow y = -2x + 12$$
$$x, y \geq 0$$

The intercepts for the first equation are (0, 8) and (8, 0). For the second equation we have (0, 12) and (6, 0). A suitable window is XMIN = 0, XMAX = 12, YMIN = 0, YMAX = 12. This will be in the first quadrant to keep the nonnegativity condition and allow the intercepts to be seen. See Screens 7 and 8.

Screen 7

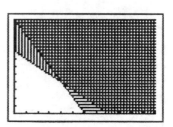

Screen 8

$[0, 12] \times [0, 12]$

To find the coordinates of the corner, either turn off the shading and use the intersection function of the calculator as shown in Screen 9 or solve using a matrix, as shown in Screen 10.

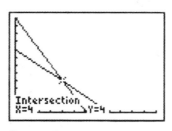

Screen 9

$[0, 12] \times [0, 12]$

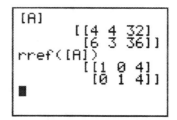

Screen 10

Self-Help Exercises 3.2

1. Graph the feasible region for the following system of inequalities and find all corner points of the feasible.

$$3x + y \geq 5$$
$$2x + 3y \geq 8$$
$$x, y \geq 0$$

2. Two types of metal connectors require for their manufacture spending a certain number of minutes on a stamping machine and also a grinding machine. A DVI connector requires 4 minutes on the stamping machine and 3 minutes on the grinding machine, while an HDMI connector requires 5 minutes on the stamping machine and 1 minute on the grinding machine. The stamping machine is available, at most,

50 minutes each hour, and the grinding machine is available, at most, 21 minutes each hour. Furthermore, each hour a total of at least two of the con-nectors must be produced. Find the feasible region and corner points for this set of constraints.

3.2 Exercises

In Exercises 1 through 24, graph the solution set.

1. $x + y < 5$

2. $2x + y < 4$

3. $x + 2y \leq 1$

3. $3x + 2y \leq 6$

5. $2x + 3y \geq 12$

6. $4x + 5y \geq 20$

7. $-2x + 3y > 5$

8. $x - 2y > 8$

9. $3x - 2y < 6$

10. $-x + 2y < 8$

11. $-6x + 2y \leq 12$

12. $6x - 3y \leq 18$

13. $2x - 3y \geq -6$

14. $2x - 3y \geq -12$

15. $x > y$

16. $2x > y + 1$

17. $y \leq 3$

18. $y > 4$

19. $x > 2$

20. $x \geq 3$

21. $y \geq -2$

22. $x < -1$

23. $x \leq 0$

24. $y < 0$

In Exercises 25 through 42, graph the feasible region and find all corner points.

25. $x + y \leq 4$
$-x + y \leq 2$

26. $x + y \geq 4$
$-x + y \geq 2$

27. $x + y < 4$
$-x + y > 2$

28. $x + y > 4$
$-x + y < 2$

29. $x + y \leq 4$
$-x + y \geq 2$
$x, y \geq 0$

30. $x + y \leq 4$
$-x + y \geq 2$

31. $x + y \leq 10$
$x \geq 2$
$y \leq 3$

32. $x + y \geq 10$
$y \leq 7$
$x \leq 8$

33. $x + y \geq 4$
$-x + y \geq 2$
$x \geq 0$

34. $x + y \leq 10$
$x + y \geq 4$
$x, y \geq 0$

35. $-x + y \leq 4$
$x + y \geq 2$
$x, y \geq 0$

36. $y \leq x$
$y \geq x - 2$
$y \leq 4$
$y \leq 0$

37. $-x + y \leq 1$
$x + y \geq 1$
$x + y \leq 4$
$y \geq 0$

38. $x + y \leq 4$
$x + y \geq 1$
$-x + y \geq -1$

39. $y \leq x$
$x + y \leq 2$

40. $x + y \leq 2$
$y \geq x$

41. $-x + y \geq 0$
$x \geq 1$
$y \leq 4$

42. $-x + y \leq 0$
$x \leq 4$
$y \geq 1$

In Exercises 43 to 48, find the system of linear inequalities that corresponds to the system shown. Find all corner points of the feasible region.

43.

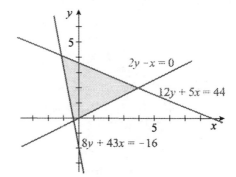

44.

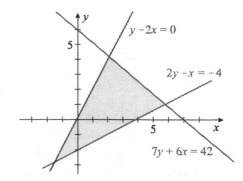

45.

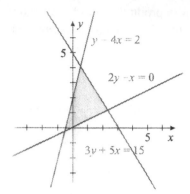

46.

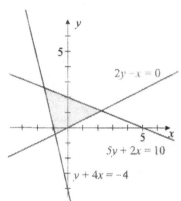

47.

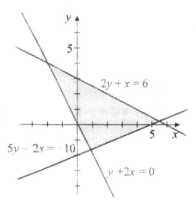

48.

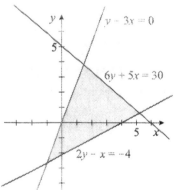

Applications

In Exercises 49 through 60, write a system of inequalities that expresses the given information and graph the feasible region. Find all corner points. Note that these correspond to Exercises 1 through 12 in Section 3.1.

49. Shipping Tractors Kubota Corporation supplies its CA35 tractor to distributors located in St. Louis and Minneapolis. The St. Louis distributor needs at least 100 of the CA35 tractors next month, while the Minneapolis distributor needs at least 50. At most 200 of the CA35 tractors can be manufactured and delivered to the distributors.

50. Transporting Crates A plane delivers cargo in two types of crates between two destinations. The light crate is 5 cubic feet in volume and 100 pounds in weight, and earns $20 in revenue. Each heavy crate is 5 cubic feet in volume and 200 pounds in weight, and earns $30 in revenue. The plane has available at most 400 cubic feet and 10,000 pounds for the crates. Finally, at least twice the number of the light crates as the heavy ones must be shipped.

51. Manufacturing Pen Tips Old-fashioned pen tips require for their manufacture time on a stamping machine, a grinding machine, and a polishing machine. The plain tip requires 1 minute on the stamping machine, 2 minutes on the grinding machine, and 2 minutes on the polishing machine. The fancy tip requires 2 minutes on the stamping machine, 2 minutes on the grinding machine, and 1 minute on the polishing machine. The stamping machine can operate a maximum of 20 minutes, the grinding machine a maximum of 22 minutes, and the polishing machine a maximum of 15 minutes each hour.

52. Diet An individual needs a daily supplement of at least 500 units of vitamin C and 200 units of vitamin E and agrees to obtain this supplement by eating two foods, I and II. Each ounce of food I contains 40 units of vitamin C and 10 units of vitamin E, while each ounce of food II contains 20 units of vitamin C and also 20 units of vitamin E. The total supplement of these two foods must be at most 30 ounces.

53. Manufacturing A firm manufactures tables and desks. To produce each table requires 1 hour of labor, 10 square feet of wood, and 2 quarts of finish. To produce each desk requires 3 hours of labor, 20 square feet of wood, and 1 quart of finish. Available is at most 45 hours of labor, at most 350 square feet of wood, and at most 55 quarts of finish.

54. Mixture A dealer has 7600 pounds of peanuts, 5800 pounds of almonds, and 3000 pounds of cashews to be used to make two mixtures. The first mixture consists of 60% peanuts, 30% almonds, and

10% cashews. The second mixture consists of 20% peanuts, 50% almonds, and 30% cashews.

55. **Fishery** A certain lake has smallmouth and largemouth bass and also three types of food for these fish: minnows, insects, and worms. Each month the lake can supply 800 pounds of minnows, 500 pounds of insects, and 700 pounds of worms. Each month each smallmouth bass requires 1 pound of minnows, 1 pound of insects, and 2 pounds of worms, and each largemouth bass requires 4 pounds of minnows, 2 pounds of insects, and 1 pound of worms.

56. **Scheduling** A firm has plants in Boston and Baltimore that manufacture three models of hot tubs: regular, fancy, and super. In one day the Boston plant can manufacture 30 of the regular model, 30 of the fancy model, and 10 of the super model. In one day the Baltimore plant can manufacture 10 of the regular model, 20 of the fancy model, and 30 of the super model. At least 240 of the regular model, 390 of the fancy model, and 410 of the super model are needed.

57. **Planting Corn** Farmer Blue has 100 acres available to plant white and yellow corn. Each acre of white corn will yield 95 bushels of corn and each acre of yellow corn will yield 120 bushels of corn. He wants to have at least three times as many bushels of white corn as he does of yellow corn.

58. **Planting Carrots** Farmer Green has 10 acres available to plant maroon and orange carrots. Each acre of maroon carrots will yield 2 tons of carrots and each acre of orange carrots will yield 4 tons of carrots. He wants to have at least three times as many tons of maroon carrots than he does of orange carrots.

59. **Baking Cookies** A baker has 50 pounds of oatmeal to make oatmeal cookies and oatmeal bars. Each batch of 36 oatmeal cookies requires 2 pounds of oatmeal. Each batch of 24 oatmeal bars requires 1.5 pounds of oatmeal. She wants at least twice as many cookies as bars.

60. **Fried Sugar** A baker has 23 pounds of sugar to make doughnuts and fritters. Each batch of 24 doughnuts requires 1.5 pounds of sugar and each batch of 15 fritters requires 2 pounds of sugar. The baker wants to have at least four times as many doughnuts as fritters.

Solutions to Self-Help Exercises 3.2

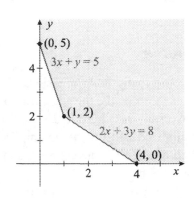

1. Since the point $(0,0)$ does not satisfy either of the first two inequalities and lies below the two lines $3x + y = 5$ and $2x + 3y = 8$, the solution set for the first two inequalities is the half-plane above and including the lines $3x + y = 5$ and $2x + 3y = 8$. This is indicated in the figure. The two inequalities $x \geq 0$ and $y \geq 0$ indicate that the solution is in the first quadrant. The feasible region is then the shaded region in the figure.

   To find the corners, note that the y-intercept of the line $3x + y = 5$ is one corner. Another corner is the x-intercept of the line $2x + 3y = 8$. The corner $(1,2)$ is found by solving the system of equations

$$
\begin{array}{c}
3x + y = 5 \\
2x + 3y = 8
\end{array}
\rightarrow
\left[\begin{array}{cc|c} 3 & 1 & 5 \\ 2 & 3 & 8 \end{array}\right]
\rightarrow
\left[\begin{array}{cc|c} 1 & 0 & 1 \\ 0 & 1 & 2 \end{array}\right]
$$

2. Recall in Self-Help Exercise 1 in the last section that we found the following system of inequalities:

$$
\begin{array}{rcl}
4x + 5y & \leq & 50 \\
3x + y & \leq & 21 \\
x + y & \geq & 2 \\
x, y & \geq & 0
\end{array}
$$

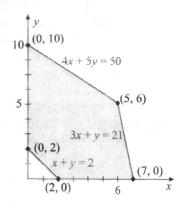

Notice that $(0,0)$ satisfies the first two inequalities and not the third and lies below each of the lines $4x + 5y = 50$, $3x + y = 21$, and $x + y = 2$. The solution set for the first two inequalities is the half-plane below and including the lines $4x + 5y = 50$ and $3x + y = 21$ and the half-plane above and including the line $x + y = 2$. This is indicated in the figure. The two inequalities $x \geq 0$ and $y \geq 0$ indicate that the solution set is in the first quadrant. The feasible region is then the shaded region in the figure.

The corners $(0,2)$ and $(2,0)$ are the x- and y-intercepts of the line $x + y = 2$. The corner $(0,10)$ is the y-intercept of the line $4x + 5y = 5$ and the corner $(7,0)$ is the x-intercept of the line $3x + y = 21$. Finally the corner $(5,6)$ is found by solving the system of equations

$$\begin{array}{rcl} 4x + 5y & = & 50 \\ 3x + y & = & 21 \end{array} \rightarrow \left[\begin{array}{cc|c} 4 & 5 & 50 \\ 3 & 1 & 21 \end{array}\right] \rightarrow \left[\begin{array}{cc|c} 1 & 0 & 5 \\ 0 & 1 & 6 \end{array}\right]$$

3.3 Graphical Solution of Linear Programming Problems

APPLICATION
Minimizing Costs

A farmer can buy two types of 100-pound bags of fertilizer, type A and type B. Each 100-pound bag of type A fertilizer costs $20 and contains 50 pounds of nitrogen, 30 pounds of phosphoric acid, and 20 pounds of potash, whereas each 100-pound bag of type B fertilizer costs $30 and contains 10 pounds of nitrogen, 30 pounds of phosphoric acid, and 60 pounds of potash. The farmer requires at least 1000 pounds of nitrogen, 1800 pounds of phosphoric acid, and 2800 pounds of potash. How many bags of each type of fertilizer should be purchased in order to minimize cost? The answer is found in Example 3.

✧ Some Linear Programming Problems

We have seen how business, economics, finance, and many other areas are replete with complex decision or allocation problems that involve the selection of specific values of many interrelated variables. We saw that there is a specific objective function that is to be maximized or minimized and we saw examples of such objectives as profit, revenue, cost, expected return on an investment, and even some measure of social welfare. The variables are normally subject to constraints that take the form of a set of inequalities that give rise to a feasible region. Maximizing or minimizing the objective function in the feasible region was called linear programming. In this section we see how to solve problems with a small number of variables using a geometric approach. In another chapter we will find an alternative method that can be used to solve the most complex linear programming problems and does not rely on the graph of the feasible region.

EXAMPLE 1   Profit and the Feasible Region for Making Boats Suppose the small, wooden-boat manufacturer of the last two sections obtained a profit of $60 for every dinghy manufactured and $80 for every skiff. How many of each type of boat should be made in order to maximize the profits?

Solution If x is the number of dinghies manufactured each week and y the number of skiffs, then the profit in dollars is $P = 60x + 80y$. Recalling the constraints that we found in Section 3.1, we have the following linear programming:

Maximize $P = 60x + 80y$ profit in dollars (the objective function)
Subject to $2x + 4y \leq 80$ cutting hours
              $4x + 2y \leq 84$ assembly hours
              $2x + 2y \leq 50$ painting hours
             $x, y \geq 0$ nonnegativity

First we need to graph the feasible region to see which values for x and y are allowed. This was done in the previous section and is shown in Figure 3.11.

Only points (x, y) in the feasible region are possible solutions. So one possible solution to the problem is to make no dinghies and eight skiffs. This is the point (0, 8) shown in Figure 3.11. The profit here is $P = 60(0) + 80(8) = 640$ or $640. At another point, say (5, 8), we will have a profit of $P = 60(5) + 80(8) = 940$ or a $940 profit. In fact, every point inside the feasible region will have enough resources to make dinghies and skiffs, but where is the profit maximized? A guess and check approach is not effective. We need to analyze the region and the profit to determine where the maximum profit occurs. To help in the analysis, the feasible region has a gradient shading in Figure 3.11. The lighter the color, the larger the profit.

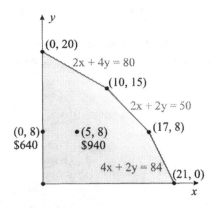

Figure 3.11

To find the place in the feasible region where P is maximized, we draw the straight lines $P = 60x + 80y = c$, called isoprofit lines, for a variety of values of c. For example, set P equal to, say 1600 (that is, show on the figure a profit of $1600). The equation $60x + 80y = 1600$ is a straight line with slope $-3/4$ and is shown in Figure 3.12. Since $P = 60x + 80y$, it is clear that we can take both x and y a little larger and still remain in the feasible region and obtain a larger profit. If we set $P = 60x + 80y = 1660$, we obtain the straight line shown in Figure 3.12. (Notice the slope is also $-3/4$.) Any point along this latter straight line gives a profit of 1660, with some points in the feasible region. But we see that we can do better. Take $P = 60x + 80y = 1800$. This line also has slope $-3/4$. Notice that this line goes through the corner A, since $A = (10, 15)$ and at this point $P = 60(10) + 80(15) = 1800$. Thus, only at the point A is the profit 1800 and also in the feasible region. If we take $P = 2000$, we see from Figure 3.12 that we obtain a straight line (parallel to the others) all of whose points are outside the feasible region. It thus appears that the profit is maximized at point A.

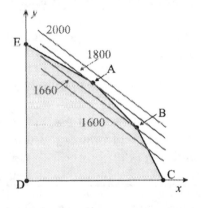

Figure 3.12

The lines for $P = 1600$, $P = 1660$, $P = 1800$, and $P = 2000$ are, as we noted, parallel. This can also be seen by setting $P = P_0$ and we find that

$$60x + 80y = P_0$$
$$y = -\frac{3}{4}x + \frac{1}{80}P_0$$

Furthermore we notice that by increasing P_0 we increase the y-intercept, and thus the line moves up (and to the right). See Figure 3.12. We then see that our strategy is to increase P_0 as much as possible while still keeping the constant profit line $P = P_0$ in contact with the feasible region. We saw that $P_0 = 1800$ meets

Technology Option

See Technology Note 1 on page 174 to see how to solve linear programming problems using a spreadsheet.

this requirement and that the point in the feasible region at which the maximum occurs is the corner point A. (As we shall see, the optimum must always occur at a corner of the feasible region.) Thus, the solution to the problem is to manufacture 10 dinghies and 15 skiffs and the weekly profit will be $1800. ✦

The problem in Example 1 has exactly one corner at which the maximum occurs. Although this is typical, the maximum can occur at more than one corner. The following is an example.

EXAMPLE 2   Problem With Multiple Solutions   Redo Example 1 if the profit is given by $P = 70x + 70y$.

Solution   The feasible region is the same as in Example 1. If we set $P = 70x + 70y = P_0$, we obtain

$$y = -x + \frac{1}{70}P_0$$

All of these lines have slope -1. Again, increasing P_0 increases the y-intercept, and thus the lines move up (and to the right), as indicated in Figure 3.13. But since the slopes of these lines are the same as the slope of the line from A to B, the maximum occurs at all points on the line segment from A to B. But again the maximum does occur at a corner, in fact, at two adjacent corners. Thus, two acceptable answers are $(10, 15)$ and $(17, 8)$, which correspond to manufacturing 10 dinghies and 15 skiffs or 17 dinghies and 8 skiffs with profits of

$$P = 70(10) + 70(15) = 1750 \quad \text{or} \quad P = 70(17) + 70(8) = 1750$$

dollars per week. Other acceptable answers are the points $(11, 14)$, $(12, 13)$, $(13, 12)$, $(14, 11)$, $(15, 10)$, and $(16, 9)$, all of which lie on the line segment between A and B and all of which have the same profit of $1750. ✦

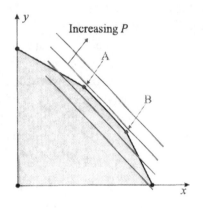

Figure 3.13

> Stillwater Mining Company needed a tool for analyzing development and production scenarios in a new area of an underground platinum and palladium mine in Stillwater, Montana. The company had a linear programming model developed that takes as input the planned mine layout, projected ore quality, and projected costs for basic mining activities, and produces as output a near-optimal schedule of activities that maximizes discounted ore revenue over a given period. The linear programming contained over 5000 constraints and over 3000 decision variables.
>
> *Source:* Carlyle and Eaves 2001

CONNECTION
Mining Activity to Optimize Production of Ore

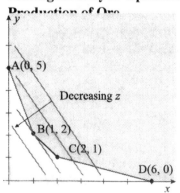

Figure 3.14

We now give an example of a linear programming problem involving minimizing the objective function.

EXAMPLE 3   A Minimizing Problem   Solve the following linear programming problem:

Minimize $z = 3x + 2y$ objective function
Subject to $3x + y \geq 5$ problem constraint
$x + y \geq 3$ problem constraint
$x + 4y \geq 6$ problem constraint
$x, y \geq 0$ nonnegative constraint

Technology Option

See Technology Note 2 on page 176 to see how to solve Example 3 using Microsoft Excel.

Solution   The feasible region is shown in Figure 3.14. If we set $z = z_0$, we obtain

$$3x + 2y = z_0$$

$$y = -\frac{3}{2}x + \frac{1}{2}z_0$$

which is a straight line with slope $-3/2$. We see that decreasing z_0 brings the line $z = z_0$ closer to the origin. Furthermore, the slope of the line segment from B to C is -1, while the slope of the line segment from A to B is -3. Since the slope of the objective function is $-3/2$ which is between these values, we see, according Figure 3.14, that the minimum occurs at a single corner point, $B(1,2)$. At this point, $z = 3(1) + 2(2) = 7$.   ◆

✧ The Geometric Method

In the previous examples the objective function was optimized at one corner point or two adjacent corner points. Careful examination of other typical feasible regions in Figure 3.15 indicates that the objective function will have its optimal values at a corner point or two adjacent corner points, if the objective function is parallel to one of the sides of the feasible region. The special case of the optimal value at two adjacent corners is considered in the last subsection. We now have the following theorem:

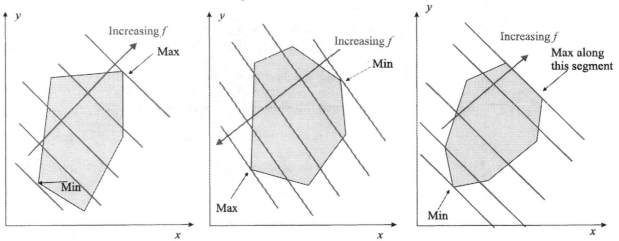

Figure 3.15

Optimal Solution Theorem for Linear Programming
If a linear programming problem has an optimal solution, then the optimal solution must occur at a corner of the feasible region. If the objective function is optimized at two corners of the feasible region, then any point on the line segment connecting these two corners also optimizes the objective function.

We will give examples later that show objective functions need not have an optimal value or may have multiple optimal values. Now, however, we list two important cases for which an optimal value exists.

Existence Theorem for Optimal Solutions

1. If the feasible region S is nonempty, bounded, and includes its boundary, then the objective function has both a minimum and a maximum in the feasible region.

2. If the feasible region S is in the first quadrant, includes its boundary, is unbounded, and the objective function $z = ax + by$ has the property that $a > 0$ and $b > 0$, then z attains a minimum value in S but has no maximum value in S.

Note that while case 2 in the theorem above is rather restrictive, the majority of applications with unbounded feasible regions will fall into this category. A more general way of determining if an unbounded feasible region has a maximum or minimum is discussed in the Extensions at the end of the Exercises for this section.

The fact that an optimal solution, if it exists, must be at a corner or adjacent corners gives rise to the following method of finding the optimal solution to a linear programming problem.

Method of Corners

Determine if a solution to a linear programming problem exists using the Existence Theorem for Optimal Solutions. If a solution exists then:

1. Graph the feasible region.

2. Locate all corners of the feasible region.

3. Evaluate the objective function at each of the corners.

4. The optimal solution will be the optimal value found in the previous step.

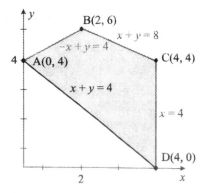

Figure 3.16

EXAMPLE 4   The Method of Corners Find both the minimum and the maximum of $z = 5x + 4y$ subject to

$$-x + y \leq 4$$
$$x + y \leq 8$$
$$x + y \geq 4$$
$$x \leq 4$$
$$x, y \geq 0$$

Solution   The feasible region is shown in Figure 3.16. Since the feasible region is nonempty, bounded, and includes its boundary, both the maximum and the minimum exist and can be found at a corner point. There are four corners, $A =$

$(0,4)$, $B = (2,6)$, $C = (4,4)$, and $D = (4,0)$. Evaluating z at these four corners yields

Corner	$z = 5x + 4y$	
$(0,4)$	$5(0) + 4(4) = 16$	← minimum
$(2,6)$	$5(2) + 4(6) = 34$	
$(4,4)$	$5(4) + 4(4) = 36$	← maximum
$(4,0)$	$5(4) + 4(0) = 20$	

Thus, the maximum is $z = 36$ at the corner $C = (4,4)$, while the minimum is $z = 16$ at the corner $A = (0,4)$.   ◆

CONNECTION
Using Linear Programming to Feed More Children

Chile's school system is using linear mathematical modeling to assign catering contracts in single-round sealed-bid combinational auctions. The Chilean state spends around \$180 million a year to feed 1,300,000 students from low-income families, making this one of the largest state auctions. To improve the quality of the assignment in the auction process, a linear programming model was constructed to allocate contract awards optimally among different concession holders. Using the model improved the price-quality of the meals with yearly savings of about \$40 million, equivalent to the cost of feeding 300,000 children during one year.

Source: Epstein, Henríquez, Catalán, Weintraub, and Martínez 2002

EXAMPLE 5   Purchasing Fertilizer at a Minimum Cost   A farmer can buy two types of 100-pound bags of fertilizer, type A and type B. Each 100-pound bag of type A fertilizer costs \$20 and contains 50 pounds of nitrogen, 30 pounds of phosphoric acid, and 20 pounds of potash, whereas each 100-pound bag of type B fertilizer costs \$30 and contains 10 pounds of nitrogen, 30 pounds of phosphoric acid, and 60 pounds of potash. The farmer requires at least 1000 pounds of nitrogen, 1800 pounds of phosphoric acid, and 2800 pounds of potash. How many bags of each type of fertilizer should be bought in order to minimize cost?

Solution   The same constraints were given in Example 6 of the last section. Recalling our work there, we can write the linear programming problem as

$$\text{Minimize } z = 20x + 30y \qquad \text{objective function}$$
$$\text{Subject to} \quad 50x + 10y \geq 1000 \quad \text{pounds of nitrogen}$$
$$30x + 30y \geq 1800 \quad \text{pounds of phosphoric acid}$$
$$20x + 60y \geq 2800 \quad \text{pounds of potash}$$
$$x, y \geq \quad 0 \quad \text{nonnegativity}$$

with x as the number of type A fertilizer bags and y the number of type B fertilizer bags. Figure 3.17 shows the feasible region found in the last section.

The region is in the first quadrant and unbounded, and the objective function $z = 20x + 30y$ has positive coefficients of x and y. Thus, a minimum will exist at a corner of the feasible region. We then have

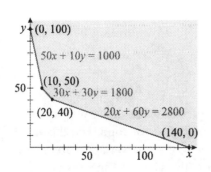

Figure 3.17

Corner	$z = 20x + 30y$	
$(0, 100)$	$20(0) + 30(100) = 3000$	
$(10, 50)$	$20(10) + 30(50) = 1700$	
$(20, 40)$	$20(20) + 30(40) = 1600$	$\leftarrow$ minimum
$(140, 0)$	$20(140) + 30(0) = 2800$	

The minimum cost is \$1600, requiring 20 bags of type A fertilizer and 40 bags of type B fertilizer.   ◆

✧ Problems With No Solution

We have now seen linear programming problems with exactly one solution and one with many solutions. We now examine two linear programming problems with no solution.

EXAMPLE 6   Unbounded Feasible Region   Solve the following linear programming problem:

$$\text{Maximize } P = x + y$$
$$\text{Subject to } \quad x, y \geq 0$$

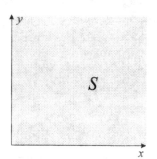

Solution   The feasible region is the first quadrant shown in Figure 3.18. This problem has no solution since one can attain any profit $P = x + y$, no matter how large, simply by taking x and y sufficiently large.   ◆

Figure 3.18

EXAMPLE 7   Empty Feasible Region   Solve the following linear programming problem:

$$\text{Maximize } z = 3x + 2y \text{ objective function}$$
$$\text{Subject to } \quad x + y \leq 2 \text{ problem constraint}$$
$$-x + y \geq 3 \text{ problem constraint}$$
$$x, y \geq 0 \text{ nonnegative constraint}$$

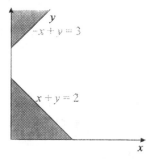

Solution   In Figure 3.19 the solution to each inequality is shaded. Note that there is no region where these inequalities are both true. Therefore the feasible region is empty. So there is no optimal solution.   ◆

Figure 3.19

✧ Technology Corner

⑦Technology Note 1   **Using Spreadsheets for Linear Programming**

Most spreadsheet programs have a built-in Solver to solve linear programming problems. Start by entering the variables, the objective function, and the values for the inequalities as shown in Worksheet 1. Note that the variables are in cells B2 and C2 and they have the value 0 to begin with. The worksheet is shown in formula auditing mode so that the formulas in each cell can be viewed. Place the cursor on the cell that calculates the Profit, B4

	A	B	C
1		Equation	Limit
2	Dinghies = x =	0	0
3	Skiffs = y =	0	0
4	Profit = P =	=60*B2+80*B3	MAX
5	Cutting Hours	=2*B2+4*B3	80
6	Assembly hours	=4*B2+2*B3	84
7	Painting hours	=2*B2+2*B3	50

Worksheet 1

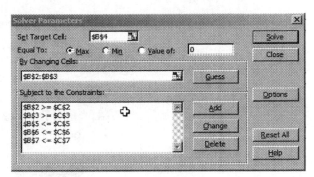

Worksheet 2

Next go to the Tools menu and choose Solver. If you do not have Solver in the list of tools, choose the Add-In option and enable the Solver. It will be available next time you click the Tools button. The solver window should look something like Worksheet 2. Choose the cell with the objective function as the target cell and the cells with the variables (*x* and *y*) as the cells to change. Next enter each constraint with the Add button which brings up a window like Worksheet 3.

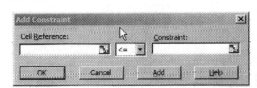

Worksheet 3

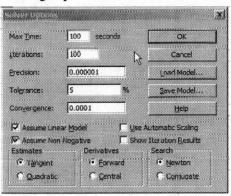

Worksheet 4

Note the pull-down for the type of inequality in Worksheet 3. Be sure the nonnegativity constraints are entered as ≥ 0. When you are done entering the five constraints, the solver box should look like Worksheet 2. Then click on the Options button and check the Assume Linear Model and Assume Non-Negative in the Solver Options box as shown in Worksheet 4. Click OK to exit and return to the solver window.

Now click the Solve button and you will get a solver results box as shown in Worksheet 5. Click OK to keep the solver solution. You will see in Worksheet 6 that the original values of 0 dinghies and 0 skiffs have been replaced by the optimal answers of 10 dinghies and 15 skiffs. Also, the objective function now shows the maximal value of 1800.

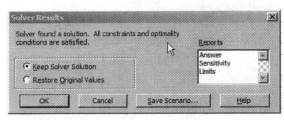

Worksheet 5

	A	B	C
1		Equation	Limit
2	Dinghies = x =	10	0
3	Skiffs = y =	15	0
4	Profit = P =	1800	MAX
5	Cutting Hours	80	80
6	Assembly hours	70	84
7	Painting hours	50	50

Worksheet 6

⑨Technology Note 2 **Using Spreadsheets for Linear Programming 2**

Enter the variables, the objective function, and the constraints as shown in Worksheet 7. Then open the solver window by clicking on Tools and then choosing Solver.... Enter the information into the solver window. Your Solver window should look like Worksheet 8. Finally, click the Solve button and then OK to see the answer shown in Worksheet 9. As found in the example, the minimum value occurs at (1, 2) with a value of $z = 7$.

	A	B	C
1		Equation	Limit
2	x	0	0
3	y	0	0
4	Objective Function	=3*B2+2*B3	MIN
5	constraint 1	=3*B2+1*B3	5
6	constraint 2	=1*B2+1*B3	3
7	constraint 3	=1*B2+3*B3	6

Worksheet 7

Solver Parameters

Set Target Cell: $B$4

Equal To: ○ Max ● Min ○ Value of: 0

By Changing Cells: $B$2:$B$3

Subject to the Constraints:
$B$2 >= $C$2
$B$3 >= $C$3
$B$5 >= $C$5
$B$6 >= $C$6
$B$7 >= $C$7

Solve Close Guess Options Add Change Reset All Delete Help

Worksheet 8

	A	B	C
1		Equation	Limit
2	x	1	0
3	y	2	0
4	Objective Function	7	MIN
5	constraint 1	5	5
6	constraint 2	3	3
7	constraint 3	7	6

Worksheet 9

Self-Help Exercises 3.3

1. a. Solve the following:

$$\text{Minimize} \quad z = 4x + 6y$$
$$\text{Subject to } 7x + 2y \geq 20$$
$$x + 2y \geq 8$$
$$x, y \geq 0$$

b. Solve with the objective function $z = 2x + 4y$.

2. Two types of metal connectors require time on a stamping machine and also time on a grinding machine. The DVI connectors require 4 minutes on the stamping machine and 3 minutes on the grinding machine. The HDMI connectors require 5 minutes on the stamping machine and 1 minute on the grinding machine. The stamping machine is available, at most, 50 minutes each hour, and the grinding machine is available, at most, 21 minutes each hour. Each hour a total of at least two of the connectors must be produced. If each of the DVI connectors brings a profit of $.50 each and the HDMI connectors a profit of $.60 each, find the number of both connectors that should be manufactured to maximize profits. (See Self-Help Exercise 2 in the last section.)

3.3 Exercises

In Exercises 1 through 6, you are given the feasible region. Find the maximum and minimum (if they exist) for the given objective function.

1. $z = x + 2y$

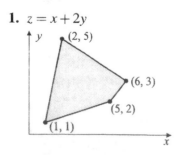

2. $z = 2x - y$

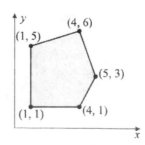

3. $z = 2x + 3y$

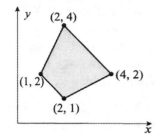

4. $z = 10x + 20y$

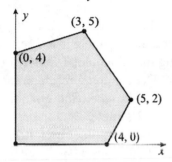

5. $z = 3x + y$

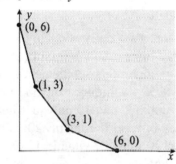

6. $z = x + y$

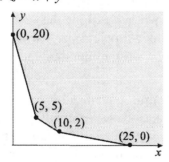

In Exercises 7 through 22, solve the linear programming problem.

7. Maximize $z = 20x + 30y$
  Subject to $x + 2y \le 90$
    $x + y \le 50$
    $x \le 30$
    $x, y \ge 0$

8. Maximize $z = 4x + y$
  Subject to $x + y \le 100$
    $3x + y \le 120$
    $y \ge 50$
    $x, y \ge 0$

9. Maximize $z = 2x + 3y$
  Subject to $2x + y \le 100$
    $y \le 40$
    $x \ge 10$
    $y \ge 20$

10. Maximize $z = 2x - 3y$
  Subject to $y \le x$
    $y \le 30$
    $y \ge 10$
    $x \le 40$

11. Minimize $z = x + y$
  Subject to $3x + y \ge 10$
    $3x + 2y \ge 17$
    $x + 2y \ge 11$
    $x, y \ge 0$

12. Minimize $z = x + 3y$
  Subject to $2x + y \ge 20$
    $x + y \ge 18$
    $x + 3y \ge 41$
    $x, y \ge 0$

13. Minimize $z = 2x + 3y$
  Subject to $x + y \le 10$
    $x \ge 1$
    $x \le 3$
    $y \ge 0$

14. Minimize $z = 4x + 5y$
  Subject to $x + y \ge 2$
    $-x + y \le 2$
    $x + y \le 6$
    $-x + y \ge -2$

15. Maximize $z = x + 10y$
  Subject to $-x + y \le 0$
    $-x + y \ge -4$
    $y \ge 1$
    $y \le 4$

16. Maximize $z = 5x + 4y$
  Subject to $-2x + y \le 0$
    $-x + y \le 0$
    $x + y \le 6$

17. Minimize $z = 4x + 5y$
Subject to $x + y \geq 5$
$-x + y \leq 1$
$-2x + y \leq 2$
$y \geq 0$

18. Minimize $z = x + y$
Subject to $2x + y \geq 9$
$x + 2y \geq 9$
$x \leq 7$
$y \leq 7$

19. Maximize $z = 2x + 4y$
Subject to $x - y \leq 0$
$x, y \geq 0$

20. Maximize $z = 3x + 2y$
Subject to $x - y \leq 0$
$2x - y \geq 0$
$x, y \geq 0$

21. Minimize $z = x + 3y$
Subject to $x + y \leq 0$
$-2x + y \geq 1$
$x, y \geq 0$

22. Minimize $z = x + y$
Subject to $x + y \leq 2$
$y \geq 3$
$x \geq 0$

Applications

Solve the following linear programming problems. Note that the problems in Exercises 23–30 correspond to those in Exercises 49–56 in Section 3.2.

23. Shipping Tractors Kubota orporation supplies its tractor CA35 to distributors located in St. Louis and in Minneapolis. The St. Louis distributer needs at least 100 of the CA35 tractors next month while the Minneapolis distributer needs at least 50. At most 200 of the CA35 tractors can be manufactured and delivered to the distributors. If it costs $30 to ship each tractor to the St. Louis distributor and $40 to the Minneapolis distributor, find the number to be shipped to each distributor which minimize cost and find the minimum cost.

24. Transportating Crates A plane delivers two types of cargo between two destinations. Each crate of cargo I is 5 cubic feet in volume and 100 pounds in weight, and earns $20 in revenue. Each crate of cargo II is 5 cubic feet in volume and 200 pounds

in weight, and earns $30 in revenue. The plane has available at most 400 cubic feet and 10,000 pounds for the crates. Finally, at least twice the number of crates of I as II must be shipped. Find the number of crates of each cargo to ship in order to maximize revenue. Find the maximum revenue.

25. Manufacturing Pen Tips Old-fashioned pen tips require for their manufacture time on a stamping machine, a grinding machine, and a polishing machine. The plain tip requires 1 minute on the stamping machine, 2 minutes on the grinding machine, and 2 minutes on the polishing machine. The fancy tip requires 2 minutes on the stamping machine, 2 minutes on the grinding machine, and 1 minute on the polishing machine. The stamping machine can operate a maximum of 20 minutes, the grinding machine a maximum of 22 minutes, and the polishing machine a maximum of 15 minutes each hour. The profit on each of the plain tips is $4 and the profit on each of the fancy tips is $5. How many of each type of tip should be made to maximize profits? What is the maximum profit?

26. Diet An individual needs a daily supplement of at least 500 units of vitamin C and 200 units of vitamin E and agrees to obtain this supplement by eating two foods, I and II. Each ounce of food I contains 40 units of vitamin C and 10 units of vitamin E, while each ounce of food II contains 20 units of vitamin C and also 20 units of vitamin E. The total supplement of these two foods must be at most 30 ounces. Unfortunately, food I contains 30 units of cholesterol per ounce, and food II contains 20 units of cholesterol per ounce. Find the appropriate amounts of the two food supplements so that cholesterol is minimized. Find the minimum amount of cholesterol.

27. Manufacturing A firm manufactures tables and desks. To produce each table requires 1 hour of labor, 10 square feet of wood, and 2 quarts of finish. To produce each desk requires 3 hours of labor, 20 square feet of wood, and 1 quart of finish. Available is at most 45 hours of labor, at most 350 square feet of wood, and at most 55 quarts of finish. The tables and desks yield profits of $4 and $3 each, respectively. Find the number of each product to be made in order to maximize profits. Find the maximum profit.

28. Mixture A dealer has 7600 pounds of peanuts, 5800 pounds of almonds, and 3000 pounds of cashews to be used to make two mixtures. The first mixture wholesales for $2 per pound and consists of 60% peanuts, 30% almonds, and 10% cashews. The second mixture wholesales for $3 per pound and consists of 20% peanuts, 50% almonds, and 30% cashews. How many pounds of each mixture should the dealer make in order to maximize revenue? Find the maximum revenue.

29. **Fishery** A certain lake has smallmouth and large-mouth bass and also three types of food for these fish, I, II, and III. Each month the lake can supply 800 pounds of food I, 500 pounds of food II, and 700 pounds of food III. Each month each small-mouth bass requires 1 pound of food I, 1 pound of food II, and 2 pounds of food III, and each large-mouth bass requires 4 pounds of food I, 2 pounds of food II, and 1 pound of food III. What is the maximum number of these fish that the lake can support?

30. **Scheduling** A firm has two plants, A and B, that manufacture three products, P_1, P_2, and P_3. In one day Plant A can manufacture 30 of P_1, 30 of P_2, and 10 of P_3, and costs $3000 a day to operate, whereas Plant B can manufacture 10 of P_1, 20 of P_2, and 30 of P_3, and costs $4000 a day to operate. At least 240 of the first product, 390 of the second, and 410 of the third are needed. How many days must each plant operate in order to minimize cost? Find the minimum cost.

31. **Scheduling** Redo the previous exercise if the cost of operating Plant A is $30,000 and of Plant B is $20,000.

32. **Diet** Redo Exercise 26 if food II contains 25 units of cholesterol and everything else is the same.

33. **Fishery** If in Exercise 29, $2 can be obtained from harvesting the smallmouth bass and $5 for the large-mouth bass, how many of each type of fish should be harvested to maximize revenue? Find the maximum revenue.

34. **Manufacturing** A firm is planning to manufacture and sell two products with the cost and profit (in thousands of dollars) given in the following table:

	Product 1	Product 2
Cost	2	1
Profit	2	3

The facilities are such that a total of at most 20 of the two products and at most 15 of product 2 can

be manufactured in any day, and at most $30,000 can be allocated for the cost in any one day. With these conditions the firm can sell all of the items manufactured. Find the number of each product to manufacture in order to maximize profit. Find the maximum profit.

35. **Manufacturing** Redo the previous exercise if the profit is given as $P = x + y$.

36. Maximize $z = 10.7x + 14.1y$
Subject to $1.22x + 3.15y \le 34.45$
$1.4x + 1.4y \le 19.6$
$1.31x + 2.46y \le 24.09$
$x, y \ge 0$

37. Minimize $z = 1.41x + 2.37y$
Subject to $1.26x + 4.17y \ge 44.31$
$2.17x + 2.17y \ge 41.23$
$1.68x + 1.03y \ge 24.12$
$x, y \ge 0$

38. **Fishery** A lake has rainbow trout and brown trout. Three foods A, B, and C are available for these trout in the lake. Each rainbow trout requires 3.42 units of food A, 2.87 units of food B, and 2.14 units of food C each day. Each brown trout requires 5.13 units of food A, 3 units of food B, and 6 units of food C each day. If at most 2701.8 units of food A, 1797.5 units of food B, and 2515 units of food C are available daily, what is the maximum number of rainbow and brown trout that this lake can support?

Extensions

For Exercises 39 through 42, we will consider the generalization of the Existence Theorem for Optimal Solution. In the theorem if the region was unbounded we could only guarantee the existence of a minimum and only if the coefficients of the objective function were positive. We can generalize this existence theorem by considering points that are in the feasible region but not at a corner. If a maximum or minimum is found at a point that is not a corner of the feasible region, then there is not a maximum or minimum solution to the problem.

39. Consider the feasible region from Example 3. Draw a box around the corner points as shown in the figure with the new "corners" E, F, and G marked. Use these new corners along with the old corners A, B, C, and D to show that this linear programming problem has a minimum but no maximum.

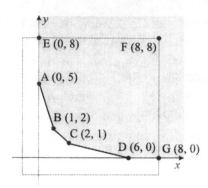

40. Using the corners in the figure above, does the objective function $z = -4x + y$ have a minimum or maximum on the feasible region?

41. Using the corners in the figure above, does the objective function $z = 5x - 6y$ have a minimum or maximum on the feasible region?

42. Using the corners in the figure above, does the objective function $z = -3x - 8y$ have a minimum or maximum on the feasible region?

Solutions to Self-Help Exercises 3.3

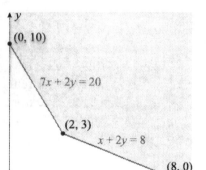

1. The feasible region is shown in the figure. The feasible region includes its boundary, is in the first quadrant, is unbounded, and the objective function $z = 4x + 6y$ has positive coefficients for x and y. Thus, a minimum exists and must occur at a corner point. By evaluating z at the three corners we see that the minimum of $z = 26$ occurs when $x = 2$ and $y = 3$.

Corner	$z = 4x + 6y$	
$(0, 10)$	$4(0) + 6(10) = 60$	
$(2, 3)$	$4(2) + 6(3) = 26$	← minimum
$(8, 0)$	$4(8) + 6(0) = 32$	

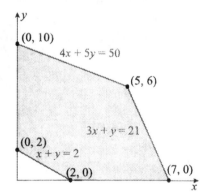

2. With x the number of the DVI connectors manufactured and y the number of the HDMI connectors, the profit is $P = 0.50x + 0.60y$. The feasible region and the corners were found in Self-Help Exercise 2 of the last section. Evaluating P at the corners yields:

Corner	$P = 0.50x + 0.60y$	
$(2, 0)$	$0.50(2) + 0.60(0) = 1.00$	
$(0, 2)$	$0.50(0) + 0.60(2) = 1.20$	
$(0, 10)$	$0.50(0) + 0.60(10) = 6.00$	
$(5, 6)$	$0.50(5) + 0.60(6) = 6.10$	← minimum
$(7, 0)$	$0.50(7) + 0.60(0) = 3.50$	

Thus, the maximum profit of $6.10 will occur if five of the DVI connectors and six of the HDMI connectors are made.

Review

✧ Summary Outline

- A linear inequality is an inequality of the form

$$ax + by < c \text{ or } \le c \text{ or } > c \text{ or } \ge c$$

- The feasible region of a system of inequalities is the set of points that satisfies all the inequalities in the system.

- Graphing a Linear Inequality
  The following steps show how to graph the linear inequality

$$ax + by < c \text{ or } \le c \text{ or } > c \text{ or } \ge c$$

  1. First graph the straight line L given by $ax + by = c$, using a dotted line if the inequalities "<" or ">" are given and a solid line if the inequalities "$\le$" or "$\ge$" are given. The dotted line indicates the straight line L is not part of the solution graph, while the solid line indicates that the line L is part of the solution graph.

  2. Pick any convenient test point not on line L and evaluate the inequality at that test point. If the inequality is true, then the solution graph is the half-plane on the same side of the line L as the test point. If the inequality is not satisfied, then the solution graph is the half-plane on that side of L that does not include the test point.

- If a linear programming problem has an optimal solution, then this optimal solution must occur at one or two corners of the feasible region. If the objective function is optimized at two corners of the feasible region, then any point on the line segment connecting these two corners also optimizes the objective function.

- The two existence theorems for optimal solutions.

  1. If the feasible region is nonempty, bounded, and includes its boundary, then the objective function has both a minimum and a maximum in the feasible region.

  2. If the feasible region S is in the first quadrant, includes its boundary, is unbounded, and the objective function $z = ax + by$ has the property that $a > 0$ and $b > 0$, then z attains a minimum value in S but has no maximum value in S.

- Determine if a solution to a linear programming problem exists using the Existence Theorem for Optimal Solutions. If a solution exists then:

  1. Graph the feasible region and locate all corners of the feasible region.

  2. Evaluate the objective function at each of the corners.

  3. The optimal solution will be the optimal value found in the previous step.

Review Exercises

1. A farmer wishes to raise corn and she must fertilize the fields with at least 100 pounds of nitrogen (N) per acre and at least 150 pounds of phosphorus (P) per acre. Two materials are available to supply these nutrients: sludge, which contains 6% N and 3% P, and bone meal, which contains 4% N and 12% P. If sludge costs $15 per 100-lb sack, and bone meal costs $20 per 100-pound sack, how many sacks of each should the farmer buy to minimize the cost of fertilizer?

2. An airline has two types of airplanes and has contracted with a tour group to provide accommodations for a minimum of each of 18 first-class, 12 tourist, and 6 economy-class passengers. The first plane costs $1 per 10 yards traveled to operate and can accommodate 4 first-class, 2 tourist, and 2 economy-class passengers, while the second plane costs $1 per 10 yards traveled to operate and can accommodate 3 first-class, 3 tourist, and 3 economy-class passengers. The airline has available at most 6 of the first type of plane and 4 of the second type. How many of each type of airplane should be used to minimize the operating cost?

3. A furniture manufacturer produces chairs and sofas. The chairs require 5 feet of wood, 5 ounces of foam rubber, and 10 square yards of material. The sofas require 20 feet of wood, 10 ounces of foam rubber, and 30 square yards of material. The manufacturer has in stock 300 feet of wood, 210 ounces of foam rubber, and 500 square yards of material. If the chairs can be sold for $200 and the sofas for $500 each, how many of each should be produced to maximize the income?

4. Refer to Exercise 3

   a. For the optimal values in the previous exercise determine which of the three commodities used in the manufacturing process is in excess and by how much.

   b. Redo the solution if the chairs can be sold for $400 and everything else remains the same. For the optimal values found determine which of the three commodities used in the manufacturing process is now in excess and by how much.

5. A small shop manufactures two styles of park bench. To manufacture the first style requires one square foot of wood, 1 pound of iron, and 3 hours of labor. The second style requires 3 square feet of wood, 1 pound of iron, and 2 hours of labor. The shop has 21 square feet of wood, 9 pounds of iron, and 24 hours of available labor. If the shop makes a profit of $10 on the first style bench and $20 on the second style bench, find the number of each style of bench to manufacture that will maximize profits.

6. Refer to Exercise 5

   a. For the optimal values determine whether iron, wood, or labor is in excess and by how much.

   b. Redo the solution if the first style of park bench yields a profit of $20 and the second $15 and everything else remains the same. For the optimal values found determine whether iron, wood, or labor is now in excess and by how much.

7. A mining company has two mines that produce three grades of ore. The North mine can produce 3 tons of low-grade ore, 1 ton of medium-grade ore, and 1 ton of high-grade ore each day. The South mine can produce 3 tons of low-grade ore, 12 tons of medium-grade ore, and 3 tons of high-grade ore each day. It costs $3000 per day to operate the North mine and $4000 a day to operate the South mine. At a particular time the company needs at least 15 tons of low-grade ore, 8 tons of medium-grade ore, and 9 tons of high-grade ore. Find the number of days each mine should be operated in order to minimize cost and find the minimum cost.

8. A farmer has 240 acres of land on which he can raise corn and/or soybeans. Raising corn yields 120 bushels per acre, which can be sold for $2.40 per bushel, and raising soybeans yields 40 bushels per acre and sells for $6.00 per bushel. To obtain this price, the farmer must be able to store his crop in bins with a total capacity of 12,000 bushels. The farmer must limit each crop to no more than 10,800 bushels. Assuming the costs of raising corn and soybeans are the same, how much of each should the farmer plant in order to maximize his revenue? What is this maximum?

9. A health food store manager is preparing two mixtures of breakfast cereal out of a supply of 10.5 pounds of oats, 0.9 pound of almonds, 0.66 pound

of raisins, and 50 pounds of wheat. The first mixture contains 50% oats, 4% almonds, 2% raisins, and the rest wheat and sells for $5 a pound. The second mixture contains 10% oats, 2% almonds, 2% raisins, and the rest wheat and sells for $4 a pound. How much of each mixture should be made to maximize profits? What is the maximum profit?

10. Refer to the linear programming problem in Exercise 1 of Section 3.4. Change the profit function to $P = 80x + 60y$. Change the paint constraint to $50 + h$.

a. Determine the new point at which the profit object function attains its maximum and find the maximum as a function of h.

b. Find the range of values that h can satisfy if the other two constraints are unchanged.

c. Find the shadow price for the painting constraint.

CHAPTER 4

Sets and Probability

In a survey of 200 people that had just returned from a trip to Europe, the following information was gathered.

- 142 visited England

- 95 visited Italy

- 65 visited Germany

- 70 visited both England and Italy

- 50 visited both England and Germany

- 30 visited both Italy and Germany

- 20 visited all three of these countries

How many went to England but not Italy or Germany?

We will learn how to solve puzzles like this in the second section of the chapter when counting the elements in a set is discussed.

4.1   Introduction to Sets

This section discusses operations on sets and the laws governing these set operations. These are fundamental notions that will be used throughout the remainder of this text. In the next two chapters we will see that probability and statistics are based on counting the elements in sets and manipulating set operations. Thus we first need to understand clearly the notion of sets and their operations.

✧ The Language of Sets

We begin here with some definitions of the language and notation used when working with sets. The most basic definition is "What is a set?" A set is a collection of items. These items are referred to as the elements or members of the set. For example, the set containing the numbers 1, 2, and 3 would be written $\{1,2,3\}$. Notice that the set is contained in curly brackets. This will help us distinguish sets from other mathematical objects.

When all the elements of the set are written out, we refer to this as roster notation. So the set containing the first 10 letters in the English alphabet would be written as $\{a,b,c,d,e,f,g,h,i,j\}$ in roster notation. If we wanted to refer to this set without writing all the elements, we could define the set in terms of its properties. This is called set-builder notation. So we write

$$\{x \mid x \text{ is one of the first 10 letters in the English alphabet}\}$$

This is read "the set of all x such that x is one of the first 10 letters in the English alphabet". If we will be using a set more than once in a discussion, it is useful to define the set with a symbol, usually an uppercase letter. So

$$S = \{a,b,c,d,e,f,g,h,i,j\}$$

We can say c is an element of the set $\{a,b,c,d,e,f,g,h,i,j\}$ or simply write $c \in S$. The symbol $\in$ is read "is an element of". We can also say that the set $R = \{c\}$ is a subset of our larger set S as every element in the set R is also in the set S.

Subsets

If every element of a set A is also an element of another set B, we say that A is a subset of B and write $A \subseteq B$. If A is not a subset of B, we write $A \nsubseteq B$.

Thus $\{1,2,4\} \subseteq \{1,2,3,4\}$, but $\{1,2,3,4\} \nsubseteq \{1,2,4\}$. Since every element in A is in A, we can write $A \subseteq A$. If there is a set B and every element in the set B is also in the set A but $B \neq A$, we say that B is a proper subset of A. This is written as $B \subset A$. Note the proper subset symbol $\subset$ is lacking the small horizontal line that the subset symbol $\subseteq$ has. The difference is rather like the difference between $<$ and $\leq$.

Some sets have no elements at all. We need some notation for this, simply leaving a blank space will not do!

> **Empty Set**
> The empty set, written as $\emptyset$ or $\{\}$, is the set with no elements.

The empty set can be used to conveniently indicate that an equation has no solution. For example

$$\{x | x \text{ is real and } x^2 = -1\} = \emptyset$$

By the definition of subset, given any set A, we must have $\emptyset \subseteq A$.

EXAMPLE 1 **Finding Subsets** Find all the subsets of $\{a, b, c\}$.

Solution The subsets are

$$\emptyset, \{a\}, \{b\}, \{c\}, \{a, b\}, \{a, c\}, \{b, c\}, \{a, b, c\} \qquad \blacklozenge$$

REMARK: Note that there are 8 subsets and 7 of them are proper subsets. In general, a set with n elements will have 2^n subsets. In the next chapter we will learn why this is so.

The empty set is the set with no elements. At the other extreme is the universal set. This set is the set of all elements being considered and is denoted by U. If, for example, we are to take a national survey of voter satisfaction with the president, the universal set is the set of all voters in this country. If the survey is to determine the effects of smoking on pregnant women, the universal set is the set of all pregnant women. The context of the problem under discussion will determine the universal set for that problem. The universal set must contain every element under discussion.

A Venn diagram is a way of visualizing sets. The universal set is represented by a rectangle and sets are represented as circles inside the universal set. For example, given a universal set U and a set A, Figure 4.1 is a Venn diagram that visualizes the concept that $A \subset U$. Figure 4.1 also visualizes the concept $B \subset A$. The U above the rectangle will be dropped in later diagrams as we will abide by the convention that the rectangle always represents the universal set.

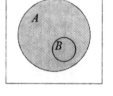

Figure 4.1

✧ Set Operations

The first set operation we consider is the complement. The complement of set A are those members of set U that do not belong to A.

> **Complement**
> Given a universal set U and a set $A \subset U$, the complement of A, written A^c, is the set of all elements that are in U but not in A, that is,
>
> $$A^c = \{x | x \in U, \ x \notin A\}$$

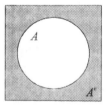

Figure 4.2
A^c is shaded.

A Venn diagram visualizing A^c is shown in Figure 4.2. Some alternate notations for the complement of a set are A' and $\bar{A}$.

EXAMPLE 2   The Complements of Sets   Let $U = \{1,2,3,4,5,6,7,8,9\}$, $A = \{1,3,5,7,9\}$, $B = \{1,2,3,4,5\}$. Find A^c, B^c, U^c, $\emptyset^c$, and $(A^c)^c$ in roster notation.

Solution   We have

$$A^c = \{2,4,6,8\}$$
$$B^c = \{6,7,8,9\}$$
$$U^c = \emptyset$$
$$\emptyset^c = \{1,2,3,4,5,6,7,8,9\} = U$$
$$(A^c)^c = \{2,4,6,8\}^c$$
$$= \{1,3,5,7,9\} = A$$

Note that in the example above we found $U^c = \emptyset$ and $\emptyset^c = U$. Additionally $(A^c)^c = A$. This can be seen using the Venn diagram in Figure 4.2, since the complement of A^c is all elements in U but not in A^c which is the set A. These three rules are called the Complement Rules.

Complement Rules
If U is a universal set, we must always have

$$U^c = \emptyset, \qquad \emptyset^c = U$$

If A is any subset of a universal set U, then

$$(A^c)^c = A$$

The next set operation is the union of two sets. This set includes the members of both sets A and B. That is, if an element belongs to set A or set B then it belongs to the union of A and B.

Set Union
The union of two sets A and B, written $A \cup B$, is the set of all elements that belong to A, or to B, or to both. Thus

$$A \cup B = \{x \mid x \in A \text{ or } x \in B \text{ or both}\}$$

REMARK: This usage of the word "or" is the same as in logic. It is the inclusive "or" where the elements that belong to both sets are part of the union. In English the use of "or" is often the exclusive "or". That is, if a meal you order at a restaurant comes with a dessert and you are offered cake or pie, you really only get one of the desserts. Choosing one dessert will exclude you from the other. If it was the logical "or" you could have both!

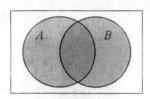

Figure 4.3
$A \cup B$ is shaded.

Our convention will be to drop the phrase "or both" but still maintain the same meaning. Note very carefully that this gives a particular definition to the word "or". Thus we will normally write

$$A \cup B = \{x | x \in A \text{ or } x \in B\}$$

It can be helpful to say that the union of A and B, $A \cup B$, is all elements in A joined together with all elements in B. A Venn diagram visualizing this is shown in Figure 4.3 with the union shaded.

EXAMPLE 3   The Union of Two Sets Let $U = \{1,2,3,4,5,6\}, A = \{1,2,3,4\}$ and $B = \{1,4,5,6\}$. Find $A \cup B$ and $A \cup A^c$.

Solution   We begin with the first set and join to it any elements in the second set that are not already there. Thus

$$\begin{aligned} A \cup B &= \{1,2,3,4\} \cup \{1,4,5,6\} \\ &= \{1,2,3,4,5,6\} \end{aligned}$$

Since $A^c = \{5,6\}$ we have

$$A \cup A^c = \{1,2,3,4\} \cup \{5,6\} = \{1,2,3,4,5,6\} = U \qquad \blacklozenge$$

The second result, $A \cup A^c = U$ is generally true. From Figure 4.2, we can see that if U is a universal set and $A \subset U$, then

$$A \cup A^c = U$$

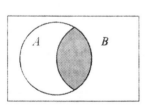

Figure 4.4

Set Intersection
The intersection of two sets A and B, written $A \cap B$, is the set of all elements that belong to both the set A and to the set B. Thus

$$A \cap B = \{x | x \in A \text{ and } x \in B\}$$

A Venn diagram is shown in Figure 4.4 with the intersection shaded.

EXAMPLE 4   The Intersection of Two Sets   Find

a. $\{a,b,c,d\} \cap \{a,c,e\}$ **b.** $\{a,b\} \cap \{c,d\}$

Solution   **a.** Only a and c are elements of both of the sets. Thus

$$\{a,b,c,d\} \cap \{a,c,e\} = \{a,c\}$$

b. The two sets $\{a,b\}$ and $\{c,d\}$ have no elements in common. Thus

$$\{a,b\} \cap \{c,d\} = \emptyset \qquad \blacklozenge$$

The sets $\{a,b\}$ and $\{c,d\}$ have no elements in common. These sets are called disjoint and can be visualized in Figure 4.5.

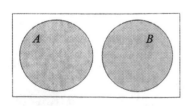

Figure 4.5
A and B are disjoint.

Disjoint Sets

Two sets A and B are **disjoint** if they have no elements in common, that is, if $A \cap B = \emptyset$.

An examination of Figure 4.2 or referring to the definition of A^c indicates that for any set A, A and A^c are disjoint. That is,

$$A \cap A^c = \emptyset$$

✧ Additional Laws for Sets

There are a number of laws for sets. They are referred to as commutative, associative, distributive, and De Morgan laws. We will consider two of these laws in the following examples.

EXAMPLE 5   Establishing a De Morgan Law   Use a Venn diagram to show that

$$(A \cup B)^c = A^c \cap B^c$$

Solution   We first consider the right side of this equation. Figure 4.6 shows a Venn diagram of A^c and B^c and $A^c \cap B^c$. We then notice from Figure 4.3 that this is $(A \cup B)^c$.

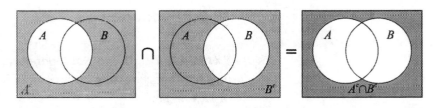

Figure 4.6   ◆

EXAMPLE 6   Establishing the Distributive Law for Union   Use a Venn diagram to show that

$$A \cup (B \cap C) = (A \cup B) \cap (A \cup C)$$

Solution   Consider first the left side of this equation. In Figure 4.7a the sets A, $B \cap C$, and the union of these two are shown. Now for the right side of the equation refer to Figure 4.7b, where the sets $A \cup B$, $A \cup C$, and the intersection of these two sets are shown. We have the same set in both cases.   ◆

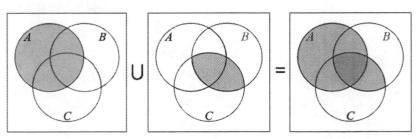

Figure 4.7a

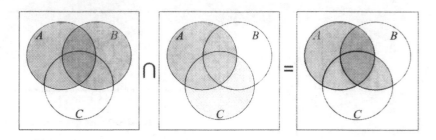

Figure 4.7b

We can summarize the laws we have found in the following list.

Laws for Set Operations	
$A \cup B = B \cup A$	Commutative law for union
$A \cap B = B \cap A$	Commutative law for intersection
$A \cup (B \cup C) = (A \cup B) \cup C$	Associative law for union
$A \cap (B \cap C) = (A \cap B) \cap C$	Associative law for intersection
$A \cup (B \cap C) = (A \cup B) \cap (A \cup C)$	Distributive law for union
$A \cap (B \cup C) = (A \cap B) \cup (A \cap C)$	Distributive law for intersection
$(A \cup B)^c = A^c \cap B^c$	De Morgan law
$(A \cap B)^c = A^c \cup B^c$	De Morgan law

✧ Applications

EXAMPLE 7   Using Set Operations to Write Expressions   Let U be the universal set consisting of the set of all students taking classes at the University of Hawaii and

$B = \{x \mid x$ is currently taking a business course$\}$

$E = \{x \mid x$ is currently taking an English course$\}$

$M = \{x \mid x$ is currently taking a math course$\}$

Write an expression using set operations and show the region on a Venn diagram for each of the following:

a. The set of students at the University of Hawaii taking a course in at least one of the above three fields.

b. The set of all students at the University of Hawaii taking both an English course and a math course but not a business course.

c. The set of all students at the University of Hawaii taking a course in exactly one of the three fields above.

Solution

a. This is $B \cup E \cup M$. See Figure 4.8a.

b. This can be described as the set of students taking an English course (E) and also (intersection) a math course (M) and also (intersection) not a business course (B^c) or

$$E \cap M \cap B^c$$

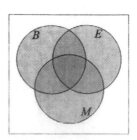

Figure 4.8a

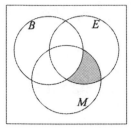

Figure 4.8b

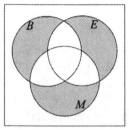

Figure 4.8c

This is the set of points in the universal set that are in both E and M but not in B and is shown in Figure 4.8b.

c. We describe this set as the set of students taking business but not taking English or math ($B \cap E^c \cap M^c$) together with (union) the set of students taking English but not business or math ($E \cap B^c \cap M^c$) together with (union) the set of students taking math but not business or English ($M \cap B^c \cap E^c$) or

$$(B \cap E^c \cap M^c) \cup (B^c \cap E \cap M^c) \cup (B^c \cap E^c \cap M)$$

This is the union of the three sets shown in Figure 4.8c. The first, $B \cap E^c \cap M^c$, consists of those points in B that are outside E and also outside M. The second set $E \cap B^c \cap M^c$ consists of those points in E that are outside B and M. The third set $M \cap B^c \cap E^c$ is the set of points in M that are outside B and E. The union of these three sets is then shown on the right in Figure 4.8c.   ◆

REMARK: The word only means the same as exactly one. So a student taking only a business course would be written as $B \cap E^c \cap M^c$.

Self-Help Exercises 4.1

1. Let $U = \{1, 2, 3, 4, 5, 6, 7\}$, $A = \{l, 2, 3, 4\}$, $B = \{3, 4, 5\}$, $C = \{2, 3, 4, 5, 6\}$. Find the following:

   a. $A \cup B$ b. $A \cap B$
   c. A^c d. $(A \cup B) \cap C$
   e. $(A \cap B) \cup C$ f. $A^c \cup B \cup C$

2. Let U denote the set of all corporations in this country and P those that made profits during the last year, D those that paid a dividend during the last year, and L those that increased their labor force during the last year. Describe the following using the three sets P, D, L, and set operations. Show the regions in a Venn diagram.

   a. Corporations in this country that had profits and also paid a dividend last year

   b. Corporations in this country that either had profits or paid a dividend last year

   c. Corporations in this country that did not have profits last year

   d. Corporations in this country that had profits, paid a dividend, and did not increase their labor force last year

   e. Corporations in this country that had profits or paid a dividend, and did not increase their labor force last year

4.1 Exercises

In Exercises 1 through 4, determine whether the statements are true or false.

1. a. $\emptyset \in A$ b. $A \in A$

2. a. $0 = \emptyset$ b. $\{x, y\} \in \{x, y, z\}$

3. a. $\{x | 0 < x < -1\} = \emptyset$
   b. $\{x | 0 < x < -1\} = 0$

4. a. $\{x | x(x - 1) = 0\} = \{0, 1\}$
   b. $\{x | x^2 + 1 < 0\} = \emptyset$

5. If $A = \{u, v, y, z\}$, determine whether the following statements are true or false.

   a. $w \in A$ b. $x \notin A$
   c. $\{u, x\} \cup A$ d. $\{y, z, v, u\} = A$

6. If $A = \{u, v, y, z\}$, determine whether the following statements are true or false.

a. $x \notin A$ **b.** $\{u, w\} \notin A$
c. $\{x, w\} \not\subset A$ **d.** $\emptyset \subset A$

7. List all the subsets of **a.** $\{3\}$, **b.** $\{3, 4\}$.

8. List all the subsets of **a.** $\emptyset$, **b.** $\{3, 4, 5\}$.

9. Use Venn diagrams to indicate the following.

a. $A \subset U, B \subset U, A \subset B^c$
b. $A \subset U, B \subset U, B \subset A^c$

10. Use Venn diagrams to indicate the following.

a. $A \subset U, B \subset U, C \subset U, C \subset (A \cup B)^c$
b. $A \subset U, B \subset U, C \subset U, C \subset A \cap B$

For Exercises 11 through 14, indicate where the sets are located on the figure below and indicate if the sets found in part a and part b are disjoint or not.

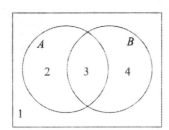

11. a. $A \cap B^c$ **b.** $A \cap B$

12. a. $A^c \cap B$ **b.** $A^c \cap B^c$

13. a. $A \cup B^c$ **b.** $(A \cup B)^c$

14. a. $A^c \cup B^c$ **b.** $(A \cap B)^c$

For Exercises 15 through 22, indicate where the sets are located on the figure below

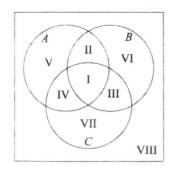

15. a. $A \cap B \cap C$ **b.** $A \cap B^c \cap C^c$

16. a. $A \cap B \cap C^c$ **b.** $B \cap A^c \cap C^c$

17. a. $A^c \cap B^c \cap C^c$ **b.** $A \cap C \cap B^c$

18. a. $B \cap C \cap A^c$ **b.** $C \cap A^c \cap B^c$

19. a. $(A \cup B) \cap C^c$ **b.** $(A \cap B)^c \cap C$

20. a. $A \cup (B \cap C)$ **b.** $A \cup B \cup C^c$

21. a. $(A \cup B)^c \cap C$ **b.** $(A^c \cap B)^c \cup C$

22. a. $A \cup (B^c \cap C^c)$ **b.** $(A \cup B \cup C)^c \cap A$

In Exercises 23 through 30, find the indicated sets with
$U = \{1, 2, 3, 4, 5, 6, 7, 8, 9, 10\}$,
$A = \{1, 2, 3, 4, 5, 6\}$,
$B = \{4, 5, 6, 7, 8\}, C = \{5, 6, 7, 8, 9, 10\}$

23. a. $A \cap B$ **b.** $A \cup B$

24. a. A^c **b.** $A^c \cap B$

25. a. $A \cap B^c$ **b.** $A^c \cap B^c$

26. a. $A^c \cup B^c$ **b.** $(A^c \cup B^c)^c$

27. a. $A \cap B \cap C$ **b.** $(A \cap B \cap C)^c$

28. a. $A \cap (B \cup C)$ **b.** $A \cap (B^c \cup C)$

29. a. $A^c \cap B^c \cap C^c$ **b.** $(A \cup B \cup C)^c$

30. a. $A^c \cap B^c \cap C$ **b.** $A^c \cap B \cap C^c$

In Exercises 31 through 34, describe each of the sets in words.

Let U be the set of all residents of your state and let
$A = \{x | x \text{ owns an automobile}\}$
$H = \{x | x \text{ owns a house}\}$

31. a. A^c **b.** $A \cup H$ **c.** $A \cup H^c$

32. a. H^c **b.** $A \cap H$ **c.** $A^c \cap H$

33. a. $A \cap H^c$ **b.** $A^c \cap H^c$ **c.** $A^c \cup H^c$

34. a. $(A \cap H)^c$ **b.** $(A \cup H)^c$ **c.** $(A^c \cap H^c)^c$

In Exercises 35 through 38, let U, A, and H be as in the previous four problems, and let
$$P = \{x \mid x \text{ owns a piano}\},$$
and describe each of the sets in words.

35. a. $A \cap H \cap P$ **b.** $A \cup H \cup P$
     c. $(A \cap H) \cup P$

36. a. $(A \cup H) \cap P$ **b.** $(A \cup H) \cap P^c$
     c. $A \cap H \cap P^c$

37. a. $(A \cap H)^c \cap P$ **b.** $A^c \cap H^c \cap P^c$
     c. $(A \cup H)^c \cap P$

38. a. $(A \cup H \cup P)^c \cap A$ **b.** $(A \cup H \cup P)^c$
     c. $(A \cap H \cap P)^c$

In Exercises 39 through 46, let U be the set of major league baseball players and let
$$N = \{x \mid x \text{ plays for the New York Yankees}\}$$
$$S = \{x \mid x \text{ plays for the San Francisco Giants}\}$$
$$F = \{x \mid x \text{ is an outfielder}\}$$
$$H = \{x \mid x \text{ has hit 20 homers in one season}\}$$
Write the set that represents the following descriptions.

39. a. Outfielders for the New York Yankees

b. New York Yankees who have never hit 20 homers in a season

40. a. San Francisco Giants who have hit 20 homers in a season.

b. San Francisco Giants who do not play outfield.

41. a. Major league ball players who play for the New York Yankees or the San Francisco Giants.

b. Major league ball players who play for neither the New York Yankees nor the San Francisco Giants.

42. a. San Francisco Giants who have never hit 20 homers in a season.

b. Major league ball players who have never hit 20 homers in a season.

43. a. New York Yankees or San Francisco Giants who have hit 20 homers in a season.

b. Outfielders for the New York Yankees who have never hit 20 homers in a season.

44. a. Outfielders for the New York Yankees or San Francisco Giants.

b. Outfielders for the New York Yankees who have hit 20 homers in a season.

45. a. Major league outfielders who have hit 20 homers in a season and do not play for the New York Yankees or the San Francisco Giants.

b. Major league outfielders who have never hit 20 homers in a season and do not play for the New York Yankees or the San Francisco Giants.

46. a. Major league players who do not play outfield, who have hit 20 homers in a season, and do not play for the New York Yankees or the San Francisco Giants.

b. Major league players who play outfield, who have never hit 20 homers in a season, and do not play for the New York Yankees or the San Francisco Giants.

In Exercises 47 through 52, let
$$U = \{1,2,3,4,5,6,7,8,9,10\}, A = \{1,2,3,4,5\},$$
$$B = \{4,5,6,7\}, C = \{5,6,7,8,9,10\}.$$
Verify that the identities are true for these sets.

47. $A \cup (B \cup C) = (A \cup B) \cup C$

48. $A \cap (B \cap C) = (A \cap B) \cap C$

49. $A \cup (B \cap C) = (A \cup B) \cap (A \cup C)$

50. $A \cap (B \cup C) = (A \cap B) \cup (A \cap C)$

51. $(A \cup B)^c = A^c \cap B^c$

52. $(A \cap B)^c = A^c \cup B^c$

Solutions to Self-Help Exercises 4.1

1. a. $A \cup B$ is the elements in A or B. Thus $A \cup B = \{1,2,3,4,5\}$.

b. $A \cap B$ is the elements in both A and B. Thus $A \cap B = \{3,4\}$.

c. A^c is the elements not in A (but in U). Thus $A^c = \{5,6,7\}$.

d. $(A \cup B) \cap C$ is those elements in $A \cup B$ and also in C. From **a** we have

$$(A \cup B) \cap C = \{1,2,3,4,5\} \cap \{2,3,4,5,6\} = \{2,3,4,5\}$$

e. $(A \cap B) \cup C$ is those elements in $A \cap B$ or in C. Thus from **b**

$$(A \cap B) \cup C = \{3,4\} \cup \{2,3,4,5,6\} = \{2,3,4,5,6\}$$

f. $A^c \cup B \cup C$ is elements in B, or in C, or not in A. Thus

$$A^c \cup B \cup C = \{2,3,4,5,6,7\}$$

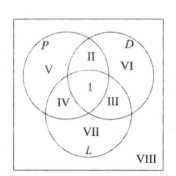

2. a. Corporations in this country that had profits and also paid a dividend last year is represented by $P \cap D$. This is regions I and II.

b. Corporations in this country that either had profits or paid a dividend last year is represented by $P \cup D$. This is regions I, II, III, IV, V, and VI.

c. Corporations in this country that did not have profits is represented by P^c. This is regions III, VI, VII, and VIII.

d. Corporations in this country that had profits, paid a dividend, and did not increase their labor force last year is represented by $P \cap D \cap L^c$. This is region II.

e. Corporations in this country that had profits or paid a dividend, and did not increase their labor force last year is represented by $(P \cup D) \cap L^c$. This is regions II, V, and VI.

4.2 The Number of Elements in a Set

APPLICATION
Breakfast Survey

> In a survey of 120 adults, 55 said they had an egg for breakfast that morning, 40 said they had juice for breakfast, and 70 said they had an egg or juice for breakfast. How many had an egg but no juice for breakfast? How many had neither an egg nor juice for breakfast? See Example 1 for the answer.

✧ Counting the Elements of a Set

This section shows the relationship between the number of elements in $A \cup B$ and the number of elements in A, B, and $A \cap B$. This is our first counting principle. The examples and exercises in this section give some applications of this. In other applications we will count the number of elements in various sets to find probability.

> **The Notation $n(A)$**
> If A is a set with a finite number of elements, we denote the number of elements in A by $n(A)$.

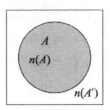

Figure 4.9

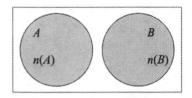

Figure 4.10

In Figure 4.9 we see the number $n(A)$ written inside the A circle and $n(A^c)$ written outside the set A. This indicates that there are $n(A)$ members in set A and $n(A^c)$ in set A^c. The number of elements in a set is also called the cardinality of the set.

There are two results that are rather apparent. First, the empty set $\emptyset$ has no elements $n(\emptyset) = 0$. For the second refer to Figure 4.10 where the two sets A and B are disjoint.

The Number in the Union of Disjoint Sets

If the sets A and B are disjoint, then

$$n(A \cup B) = n(A) + n(B)$$

A consequence of the last result is the following. In Figure 4.9, we are given a universal set U and a set $A \subset U$. Then since $A \cap A^c = \emptyset$ and $U = A \cup A^c$,

$$n(U) = n(A \cup A^c) = n(A) + n(A^c)$$

✧ Union Rule for Two Sets

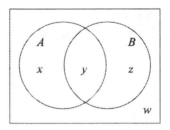

Figure 4.11

Now consider the more general case shown in Figure 4.11. We assume that x is the number in the set A that are not in B, that is, $n(A \cap B^c)$. Next we have z, the number in the set B that are not in A, $n(A^c \cap B)$. Finally, y is the number in both A and B, $n(A \cap B)$ and w is the number of elements that are neither in A nor in B, $n(A^c \cap B^c)$. Then

$$\begin{aligned} n(A \cup B) &= x + y + z \\ &= (x + y) + (y + z) - y \\ &= n(A) + n(B) - n(A \cap B) \end{aligned}$$

Alternatively, we can see that the total $n(A) + n(B)$ counts the number in the intersection $n(A \cap B)$ twice. Thus to obtain the number in the union $n(A \cup B)$, we must subtract $n(A \cap B)$ from $n(A) + n(B)$.

The Number in the Union of Two Sets

For any finite sets A and B,

$$n(A \cup B) = n(A) + n(B) - n(A \cap B)$$

EXAMPLE 1   An Application of Counting   In a survey of 120 adults, 55 said they had an egg for breakfast that morning, 40 said they had juice for breakfast, and 70 said they had an egg or juice for breakfast. How many had an egg but no juice for breakfast? How many had neither an egg nor juice for breakfast?

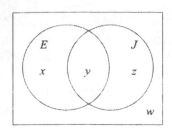

Figure 4.12a

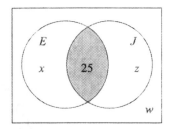

Figure 4.12b

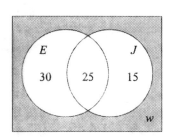

Figure 4.12c

Solution   Let U be the universal set of adults surveyed, E the set that had an egg for breakfast, and J the set that had juice for breakfast. A Venn diagram is shown in Figure 4.12a. From the survey, we have that

$$n(E) = 55 \qquad n(J) = 40, \qquad n(E \cup J) = 70$$

Note that each of these is a sum. That is $n(E) = 55 = x + y$, $n(J) = 40 = y + z$ and $n(E \cup J) = 70 = x + y + z$. Since 120 people are in the universal set, $n(U) = 120 = x + y + z + w$.

The number that had an egg and juice for breakfast is given by $n(E \cap J)$ and is shown as the shaded region in Figure 4.12b. We apply the union rule:

$$\begin{aligned} n(E \cap J) &= n(E) + n(J) - n(E \cup J) \\ &= 55 + 40 - 70 \\ &= 25 \end{aligned}$$

We first place the number 25, just found, in the $E \cap J$ area in the Venn diagram in Figure 4.12b. Since the number of people who had eggs (with and without juice) is 55, then according to Figure 4.12b,

$$\begin{aligned} n(E) = 55 &= x + 25 \\ x &= 30 \end{aligned}$$

Similarly, the number who had juice (with and without an egg) is 40. Using Figure 4.12b,

$$\begin{aligned} n(J) = 40 &= z + 25 \\ z &= 15 \end{aligned}$$

These two results are shown in Figure 4.12c. We wish to find $w = n((E \cup J)^c)$. This is shown as the shaded region in Figure 4.12c. The unshaded region is $E \cup J$. We then have that

$$\begin{aligned} n(E \cup J) + n((E \cup J)^c) &= n(U) \\ n((E \cup J)^c) &= n(U) - n(E \cup J) \\ w &= 120 - 70 \\ w &= 50 \end{aligned}$$

And so there were 50 people in the surveyed group that had neither an egg nor juice for breakfast.   ◆

✧ Counting With Three Sets

Many counting problems with sets have two sets in the universal set. We will also study applications with three sets in the universal set. The union rule for three sets is studied in the extensions for this section. In the example below, deductive reasoning is used to solve for the number of elements in each region of the Venn diagram. In cases where this will not solve the problem, systems of linear equations can be used to solve the Venn diagram. This is studied in the Chapter Project found in the Review section.

EXAMPLE 2   European Travels   In a survey of 200 people that had just returned from a trip to Europe, the following information was gathered.

- 142 visited England

- 95 visited Italy

- 65 visited Germany

- 70 visited both England and Italy

- 50 visited both England and Germany

- 30 visited both Italy and Germany

- 20 visited all three of these countries

a. How many went to England but not Italy or Germany?
b. How many went to exactly one of these three countries?
c. How many went to none of these three countries?

Solution   Let U be the set of 200 people that were surveyed and let
$$E = \{x|x \text{ visited England}\}$$
$$I = \{x|x \text{ visited Italy}\}$$
$$G = \{x|x \text{ visited Germany}\}$$

We first note that the last piece of information from the survey indicates that

$$n(E \cap I \cap G) = 20$$

Place this in the Venn diagram shown in Figure 4.13a. Recall that 70 visited both England and Italy, that is, $n(E \cap I) = 70$. If a is the number that visited England and Italy but not Germany, then, according to Figure 4.13a, $20 + a = n(E \cap I) = 70$. Thus $a = 50$. In the same way, if b is the number that visited England and Germany but not Italy, then $20 + b = n(E \cap G) = 50$. Thus $b = 30$. Also if c is the number that visited Italy and Germany but not England, then $20 + c = n(G \cap I) = 30$. Thus $c = 10$. All of this information is then shown in Figure 4.13b.

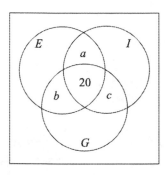

Figure 4.13a

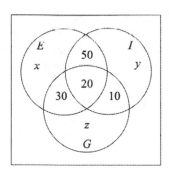

Figure 4.13b

a. Let x denote the number that visited England but not Italy or Germany. Then, according to Figure 4.13b, $20 + 30 + 50 + x = n(E) = 142$. Thus $x = 42$, that is, the number that visited England but not Italy or Germany is 42.

b. Since $n(I) = 95$, the number that visited Italy but not England or Germany is given from Figure 4.13b by $95 - (50 + 20 + 10) = 15$. Since $n(G) = 65$, the number that visited Germany but not England or Italy is, according to Figure 4.13b, given by $65 - (30 + 20 + 10) = 5$. Thus, according to Figure 4.13c, the number who visited just one of the three countries is

$$42 + 15 + 5 = 62$$

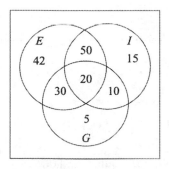

Figure 4.13c

c. There are 200 people in the U and so according to Figure 4.13c, the number that visited none of these three countries is given by
$$200 - (42 + 15 + 5 + 50 + 30 + 10 + 20) = 200 - 172 = 28 \qquad \blacklozenge$$

EXAMPLE 3   Pizzas   At the end of the day the manager of Blue Baker wanted to know how many pizzas were sold. The only information he had is listed below. Use the information to determine how many pizzas were sold.

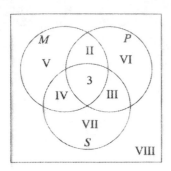

Figure 4.14a

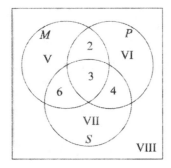

Figure 4.14b

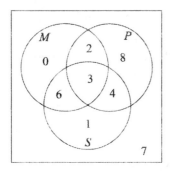

Figure 4.14c

- 3 pizzas had mushrooms, pepperoni, and sausage

- 7 pizzas had pepperoni and sausage

- 6 pizzas had mushrooms and sausage but not pepperoni

- 15 pizzas had two or more of these toppings

- 11 pizzas had mushrooms

- 8 pizzas had only pepperoni

- 24 pizzas had sausage or pepperoni

- 17 pizzas did not have sausage

Solution Begin by drawing a Venn diagram with a circle for pizzas that had mushrooms, a circle for pizzas that had pepperoni, and, pizzas that had sausage. In the center place a 3 since three pizzas had all these toppings. See Figure 4.14a.

Since 7 pizzas have pepperoni and sausage, 7 = 3 + III or III = 4. If 6 pizzas had mushrooms and sausage but not pepperoni, then IV = 6. The region for two or more of these toppings is 3 + II + III + IV = 15. Using III = 4 and IV = 6, that gives 3 + II + 4 + 6 = 15 or II = 2. This information is shown in Figure 4.14b.

Given that 11 pizzas had mushrooms, V + 2 + 3 + 6 = 11 and therefore V = 0. Since 8 pizzas had only pepperoni, VI = 8. With a total of 24 pizzas in the sausage or pepperoni region and knowing that VI = 8, we have 2 + 8 + 6 + 3 + 4 + VII = 24 or VII = 1. Finally, if 17 pizzas did not have sausage then 17 = V + 2 + VI + VIII = 0 + 2 + 8 + VIII. This gives VIII = 7 and our complete diagram is shown in Figure 4.14c.

To find the total number of pizzas sold, the 8 numbers in the completed Venn diagram are added:

$$0 + 2 + 8 + 6 + 3 + 4 + 1 + 7 = 31$$ ◆

Self-Help Exercises 4.2

1. Given that $n(A \cup B) = 100$, $n(A \cap B^c) = 50$, and $n(A \cap B) = 20$, find $n(A^c \cap B)$.

2. The registrar reported that among 2000 students, 700 did not register for a math or English course, while 400 registered for both of these two courses. How many registered for exactly one of these courses?

3. One hundred shoppers are interviewed about the contents of their bags and the following results are found:

- 40 bought apple juice
- 19 bought cookies
- 13 bought broccoli
- 1 bought broccoli, apple juice, and cookies
- 11 bought cookies and apple juice
- 2 bought cookies and broccoli but not apple juice
- 24 bought only apple juice

Organize this information in a Venn diagram and find how many shoppers bought none of these items.

4.2 Exercises

1. If $n(A) = 100$, $n(B) = 75$, and $n(A \cap B) = 40$, what is $n(A \cup B)$?

2. If $n(A) = 200$, $n(B) = 100$, and $n(A \cup B) = 250$, what is $n(A \cap B)$?

3. If $n(A) = 100$, $n(A \cap B) = 20$, and $n(A \cup B) = 150$, what is $n(B)$?

4. If $n(B) = 100$, $n(A \cup B) = 175$, and $n(A \cap B) = 40$, what is $n(A)$?

5. If $n(A) = 100$ and $n(A \cap B) = 40$, what is $n(A \cap B^c)$?

6. If $n(U) = 200$ and $n(A \cup B) = 150$, what is $n(A^c \cap B^c)$?

7. If $n(A \cup B) = 500$, $n(A \cap B^c) = 200$, $n(A^c \cap B) = 150$, what is $n(A \cap B)$?

8. If $n(A \cap B) = 50$, $n(A \cap B^c) = 200$, $n(A^c \cap B) = 150$, what is $n(A \cup B)$?

9. If $n(A \cap B) = 150$ and $n(A \cap B \cap C) = 40$, what is $n(A \cap B \cap C^c)$?

10. If $n(A \cap C) = 100$ and $n(A \cap B \cap C) = 60$, what is $n(A \cap B^c \cap C)$?

11. If $n(A) = 200$ and $n(A \cap B \cap C) = 40$, $n(A \cap B \cap C^c) = 20$, $n(A \cap B^c \cap C) = 50$, what is $n(A \cap B^c \cap C^c)$?

12. If $n(B) = 200$ and $n(A \cap B \cap C) = 40$, $n(A \cap B \cap C^c) = 20$, $n(A^c \cap B \cap C) = 50$, what is $n(A^c \cap B \cap C^c)$?

For Exercises 13 through 20, let A, B, and C be sets in a universal set U. We are given $n(U) = 100$, $n(A) = 40$, $n(B) = 37$, $n(C) = 35$, $n(A \cap B) = 25$, $n(A \cap C) = 22$, $n(B \cap C) = 24$, and $n(A \cap B \cap C^c) = 10$. Find the following values.

13. $n(A \cap B \cap C)$

14. $n(A^c \cap B \cap C)$

15. $n(A \cap B^c \cap C)$

16. $n(A \cap B^c \cap C^c)$

17. $n(A^c \cap B \cap C^c)$

18. $n(A^c \cap B^c \cap C)$

19. $n(A \cup B \cup C)$

20. $n((A \cup B \cup C))^c$

Applications

21. **Headache Medicine** In a survey of 1200 households, 950 said they had aspirin in the house, 350 said they had acetaminophen, and 200 said they had both aspirin and acetaminophen.

    a. How many in the survey had at least one of the two medications?

    b. How many in the survey had aspirin but not acetaminophen?

    c. How many in the survey had neither aspirin nor acetaminophen?

22. **Newspaper Subscriptions** In a survey of 1000 households, 600 said they received the morning paper but not the evening paper, 300 said they received both papers, and 100 said they received neither paper.

    a. How many received the evening paper but not the morning paper?

    b. How many received at least one of the papers?

23. **Course Enrollments** The registrar reported that among 1300 students, 700 students did not register for either a math or English course, 400 registered for an English course, and 300 registered for both types of courses.

    a. How many registered for an English course but not a math course?

    b. How many registered for a math course?

24. **Pet Ownership** In a survey of 500 people, a pet food manufacturer found that 200 owned a dog but not a cat, 150 owned a cat but not a dog, and 100 owned neither a dog or cat.

    a. How many owned both a cat and a dog?

    b. How many owned a dog?

25. **Fast Food** A survey by a fast-food chain of 1000 adults found that in the past month 500 had been to Burger King, 700 to McDonald's, 400 to Wendy's, 300 to Burger King and McDonald's, 250 to McDonald's and Wendy's, 220 to Burger King and Wendy's, and 100 to all three. How many went to

    a. Wendy's but not the other two?

    b. only one of them?

    c. none of these three?

26. **Investments** A survey of 600 adults over age 50 found that 200 owned some stocks and real estate but no bonds, 220 owned some real estate and bonds but no stock, 60 owned real estate but no stocks or bonds, and 130 owned both stocks and bonds. How many owned none of the three?

27. **Entertainment** A survey of 500 adults found that 190 played golf, 200 skied, 95 played tennis, 100 played golf but did not ski or play tennis, 120 skied but did not play golf or tennis, 30 played golf and skied but did not play tennis, and 40 did all three.

    a. How many played golf and tennis but did not ski?

    b. How many played tennis but did not play golf or ski?

    c. How many participated in at least one of the three sports?

28. **Transportation** A survey of 600 adults found that during the last year, 100 traveled by plane but not by train, 150 traveled by train but not by plane, 120 traveled by bus but not by train or plane, 100 traveled by both bus and plane, 40 traveled by all three, and 360 traveled by plane or train. How many did not travel by any of these three modes of transportation?

29. **Magazines** In a survey of 250 business executives, 40 said they did not read Money, Fortune, or Business Week, while 120 said they read exactly one of these three and 60 said they read exactly two of them. How many read all three?

30. **Sales** A furniture store held a sale that attracted 100 people to the store. Of these, 57 did not buy anything, 9 bought both a sofa and love seat, 8 bought both a sofa and chair, 7 bought both a love seat and chair. There were 24 sofas, 18 love seats, and 20 chairs sold. How many people bought all three items?

Extensions

31. Use a Venn diagram to show that

$$n(A \cup B \cup C) = n(A) + n(B) + n(C) \\ -n(A \cap B) - n(A \cap C) \\ -n(B \cap C) + n(A \cap B \cap C)$$

32. Give a proof of the formula in Exercise 31. Hint: Set $B \cup C = D$ and use union rule on $n(A \cup D)$. Now use the union rule two more times, recalling from the last section that $A \cap (B \cup C) = (A \cap B) \cup (A \cap C)$.

Solutions to Self-Help Exercises 4.2

1. The accompanying Venn diagram indicates that

$$n(A \cap B^c) = 50, \quad n(A \cap B) = 20, \quad z = n(A^c \cap B)$$

Then, according to the diagram,

$$50 + 20 + z = n(A \cup B) = 100$$

Thus $z = 30$.

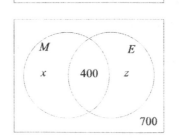

2. The number of students that registered for exactly one of the courses is the number that registered for math but not English, $x = n(M \cap E^c)$, plus the number that registered for English but not math, $z = n(M^c \cap E)$. Then, according to the accompanying Venn diagram, $x + z + 400 + 700 = 2000$. Thus $x + z = 900$. That is, 900 students registered for exactly one math or English course.

3. Let A be the set of shoppers who bought apple juice, B the set of shoppers who bought broccoli, and C the set of shoppers who bought cookies. This is shown in the first figure below. Since one shopper bought all three items, a 1 is placed in region I. Twenty-four shoppers bought only apple juice and this is region V.

Given 2 shoppers bought cookies and broccoli but not apple juice, a 2 is placed in region III. This is shown in the next figure below.

The statement "11 bought cookies and apple juice" includes those who bought broccoli and those who did not. We now know that one person bought all 3 items, so $11 - 1 = 10$ people bought cookies and apple juice but not broccoli. A 10 is placed in region IV.

Now $I + II + IV + V = 40$ as we are told "40 bought apple juice." With the 10 in region IV we know 3 of the 4 values for set A and we can solve for region II: $40 = 24 + 10 + 1 + II$ gives $II = 5$. Place this in the Venn diagram as shown in the third figure below.

Examining the figure, we can use the total of 13 in the broccoli circle to solve for VI: $18 = 5 + 1 + 2 + VI$ gives $VI = 10$. The total of 19 in the cookies circle lets us solve for VII: $10 + 1 + 2 + VII = 13$ gives $VII = 0$. The very last piece of information is that there were 100 shoppers. To solve for VIII we have $100 = 24 + 5 + 10 + 10 + 1 + 2 + 0 + VIII$ or $VIII = 48$. That is, 48 shoppers bought none of these items. The completed diagram is the final figure below.

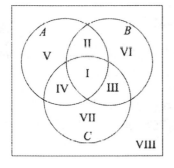 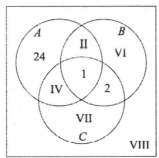 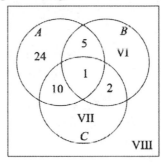 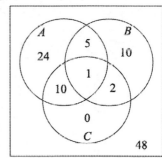

4.3 Sample Spaces and Events

Many people have a good idea of the basics of probability. That is, if a fair coin is flipped, you have an equal chance of a head or a tail showing. However, as we proceed to study more advanced concepts in probability we need some formal definitions that will both agree with our intuitive understanding of probability and allow us to go deeper into topics such as conditional probability. This will tie closely to work we have done learning about sets.

✧ The Language of Probability

We begin the preliminaries by stating some definitions. It is very important to have a clear and precise language to discuss probability so pay close attention to the exact meanings of the terms below.

Experiments and Outcomes

An experiment is an activity that has observable results.

An outcome is the result of the experiment.

The following are some examples of experiments. Flip a coin and observe whether it falls "heads" or "tails." Throw a die (a small cube marked on each face with from one to six dots[1]) and observe the number of dots on the top face. Select a transistor from a bin and observe whether or not it is defective.

The following are some additional terms that are needed.

Sample Spaces and Trials
A sample space of an experiment is the set of all possible outcomes of the experiment. Each repetition of an experiment is called a trial.

For the experiment of throwing a die and observing the number of dots on the top face the sample space is the set

$$S = \{1,2,3,4,5,6\}$$

In the experiment of flipping a coin and observing whether it falls heads or tails, the sample space is $S = \{\text{heads}, \text{tails}\}$ or simply $S = \{H, T\}$.

EXAMPLE 1   Determining the Sample Space   An experiment consists of noting whether the price of the stock of the Ford Corporation rose, fell, or remained unchanged on the most recent day of trading. What is the sample space for this experiment?

Solution   There are three possible outcomes depending on whether the price rose, fell, or remained unchanged. Thus the sample space S is

$$S = \{\text{rose}, \text{fell}, \text{unchanged}\}$$ ◆

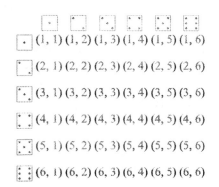

$(1, 1)\,(1, 2)\,(1, 3)\,(1, 4)\,(1, 5)\,(1, 6)$

$(2, 1)\,(2, 2)\,(2, 3)\,(2, 4)\,(2, 5)\,(2, 6)$

$(3, 1)\,(3, 2)\,(3, 3)\,(3, 4)\,(3, 5)\,(3, 6)$

$(4, 1)\,(4, 2)\,(4, 3)\,(4, 4)\,(4, 5)\,(4, 6)$

$(5, 1)\,(5, 2)\,(5, 3)\,(5, 4)\,(5, 5)\,(5, 6)$

$(6, 1)\,(6, 2)\,(6, 3)\,(6, 4)\,(6, 5)\,(6, 6)$

Figure 4.15

EXAMPLE 2   Determining the Sample Space   Two dice, identical except that one is green and the other is red, are tossed and the number of dots on the top face of each is observed. What is the sample space for this experiment?

Solution   Each die can take on its six different values with the other die also taking on all of its six different values. We can express the outcomes as order pairs. For example, (2, 3) will mean 2 dots on the top face of the green die and 3 dots on the top face of the red die. The sample space S is below. A more colorful version is shown in Figure 4.15.

$$\begin{aligned}
S = \{&(1,1),(1,2),(1,3),(1,4),(1,5),(1,6),\\
&(2,1),(2,2),(2,3),(2,4),(2,5),(2,6),\\
&(3,1),(3,2),(3,3),(3,4),(3,5),(3,6),\\
&(4,1),(4,2),(4,3),(4,4),(4,5),(4,6),\\
&(5,1),(5,2),(5,3),(5,4),(5,5),(5,6),\\
&(6,1),(6,2),(6,3),(6,4),(6,5),(6,6)\}
\end{aligned}$$ ◆

---

[1]There are also four-sided die, eight-sided die, and so on. However, the six-sided die is the most common and six-sided should be assumed when we refer to a die, unless otherwise specified.

If the experiment of tossing 2 dice consists of just observing the total number of dots on the top faces of the two dice, then the sample space would be

$$S = \{2, 3, 4, 5, 6, 7, 8, 9, 10, 11, 12\}$$

In short, the sample space depends on the precise statement of the experiment.

EXAMPLE 3   Determining the Sample Space   A coin is flipped twice to observe whether heads or tails shows; order is important. What is the sample space for this experiment?

Solution   The sample space S consists of the 4 outcomes
$$S = \{(H,H), (H,T), (T,H), (T,T)\}$$ ◆

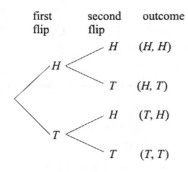

first flip   second flip   outcome

Figure 4.16

◇ Tree Diagrams

In Example 3 we completed a task (flipped a coin) and then completed another task (flipped the coin again). In these cases, the experiment can be diagrammed with a tree. The tree diagram for Example 3 is shown in Figure 4.16. We see we have a first set of branches representing the first flip of the coin. From there we flip the coin again and have a second set of branches. Then trace along each branch to find the outcomes of the experiment. If the coin is tossed a third time, there will be eight outcomes.

EXAMPLE 4   Determining the Sample Space   A die is rolled. If the die shows a 1 or a 6, a coin is tossed. What is the sample space for this experiment?

Solution   Figure 4.17 shows the possibilities. We then have

$$S = \{(1,H), (1,T), 2, 3, 4, 5, (6,H), (6,T)\}$$ ◆

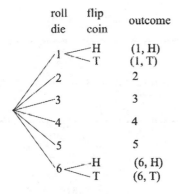

roll die   flip coin   outcome

Figure 4.17

◇ Events

We start this subsection with the following definition of an event.

> **Events and Elementary Events**
> Given a sample space S for an experiment, an **event** is any subset E of S. An **elementary (or simple) event** is an event with a single outcome.

EXAMPLE 5   Finding Events   Using the sample space from Example 3 find the events: "At least one head comes up" and "Exactly two tails come up." Are either events elementary events?

Solution   "At least one head comes up" $= \{(H,H), (H,T), (T,H)\}$
  "Exactly two tails come up" $= \{(T,T)\}$
  The second event, "Exactly two tails come up" has only one outcome and so it is an elementary event.   ◆

We can use our set language for union, intersection, and complement to describe events.

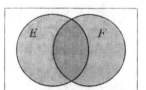

Figure 4.18

> **Union of Two Events**
> If E and F are two events, then $E \cup F$ is the union of the two events and consists of the set of outcomes that are in E or F.

Thus the event $E \cup F$ is the event that "E or F occurs." Refer to Figure 4.18 where the event $E \cup F$ is the shaded region on the Venn diagram.

> **Intersection of Two Events**
> If E and F are two events, then $E \cap F$ is the intersection of the two events and consists of the set of outcomes that are in both E and F.

Thus the event $E \cap F$ is the event that "E and F both occur." Refer to Figure 4.18 where the event $E \cap F$ is the region where E and F overlap.

> **Complement of an Event**
> If E is an event, then E^c is the complement of E and consists of the set of outcomes that are not in E.

Thus the event E^c is the event that "E does not occur."

EXAMPLE 6   Determining Union, Intersection, and Complement   Consider the sample space given in Example 2. Let E consist of those outcomes for which the number of dots on the top faces of both dice is 2 or 4. Let F be the event that the sum of the number of dots on the top faces of the two dice is 6. Let G be the event that the sum of the number of dots on the top faces of the two dice is less than 11.

a. List the elements of E and F.
b. Find $E \cup F$.
c. Find $E \cap F$.
d. Find G^c.

Solution
a. $E = \{(2,2),(2,4),(4,2),(4,4)\}$ and $F = \{(1,5),(2,4),(3,3),(4,2),(5,1)\}$
b. $E \cup F = \{(2,2),(2,4),(4,2),(4,4),(1,5),(3,3),(5,1)\}$
c. $E \cap F = \{(2,4),(4,2)\}$
d. $G^c = \{(5,6),(6,5),(6,6)\}$ ✦

If S is a sample space, $\emptyset \subseteq S$, and thus $\emptyset$ is an event. We call the event $\emptyset$ the impossible event since the event $\emptyset$ means that no outcome has occurred, whereas, in any experiment some outcome *must* occur.

The Impossible Event

The empty set, $\emptyset$, is called the **impossible event**.

For example, if H is the event that a head shows on flipping a coin and T is the event that a tail shows, then $H \cap T = \emptyset$. The event $H \cap T$ means that both heads and tails shows, which is impossible.

Since $S \subseteq S$, S is itself an event. We call S the **certainty event** since any outcome of the experiment must be in S. For example, if a fair coin is flipped, the event $H \cup T$ is certain since a head or tail must occur.

The Certainty Event

Let S be a sample space. The event S is called the **certainty event**.

We also have the following definition for mutually exclusive events. See Figure 4.19.

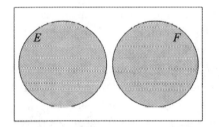

Figure 4.19

Mutually Exclusive Events

Two events E and F are said to be **mutually exclusive** if the sets are **disjoint**. That is,

$$E \cap F = \emptyset$$

Standard Deck of 52 Playing Cards

A standard deck of 52 playing cards has four 13-card suits: clubs ♣, diamonds ♢, hearts ♡, and spades ♠. The diamonds and hearts are red, while the clubs and spades are black. Each 13-card suit contains cards numbered from 2 to 10, a jack, a queen, a king, and an ace. The jack, queen, king, and ace can be considered respectively as number 11, 12, 13, and 14. In poker the ace can be either a 14 or a 1. See Figure 4.20.

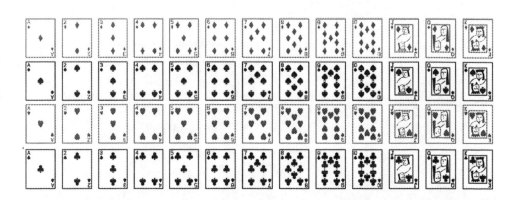

Figure 4.20

EXAMPLE 7   Determining if Sets Are Mutually Exclusive   Let a card be chosen from a standard deck of 52 cards. Let E be the event consisting of drawing a 3. Let F be the event of drawing a heart. Let G be the event of drawing a Jack. Are E and F mutually exclusive? Are E and G?

Solution   Since $E \cap F$ is the event that the card is a 3 and is a heart,

$$E \cap F = \{3\heartsuit\} \neq \emptyset$$

and so these events are not mutually exclusive. The event $E \cap G$ is the event that the card is a 3 and a jack, so

$$E \cap G = \emptyset$$

therefore E and G are mutually exclusive.   ◆

✧ Continuous Sample Spaces

In all the previous examples we were able to list each outcome in the sample space, even if the list is rather long. But consider the outcomes of an experiment where the time spent running a race is measured. Depending on how the time is measured, an outcome could be 36 seconds or 36.0032 seconds. The values of the outcomes are not restricted to whole numbers and so the sample space must be described, rather than listed. In the case of the race we could say $S = \{t | t \geq 0, t \text{ in seconds}\}$. Then the event E that a person takes less than 35 seconds to run the race would be written $E = \{t | t < 35 \text{ seconds}\}$.

EXAMPLE 8   Weighing Oranges   At a farmer's market there is a display of fresh oranges. The oranges are carefully weighed. What is a sample space for this experiment? Describe the event that a orange weighs 100 grams or more. Describe the event that a orange weighs between 200 and 250 grams.

Solution   Since the weight of the orange can be any positive number,

$$S = \{w | w > 0, w \text{ in grams}\}$$

Note that $w = 0$ is not included as if the weight was zero there would be no orange! The event that an orange weighs 100 grams or more is

$$E = \{w | w \geq 100, w \text{ in grams}\}$$

Here note that we use $\geq$, not $>$ as the value of exactly 100 grams needs to be included. The event that the orange weighs between 200 and 250 grams is

$$F = \{w | 200 < w < 250, w \text{ in grams}\}$$

where strict inequalities are used as the weight is between those values.   ◆

Self-Help Exercises 4.3

1. Two tetrahedrons (4 sided), each with equal sides numbered from 1 to 4, are identical except that one is red and the other green. If the two tetrahedrons are tossed and the number on the bottom face of each is observed, what is the sample space for this experiment?

2. Consider the sample space given in the previous exercise. Let E consist of those outcomes for which both (tetrahedron) dice show an odd number. Let F be the event that the sum of the two numbers on these dice is 5. Let G be the event that the sum of the two numbers is less than 7.

   a. List the elements of E and F.

   b. Find $E \cap F$.

   c. Find $E \cup F$.

   d. Find G^c.

3. A hospital carefully measures the length of every baby born. What is a sample space for this experiment? Describe the events

   a. the baby is longer than 22 inches.

   b. the baby is 20 inches or shorter.

   c. the baby is between 19.5 and 21 inches long.

4.3 Exercises

1. Let $S = \{a, b, c\}$ be a sample space. Find all the events.

2. Let the sample space be $S - \{a, b, c, d\}$. How many events are there?

3. A coin is flipped three times, and heads or tails is observed after each flip. What is the sample space? Indicate the outcomes in the event "at least 2 heads are observed."

4. A coin is flipped, and it is noted whether heads or tails show. A die is tossed, and the number on the top face is noted. What is the sample space of this experiment?

5. A coin is flipped three times. If heads show, one is written down. If tails show, zero is written down. What is the sample space for this experiment? Indicate the outcomes if "one is observed at least twice."

6. Two tetrahedrons (4 sided), each with equal sides numbered from 1 to 4, are identical except that one is red and the other green. If the two tetrahedrons are tossed and the number on the bottom face of each is observed, indicate the outcomes in the event "the sum of the numbers is 4."

7. An urn holds 10 identical balls except that 1 is white, 4 are black, and 5 are red. An experiment consists of selecting a ball from the urn and observing its color. What is a sample space for this experiment? Indicate the outcomes in the event "the ball is not white."

8. For the urn in Exercise 7, an experiment consists of selecting 2 balls in succession without replacement and observing the color of each of the balls. What is the sample space of this experiment? Indicate the outcomes of the event "no ball is white."

9. Ann, Bubba, Carlos, David, and Elvira are up for promotion. Their boss must select three people from this group of five to be promoted. What is the sample space? Indicate the outcomes of the event "Bubba is selected."

10. A restaurant offers six side dishes: rice, macaroni, potatoes, corn, broccoli, and carrots. A customer must select two different side dishes for his dinner. What is the sample space? List the outcomes of the event "Corn is selected."

11. An experiment consists of selecting a digit from the number 112964333 and observing it. What is a sample space for this experiment? Indicate the outcomes in the event that "an even digit."

12. An experiment consists of selecting a letter from the word CONNECTICUT and observing it. What is a

sample space for this experiment? Indicate the outcomes of the event "a vowel is selected."

13. An inspector selects 10 transistors from the production line and notes how many are defective.

    a. Determine the sample space.

    b. Find the outcomes in the set corresponding to the event E "at least 6 are defective."

    c. Find the outcomes in the set corresponding to the event F "at most 4 are defective."

    d. Find the sets $E \cup F, E \cap F, E^c, E \cap F^c, E^c \cap F^c$.

    e. Find all pairs of sets among the nonempty ones listed in part (d) that are mutually exclusive.

14. A survey indicates first whether a person is in the lower income group (L), middle income group (M), or upper income group (U), and second which of these groups the father of the person is in.

    a. Determine the sample space using the letters L, M, and U.

    b. Find the outcomes in the set corresponding to the event E "the person is in the lower income group."

    c. Find the outcomes in the set corresponding to the event F "the person is in the higher income group."

    d. Find the sets $E \cup F, E \cap F, E^c, E \cap F^c, E^c \cap F^c$.

    e. Find all pairs of sets listed in part (d) that are mutually exclusive.

15. A corporate president decides that for each of the next three fiscal years success (S) will be declared if the earnings per share of the company go up at least 10% that year and failure (F) will occur is less than 10%.

    a. Determine the sample space using the letters S and F.

    b. Find the outcomes in the set corresponding to the event E "at least 2 of the next 3 years is a success."

    c. Find the outcomes in the set corresponding to the event G "the first year is a success."

    d. Find and describe the sets $E \cup G, E \cap G, G^c$, $E^c \cap G$, and $(E \cup G)^c$.

    e. Find all pairs of sets listed in part (d) that are mutually exclusive.

16. Let E be the event that the life of a certain light bulb is at least 100 hours and F that the life is at most 200 hours. Describe the sets:

    a. $E \cap F$ **b.** F^c **c.** $E^c \cap F$ **d.** $(E \cup F)^c$

17. Let E be the event that a pencil is 10 cm or longer and F the event that the pencil is less than 25 cm. Describe the sets:

    a. $E \cap F$ **b.** E^c **c.** $E \cap F^c$ **d.** $(E \cup F)^c$

In Exercises 18 through 23, S is a sample space and E, F, and G are three events. Use the symbols $\cap$, $\cup$, and ^{c} to describe the given events.

18. F but not E

19. E but not F

20. Not F or not E

21. Not F and not E

22. Not F, nor E, nor G

23. E and F but not G

24. Let S be a sample space consisting of all the integers from 1 to 20 inclusive, E the first 10 of these, and F the last 5 of these. Find $E \cap F, E^c \cap F, (E \cup F)^c$, and $E^c \cap F^c$.

25. Let S be the 26 letters of the alphabet, E be the vowels $\{a, e, i, o, u\}$, F the remaining 21 letters, and G the first 5 letters of the alphabet. Find the events $E \cup F \cup G, E^c \cup F^c \cup G^c, E \cap F \cap G$, and $E \cup F^c \cup G$.

26. A bowl contains a penny, a nickel, and a dime. A single coin is chosen at random from the bowl. What is the sample space for this experiment? List the outcomes in the event that a penny or a nickel is chosen.

27. A cup contains four marbles. One red, one blue, one green, and one yellow. A single marble is drawn at random from the cup. What is the sample space for this experiment? List the outcomes in the event that a blue or a green marble is chosen.

Solutions to Self-Help Exercises 4.3

1. Consider the outcomes as ordered pairs, with the number on the bottom of the red one the first number and the number on the bottom of the white one the second number. The sample space is

$$S = \{\, (1,1),(1,2),(1,3),(1,4),$$
$$(2,1),(2,2),(2,3),(2,4),$$
$$(3,1),(3,2),(3,3),(3,4),$$
$$(4,1),(4,2),(4,3),(4,4)\}$$

2. **a.** $E = \{(1,1),(1,3),(3,1),(3,3)\}$, and $F = \{(1,4),(2,3),(3,2),(4,1)\}$

   b. $E \cap F = \emptyset$

   c. $E \cup F = \{(1,1),(1,3),(3,1),(3,3),(1,4),(2,3),(3,2),(4,1)\}$

   d. $G^c = \{(3,4),(4,3),(4,4)\}$

3. Since the baby can be any length greater than zero, the sample space is

$$S = \{x | x > 0, x \text{ in inches}\}$$

   a. $E = \{x | x > 22, x \text{ in inches}\}$

   b. $F = \{x | x \le 20, x \text{ in inches}\}$

   c. $G = \{x | 19.5 < x < 21, x \text{ in inches}\}$

4.4 Basics of Probability

✧ Introduction to Probability

We first consider sample spaces for which the outcomes (elementary events) are equally likely. For example, a head or tail is equally likely to come up on a flip of a fair coin. Any of the six numbers on a fair die is equally likely to come up on a roll. We will refer to a sample space S whose individual elementary events are equally likely as a uniform sample space. We then give the following definition of the probability of any event in a uniform sample space.

Probability of an Event in a Uniform Sample Space

If S is a finite uniform sample space and E is any event, then the probability of E, $P(E)$, is given by

$$P(E) = \frac{\text{Number of elements in } E}{\text{Number of elements in } S} = \frac{n(E)}{n(S)}$$

EXAMPLE 1 **Probability for a Single Die** Suppose a fair die is rolled and the sample space is $S = \{1, 2, 3, 4, 5, 6\}$. Determine the probability of each of the following events.

a. The die shows an odd number.
b. The die shows the number 9.
c. The die shows a number less than 8.

Solution **a.** We have $E = \{1, 3, 5\}$. Then

$$P(E) = \frac{n(E)}{n(S)} = \frac{3}{6} = \frac{1}{2}$$

b. The event F that the die shows a 9 is the impossible event. So $n(F) = 0$ and

$$P(F) = \frac{n(F)}{n(S)} = \frac{0}{6} = 0$$

c. The event G that the die shows a number less than 8 is just the certainty event. So $G = \{1, 2, 3, 4, 5, 6\} = S$ and

$$P(G) = \frac{n(G)}{n(S)} = \frac{6}{6} = 1 \qquad \blacklozenge$$

EXAMPLE 2 **Probability for a Single Card** Suppose a single card is randomly drawn from a standard 52-card deck. Determine the probability of each of the following events.

a. A king is drawn.
b. A heart is drawn.

Solution **a.** The event is $E = \{$ K$\diamondsuit$, K$\heartsuit$, K$\spadesuit$, K$\clubsuit \}$. So,

$$P(E) = \frac{n(E)}{n(S)} = \frac{4}{52} = \frac{1}{13}$$

b. The event F contains 13 hearts. So
$$P(F) = \frac{n(F)}{n(S)} = \frac{13}{52} = \frac{1}{4} \qquad \blacklozenge$$

EXAMPLE 3 **Probability for Transistors** A bin contains 15 identical (to the eye) transistors except that 6 are defective and 9 are not. What is the probability that a transistor selected at random is defective?

Solution Let us denote the set S to be the set of all 15 transistors and the set E to be the set of defective transistors. Then,
$$P(E) = \frac{n(E)}{n(S)} = \frac{6}{15} = \frac{2}{5} \qquad \blacklozenge$$

REMARK: What if we selected two transistors or two cards? We will learn how to handle this type of experiment in the next chapter.

EXAMPLE 4 **Probability for Two Coin Flips** A fair coin is flipped twice to observe whether heads or tails shows; order is important. What is the probability that tails occurs both times?

Solution The sample space S consists of the 4 outcomes

$$S = \{(H, H), (H, T), (T, H), (T, T)\}$$

Since we are using a fair coin, each of the individual four elementary events are equally likely. The set E that tails occurs both times is $E = \{(T, T)\}$ and contains one element. We have

$$P(E) = \frac{n(E)}{n(S)} = \frac{1}{4}$$
◆

✧ Empirical Probability

A very important type of problem that arises every day in business and science is to find a practical way to estimate the likelihood of certain events. For example, a food company may seek a practical method of estimating the likelihood that a new type of candy will be enjoyed by consumers. The most obvious procedure for the company to follow is to randomly select a consumer, have the consumer taste the candy, and then record the result. This should be repeated many times and the final totals tabulated to give the fraction of tested consumers who enjoy the candy. This fraction is then a practical estimate of the likelihood that all consumers will enjoy this candy. We refer to this fraction or number as empirical probability.

The London merchant John Graunt (1620–1674) with the publication of *Natural and Political Observations Made upon the Bills of Mortality* in 1662 seems to have been the first person to have gathered data on mortality rates and determined empirical probabilities from them. The data were extremely difficult to obtain. His then-famous London Life Table is reproduced below, showing the number of survivors through certain ages per 100 people.

Age	0	6	16	26	36	46	56	66	76
Survivors	100	64	40	25	16	10	6	3	1
London Life Table									

EXAMPLE 5 **Finding Empirical Probability** Using the London Life Table, find the empirical probability of a randomly chosen person living in London in the first half of the 17th century surviving until age 46.

Solution In the London Life Table $N = 100$. If E is the event "survive to age 46," then according to the table the corresponding number is 10. Thus, the empirical probability of people living in London at that time surviving until age 46 was $10/100 = 0.1$.
◆

Consider now a poorly made die purchased at a discount store. Dice are made by drilling holes in the sides and then backfilling. Cheap dice are, of course, not carefully backfilled. So when a lot of holes are made in a face, such as for a side with 6, and they are not carefully backfilled, that side will not be quite as heavy as the others. Thus a 6 will tend to come up more often on the top. Even a die taken from a craps table in Las Vegas, where the dice are of very high quality, will have some tiny imbalance.

EXAMPLE 6 **Finding Empirical Probability** A die with 6 sides numbered from 1 to 6, such as used in the game of craps, is suspected to be somewhat lopsided. A laboratory has tossed this die 1000 times and obtained the results shown in the table. Find the empirical probability that a 2 will occur and the probability that a 6 will occur.

Outcome	1	2	3	4	5	6
Number Observed	161	179	148	177	210	125

Solution The total number observed is 1000. The number observed for the 2 and 6, respectively is 179 and 125. So dividing these numbers by 1000 gives

$$P(2) = {}^{179}/_{1000} = 0.179$$
$$P(6) = {}^{125}/_{1000} = 0.125 \qquad \blacklozenge$$

CONNECTION
Frederick Mosteller and the Dice Experiment

Frederick Mosteller has been president of the American Association for the Advancement of Science, the Institute of Mathematical Statistics, and the American Statistical Association. He once decided that "It would be nice to see if the actual outcome of a real person tossing real dice would match up with the theory." He then engaged Willard H. Longcor to buy some dice, toss them, and keep careful records of the outcomes. Mr. Longcor then tossed the dice on his floor at home so that the dice would bounce on the floor and then up against the wall and then land back on the floor. After doing this several thousand times his wife became troubled by the noise. He then placed a rug on the floor and on the wall, and then proceeded to quietly toss his dice *millions* of times, keeping careful records of the outcomes. In fact, he was so careful and responsible about his task, that he threw away his data on the first 100,000 tosses, since he had a nagging worry that he might have made some mistake keeping perfect track.

✧ Probability Distribution Tables

A probability distribution table is a useful way to display probability data for an experiment. In a probability distribution table there is one column (or row) for the events that take place and one column (or row) for the probability of the event. The events chosen must be mutually exclusive and therefore the total probability will add to 1. This is best demonstrated through an example.

EXAMPLE 7   Flipping a Coin Twice Write the probability distribution table for the number of heads when a coin is flipped twice.

Solution Recall from Example 4 that the uniform sample space is $S = \{(H,H), (H,T), (T,H), (T,T)\}$. Next, we are asked to organize the events by the number of heads, so we will have three events

$E_1 = \{(H,H)\}$ with two heads and a probability of $1/4$,
$E_2 = \{(H,T), (T,H)\}$ with exactly one head and a probability of $2/4$
$E_3 = \{(T,T)\}$ with zero heads and a probability of $1/4$.

This is shown in the table on the left. $\blacklozenge$

Event	Probability
2 heads	$1/4$
1 head	$1/2$
0 heads	$1/4$

Note how the list of events covered all the possibilities for the number of heads and that the events are all mutually exclusive. You can't have exactly two heads and exactly one head at the same time! Next see that the sum of the probabilities is equal to one. This will always be the case when your probability distribution table is correct.

EXAMPLE 8 **Sum of the Numbers for Two Dice** Two fair dice are rolled. Find the probability distribution table for the sum of the numbers shown uppermost.

Solution Recall the uniform sample space in Example 2 of the last section for rolling two dice. We see the smallest sum is 2 from the roll (1,1) and the largest sum is 12 from the roll (6,6). Count the number of outcomes in each event to find the probability:

Sum	2	3	4	5	6	7	8	9	10	11	12
Probability	1/36	2/36	3/36	4/36	5/36	6/36	5/36	4/36	3/36	2/36	1/36

◆

EXAMPLE 9 **Weight of Oranges** A crate contains oranges and each orange is carefully weighed. It was found that 12 oranges weighed less than 100 grams, 40 oranges weighed 100 grams or more, but less than 150 grams, 60 oranges weighed 150 grams or more, but less than 200 grams, and 8 oranges weighed 200 grams or more. Organize this information in a probability distribution table

Solution The sample space for this experiment was found in the previous section to be $S = \{w | w > 0, w \text{ in grams}\}$. There are four mutually exclusive events described in this sample space and these form the basis of the probability distribution table. A total of $12 + 40 + 60 + 8 = 120$ oranges were weighed. The empirical probability that an orange weighs less than 100 grams will be the ratio $12/120$. The remaining probabilities are found in the same way. This gives the probability distribution table below where w is the weight of an orange in grams.

Event	Probability
$w < 100$	$12/120 = 1/10$
$100 \leq w < 150$	$40/120 = 1/3$
$150 \leq w < 200$	$60/120 = 1/2$
$w \geq 200$	$8/120 = 2/30$

◆

REMARK: Notice that in the probability distribution table above that there were no gaps and no overlap. It is important to be able to translate the statements like "100 grams or more" into an event $100 \leq w$.

Self-Help Exercises 4.4

1. Two tetrahedrons (4 sided), each with equal sides numbered from 1 to 4, are identical except that one is red and the other white. If the two tetrahedrons are tossed and the number on the bottom face of each is observed, what is the sample space for this experiment? Write the probability distribution table for the sum of the numbers on the bottom of the dice.

2. In the past month 72 babies were born at a local hospital. Each baby was carefully measured and it was found that 10 babies were less than 19 inches long, 12 babies were 19 inches or longer but less than 20 inches long, 32 babies were 20 inches or longer but less than 21 inches long. Organize this information in a probability distribution table.

3. An experiment consists of randomly selecting a letter from the word FINITE and observing it. What is the probability of selecting a vowel?

4.4 Exercises

In Exercises 1 through 4, a fair die is tossed. Find the probabilities of the given events.

1. an even number

2. the numbers 4 or 5

3. a number less than 5

4. any number except 2 or 5

In Exercises 5 through 10, a card is drawn randomly from a standard deck of 52 cards. Find the probabilities of the given events.

5. an ace

6. a spade

7. a red card

8. any number between 3 and 5 inclusive

9. any black card between 5 and 7 inclusive

10. a red 8

In Exercises 11 through 14, a basket contains 3 white, 4 yellow, and 5 black transistors. If a transistor is randomly picked, find the probability of each of the given events.

11. white

12. black

13. not yellow

14. black or yellow

15. A somewhat lopsided die is tossed 1000 times with 1 showing on the top face 150 times. What is the empirical probability that a 1 will show?

16. A coin is flipped 10,000 times with heads showing 5050 times. What is the empirical probability that heads will show?

17. The speed of 500 vehicles on a highway with limit of 55 mph was observed, with 400 going between 55 and 65 mph, 60 going less than 55 mph, and 40 going over 65 mph. What is the empirical probability that a vehicle chosen at random on this highway will be going **a.** under 55 mph, **b.** between 55 and 65 mph, **c.** over 65 mph.

18. In a survey of 1000 randomly selected consumers, 50 said they bought brand A cereal, 60 said they bought brand B, and 80 said they bought brand C. What is the empirical probability that a consumer will purchase **a.** brand A cereal, **b.** brand B, **c.** brand C?

19. A large dose of a suspected carcinogen has been given to 500 white rats in a laboratory experiment. During the next year, 280 rats get cancer. What is the empirical probability that a rat chosen randomly from this group of 500 will get cancer?

20. A new brand of sausage is tested on 200 randomly selected customers in grocery stores with 40 saying they like the product, the others saying they do not. What is the empirical probability that a consumer will like this brand of sausage?

21. Over a number of years the grade distribution in a mathematics course was observed to be

A	B	C	D	F
25	35	80	40	20

What is the empirical probability that a randomly selected student taking this course will receive a grade of A? B? C? D? F?

22. A store sells four different brands of VCRs. During the past year the following number of sales of each of the brands were found.

Brand A	Brand B	Brand C	Brand D
20	60	100	70

What is the empirical probability that a randomly selected customer who buys a VCR at this store will pick brand A'? brand B:' brand C'? brand D?

23. A somewhat lopsided die is tossed 1000 times with the following results. What is the empirical probability that an even number shows?

1	2	3	4	5	6
150	200	140	250	160	100

24. A retail store that sells sneakers notes the following number of sneakers of each size that were sold last year.

7	8	9	10	11	12
20	40	60	30	40	10

What is the empirical probability that a customer buys a pair of sneakers of size 7 or 12?

25. A fair coin is flipped three times, and heads or tails is observed after each flip. What is the probability of the event "at least 2 heads are observed." Refer to the answer in Exercise 3 in Section 4.3.

26. A fair coin is flipped, and it is noted whether heads or tails show. A fair die is tossed, and the number on the top face is noted. What is the probability of the event "heads shows on the coin and an even number on the die." Refer to the answer in Exercise 4 in Section 4.3.

27. A coin is flipped three times. If heads show, one is written down. If tails show, zero is written down. What is the probability of the event "one is observed at least twice." Refer to the answer in Exercise 5 in Section 4.3.

28. Two fair tetrahedrons (4 sided), each with equal sides numbered from 1 to 4, are identical except that one is red and the other white. If the two tetrahedrons are tossed and the number on the bottom face of each is observed, what is the probability of the event "the sum of the numbers is 4." Refer to the answer in Exercise 6 in Section 4.3.

In Exercises 29 through 34, assume that all elementary events in the same sample space are equally likely.

29. A fair coin is flipped three times. What is the probability of obtaining exactly 2 heads? At least 1 head?

30. A family has three children. Assuming a boy is as likely as a girl to have been born, what is the probability that two are boys and one is a girl? That at least one is a boy?

31. A fair coin is flipped and a fair die is tossed. What is the probability of obtaining a head and a 3?

32. A fair coin is flipped twice and a fair die is tossed. What is the probability of obtaining 2 heads and a 3?

33. A pair of fair dice are tossed. What is the probability of obtaining a sum of 2? 4? 8?

34. A pair of fair dice are tossed. What is the probability of obtaining a sum of 5? 6? 11?

35. An experiment consists of selecting a digit from the number 112964333 and observing it. What is the probability that "an even digit is selected."

36. An experiment consists of selecting a letter from the word CONNECTICUT and observing it. What is the probability that "a vowel is selected."

Solutions to Self-Help Exercises 4.4

1. The sample space was found in the previous section and is

$$S = \{ (1,1),(1,2),(1,3),(1,4),$$
$$(2,1),(2,2),(2,3),(2,4),$$
$$(3,1),(3,2),(3,3),(3,4),$$
$$(4,1),(4,2),(4,3),(4,4)\}$$

The sum of the numbers ranges from $1+1 = 2$ to $4+4 = 8$. Count the outcomes in each event to find

Sum	2	3	4	5	6	7	8
Probability	1/16	2/16	3/16	4/16	3/16	2/16	1/16

2. The sample space for this experiment is $S = \{x|x > 0, x \text{ in inches}\}$. The lengths of $10 + 12 + 32 = 54$ babies is given. A careful examination of the events shows that no mention was made of babies longer than 21 inches. We deduce that $72 - 54 = 18$ babies must be 21 inches or longer. This can now be arranged in a probability distribution table where x is the length of the baby in inches.

Event	Probability
$x < 19$	$10/72 = 5/36$
$19 \leq x < 20$	$12/72 = 1/6$
$20 \leq x < 21$	$32/72 = 4/9$
$x \geq 21$	$18/72 = 1/4$

3. FINITE has six letters and there are three vowels. So

$$P(\text{vowel}) = \frac{3}{6} = \frac{1}{2}$$

4.5 Rules for Probability

✧ Elementary Rules

Recall that if S is a finite uniform sample space, that is, a space for which all individual elementary elements are equally likely, and E is any event, then the probability of E, denoted by $P(E)$, is given by

$$P(E) = \frac{\text{Number of elements in } E}{\text{Number of elements in } S} = \frac{n(E)}{n(S)}$$

If E is an event in a sample space then $0 \leq n(E) \leq n(S)$. Dividing this by $n(S)$ then gives

$$0 \leq \frac{n(E)}{n(S)} \leq \frac{n(S)}{n(S)} = 1$$

Using the definition of probability given above yields

$$0 \leq P(E) \leq 1$$

This is our first rule for probability. Notice also that

$$P(S) = \frac{n(S)}{n(S)} = 1 \quad \text{and} \quad P(\emptyset) = \frac{n(\emptyset)}{n(S)} = \frac{0}{n(S)} = 0$$

These rules apply for events in any sample space; however, the derivations just given are valid only for spaces with equally likely events.

Elementary Rules for Probability

For any event E in a sample space S we have

$$0 \leq P(E) \leq 1 \qquad P(S) = 1 \qquad P(\emptyset) = 0$$

✧ Union Rule for Probability

We would now like to determine the probability of the union of two events E and F. We start by recalling the union rule for sets:

$$n(E \cup F) = n(E) + n(F) - n(E \cap F)$$

Now divide both sides of this last equation by $n(S)$ and obtain

$$\frac{n(E \cup F)}{n(S)} = \frac{n(E)}{n(S)} + \frac{n(F)}{n(S)} - \frac{n(E \cap F)}{n(S)}$$

By the definition of probability given above this becomes

$$P(E \cup F) = P(E) + P(F) - P(E \cap F)$$

This is called the **union rule for probability**. This rule applies for events in any sample space; however, the derivation just given is valid only for spaces with equally likely events.

Union Rule for Probability

$$P(E \cup F) = P(E) + P(F) - P(E \cap F)$$

EXAMPLE 1 Union Rule With Drawing a Card A single card is randomly drawn from a standard deck of cards. What is the probability that it will be a red card or a king.

Solution Let R be the set of red cards and let K be the set of kings. Red cards consist of hearts and diamonds, so there are 26 red cards. Therefore $P(R) = 26/52$. There are 4 kings, so $P(K) = 4/52$. Among the 4 kings, there are 2 red cards. So, $P(R \cap K) = 2/52$. Using the union rule gives

$$P(R \cup K) = P(R) + P(K) - P(R \cap K)$$
$$= \frac{26}{52} + \frac{4}{52} - \frac{2}{52}$$
$$= \frac{28}{52} = \frac{7}{13}$$

◆

REMARK: It is likely that you would intuitively use the union rule had you been asked to pick out all of the cards from the deck that were red or kings. You would choose out all of the red cards along with all of the kings for a total of 28 cards.

EXAMPLE 2 Union Rule With Two Dice Two dice, identical except that one is green and the other is red, are tossed and the number of dots on the top face of each is observed. Let E consist of those outcomes for which the number of dots on the top face of the green dice is a 1 or 2. Let F be the event that the sum of the number of dots on the top faces of the two dice is 6. Find the probability that a 1 or 2 will be on the top of the green die or the sum of the two numbers will be 6.

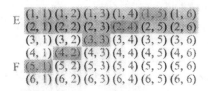

$$E \begin{array}{llllll} (1,1) & (1,2) & (1,3) & (1,4) & (1,5) & (1,6) \\ (2,1) & (2,2) & (2,3) & (2,4) & (2,5) & (2,6) \\ (3,1) & (3,2) & (3,3) & (3,4) & (3,5) & (3,6) \\ (4,1) & (4,2) & (4,3) & (4,4) & (4,5) & (4,6) \\ (5,1) & (5,2) & (5,3) & (5,4) & (5,5) & (5,6) \\ (6,1) & (6,2) & (6,3) & (6,4) & (6,5) & (6,6) \end{array}$$

Figure 4.21

Solution   Notice that

$$E = \{(1,1),(1,2),\cdots,(1,6),(2,1),(2,2),\cdots,(2,6)\}$$
$$F = \{(1,5),(2,4),(3,3),(4,2),(5,1)\}$$
$$E \cap F = \{(1,5),(2,4)\}$$

The set that a 1 or 2 will be on the top of the green die and the sum of the two numbers will be 6 is $E \cap F$. To find $p(E \cap F)$ use the union rule of probability and obtain

$$P(E \cup F) = P(E) + P(F) - P(E \cap F)$$
$$= \frac{12}{36} + \frac{5}{36} - \frac{2}{36} = \frac{15}{36}$$

Alternatively, you can draw the sample space for two dice and circle all outcomes that have a 1 or 2 on the top of the green die or the sum of the two numbers shown uppermost is 6. This is done in Figure 4.21. Counting the circled outcomes we find there are 15 of them.   ◆

Consider two events E and F that are mutually exclusive, that is, $E \cap F) = \emptyset$. Then $P(E \cap F) = 0$. Using the union rule of probability for these two sets gives

$$P(E \cup F) = P(E) + P(F) - P(E \cap F)$$
$$= P(E) + P(F) - 0$$
$$= P(E) + P(F)$$

We then have the following rule:

Union Rule for Mutually Exclusive Events
If E and F are mutually exclusive events, then

$$P(E \cup F) = P(E) + P(F)$$

For any event E in a sample space, $E \cup E^c = S$ and $E \cap E^c = \emptyset$. So, E and E^c are mutually exclusive. Using the union rule for mutually exclusive events we have that

$$P(E) + P(E^c) = P(E \cup E^c) = P(S) = 1$$

So, $P(E^c) = 1 - P(E)$ and $P(E) = 1 - P(E^c)$. We call this the complement rule.

Complement Rule for Probability

$$P(E^c) = 1 - P(E) \qquad P(E) = 1 - P(E^c)$$

EXAMPLE 3   Complement Rule for Two Dice   Consider the dice described in Example 2. What is the probability that the sum of the two numbers is less than 12.

Solution   Let E be the event that the sum of the two numbers is less than 12. Then we wish to find $P(E)$. It is tedious to find this directly. Notice that $E^c = \{(6,6)\}$. Now use the complement rule.

$$P(E) = 1 - P(E^c) = 1 - \frac{1}{36} = \frac{35}{36} \qquad \blacklozenge$$

EXAMPLE 4   Finding Empirical Probability   A die with 6 sides numbered from 1 to 6, such as used in the game of craps, is suspected to be somewhat lopsided. A laboratory has tossed this die 1000 times and obtained the results shown in the table. Find the empirical probability that an even number will occur.

Outcome	1	2	3	4	5	6
Number Observed	161	179	148	177	210	125

Solution   The total number observed is 1000. The number observed for the 2, 4, and 6, respectively is 179, 177, and 125. So dividing these numbers by 1000 gives

$$P(2) = {}^{179}/_{1000} = 0.179$$
$$P(4) = {}^{177}/_{1000} = 0.177$$
$$P(6) = {}^{125}/_{1000} = 0.125$$

To find the empirical probability of an even number these three values can be added as the events are mutually exclusive. That is,

$$P(\text{even}) = P(2) + P(4) + P(6) = 0.179 + 0.177 + 0.125 = 0.481 \qquad \blacklozenge$$

EXAMPLE 5   Finding the Probability of an Event   A salesman makes two stops when in Pittsburgh. The first stop yields a sale 10% of the time, the second stop 15% of the time, and both stops yield a sale 4% of the time. What proportion of the time does a trip to Pittsburgh result in no sales?

Solution   Let E be the event a sale is made at the first stop and F the event that a sale is made at the second stop. What should we make of the statement that the first stop yields a sale 10% of the time. It seems reasonable to assume that the salesman or his manager have looked at his sales data and estimated the 10% number. We then take the 10% or 0.10 as the empirical probability. We interpret the other percentages in a similar way. We then have

$$P(E) = 0.10 \qquad P(F) = 0.15 \qquad P(E \cap F) = 0.04$$

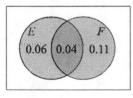

Figure 4.22

Since $P(E \cap F) = 0.04$, we place 0.04 in the region $E \cap F$ in Figure 4.22. Now since $P(E) = 0.10$, we can see that $P(E \cap F^c) = 0.10 - 0.04 = 0.06$. In a similar fashion we have $P(E^c \cap F) = 0.15 - 0.04 = 0.11$. Thus, we readily see from Figure 4.22 that

$$P(E \cup F) = 0.06 + 0.04 + 0.11 = 0.21$$

Then by the complement rule we have

$$P((E \cup F)^c) = 1 - P(E \cup F) = 1 - 0.21 = 0.79$$

Thus no sale is made in Pittsburgh 79% of the time. $\qquad \blacklozenge$

REMARK: We could have obtained $P(E \cup F)$ directly from the union rule as follows:

$$P(E \cup F) = P(E) + P(F) - P(E \cap F) = 0.10 + 0.15 - 0.04 = 0.21$$

EXAMPLE 6 **Finding the Probability of an Event** The probability that any of the first five numbers of a loaded die will come up is the same while the probability that a 6 comes up is 0.25. What is the probability that a 1 will come up?

Solution We are given $P(1) = P(2) = P(3) = P(4) = P(5)$, $P(6) = 0.25$. Also, all the probabilities must add up to 1, so

$$
\begin{aligned}
1 &= P(1) + P(2) + P(3) + P(4) + P(5) + P(6) \\
&= 5P(1) + 0.25 \\
5P(1) &= 0.75 \\
P(1) &= 0.15
\end{aligned}
$$

$\blacklozenge$

EXAMPLE 7 **Continuous Sample Space** Arrange the following information in a probability distribution table: A crop of apples is brought in for weighing. It is found that 10% of the apples weigh less than 100 gm, 40% weigh 200 gm or less, and 25% weigh more than 300 gm.

Solution If we let x = weight of an apple in grams then

Event	Probability
$0 \leq x < 100$ gm	0.10
100 gm $\leq x \leq 200$ gm	0.30
200 gm $< x \leq 300$ gm	0.35
$x > 300$ gm	0.25

Note that the 40% of the apples that weigh 200 gm or less includes the 10% that weigh less than 100 grams. Since the events in a probability distribution table must be mutually exclusive, the 30% that weigh 100 grams or more and 200 grams or less are shown in the second row. The third row of the table is found using deductive reasoning as the total probability must be 1 and there is a gap in the events. $\blacklozenge$

$\diamondsuit$ Odds (Optional)

One can interpret probabilities in terms of odds in a bet. Suppose in a sample space S we are given an event E with probability $P = P(E) = \frac{5}{7}$. In the long term we expect E to occur 5 out of 7 times. Now, $P(E^c) = \frac{2}{7}$ and in the long term we expect that E^c to occur 2 out of 7 times. Then we say that the odds in favor of E are 5 to 2.

> **Odds**
>
> The odds in favor of an event E are defined to be the ratio of $P(E)$ to $P(E^c)$, or
>
> $$\frac{P(E)}{P(E^c)} = \frac{P(E)}{1 - P(E)}$$

Often the ratio $P(E)/P(E^c)$ is reduced to lowest terms, a/b, and then we say that the odds are a to b or a:b.

EXAMPLE 8   Determining the Odds of an Event   You believe that a horse has a probability of $1/4$ of winning a race. What are the odds of this horse winning? What are the odds of this horse losing? What profit should a winning $2 bet return to be fair?

Solution   Since the probability of winning is $P = 1/4$, the odds of winning are

$$\frac{P}{1 - P} = \frac{1/4}{1 - 1/4} = \frac{1/4}{3/4} = \frac{1}{3}$$

that is: 1 to 3 or 1:3.

Since the probability of winning is $\frac{1}{4}$, the probability of losing is $1 - 1/4 = 3/4$. Then the odds for losing is

$$\frac{3/4}{1 - 3/4} = \frac{3/4}{1/4} = \frac{3}{1}$$

or 3 to 1 or 3:1. Since the fraction $3/1$ can also be written as $6/2$ with odds 6 to 2, a fair $2 bet should return $6 for a winning ticket.   ◆

Notice that making this same bet many times, we expect to win $6 one-fourth of the time and lose $2 three-fourths of the time. So, for example, on every four bets we would expect to win $6 once and lose $2 three times. Our average winnings would be $6(1) - 2(3) = 0$ dollars.

If the odds for an event E are given as a/b, we can calculate the probability $P(E)$. We have

$$\frac{a}{b} = \frac{P(E)}{1 - P(E)}$$
$$a(1 - P(E)) = bP(E)$$
$$a = bP(E) + aP(E)$$
$$= P(E)(a + b)$$
$$P(E) = \frac{a}{a + b}$$

> **Obtaining Probability From Odds**
> Suppose that the odds for an event E occurring is given as a/b or $a : b$, then
>
> $$P(E) = \frac{a}{a + b}$$

REMARK: One can think of the odds a:b of event E as saying if this experiment was carried out $a+b$ times, then a of those times E would have occurred. Our definition of empirical probability then says $P(E) = \frac{a}{a+b}$

EXAMPLE 9 **Obtaining Probability From Odds** At the race track, the odds for a horse winning is listed at $3/2$. What is the probability that the horse will win.

Solution Using the above formula for odds a/b, we have

$$P = \frac{a}{a+b} = \frac{3}{3+2} = 0.60$$

◆

Self-Help Exercises 4.5

1. If $S = \{a,b,c\}$ with $P(a) = P(b) = 2P(c)$, find $P(a)$.

2. A company has bids on two contracts. They believe that the probability of obtaining the first contract is 0.4 and of obtaining the second contract is 0.3, while the probability of obtaining both contracts is 0.1.

   a. Find the probability that they will obtain exactly one of the contracts.

   b. Find the probability that they will obtain neither of the contracts.

3. What are the odds that the company in the previous exercise will obtain both of the contracts?

4.5 Exercises

In all the following, S is assumed to be a sample space.

1. Let $S = \{a,b,c\}$ with $P(a) = 0.1$, $P(b) = 0.4$, and $P(c) = 0.5$. Let $E = \{a,b\}$ and $F = \{b,c\}$. Find $P(E)$ and $P(F)$.

2. Let $S = \{a,b,c,d,e,f\}$ with $P(a) = 0.1$, $P(b) = 0.2$, $P(c) = 0.25$, $P(d) = 0.15$, $P(e) = 0.12$, and $P(f) = 0.18$. Let $E = \{a,b,c\}$ and $F = \{c,d,e,f\}$ and find $P(E)$ and $P(F)$.

3. Let $S = \{a,b,c,d,e,f\}$ with $P(b) = 0.2$, $P(c) = 0.25$, $P(d) = 0.15$, $P(e) = 0.12$, and $P(f) = 0.1$. Let $E = \{a,b,c\}$ and $F = \{c,d,e,f\}$. Find $P(a)$, $P(E)$, and $P(F)$.

4. Let $S = \{a,b,c,d,e,f\}$ with $P(b) = 0.3$, $P(c) = 0.15$, $P(d) = 0.05$, $P(e) = 0.2$, $P(f) = 0.13$. Let $E = \{a,b,c\}$ and $F = \{c,d,e,f\}$. Find $P(a)$, $P(E)$, and $P(F)$.

5. If $S = \{a,b,c,d\}$ with $P(a) = P(b) = P(c) = P(d)$, find $P(a)$.

6. If $S = \{a,b,c\}$ with $P(a) = P(b)$ and $P(c) = 0.4$, find $P(a)$.

7. If $S = \{a,b,c,d,e,f\}$ with $P(a) = P(b) = P(c) = P(d) = P(e) = P(f)$, find $P(a)$.

8. If $S = \{a,b,c\}$ with $P(a) = 2P(b) = 3P(c)$, find $P(a)$.

9. If $S = \{a,b,c,d,e,f\}$ with $P(a) = P(b) = P(c)$, $P(d) = P(e) = P(f) = 0.1$, find $P(a)$.

10. If $S = \{a,b,c,d,e,f\}$ and if $P(a) = P(b) = P(c)$, $P(d) = P(e) = P(f)$, $P(d) = 2P(a)$, find $P(a)$.

11. If E and F are two disjoint events in S with $P(E) = 0.2$ and $P(F) = 0.4$, find $P(E \cup F)$, $P(E^c)$, and $P(E \cap F)$.

12. Why is it not possible for E and F to be two disjoint events in S with $P(E) = 0.5$ and $P(F) = 0.7$?

13. If E and F are two disjoint events in S with $P(E) = 0.4$ and $P(F) = 0.3$, find $P(E \cup F)$, $P(F^c)$, $P(E \cap F)$, $P((E \cup F)^c)$, and $P((E \cap F)^c)$.

14. Why is it not possible for $S = \{a,b,c\}$ with $P(a) = 0.3$, $P(b) = 0.4$, and $P(c) = 0.5$?

15. Let E and F be two events in S with $P(E) = 0.3$, $P(F) = 0.5$, and $P(E \cap F) = 0.2$. Find $P(E \cap F)$ and $P(E \cap F^c)$.

16. Let E and F be two events in S with $P(E) = 0.3$, $P(F) = 0.5$, and $P(E \cap F) = 0.2$. Find $P(E^c \cap F)$ and $P(E^c \cap F^c)$.

17. Let E and F be two events in S with $P(E) = 0.3$, $P(F) = 0.5$, and $P(E \cup F) = 0.6$. Find $P(E \cap F)$ and $P(E \cap F^c)$.

18. Why is it not possible to have E and F two events in S with $P(E) = 0.3$ and $P(E \cap F) = 0.5$?

In Exercises 19 through 22, let E, F, and G be events in S with $P(E) = 0.55$, $P(F) = 0.4$, $P(G) = 0.45$, $P(E \cap F) = 0.3$, $P(E \cap G) = 0.2$, $P(F \cap G) = 0.15$, and $P(E \cap F \cap G) = 0.1$.

19. Find $P(E \cap F \cap G^c)$, $P(E \cap F^c \cap G)$, and $P(E \cap F^c \cap G^c)$.

20. Using the results of the previous exercise, find $P(E^c \cap F \cap G)$, $P(E^c \cap F \cap G^c)$, and $P(E^c \cap F^c \cap G)$.

21. Using the results of the previous two exercises, find $P(E \cup F \cup G)$.

22. Using the results of the previous three exercises, find $P(E^c \cup F^c \cup G^c)$.

23. For the loaded die in Example 6 of the text, what are the odds that

a. a 2 will occur   **b.** a 6 will occur?

24. For the loaded die in Example 6 of the text, what are the odds that

a. a 3 will occur   **b.** a 1 will occur?

25. A company believes it has a probability of 0.40 of receiving a contract. What is the odds that it will?

26. In Example 5 of the text, what are the odds that the salesman will make a sale on

a. the first stop   **b.** on the second stop

c. on both stops?

27. It is known that the odds that E will occur are 1:3 and that the odds that F will occur are 1:2, and that both E and F cannot occur. What are the odds that E or F will occur?

28. If the odds for a successful marriage are 1:2, what is the probability for a successful marriage?

29. If the odds for the Giants winning the World Series are 1:4, what is the probability that the Giants will win the Series?

Applications

30. **Bidding on Contracts** An aerospace firm has three bids on government contracts and knows that the contracts are most likely to be divided up among a number of companies. The firm decides that the probability of obtaining exactly one contract is 0.6, of exactly two contracts is 0.15, and of exactly three contracts is 0.04. What is the probability that the firm will obtain at least one contracts? No contracts?

31. **Quality Control** An inspection of computers manufactured at a plant reveals that 2% of the monitors are defective, 3% of the keyboards are defective, and 1% of the computers have both defects.

a. Find the probability that a computer at this plant has at least one of these defects.

b. Find the probability that a computer at this plant has none of these defects.

32. **Medicine** A new medication produces headaches in 5% of the users, upset stomach in 15%, and both in 2%.

a. Find the probability that at least one of these side effects occurs.

b. Find the probability that neither of these side effects occurs.

33. **Manufacturing** A manufactured item is guaranteed for one year and has three critical parts. It has been decided that during the first year the probability of failure of the first part is 0.03, of the second part 0.02, the third part 0.01, both the first and second is 0.005, both the first and third is 0.004, both the second and third is 0.003, and all three parts 0.001.

a. What is the probability that exactly one of these parts will fail in the first year?

b. What is the probability that at least one of these parts will fail in the first year?

c. What is the probability that none of these parts will fail in the first year?

34. **Marketing** A survey of business executives found that 40% read *Business Week*, 50% read *Fortune*, 40% read *Money*, 17% read both *Business Week* and *Fortune*, 15% read both both *Business Week* and *Money*, 14% read both *Fortune* and *Money*, and 8% read all three of these magazines.

a. What is the probability that one of these executives reads exactly one of these three magazines?

b. What is the probability that one of these executives reads at least one of these three magazines?

c. What is the probability that one of these executives reads none of these three magazines?

35. **Advertising** A firm advertises three different products, A, B, and C, on television. From past experience, it expects 1.5% of listeners to buy exactly one of the products, 1% to buy exactly two of the products, 1.2% to buy A, 0.4% to buy both A and B, 0.3% to buy both A and C, and 0.6% to buy A but not the other two.

a. Find the probability that a listener will buy only B or only C.

b. Find the probability that a listener will buy all three.

c. Find the probability that a listener will buy both B and C.

d. Find the probability that a listener will buy none of the three.

36. **Sales** A salesman always makes a sale at one of the three stops in Atlanta and 30% of the time makes a sale at only the first stop, 15% at only the second stop, 20% at only the third stop, and 35% of the time at exactly two of the stops. Find the probability that the salesman makes a sale at all three stops in Atlanta.

Extensions

37. Let E and F be two events in S with $P(E) = 0.5$ and $P(F) = 0.7$. Just how small could $P(E \cap F)$ possibly be?

38. Let E and F be two events in S with $P(E) = 0.3$ and $P(F) = 0.4$. Just how large could $P(F \cup F)$ possibly be?

39. You buy a new die and toss it 1000 times. A 1 comes up 165 times. Is it true that the probability of a 1 showing on this die is 0.165?

40. A fair coin is to be tossed 100 times. Naturally you expect tails to come up 50 times. After 60 tosses, heads has come up 40 times. Is it true that now heads is likely to come up less often than tails during the next 40 tosses?

41. You are playing a game at a casino and have correctly calculated the probability of winning any one game to be 0.48. You have played for some time and have won 60% of the time. You are on a roll. Should you keep playing?

42. You are watching a roulette game at a casino and notice that red has been coming up unusually often. (Red should come up as often as black.) Is it true that, according to "the law of averages," black is likely to come up unusually often in the next number of games to "even things up"?

43. You buy a die and toss it 1000 times and notice that a 1 came up 165 times. You decide that the probability of a 1 on this die is 0.165. Your friend takes this die and tosses it 1000 times and notes that a 1 came up 170 times. He concludes that the probability of a 1 is 0.17. Who is correct?

44. People who frequent casinos and play lotteries are gamblers, but those who run the casinos and lotteries are not. Do you agree? Why or why not?

Solutions to Self-Help Exercises 4.5

1. If $S = \{a, b, c\}$ and $P(a) = P(b) = 2P(c)$, then

$$1 = P(a) + P(b) + P(c)$$
$$= P(a) + P(a) + 0.5P(a)$$
$$= 2.5P(a)$$
$$P(a) = 0.4$$

2. **a.** Let E be the event that the company obtains the first contract and let F be the event that the company obtains the second contract. The event that the company obtains the first contract but not the second is $E \cap F^c$, while

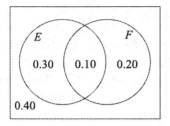

the event that the company obtains the second contract but not the first is $E^c \cap F$. These two sets are mutually exclusive, so the probability that the company receives exactly one of the contracts is

$$P(E \cap F^c) + P(E^c \cap F)$$

Now $P(E) = 0.40$, $P(F) = 0.30$, and since $E \cap F$ is the event that the company receives both contracts, $P(E \cap F) = 0.10$. Notice on the accompanying diagram that $E \cap F^c$ and $E \cap F$ are mutually disjoint and that $(E \cap F^c) \cup (E \cap F) = E$. Thus

$$P(E \cap F^c) + P(E \cap F) = P(E)$$
$$P(E \cap F^c) + 0.10 = 0.40$$
$$P(E \cap F^c) = 0.30$$

Also notice on the accompanying diagram that $E^c \cap F$ and $E \cap F$ are mutually disjoint and that $(E^c \cap F) \cup (E \cap F) = F$. Thus

$$P(E^c \cap F) + P(E \cap F) = P(F)$$
$$P(E^c \cap F) + 0.10 = 0.30$$
$$P(E \cap F^c) = 0.20$$

Thus the probability that the company will receive exactly one of the contracts is

$$P(E \cap F^c) + P(E^c \cap F) = 0.30 + 0.20 = 0.50$$

b. The event that the company obtains neither contract is given by $(E \cup F)^c$. From the diagram

$$P(E \cup F) = 0.30 + 0.10 + 0.20 = 0.60$$

Thus

$$P((E \cup F)^c) = 1 - P(E \cup F) = 1 - 0.60 = 0.40$$

The probability that the company receives neither contract is 0.40.

4.6 Conditional Probability

APPLICATION
Locating Defective Parts

A company makes the components for a product at a central location. These components are shipped to three plants, 1, 2, and 3, for assembly into a final product. The percentages of the product assembled by the three plants are, respectively, 50%, 20%, and 30%. The percentages of defective products coming from these three plants are, respectively, 1%, 2%, and 3%. What is the probability of randomly choosing a product made by this company that is defective from Plant 1? See Example 4 for the answer.

✦ Definition of Conditional Probability

The probability of an event is often affected by the occurrences of other events. For example, there is a certain probability that an individual will die of lung cancer. But if a person smokes heavily, then the probability that this person will die of lung cancer is higher. That is, the probability has changed with the additional information. In this section we study such conditional probabilities. This important idea is further developed in the next section.

Given two events E and F, we call the probability that E will occur given that F has occurred the conditional probability and write $P(E|F)$. Read this as "*the probability of E given F.*"

Conditional probability normally arises in situations where the old probability is "updated" based on new information. This new information is usually a change in the sample space. Suppose, for example, a new family moves in next door. The real estate agent mentions that this new family has two children. Based on this information, you can calculate the probability that both children are boys. Now a neighbor mentions that they met one child from the new family and this child is a boy. Now the probability that both children from the new family are boys has changed given this new information. We will find this new probability in Example 2.

EXAMPLE 1   Finding Conditional Probability   A card is drawn randomly from a deck of 52 cards.

a. What is the probability that this card is an ace?

b. What is the probability that this card is an ace given that the card is known to be red and 10 or higher?

Solution

a. The uniform sample space consists of 52 cards and has the uniform probability. Thus, if $E = \{x|x \text{ is an ace}\}$,

$$P(E) = \frac{n(E)}{n(S)} = \frac{4}{52}$$

b. Let F be the event in S consisting of all red cards 10 or higher. We have $n(S) = 52$ and $n(F) = 10$. Since we are certain that the card chosen was red and 10 or higher, our sample space is no longer the entire deck of 52 cards, but simply those 10 cards in F. This will be our denominator in the ratio of outcome in our event to outcomes in our sample space. The event ace and known to be red and 10 or higher, has two outcomes as there are two red aces. So the numerator will be $n(E \cap F) = 2$. Putting this together we have the probability of E given that F has occurred is

$$P(E|F) = \frac{n(E \cap F)}{n(F)} = \frac{2}{10} \qquad \blacklozenge$$

It can be helpful to divide the numerator and denominator in the last fraction by $n(S)$ and obtain

$$P(E|F) = \frac{n(E \cap F)}{n(F)} = \frac{n(E \cap F)/n(S)}{n(F)/n(S)}$$

But this is just

$$P(E|F) = \frac{P(E \cap F)}{P(F)}$$

This motivates the following definition for any event E and F in a sample space S.

Conditional Probability

Let E and F be two events in a sample space S. The conditional probability that E occurs given that F has occurred is defined to be

$$P(E|F) = \frac{P(E \cap F)}{P(F)}$$

REMARK: It is worthwhile to notice that the events E, F, and $E \cap F$ are all in the original sample space S and $P(E)$, $P(F)$, and $P(E \cap F)$ are all probabilities defined on S. However, we can think of $P(E|F)$ as a probability defined on the new sample space $S' = F$. See Figure 4.23.

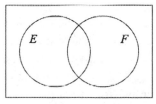

Old Sample Space   New Sample Space

Figure 4.23

EXAMPLE 2 **Calculating a Conditional Probability** A new family has moved in next door and is known to have two children. Find the probability that both children are boys given that at least one is a boy. Assume that a boy is as likely as a girl.

Solution Let E be the event that both children are a boy and F the event that at least one is a boy. Then

$$S = \{BB, BG, GB, GG\}, E = \{BB\}, F = \{BB, BG, GB\}, E \cap F = \{BB\}$$

and

$$P(E|F) = \frac{P(E \cap F)}{P(F)} = \frac{1/4}{3/4} = \frac{1}{3} \qquad \blacklozenge$$

✧ The Product Rule

We will now see how to write $P(E \cap F)$ in terms of a product of two probabilities. From the definition of conditional probability, we have

$$P(E|F) = \frac{P(E \cap F)}{P(F)}, \qquad P(F|E) = \frac{P(F \cap E)}{P(E)}$$

if $P(E) > 0$ and $P(F) > 0$. Solving for $P(E \cap F)$ and $P(F \cap E)$, we obtain

$$P(E \cap F) = P(F)P(E|F), \qquad P(F \cap E) = P(E)P(F|E)$$

Since $P(E \cap F) = P(F \cap E)$, it follows that

$$P(E \cap F) = P(F)P(E|F) = P(E)P(F|E)$$

This is called the product rule.

Product Rule
If E and F are two events in a sample space S with $P(E) > 0$ and $P(F) > 0$, then

$$P(E \cap F) = P(F)P(E|F) = P(E)P(F|E)$$

EXAMPLE 3   Using the Product Rule   Two bins contain transistors. The first bin has 5 defective and 15 non-defective transistors while the second bin has 3 defective and 17 non-defective transistors. If the probability of picking either bin is the same, what is the probability of picking the first bin and a good transistor?

Solution   The sample space is $S = \{1D, 1N, 2D, 2N\}$ where the number refers to picking the first or second bin and the letter refers to picking a defective (D) or non-defective (N) transistor.

If E is the event "pick the first bin" and F is the event "pick a non-defective transistor," then $E = \{1D, 1N\}$ and $F = \{1N, 2N\}$. The probability of picking a non-defective transistor given that the first bin has been picked is the conditional probability $P(F|E) = 15/20$. The event "picking the first bin and a non-defective transistor" is $E \cap F$. From the product rule

$$P(E \cap F) = P(E)P(F|E) = \frac{1}{2} \cdot \frac{15}{20} = \frac{3}{8} \qquad \blacklozenge$$

✧ Probability Trees

We shall now consider a finite sequence of experiments in which the outcomes and associated probabilities of each experiment depend on the outcomes of the preceding experiments. For example, we can choose a card from a deck of cards, place the picked card on the table, and then pick another card from the deck. This process could continue until all the cards are picked.

Such a finite sequence of experiments is called a finite stochastic process. Stochastic processes can be effectively described by probability trees that we now consider. The following example should be studied carefully since we will return to it in the next section.

EXAMPLE 4   Using a Probability Tree   A company makes the components for a product at a central location. These components are shipped to three plants, 1, 2, and 3, for assembly into a final product. The percentage of the product assembled by the three plants are, respectively, 50%, 20%, and 30%. The percentages of defective products coming from these three plants are, respectively, 1%, 2%, and 3%.

a. What is the probability of randomly choosing a product made by this company that is defective from Plant 1?, 2?, 3?

b. What is the probability of randomly choosing a product made by this company that is defective?

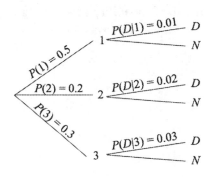

Figure 4.24

Solution   The probability of the part being assembled in Plant 1 is $P(1) = 0.5$, in Plant 2 is $P(2) = 0.2$, and in Plant 3 is $P(3) = 0.3$. We begin our tree with this information as shown in Figure 4.24. Notice how this is similar to the trees drawn in earlier sections with the only difference being the probability of the outcome being placed on the branch leading to that outcome.

We are also given the conditional probabilities, $P(D|1) = 0.01$, $P(D|2) = 0.02$, and $P(D|3) = 0.03$. The branch leading from Plant 1 to a defective item tells us that we are referring to items from Plant 1 and therefore the number that should be placed on this branch is the probability the component is defective given that it was made at Plant 1, $P(D|1) = 0.01$. Continue with the conditional probabilities given for the other plants. This is all shown in the tree diagram in Figure 4.24.

a. Notice that the product rule, $P(1 \cap D) = P(1)P(D|1)$, represents multiplying along the branches 1 and D. So using the product rule we have

$$P(1 \cap D) = P(1)P(D|1) = (0.5)(0.01) = 0.005 = 0.5\%$$
$$P(2 \cap D) = P(2)P(D|2) = (0.2)(0.02) = 0.004 = 0.4\%$$
$$P(3 \cap D) = P(3)P(D|3) = (0.3)(0.03) = 0.009 = 0.9\%$$

b. For a component to be defective it came from Plant 1 or Plant 2 or Plant 3. These events are mutually exclusive since a component can only come from one plant. We have the following:

$$P(D) = P(1 \cap D) + P(2 \cap D) + P(3 \cap D)$$
$$= 0.005 + 0.004 + 0.009 = 0.018$$

EXAMPLE 5   Using a Probability Tree   A box contains three blue marbles and four red marbles. A marble is selected at random until a red one is picked.

a. What is the probability that the number of marbles selected is one?

b. What is the probability that the number of marbles selected is two?

c. What is the probability that the number of marbles selected is three?

Solution   The process for selecting a marble one at a time from the box is shown in Figure 4.25.

a. On the first draw there are four red marbles in a box of seven. So the probability of selecting a red marble is 4/7. We note for further reference that the probability of selecting a blue marble is 3/7. These probabilities are on the first legs of the tree diagram.

b. The only way it can take two selections to obtain a blue marble is for the first selection be a blue marble. In this case there are two blue marbles and four red marbles. Thus, the probability of selecting a red marble given that a blue marble was chosen first is 4/6.

From the tree in Figure 4.25, the probability of the branch $B_1 R_2$ is $(3/7) \cdot (4/6) = 2/7$. We note for further reference that the probability of selecting a blue marble on the second selection given that a blue marble was selected first is $2/6$. See Figure 4.25.

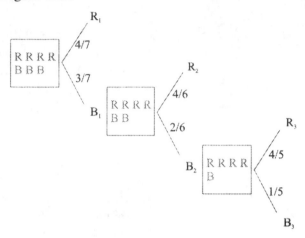

Figure 4.25

c. The only way it can take three selections to obtain a red marble is for the first two selections to be blue marbles. At this point (with two blue marbles missing) there is one blue marble and four red marbles left in the box. The probability of selecting a red marble given that a blue marble was chosen the first and second time is $4/5$. Now the probability of the branch $B_1 B_2 R_3$ can be found by applying the product rule (multiply along the branches) to find

$$\frac{3}{7} \cdot \frac{2}{6} \cdot \frac{4}{5} = \frac{4}{35} \qquad \blacklozenge$$

✧ Independent Events

We say that two events E and F are independent if the outcome of one does not affect the outcome of the other. For example, the probability of obtaining a head on a second flip of a coin is independent from what happened on the first flip. This is intuitively clear since the coin cannot have any memory of what happened on the first flip. Indeed the laws of physics determine the probability of heads occurring. Thus for the probability of heads to be different on the second flip the laws of physics must be different on the second flip. On the other hand, if we are selecting cards one at time without replacement from a standard deck of cards, the probability of selecting the queen of spades on the second draw clearly depends on what happens on the first draw. If the queen of spades was already picked, the probability of picking her on the second draw would be zero. Thus drawing the queen of spades on the second draw without replacement is not independent from drawing the queen of spades on the first draw.

That is, two events E and F are independent if

$$P(E|F) = P(E) \qquad \text{and} \qquad P(F|E) = P(F)$$

In words, the probability of E given that F has occurred is the same probability of E if F had not occurred. Similarly, the probability of F given that E has occurred is just the probability of F if E had not occurred.

Independent Events

Two events E and F are said to be independent if

$$P(E|F) = P(E) \qquad \text{and} \qquad P(F|E) = P(F)$$

We shall now obtain a result that is more convenient to apply when attempting to determine if two events are independent. It will also be useful when finding the probability that a series of independent events occurred.

If then two events E and F are independent, the previous comments together with the product rule indicate that

$$P(E \cap F) = P(E|F)P(F) = P(E)P(F)$$

Now consider the case that $P(E) > 0$ and $P(F) > 0$. Assume that $P(E \cap F) = P(E)P(F)$, then

$$P(E|F) - \frac{P(E \cap F)}{P(F)} = \frac{P(E)P(F)}{P(F)} = P(E)$$

$$P(F|E) = \frac{P(E \cap F)}{P(E)} = \frac{P(E)P(F)}{P(E)} = P(F)$$

This discussion then yields the following theorem.

Independent Events Theorem

Let E and F be two events with $P(E) > 0$ and $P(F) > 0$. Then E and F are independent if, and only if,

$$P(E \cap F) = P(E)P(F)$$

Although at times one is certain whether or not two events are independent, often one can only tell by doing the calculations.

EXAMPLE 6   Smoking and Heart Disease   A study of 1000 men over 65 indicated that 250 smoked and 50 of these smokers had some signs of heart disease, while 100 of the nonsmokers showed some signs of heart disease. Let E be the event "smokes" and H be the event "has signs of heart disease." Are these two events independent?

Solution   The Venn diagram is given in Figure 4.26. From this diagram $P(H) = 0.15$, $P(E) = 0.25$, and $P(H \cap E) = 0.05$. Thus

$$P(H)P(E) = (0.15)(0.25) = 0.0375$$
$$P(H \cap E) = 0.05$$

Since $0.0375 \neq 0.05$, these two events are not independent.   ◆

EXAMPLE 7   Determining if Two Events Are Independent   In a medical trial a new drug was effective for 60% of the patients and 30% of the patients suffered

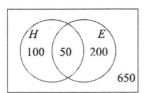

Figure 4.26

from a side effect. If 28% of the patients did not find the drug effective nor had a side effect, are the events E (drug was effective) and F (patient had a side effect) independent?

Solution   We can organize this information in a Venn diagram. If 28% of the patients did not find the drug effective nor had a side effect, this means that 0.28 is placed in the region outside the E and F circles. See Figure 4.27. The region inside will have the probability $(E \cup F) = 1 - 0.28 = 0.72$. Since we are not told how many found the drug effective and had a side effect, $P(E \cap F)$, we will need to use the union rule to find this number,

$$P(E \cup F) = P(E) + P(F) - P(E \cap F)$$
$$0.72 = 0.6 + 0.3 - P(E \cap F)$$
$$P(E \cap F) = 0.9 - 0.72 = 0.18$$

Place this in the Venn diagram in Figure 4.27. For completeness we could find $P(E \cap F^c) = 0.6 - 0.18 = 0.42$ and $P(E^c \cap F) = 0.3 - 0.18 = 0.12$ and place those in the diagram. However, to check for independence we need only place the three values needed in the formula:

$$P(E)P(F) = (0.60)(0.30) = 0.18$$
$$P(E \cap F) = 0.18$$

Since $0.18 = 0.18$, these events are independent.   ◆

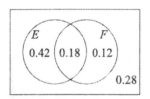

Figure 4.27

REMARK: Notice that saying two events are independent is not the same as saying that they are mutually exclusive. The sets in both previous examples were not mutually exclusive, but in one case the sets were independent and in the other case they were not.

The notion of independence can be extended to any number of finite events.

Independent Set of Events
A set of events $\{E_1, E_2, \ldots, E_n\}$ is said to be independent if, for any k of these events, the probability of the intersection of these k events is the product of the probabilities of each of the k events. This must hold for any $k = 2, 3, \ldots, n$.

For example, for the set of events $\{E, F, G\}$ to be independent all of the following must be true:

$$P(E \cap F) = P(E)P(F), \quad P(E \cap G) = P(E)P(G)$$

$$P(F \cap G) = P(F)P(G), \quad P(E \cap F \cap G) = P(E)P(F)P(G)$$

It is intuitively clear that if two events E and F are independent, then so also are E and F^c, E^c and F, E^c and F^c. (See Exercises 52 and 53.) Similar statements are true about a set of events.

EXAMPLE 8   Independent Events and Safety   An aircraft has a system of three computers, each independently able to exercise control of the flight. The computers are considered 99.9% reliable during a routine flight. What is the probability of having a failure of the control system during a routine flight?

Solution   Let the events E_i, $i = 1, 2, 3$ be the three events given by the reliable performance of respectively the first, second, and third computer. Since the set of events $\{E_1, E_2, E_3\}$ is independent, so is the set of events $\{E_1^c, E_2^c, E_3^c\}$. The system will fail only if all three computers fail. Thus the probability of failure of the system is given by

$$\{E_1^c \cap E_2^c \cap E_3^c\} = P(E_1^c)P(E_2^c)P(E_3^c) = (0.001)^3$$

which, of course, is an extremely small number.   ✦

EXAMPLE 9   Broken Elevators   A building has three elevators. The chance that elevator A is not working is 12%, the chance that elevator B is not working is 15% and the chance that elevator C is not working is 9%. If these probabilities are independent, what is the probability that exactly one elevator is not working?

Solution   The probability that elevator A is not working but the other two are working is $(0.12)(0.85)(0.91)$. The probability that only elevator B is working is $(0.88)(0.15)(0.91)$ and only elevator C working has probability $(0.88)(0.85)(0.09)$ of occurring. The probability that exactly one does not work is the sum of these three probabilities:

$$P = (0.12)(0.85)(0.91) + (0.88)(0.15)(0.91) + (0.88)(0.85)(0.09)$$
$$= 0.28026$$
✦

Self-Help Exercises 4.6

1. Three companies A, B, and C, are competing for a contract. The probabilities that they receive the contract are, respectively, $P(A) = 1/6$, $P(B) = 1/3$, and $P(C) = 1/2$. What is the probability that A will receive the contract if C pulls out of the bidding?

2. Two bins contain transistors. The first has 4 defective and 15 non-defective transistors, while the second has 3 defective and 22 non-defective ones. If the probability of picking either bin is the same, what is the probability of picking the second bin and a defective transistor?

3. Success is said to breed success. Suppose you are in a best of 3 game tennis match with an evenly matched opponent. However, if you win a game, your probability of winning the next increases from $1/2$ to $2/3$. Suppose, however, that if you lose, the probability of winning the next match remains the same. (Success does not breed success for your opponent.) What is your probability of winning the match? Hint: Draw a tree.

4. A family has three children. Let E be the event "at most one boy" and F the event "at least one boy and at least one girl." Are E and F independent if a boy is as likely as a girl? Hint: Write down every element in the sample space S and the events E, F, and $E \cap F$, and find the appropriate probabilities by counting.

4.6 Exercises

In Exercises 1 through 6, refer to the accompanying Venn diagram to find the conditional probabilities.

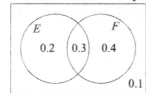

1. a. $P(E|F)$ **b.** $P(F|E)$

2. a. $P(E^c|F)$ **b.** $P(F^c|E)$

3. a. $P(E|F^c)$ **b.** $P(F|E^c)$

4. a. $P(E^c|F^c)$ **b.** $P(F^c|E^c)$

5. a. $P(F|E \cap F)$ **b.** $P(F^c|F)$

6. a. $P(E^c \cap F|F)$ **b.** $P(E \cap F^c|F)$

In Exercises 7 through 12, let $P(E) = 0.4$, $P(F) = 0.6$, and $P(E \cap F) = 0.2$. Draw a Venn diagram and find the conditional probabilities.

7. a. $P(E^c|F)$ **b.** $P(F^c|E)$

8. a. $P(E|F)$ **b.** $P(F|E)$

9. a. $P(F^c|E^c)$ **b.** $P(E \cup F|E)$

10. a. $P(E|F^c)$ **b.** $P(F|E^c)$

11. a. $P(E^c \cap |F)$ **b.** $P(E \cap F^c|E)$

12. a. $P(F|E \cap F)$ **b.** $P(E^c|E)$

In Exercises 13 through 20, determine if the given events E and F are independent.

13. $P(E) = 0.3$, $P(F) = 0.5$, $P(E \cap F) = 0.2$

14. $P(E) = 0.5$, $P(F) = 0.7$, $P(E \cap F) = 0.3$

15. $P(E) = 0.2$, $P(F) = 0.5$, $P(E \cap F) = 0.1$

16. $P(E) = 0.4$, $P(F) = 0.5$, $P(E \cap F) = 0.2$

17. $P(E) = 0.4$, $P(F) = 0.3$, $P(E \cup F) = 0.6$

18. $P(E \cap F^c) = 0.3$, $P(E \cap F) = 0.2$, $P(E^c \cap F) = 0.2$

19. $P(E \cap F^c) = 0.3$, $P(E \cap F) = 0.3$, $P(E^c \cap F) = 0.2$

20. $P(E) = 0.2$, $P(F) = 0.5$, $P(E \cup F) = 0.6$

21. A pair of fair dice is tossed. What is the probability that a sum of seven has been tossed if it is known that at least one of the numbers is a 3.

22. A single fair die is tossed. What is the probability that a 3 occurs on the top if it is known that the number is a prime?

23. A fair coin is flipped three times. What is the probability that heads occurs three times if it is known that heads occurs at least once?

24. A fair coin is flipped four times. What is the probability that heads occurs three times if it is known that heads occurs at least twice?

25. Three cards are randomly drawn without replacement from a standard deck of 52 cards.
   a. What is the probability of drawing an ace on the third draw?
   b. What is the probability of drawing an ace on the third draw given that at least one ace was drawn on the first two draws?

26. Three balls are randomly drawn from an urn that contains four white and six red balls.
   a. What is the probability of drawing a red ball on the third draw?
   b. What is the probability of drawing a red ball on the third draw given that at least one red ball was drawn on the first three draws?

27. From the tree diagram find
   a. $P(A \cap E)$ **b.** $P(A)$ **c.** $P(A|E)$

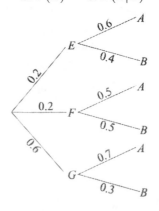

28. From the tree diagram find

    a. $P(A \cap E)$ **b.** $P(A)$ **c.** $P(A|E)$

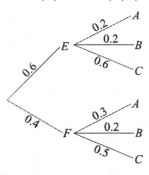

29. An urn contains five white, three red, and two blue balls. Two balls are randomly drawn. What is the probability that one is white and one is red if the balls are drawn

    a. without replacement?

    b. with replacement after each draw?

30. An urn contains four white and six red balls. Two balls are randomly drawn. If the first one is white, the ball is replaced. If the first one is red, the ball is not replaced. What is the probability of drawing at least one white ball?

31. In a family of four children, let E be the event "at most one boy" and F the event "at least one girl and at least one boy." If a boy is as likely as a girl, are these two events independent?

32. A fair coin is flipped three times. Let E be the event "at most one head" and F the event "at least one head and at least one tail." Are these two events independent?

33. The two events E and F are independent with $P(E) = 0.3$ and $P(F) = 0.5$. Find $P(E \cup F)$.

34. The two events E and F are independent with $P(E) = 0.4$ and $P(F) = 0.6$. Find $P(E \cup F)$.

35. The three events E, F, and G are independent with $P(E) = 0.2$, $P(F) = 0.3$, and $P(G) = 0.5$. What is $P(E \cup F \cup G)$?

36. The three events E, F, and G are independent with $P(E) = 0.3$, $P(F) = 0.4$, and $P(G) = 0.6$. What is $P(E^c \cup F^c \cup G^c)$?

Applications

37. Manufacturing A plant has three assembly lines with the first line producing 50% of the product and the second 30%. The first line produces defective products 1% of the time, the second line 2% of the time, and the third 3% of the time.

    a. What is the probability that a defective product is produced at this plant given that it was made on the second assembly line?

    b. What is the probability that a defective product is produced at this plant?

38. Manufacturing Two machines turn out all the products in a factory, with the first machine producing 40% of the product and the second 60%. The first machine produces defective products 2% of the time and the second machine 4% of the time.

    a. What is the probability that a defective product is produced at this factory given that it was made on the first machine?

    b. What is the probability that a defective product is produced at this factory?

39. Suppliers A manufacturer buys 40% of a certain part from one supplier and the rest from a second supplier. It notes that 2% of the parts from the first supplier are defective, and 3% are defective from the second supplier. What is the probability that a part is defective?

40. Advertising A television ad for a company's product has been seen by 20% of the population. Of those who see the ad, 10% then buy the product. Of those who do not see the ad, 2% buy the product. Find the probability that a person buys the product.

41. Reliability A firm is making a very expensive optical lens to be used in an earth satellite. To be assured that the lens has been ground correctly, three independent tests using entirely different techniques are used. The probability is 0.99 that any of one of these tests will detect a defect in the lens. What is the probability that the lens has a defect even though none of the three tests so indicates?

42. Psychology and Sales A door-to-door salesman expects to make a sale 10% of the time when starting the day. But making a sale increases his enthusiasm so much that the probability of a sale to the next customer is 0.2. If he makes no sale, the probability for a sale stays at 0.1. What is the probability that he will make at least two sales with his first three visits?

43. Quality Control A box contains two defective (D) parts and five non-defective (N) ones. You randomly select a part (without replacement) until you get a non-defective part. What is the probability that the number of parts selected is

a. one   **b.** two   **c.** three?

44. **Sales** A company sells machine tools to two firms in a certain city. In 40% of the years it makes a sale to the first firm, in 30% of the years to the second firm, and in 10% to both. Are the two events "a sale to the first firm" and "a sale to the second firm" independent?

45. **Medicine** In a study of 250 men over 65, 100 smoked, 60 of the smokers had some signs of heart disease, and 90 of the nonsmokers showed some signs of heart disease. Let E be the event "smokes" and H be the event "has signs of heart disease." Are these two events independent?

46. **Contracts** A firm has bids on two contracts. It is known that the awarding of these two contracts are independent events. If the probability of receiving the contracts are 0.3 and 0.4, respectively, what is the probability of not receiving either?

47. **Stocks** A firm checks the last 200 days on which its stock has traded. On 100 of these occasions the stock has risen in price with a broad-based market index also rising on 70 of these particular days. The same market index has risen 90 of the 200 trading days. Are the movement of the firm's stock and the movement of the market index independent?

48. **Bridges** Dystopia County has three bridges. In the next year, the Elder bridge has a 15% chance of collapse, the Younger bridge has a 5% chance of collapse and the Ancient bridge has a 20% chance of collapse. What is the probability that exactly one bridge will collapse in the next year?

49. **Missing Parts** A store sells desk kits. In each kit there is a 2% chance that a screw is missing, a 3% chance that a peg is missing, and a 1% chance that a page of directions is missing. If these events are independent, what is the probability that a desk kit has exactly one thing missing?

Extensions

50. **Medicine** The probability of residents of a certain town contracting cancer is 0.01. Let x be the percent of residents that work for a certain chemical plant and suppose that the probability of both working for this plant and of contracting cancer is 0.001.

What must x be for the two events "gets cancer" and "work for the chemical plant" to be independent?

51. Given the probabilities shown in the accompanying Venn diagram, show that the events E and F are independent if, and only if,

$$p_1 p_3 = p_2 p_4$$

What must the Venn diagram look like if the sets are mutually disjoint?

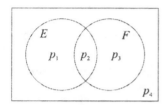

52. Show that if E and F are independent, then so are E and F^c.

53. Show that if E and F are independent, then so are E^c and F^c.

54. Show that two events are independent if they are mutually exclusive and the probability of one of them is zero.

55. Show that two events E and F are not independent if they are mutually exclusive and both have nonzero probability.

56. Show that if E and F are independent events, then

$$P(E \cup F) = 1 - P(E^c)P(F^c)$$

57. If $P(F) > 0$, then show that

$$P(E^c | F) = 1 - P(E | F)$$

58. If E, F, and G are three events and $P(G) > 0$, show that

$$P(E \cup G | G) = P(E | G) + P(F | G) - P(E \cap F | G)$$

59. If E and F are two events with $F \subset E$, then show that $P(E | F) = 1$.

60. If E and F are two events with $E \cap F = \emptyset$, then show that $P(E | F) = 0$.

61. If E and F are two events, show that

$$P(E | F) + P(E^c | F) = 1$$

Solutions to Self-Help Exercises 4.6

1. If E is the event that A obtains the contract and F the event that either A or B obtain the contract, then $E = \{A\}$, $F = \{A, B\}$, and $E \cap F = \{A\}$, and the conditional probability that A will receive the contract if C pulls out of the bidding is

$$P(E|F) = \frac{P(E \cap F)}{P(F)} = \frac{^1\!/_6}{^1\!/_2} = \frac{1}{3}$$

2. The sample space is $S = \{1D, 1N, 2D, 2N\}$ where the number refers to picking the first or second bin and the letter refers to picking a defective (D) or non-defective (N) transistor. If E is picking the first bin and F is picking a defective transistor then

$$P(E \cap F) = P(E)P(F|E) = \frac{1}{2} \cdot \frac{3}{25} = \frac{3}{50}$$

3. The appropriate tree is given.

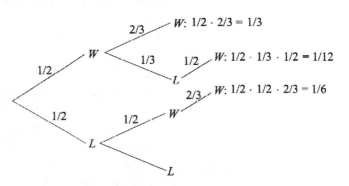

The probability of winning the match is then

$$\frac{1}{3} + \frac{1}{12} + \frac{1}{6} = \frac{7}{12}$$

4. The elements in the spaces S, E, and F are

$$S = \{BBB, BBG, BGB, BGG, GBB, GBG, GGB, GGG\}$$
$$E = \{BGG, GBG, GGB, GGG\}$$
$$F = \{BBG, BGB, BGG, GBB, GBG, GGB\}$$

With $E \cap F = \{BGG, GBG, GGB\}$. Thus counting elements gives

$$P(E \cap F) = \frac{3}{8} \qquad P(E)P(F) = \frac{4}{8} \cdot \frac{6}{8} = \frac{3}{8}$$

Since these two numbers are the same, the two events are independent.

4.7 Bayes' Theorem

APPLICATION
Probability of a Defective Part

> Recall Example 4 of the last section. A company makes the components for a product at a central location. These components are shipped to three plants, 1, 2, and 3, for assembly into a final product. The percentages of the product assembled by the three plants are, respectively, 50%, 20%, and 30%. The percentages of defective products coming from these three plants are, respectively, 1%, 2%, and 3%. Given a defective product, what is the probability it was assembled at Plant 1? At Plant 2? At Plant 3? See Example 1 for the answers to these questions.

✧ Bayesian Reasoning

We have been concerned with finding the probability of an event that will occur in the future. We now look at calculating probabilities after the events have occurred. This is a surprisingly common and important application of conditional probability. For example, when an e-mail message is received, the e-mail program does not know if the message is junk or not. But, given the number of misspelled words or the presence of certain keywords, the message is probably junk and is appropriately filtered. This is called Bayesian filtering and knowledge of what happened second (the misspelled words) allows an estimate of what happened first (the mail is junk).

We will now consider a situation where we will use Bayesian reasoning to estimate what happened in the first part of an experiment when you only know the results of the second part. Your friend has a cup with five green marbles and two red marbles and a bowl with one green, and three red, as shown in Figure 4.28a. There is an equal chance of choosing the cup or the bowl. After the cup or bowl has been chosen, a marble is selected from the container. A tree diagram for this experiment is shown in Figure 4.28b. Notice that on the branches of the tree diagram we have the conditional probabilities such as $P(G|C)$ which is the probability you choose a green marble given you are choosing from the cup.

Now your friend hides the bowl and cup and performs the experiment. He then shows you he has picked a green marble and asks, "what is the probability this green marble came from the cup"? That is, what is $P(C|G)$? Notice this is **not** what we have on the tree diagram. How can we figure this out?

Intuitively, if you had to guess if it was more likely to have come from the cup or the bowl, you would say it came from the cup. Looking at the figure, the cup has relatively more green ones, and if it was equally likely to have been picked from the cup or bowl, given it is green, more likely than not it came from the cup. But how can we get an exact value for the probability? Recall the formula used in the previous section for conditional probability,

$$P(C|G) = \frac{P(C \cap G)}{P(G)}$$

We can find $P(C \cap G)$ from the product rule. From multiplying along the branches it is

$$P(C \cap G) = P(C) \cdot P(G|C) = \frac{1}{2} \cdot \frac{5}{7} = \frac{5}{14}$$

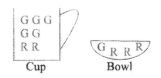

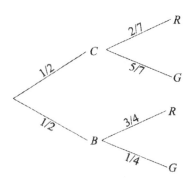

Figure 4.28a

Figure 4.28b

What about the denominator, $P(G)$? We can get green marbles from the cup or green marbles from the bowl. The total probability will be the sum of the probabilities of those two mutually exclusive events:

$$P(G) = P(G \cap C) + P(G \cap B) = \frac{1}{2} \cdot \frac{5}{7} + \frac{1}{2} \cdot \frac{1}{4} = \frac{27}{56}$$

.

Putting the pieces together we have

$$P(C|G) = \frac{5/14}{27/56} = \frac{20}{27} \approx 0.74$$

So there was about a 74% chance that the marble came from the cup, given that it was green.

This is an example of **Bayes' theorem**. This theorem was discovered by the Presbyterian minister Thomas Bayes (1702–1763). We now state this in a more general form.

✦ Bayes' Theorem

We suppose that we are given a sample space S and three mutually exclusive events E_1, E_2, and E_3, with $E_1 \cup E_2 \cup E_3 = S$ as indicated in Figure 4.29. Notice that the three events divide the same space S into 3 partitions. Given another event F, the tree diagram of possibilities is shown in Figure 4.30.

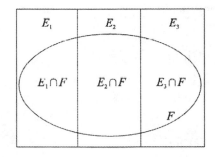

Figure 4.29

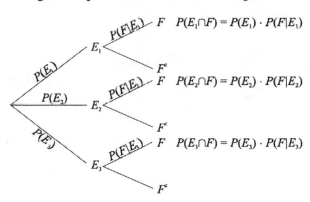

Figure 4.30

The probability $P(F|E_1)$ is the fraction with the numerator given by the probability off the branch $E_1 \cap F$ while the denominator is the sum of all the probabilities of all branches that end in F. This is

$$P(E_1|F) = \frac{P(E_1)P(F|E_1)}{P(E_1)P(F|E_1) + P(E_2)P(F|E_2) + P(E_3)P(F|E_3)}$$

The same for $P(F|E_2)$.

$$P(E_2|F) = \frac{P(E_2)P(F|E_2)}{P(E_1)P(F|E_1) + P(E_2)P(F|E_2) + P(E_3)P(F|E_3)}$$

and so on. We then state Bayes' theorem in even more general form.

Bayes' Theorem

Let $E_1, E_2, \ldots, E_n$, be mutually exclusive events in a sample space S with $E_1 \cup E_2 \cup \ldots \cup E_n = S$. If F is any event in S, then for $i = 1, 2, \ldots, n,$

$$P(E_i | F) = \frac{\text{probability of branch } E_i \cap F}{\text{sum of all probabilities of all branches that end in } F}$$

$$= \frac{P(E_i)P(F | E_i)}{P(E_1)P(F | E_1) + P(E_2)P(F | E_2) + \cdots + P(E_n)P(F | E_n)}$$

REMARK: The formula above looks quite complex. However, Bayes' theorem is much easier to remember by simply keeping in mind the original formula is simply $P(E|F) = P(E \cap F)/P(F)$ and that sometimes to find $P(F)$ you need to add together all the different ways that F can occur.

EXAMPLE 1   Defective Components   At the start of this section a question was posed to find the probability that a defective component came from a certain plant. Find these probabilities.

Solution   Refer to Figure 4.31 for the probabilities that are given. Using the product rule we have

$$P(1 \cap D) = P(1)P(D|1) = (0.5)(0.01) = 0.005$$
$$P(2 \cap D) = P(2)P(D|2) = (0.2)(0.02) = 0.004$$
$$P(3 \cap D) = P(3)P(D|3) = (0.3)(0.03) = 0.009$$

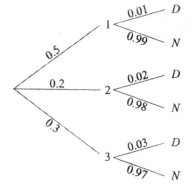

Figure 4.31

and thus

$$P(D) = = P(1 \cap D) + P(2 \cap D) + P(3 \cap D)$$
$$= 0.005 + 0.004 + 0.009$$
$$= 0.018$$

Using this information and the definition of conditional probability, we then have

$$P(1|D) = \frac{P(1 \cap D)}{P(D)} = \frac{0.005}{0.005 + 0.004 + 0.009} = \frac{0.005}{0.018} = \frac{5}{18}$$

We now notice that the numerator of this fraction is the probability of the branch $1 \cap D$, while the denominator is the sum of all the probabilities of all branches that end in D. We also have

$$P(2|D) = \frac{P(2 \cap D)}{P(D)} = \frac{0.004}{0.018} = \frac{4}{18}$$

Now notice that the numerator of this fraction is the probability of the branch $2 \cap D$, while the denominator is the sum of all the probabilities of all branches that end in D. A similar statement can be made for

$$P(3|D) = \frac{P(3 \cap D)}{P(D)} = \frac{0.009}{0.018} = \frac{9}{18} \qquad \blacklozenge$$

A very interesting example occurs in medical tests for disease. All medical tests have what are called false positives and false negatives. That is, a test result could come back positive and the patient does not have the disease or a test could come back negative and the patient does have the disease. Many modern tests have low rates of false positives and false negatives, but even then there can be difficulties with a diagnosis. We begin with a test that gives every appearance of being excellent, but an important consequence may be disappointing.

EXAMPLE 2   A Medical Application of Bayes' Theorem   The standard tine test for tuberculosis attempts to identify carriers, that is, people who have been infected by the tuberculin bacteria. The probability of a false negative is 0.08, that is, the probability of the tine test giving a negative reading to a carrier is $P(-|C) = 0.08$. The probability of a false positive is 0.04, that is, the probability of the tine test giving a positive indication when a person is a non-carrier is $P(+|N) = 0.04$.

The probability of a random person in the United States having tuberculosis is 0.0075. Find the probability that a person is a carrier given that the tine test gives a positive indication.

Solution   The probability we are seeking is $P(C|+)$. Figure 4.32 shows the appropriate diagram where C is the event "is a carrier," N the event "is a non-carrier," $+$ the event "test yields positive result," and $-$ is the event "test is negative."

Then Bayes' theorem can be used and $P(C|+)$ is the probability of branch $C \cap +$ divided by the sum of all probabilities that end in $+$. Then

$$P(C|+) = \frac{P(C \cap +)}{P(+)} = \frac{P(C)P(+|C)}{P(C)P(+|C) + P(N)P(+|N)}$$

$$= \frac{(0.0075)(0.92)}{(0.0075)(0.92) + (0.9925)(0.04)} \approx 0.15$$

So only 15% of people with positive tine test results actually carry TB.   ✦

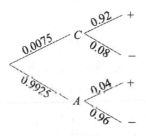

Figure 4.32

REMARK: This number is surprisingly low. Does this indicate that the test is of little value? As Self-Help Exercise 1 will show, a person whose tine test is negative has a probability of 0.999 of not having tuberculosis. Such an individual can feel safe. The individuals whose tine test is positive are probably all right also but will need to undergo further tests, such as a chest x-ray.

In some areas of the United States the probability of being a carrier can be as high as 0.10. The following example examines the tine test under these conditions.

EXAMPLE 3   A Medical Application of Bayes' Theorem   Using the information found in Example 2, find $P(C|+)$ again when $P(C) = 0.10$.

Solution   See Figure 4.33 for the tree diagram with the probabilities. Using Bayes' theorem exactly as before, we obtain

$$P(C|+) = \frac{P(C)P(+|C)}{P(C)P(+|C) + P(N)P(+|N)}$$

$$= \frac{(0.10)(0.92)}{(0.10)(0.92) + (0.90)(0.04)} \approx 0.72$$

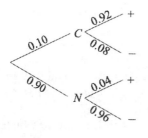

Figure 4.33

Thus 72% of these individuals who have a positive tine test result are carriers. ✦

Thus in the first example, when the probability of being a carrier is low, the tine test is useful for determining those who do not have TB. In the second example, when the probability of being a carrier is much higher, the tine test is useful for determining those who are carriers, although, naturally, these latter individuals will undergo further testing.

EXAMPLE 4   An Application of Bayes' Theorem   Suppose there are only four economic theories that can be used to predict expansions and contractions in the economy. By polling economists on their beliefs on which theory is correct, the probability that each of the theories is correct has been determined as follows:

$$P(E_1) = 0.40, P(E_2) = 0.25, P(E_3) = 0.30, P(E_4) = 0.05$$

The economists who support each theory then use the theory to predict the likelihood of a recession (R) in the next year. These are as follows:

$$P(R|E_1) = 0.01, P(R|E_2) = 0.02, P(R|E_3) = 0.03, P(R|E_4) = 0.90$$

Now suppose a recession actually occurs in the next year. How would the probabilities of the correctness of the fourth and first theories be changed?

Solution   We first note that the fourth theory E_4, has initially a low probability of being correct. Also notice that this theory is in sharp disagreement with the other three on whether there will be a recession in the next year.

Bayes' theorem gives $P(E_4|R)$ the probability of the branch $E_4 \cap R$ divided by the sum of all the probabilities of all the branches that end in R. See Figure 4.34. Similarly for the other theories. Thus $P(E_4|R)$ and and $P(E_1|R)$ are

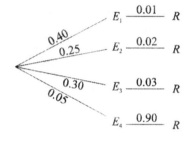

Figure 4.34

$$P(E_4|R) = \frac{P(E_4 \cap R)}{P(R)}$$

$$= \frac{P(E_4)P(R|E_4)}{P(E_1)P(R|E_1) + P(E_2)P(R|E_2) + P(E_3)P(R|E_3) + P(E_4)P(R|E_4)}$$

$$= \frac{(0.05)(0.90)}{(0.40)(0.01) + (0.25)(0.02) + (0.30)(0.03) + (0.05)(0.90)}$$

$$= \frac{0.045}{0.063} \approx 0.71$$

$$P(E_1|R) = \frac{P(E_1 \cap R)}{P(R)}$$

$$= \frac{P(E_1)P(R|E_1)}{P(E_1)P(R|E_1) + P(E_2)P(R|E_2) + P(E_3)P(R|E_3) + P(E_4)P(R|E_4)}$$

$$= \frac{(0.04)(0.10)}{(0.40)(0.01) + (0.25)(0.02) + (0.30)(0.03) + (0.05)(0.90)}$$

$$= \frac{0.004}{0.063} \approx 0.06$$

Thus, given that the recession did occur in the next year, the probability that E_4 is correct has jumped, while the probability that E_1 is true has plunged.   ✦

Although this is an artificial example probabilities indeed are revaluated in this way based on new information.

Self-Help Exercises 4.7

1. Referring to Example 2 of the text, find the probability that an individual in the United States is not a carrier given that the tine test is negative.

2. A gym has three trainers, Aldo, Bertha, and Coco, who each have $1/3$ of the new members. A person who trains with Aldo has a 60% chance of being successful, a person who trains with Bertha has a 30% chance of being successful and a person who trains with Coco has a 90% chance of being suc-

cessful. What is the probability that a successful member had Bertha as her trainer?

3. A purse has three nickels and five dimes. A wallet has two nickels and one dime. A coin is chosen at random from the purse and placed in the wallet. A coin is then drawn from the wallet. If a dime is chosen from the wallet, what is the probability that the transferred coin was a nickel?

4.7 Exercises

1. Find $P(E_1|F)$ and $P(E_2|F^c)$ using the tree diagram below.

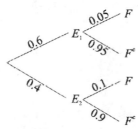

2. Find $P(E_1|F^c)$ and $P(E_2|F)$ using the tree diagram in the previous exercise.

3. Find $P(E_1|F)$ and $P(E_1|F^c)$ using the tree diagram below.

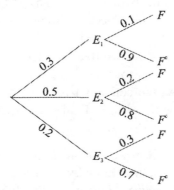

4. Find $P(E_3|F)$ and $P(E_3|F^c)$ using the tree diagram in the previous exercise.

Exercises 5 through 8 refer to two urns that each contain 10 balls. The first urn contains 2 white and 8 red balls. The second urn contains 7 white and 3 red balls. An

urn is selected, and a ball is randomly drawn from the selected urn. The probability of selecting the first urn is $2/3$.

5. If the ball is white, find the probability that the first urn was selected.

6. If the ball is white, find the probability that the second urn was selected.

7. If two balls are drawn from the selected urn without replacement and both are white, what is the probability that the urn selected was the
   a. the first one?
   b. the second one?

8. A ball is drawn from the selected urn and replaced. Then another ball is drawn and replaced from the same urn. If both balls are white, what is the probability that the urn selected was
   a. the first one?
   b. the second one?

Exercises 9 through 12 refer to three urns that each contain 10 balls. The first contains 2 white and 8 red balls, the second 5 white and 5 red, and the third all 10 white. Each urn has an equal probability of being selected. After an urn is selected a ball is randomly drawn from this urn.

9. If the ball drawn was white, find the probability that the first urn was selected.

10. If the ball drawn was white, find the probability that the third urn was selected.

11. Suppose two balls are drawn from the selected urn without replacement and both are white. What is the probability that the urn selected was

a. the first one?   **b.** the second one?

12. Now a ball is drawn, replaced, and then another drawn. Suppose both are white. What is the probability that the urn selected was

a. the first one?   **b.** the second one?

Exercises 13 through 16 refer to the following experiment: A box has two blue and six green jelly beans. A bag has five blue and four green jelly beans. A jelly bean is selected at random from the box and placed in the bag. Then a jelly bean is selected at random from the bag.

13. If a blue jelly bean is selected from the bag, what is the probability that the transferred jelly bean was blue?

14. If a green jelly bean is selected from the bag, what is the probability that the transferred jelly bean was green?

15. If a green jelly bean is selected from the bag, what is the probability that the transferred jelly bean was blue?

16. If a blue jelly bean is selected from the bag, what is the probability that the transferred jelly bean was green?

Exercises 17 through 20 refer to the following experiment: Two cards are drawn in succession without replacement from a standard deck of 52 playing cards.

17. What is the probability that the first card drawn was a spade given that the second card drawn was not a spade?

18. What is the probability that the first card drawn was a queen given that the second card drawn was not a queen?

19. What is the probability that the first card drawn was a heart given that the second card drawn was a diamond?

20. What is the probability that the first card drawn was an ace given that the second card drawn was a king?

Applications

21. Manufacturing A plant has three assembly lines with the first line producing 50% of the product and the second 30%. The first line produces defective products 1% of the time, the second line 2% of the time, and the third 3% of the time. Given a defective product, what is the probability it was produced on the second assembly line? See Exercise 37 of the previous section.

22. Manufacturing Two machines turn out all the products in a factory, with the first machine producing 40% of the product and the second 60%. The first machine produces defective products 2% of the time and the second machine 4% of the time. Given a defective product, what is the probability it was produced on the first machine? See Exercise 38 of the previous section.

23. Medicine Do Example 2 of the text if all the information remains the same except that the tine test has the remarkable property that $P(+|C) = 1$. Compare your answer to the one in Example 2.

24. Medicine Using the information in Example 2 of the text, find $P(N|-)$, where $-$ is the event "test shows negative."

25. Economics Using the information in Example 4 of the text, find $P(E_1|R^c)$ and $P(E_4|R_c)$. Compare your answers with $P(E_1)$ and $P(E_4)$.

26. Manufacturing For Example 1, find $P(E_1|F^c)$.

27. Quality Control One of two bins is selected at random, one as likely to be selected as the other, and from the bin selected a transistor is chosen at random. The transistor is tested and found to be defective. It is known that the first bin contains two defective and four nondefective transistors, while the second bin contains five defective and one nondefective transistors. Find the probability that second bin was selected.

28. Quality Control Suppose in the previous exercise there is a third bin with five transistors, all of which are defective. Now one of the three bins is selected at random, one as likely to be selected as any other, and from this bin a transistor is chosen at random. If the transistor is defective find the probability it came from the third one.

29. Quality Control A typical box of 100 transistors contains only 1 defective one. It is realized that among the last 10 boxes, one box has 10 defective transistors. An inspector picks a box at random, and the first transistor selected is found to be defective. What is the probability that this box is the bad one?

30. **Quality Control** A typical box of 100 transistors contains only 1 defective one. It is realized that among the last 10 boxes, one box has 10 defective transistors. An inspector picks a box at random, inspects two transistors from this box on a machine and discovers that one of them is defective and one is not. What is the probability that this box is the bad one?

31. **Manufacturing** A manufacturing firm has four machines that produce the same component. Using the table, given that a component is defective find the probability that the defective component was produced by

a. machine 1   b. machine 2.

Machine	Percentage of Components Produced	Percentage of Defective Components
1	20	1
2	30	2
3	40	3
4	10	4

32. **Social Sciences** A man claimed not to be the father of a certain child. On the basis of evidence presented, the court felt that this man was twice as likely to be the father as not, and, hardly satisfied with these odds, required the man to take a blood test. The mother of the child had a different blood type than the child: therefore the blood type of the child was completely determined by the father. If the man's blood type was different than the child, then he could not be the father. The blood type of the child occurred in only 10% of the population. The blood tests indicated that the man had the same blood type as the child. What is the probability that the man is the father?

33. **Medical Diagnosis** A physician examines a patient and, on the basis of the symptoms, determines that he may have one of four diseases; the probability of each is given in the table. She orders a blood test, which indicates that the blood is perfectly normal. Data are available on the percentage of patients with each disease whose blood tests are normal. On the basis of the normal blood test, find all probabilities that the patient has each disease.

Diseases	Probability of Disease of Disease	Percentage of Normal Blood With This Disease
1	0.1	60
2	0.2	20
3	0.3	20
4	0.4	10

Solutions to Self-Help Exercises 4.7

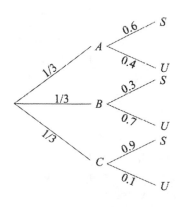

1. Bayes' theorem can be used, and $F = -$. Then

$$P(N|-) = \frac{P(N \cap -)}{P(-)} = \frac{P(N)P(-|N)}{P(N)P(-|N) + P(C)P(-|C)}$$

$$= \frac{(0.9925)(0.96)}{(0.9925)(0.96) + (0.0075)(0.08)} \approx 0.999$$

2. Begin with a tree diagram as shown in the figure on the left where S is a successful member and U is an unsuccessful member. To find $P(B|S)$ use Bayes' theorem.

$$P(B|S) = \frac{P(B \cap S)}{P(S)} = \frac{\frac{1}{3} \cdot 0.3}{\frac{1}{3} \cdot 0.6 + \frac{1}{3} \cdot 0.3 + \frac{1}{3} \cdot 0.9}$$

$$= \frac{0.1}{0.2 + 0.1 + 0.3} = \frac{1}{6} \approx 0.1667$$

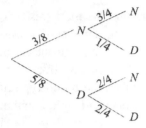

3. Begin with a tree diagram. On the first set of branches we show the selection of a coin from the purse. Following the top branch, the nickel is placed in the wallet. Now the wallet has three nickels and one dime and a coin is chosen. Following the lower branch we place a dime in the wallet. The wallet then has two nickels and two dimes from which a coin is chosen.

We are asked to find $P(N_1|D_2)$ so we use Bayes' theorem:

$$P(N_1|D_2) = \frac{P(N_1 \cap D_2)}{P(D_2)} = \frac{P(N_1 \cap D_2)}{P(N_1 \cap D_2) + P(D_1 \cap D_2)}$$

$$= \frac{\frac{3}{8} \cdot \frac{1}{4}}{\frac{3}{8} \cdot \frac{1}{4} + \frac{5}{8} \cdot \frac{2}{4}} = \frac{3}{13}$$

Review

✧ Summary Outline

- If every element of a set A is also an element of another set B, we say that A is a *subset* of B and write $A \subseteq B$. If A is not a subset of B, we write $A \nsubseteq B$.

- If every element of a set A is also an element of another set B and $A \neq B$, we say that A is a *proper subset* of B and write $A \subset B$. If A is not a proper subset of B, we write $A \not\subset B$.

- The *empty set*, written as $\emptyset$, is the set with no elements.

- Given a universal set U and a set $A \subset U$, the *complement* of A, written A^c, is the set of all elements that are in U but not in A, that is,

$$A^c = \{x | x \in U, x \notin A\}$$

- The *union* of two sets A and B, written $A \cup B$, is the set of all elements that belong to A, or to B, or to both. Thus

$$A \cup B = \{x | x \in A \text{ or } x \in B \text{ or both}\}$$

- The *intersection* of two sets A and B, written $A \cap B$, is the set of all elements that belong to both the set A and to the set B.

- If $A \cap B = \emptyset$ then the sets A and B are *disjoint*.

- Rules for Set Operations

$A \cup B = B \cup A$	Commutative law for union
$A \cap B = B \cap A$	Commutative law for intersection
$A \cup (B \cup C) = (A \cup B) \cup C$	Associative law for union
$A \cap (B \cap C) = (A \cap B) \cap C)$	Associative law for intersection
$A \cup (B \cap C) = (A \cup B) \cap (A \cup C)$	Distributive law for union
$A \cap (B \cup C) = (A \cap B) \cup (A \cap C)$	Distributive law for intersection
$(A \cup B)^c = A^c \cap B^c$	De Morgan law
$(A \cap B)^c = A^c \cup B^c$	De Morgan law

- If A is a set with a finite number of elements, we denote the number of elements in A by $n(A)$

- If the sets A and B are disjoint, then $n(A \cup B) = n(A) + n(B)$.

- For any finite sets A and B we have the union rule,

$$n(A \cup B) = n(A) + n(B) - n(A \cap B)$$

- An experiment is an activity that has observable results. The results of the experiment are called outcomes.

- A sample space of an experiment is the set of all possible outcomes of the experiment. Each repetition of an experiment is called a trial.

- Given a sample space S for an experiment, an event is any subset E of S. An elementary event is an event with a single outcome.

- If E and F are two events, then $E \cup E$ is the union of the two events and consists of the set of outcomes that are in E or F or both.

- If E and F are two events, then $E \cap F$ is the intersection of the two events and consists of the set of outcomes that are in both E and F.

- If E is an event, then E^c is the complement of E and consists of the set of outcomes that are not in E.

- The empty set, $\emptyset$, is called the impossible event.

- Let S be a sample space. The event S is called the certainty event.

- Two events E and F are said to be mutually exclusive or disjoint if $E \cap F = \emptyset$.

- Properties of Probability Let S be a sample space and E, A, and B be events in S, $P(E)$ the probability of E, and so on. Then

$0 \leq P(E) \leq 1$

$P(S) = 1$

$P(\emptyset) = 0$

$P(A \cup B) = P(A) + P(B)$, if $A \cap B = \emptyset$

$P(E^c) = 1 - P(E)$

$P(A \cup B) = P(A) + P(B) - P(A \cap B)$

$P(A) \leq P(B)$, if $A \subset B$

- Let $P(E)$ be the probability of E, then the odds for E are

$$\frac{P(E)}{1 - P(E)} \text{ if } P(E) \neq 1$$

This fraction reduced to lowest terms is $\frac{a}{b}$ and the odds are a:b.

- If the odds for an event E occurring is given as $\frac{a}{b}$ or a:b, then

$$P(E) = \frac{a}{a + b}$$

- If S is a finite uniform sample space and E is any event, then

$$P(E) = \frac{\text{Number of elements in } E}{\text{Number of elements in } S} = \frac{n(E)}{n(S)}$$

- Let E and F be two events in a sample space S. The conditional probability that E occurs given that F has occurred is defined to be

$$P(E|F) = \frac{P(E \cap F)}{P(F)} \quad \text{if} \quad P(F) > 0$$

- Product rule: If E and F are two events in a sample space S with $P(E) > 0$ and $P(F) > 0$, then

$$P(E \cap F) = P(F)P(E|F) = P(E)P(F|E)$$

- Two events E and F are said to be independent if

$$P(E|F) = P(E) \quad \text{and} \quad P(F|E) = P(F)$$

- Let E and F be two events with $P(E) > 0$ and $P(F) > 0$. Then E and F are independent if, and only if, $P(E \cap F) = P(E)P(F)$.

- A set of events $\{E_1, E_2, \dots, E_n\}$ is said to be independent if, for any k of these events, the probability of the intersection of these k events is the product of the probabilities of each of the k events. This must hold for any $k = 2, 3, \dots, n$.

- Bayes' Theorem Let $E_1, E_2, \dots, E_n$, be mutually exclusive events in a sample space S with $E_1 \cup E_2 \cup \dots \cup E_n = S$. If F is any event in S, then for $i = 1, 2, \dots, n$,

$$P(E_i|F) = \frac{\text{probability of branch } E_i F}{\text{sum of all probabilities of all branches that end in } F}$$
$$= \frac{P(E_i \cap F)}{P(F)}$$
$$= \frac{P(E_i)P(F|E_i)}{P(E_1)P(F|E_1) + P(E_2)P(F|E_2) + \dots + P(E_n)P(F|E_n)}$$

✦ Review Exercises

1. Determine which of the following are sets:

   a. current members of the board of Bank of America

   b. past and present board members of Bank of America that have done an outstanding job

   c. current members of the board of Bank of America who are over 10 feet tall

2. Write in set-builder notation:

   $\{5, 10, 15, 20, 25, 30, 35, 40\}$.

3. Write in roster notation: $\{x|x^3 - 2x = 0\}$

4. List all the subsets of $\{A, B, C\}$.

5. On a Venn diagram indicate where the following sets are:

   a. $A \cap B \cap C$ **b.** $A^c \cap B \cap C$ **c.** $(A \cup B)^c \cap C$

6. Let $U = \{1,2,3,4,5,6\}$, $A = \{1,2,3\}$, $B = \{2,3,4\}$, and $C = \{4,5\}$. Find the following sets: $A \cup B$, $A \cap B$, B^c, $A \cap B \cap C$, $(A \cup B) \cap C$, $A \cap B^c \cap C$

7. Let U be the set of all your current instructors and let

   $H = \{x | x$ is at least 6 feet tall$\}$

   $M = \{x | x$ is a male$\}$

   $W = \{x | x$ weighs more than 180 pounds$\}$

   Describe each of the following sets in words:

   a. H^c **b.** $H \cup M$

   c. $M^c \cap W^c$ **d.** $H \cap M \cap W$

   e. $H^c \cap M \cap W$ **f.** $(H \cap M^c) \cup W$

8. Using the set H, M, and W in the previous exercise and set operations, write the set that represents the following statements:

   a. my current female instructors

   b. my current female instructors who weigh at most 180 pounds

   c. my current female instructors who are at least 6 feet tall or else weigh more than 180 pounds

9. For the sets given in Exercise 6, verify that

   $$A \cup (B \cap C) = (A \cup B) \cap (A \cup C)$$

10. Use a Venn diagram to show that $(A \cap B)^c = A^c \cup B^c$

11. If $n(A) = 100$, $n(B) = 40$, and $n(A \cap B) = 20$, find $n(A \cup B)$.

12. If $n(A) = 40$ and $n(A \cap B^c) = 30$, find $n(A \cap B)$.

13. In a consumer advertising survey of 100 men, it was found that 20 watched the first game of the World Series, 15 watched the first game of the World Series and also watched the Super Bowl, while 30 did not watch either. How many watched the Super Bowl but not the first game of the World Series.

14. A consumer survey of 100 children found that

    - 57 had a Barbie doll
    - 68 had a teddy bear
    - 11 had a toy piano
    - 45 had a Barbie doll and a teddy bear
    - 8 had a teddy bear and a toy piano
    - 7 had a Barbie doll and a toy piano
    - 5 had all three

    a. How many had a Barbie doll and a teddy bear but not a toy piano?

    b. How many had exactly 2 of these toys?

    c. How many had none of these toys?

15. During a recent four-round golf tournament the number of strokes were recorded on a par 5 hole. The following table lists the frequencies of each number of strokes.

Strokes	3	4	5	6	7	8
Frequency	4	62	157	22	4	1

    a. Find the probability for each number of strokes.

    b. Find the probability that the number of strokes were less or equal to 5.

    c. Find the probability that the number of strokes were less than 5.

16. An urn has 10 white, 5 red, and 15 blue balls. A ball is drawn at random. What is the probability that the ball will be

    a. red?   **b.** red or white?   **c.** not white?

17. If E and F are disjoint sets in a sample space S with $P(E) = 0.25$ and $P(F) = 0.35$, find

    a. $P(E \cup F)$ **b.** $n(E \cap F)$ **c.** $P(E^c)$

18. If E and F are two events in the sample space S with $P(E) = 0.20$, $P(F) = 0.40$, and $P(E \cap F) = 0.05$, find

    a. $P(E \cup F)$ **b.** $P(E^c \cap F)$ **c.** $P((E \cup F)^c)$

19. Consider the sample space $S = \{a,b,c,d\}$ and suppose that $P(a) = P(b)$, $P(c) = P(d)$, and $P(d) = 2P(a)$. Find $P(b)$.

20. If the odds for a company obtaining a certain contract are 3:1, what is the probability that the company will receive the contract?

21. A furniture manufacturer notes the 6% of its reclining chairs have a defect in the upholstery, 4% a defect in the reclining mechanism, and 1% have both defects.

    a. Find the probability that a recliner has at least one of these defects.

    b. Find the probability that a recliner has none of these defects.

22. A survey of homeowners indicated that during the last year: 22% had planted vegetables, 30% flowers, 10% trees, 9% vegetables and flowers, 7% vegetables and trees, 5% flowers and trees, and 4%, all three of these.

a. Find the probability that a homeowner planted vegetables but not flowers.

b. Find the probability that exactly two of the items were planted.

c. Find the probability that none of these three items were planted.

23. Let $P(E) = 0.3$, $P(F) = 0.5$, and $P(E \cap F) = 0.2$. Draw a Venn diagram and find the indicated conditional probabilities:

a. $P(E|F)$ **b.** $P(E^c|F)$ **c.** $P(F^c|E^c)$

24. If $P(E) = 0.5$, $P(F) = 0.6$, and $P(E \cap F) = 0.4$, determine if E and F are independent events.

25. **Reliability** A spacecraft has three batteries that can operate all systems independently. If the probability that any battery will fail is 0.05, what is the probability that all three will fail?

26. **Basketball** A basketball player sinks a free throw 80% of the time. If she sinks one, the probability of sinking the next goes to 0.90. If she misses, the probability of sinking the next goes to 0.70. Find the probability that she will sink exactly two out of three free throws.

27. **Manufacturing** A manufacturing firm has 5 machines that produce the same component. Using the table, find the probability that a defective component was produced by

a. machine 1   **b.** machine 4

Machine	Components Produced	Defective Components
1	20%	1%
2	30%	2%
3	30%	3%
4	10%	4%
5	10%	10%

28. **Drug Testing** A company tests its employees for drug usage with a test that gives a positive reading 95% of the time when administered to a drug user and gives a negative reading 95% of the time when administered to a non-drug user. If 5% of the employees are drug users, find the probability that an employee is a non-drug user given that this person had a positive reading on the test. (The answer is shocking and illustrates the care that must be exercised in using such tests in determining guilt.)

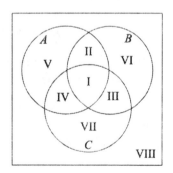

Figure 4.35

◇ Project: Venn Diagrams and Systems of Linear Equations

Sometimes the numbers do not arrange themselves in the Venn diagram as neatly as they did in the exercises in Section 2. If this happens you can often use deductive reasoning to fill in the diagram. However, sometimes a system of equations must be used to complete the diagram. If we use a system of linear equations to fill in the Venn diagram, we need a consistent way to refer to the eight regions of the Venn diagram. In Figure 4.35 we see the eight regions on the diagram labeled with the Roman numerals I through VIII. That is, $n(A \cap B^c \cap C^c)$ is V.

The next example will be solved using two different methods. If the solution is not unique, techniques from our study of linear systems can be used.

EXAMPLE 5   Vegetable Survey There were 32 students surveyed and asked if they did or did not like tomatoes, spinach, or peas with the results listed below. Arrange this information in a Venn diagram.

- 7 students liked all three vegetables

- 6 students did not like spinach or peas

- 1 student liked only tomatoes

- 9 students liked tomatoes and spinach

- 23 students liked two or more of these vegetables

- 5 students liked spinach but not peas

- 18 students liked spinach

Solution   Begin with a blank Venn diagram. Let
$S = \{x | x \text{ is a student who likes spinach}\}$
$T = \{x | x \text{ is a student who likes tomatoes}\}$
$P = \{x | x \text{ is a student who likes peas}\}$

DEDUCTIVE REASONING METHOD:

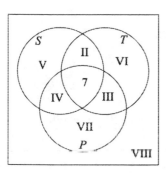

Figure 4.36

- The first clue that "7 students liked all three vegetables" tells us that we can place the number 7 in the intersection of all three sets: $n(S \cap T \cap P) = 7$. See Figure 4.36 You can scratch out this clue as each clue is used only once.

- The second clue that "6 students did not like spinach or peas" is not useful yet as both VI and VIII are outside of the region corresponding to liking spinach or peas. All we know is that those two numbers add to 6. Move on to the next clue.

- The third clue says "1 student liked only tomatoes" and so the number 1 is placed in region VI ($S^c \cap T \cap P^c$). Scratch out this clue as it has been used.

- The fourth clue says "9 students liked tomatoes and spinach" and this means $7 + \text{II} = 9$. So there must be 2 students who like tomatoes and spinach but not peas. A 2 is placed in the region $S \cap T \cap P^c$ as shown in Figure 4.37. This clue can be scratched out.

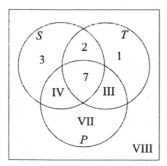

Figure 4.37

- The fifth clue states that "23 students liked two or more of these vegetables." The region representing two or more vegetables is shaded in Figure 4.37 and we see that is the sum of four numbers and at this point we only know the value of two of them. This clue is skipped for now.

- The sixth clue states "5 students liked spinach but not peas." This is the region that is in the S circle but outside the P circle. We see that 2 of the 5 students have been accounted for as they like spinach and tomatoes but not peas. Therefore 3 students like only spinach and a 3 is placed in the region $S \cap T^c \cap P^c$ and this clue is scratched out.

- The seventh clue is that "18 students liked spinach" and we see that the S circle is nearly complete. If there are 18 students in all in this circle and $3 + 2 + 7 = 12$ of them are accounted for, then $18 - 12 = 6$ students must be in the remaining empty spot in the S circle for students who like spinach and peas but not tomatoes, $S \cap T^c \cap P$. This is shown in Figure 4.38.

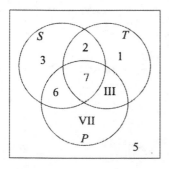

Figure 4.38

- The eighth clue is that 32 students are surveyed, so $n(U) = 32$. Since three numbers are still missing in the diagram, we are not ready for this clue yet.

We have three missing numbers in our diagram and three un-used clues:

- 6 students did not like spinach or peas

- 23 students liked two or more of these vegetables

- 32 students were surveyed

The region representing not spinach or peas will be those students who like only tomatoes (which is 1 student) and those students who do not like any of the vegetables, so $6 - 1 = 5$ students did not like any of the vegetables.

Referring back to the shaded region in Figure 4.37 we now know 3 of the four numbers that represent liking two or more of these vegetables so we can find the missing number by subtraction, $23 - 2 - 6 - 7 = 8$ students liked tomatoes and peas but not spinach. Place the 8 in the region $S^c \cap T \cap P$.

Finally we do not know how many students liked only peas, but we do know there are 32 students who were surveyed and so by subtraction, $32 - 3 - 2 - 1 - 6 - 7 - 8 - 5 = 0$, so a zero is placed in the region $S^c \cap T^c \cap P$. The completed diagram is shown in Figure 4.39.

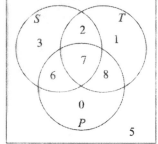

Figure 4.39

SYSTEMS OF EQUATIONS METHOD:

Referring to Figure 4.40 with the Roman numerals, we translate each clue into a linear equation.

- 32 students were surveyed $\rightarrow$ I + II + III + IV + V + VI + VII + VIII = 32

- 7 students liked all three vegetables $\rightarrow$ V = 7

- 6 students did not like spinach or peas $\rightarrow$ III + VIII = 6

- 1 student liked only tomatoes $\rightarrow$ III = 1

- 9 students liked tomatoes and spinach $\rightarrow$ II + V = 9

- 23 students liked two or more of these vegetables $\rightarrow$ II + IV + V + VI = 23

- 5 students liked spinach but not peas $\rightarrow$ I + II = 5

- 18 students liked spinach $\rightarrow$ I + II + IV + V = 18

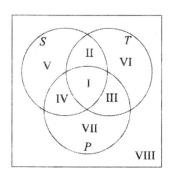

Figure 4.40

Place this information into an augmented matrix and use the methods of Chapter 1 to solve the system. This method is particularly useful if a calculator is used. With $x_1 = $ I, $x_2 = $ II, and so on we have

$$
\begin{aligned}
x_1 + x_2 + x_3 + x_4 + x_5 + x_6 + x_7 + x_8 &= 32 \\
x_5 &= 7 \\
x_3 \qquad\qquad\qquad + \; x_8 &= 6 \\
x_3 &= 1 \\
x_2 \qquad + \; x_5 &= 9 \\
x_2 \quad + \; x_4 + x_5 + x_6 &= 5 \\
x_1 + x_2 &= 32 \\
x_1 + x_2 + \quad x_4 + x_5 &= 18
\end{aligned}
$$

The solution to the system is

I = 3, II = 2, III = 1, IV = 6, V = 7, VI = 8, VII = 0, VIII = 5. ✦

Complete a Venn diagram for each of the exercises below.

1. $n(A) = 11, n(B) = 14, n(C) = 19, n(U) = 36, n(A \cap B) = 4, n(A \cap C) = 8, n(B \cap C) = 7$ and $n(A \cup B \cup C) = 28$

2. A class of 6th grade boys is surveyed and asked if they were wearing one or more of the following items of clothing that day: a T-shirt, shorts or athletic shoes. The results were:

   - 40 wore a T-shirt, shorts, and athletic shoes
   - 23 wore exactly two of these items
   - 57 wore shorts
   - 12 did not wear a T-shirt
   - 4 wore only athletic shoes
   - 7 did not wear shorts or athletic shoes
   - 11 wore only shorts and a T-shirt
   - 52 wore a T-shirt and athletic shoes

3. Two hundred tennis players were asked which of these strokes they considered their weakest stroke(s): the serve, the backhand, and the forehand.

   - 20 players said none of these were their weakest stroke
   - 30 players said all three of these were their weakest stroke
   - 40 players said their serve and forehand were their weakest strokes
   - 40 players said that only their serve and backhand were their weakest strokes.
   - 15 players said that their forehand but not their backhand was their weakest stroke
   - 52 players said that only their backhand was their weakest stroke
   - 115 players said their serve was their weakest stroke

   Source: Joe Kahlig

4. Thirty-one children were asked about their lunch preferences and the following results were found:

   - 12 liked cheeseburgers
   - 14 liked pizza
   - 9 liked burritos
   - 5 liked cheeseburgers and pizza
   - 4 liked cheeseburgers and burritos
   - 8 liked pizza and burritos
   - 10 liked none of these items

CHAPTER 5

Counting and Probability

CONNECTION

Texas Hold'em Poker

In this game of poker a player tries to make the best hand possible using the two cards in the player's hand along with three of the cards on the table.

How is the ranking of poker hands determined? For example, why does a straight flush beat a four-of-a-kind? In this chapter we will learn how to find the probability of a poker hand. See page 273 to find the probability of a flush.

5.1 The Multiplication Principle and Permutations

APPLICATION
Number of License Plates

> A certain state uses license plates with three letters followed by three numbers with no repeats of letters or numbers. How many such license plates can be made? See Example 10 for the answer.

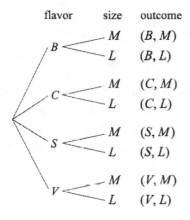

Figure 5.41

✧ The Multiplication Principle

Some of the basic counting techniques that are used in the study of probability will now be considered. The multiplication principle given here is fundamental to all of the counting methods that will follow. Before stating the multiplication principle, we consider two examples.

EXAMPLE 1   A Simple Counting Problem   A manufacturer makes four flavors of yogurt and each flavor comes in medium and large sizes. The available flavors are blueberry, cherry, strawberry, and vanilla. How many different flavors and sizes of yogurt are there? What is the set of all possible choices?

Solution   We can think of the procedure as a sequence of two choices or tasks. The first task is to pick a flavor and the second task is to pick a size. We can denote the choice of picking cherry in the large size as the ordered pair (cherry, large) or simply (C, L). All possible outcomes can be visualized in the tree diagram in Figure 5.41. Counting all the possibilities gives eight different yogurts. The set of all possible choices is

$$S = \{(B,M), (B,L), (C,M), (C,L), (S,M), (S,L), (V,M), (V,L)\} \qquad \blacklozenge$$

If we examine more closely why we obtained the answer $n(S) = 8$, we can notice from Figure 5.41 that we had four groups of two each. This gives $4 \times 2 = 8$, where there were four choices for flavors, and for each flavor there were two choices for the size. If you are asked to list all of the different outcomes, a tree diagram is essential. However, if you are only asked how many different outcomes there are, the shortcut below is effective.

Rather than list the branches, draw a blank for each place you need to make a choice. Under the blank list what you are choosing. Then determine how many choices you have for each task and multiply, as shown below

$$\frac{}{\text{flavor}} \times \frac{}{\text{size}} = \frac{4}{\text{flavor}} \times \frac{2}{\text{size}} = 8$$

You can abbreviate this shortcut further by simply writing $(\_\_, \_\_)$ to indicate that there are two tasks to be done and then write $(\_\_, \_\_) = (4, 2)$ to show that the first task can be completed four ways and the second task can be completed two ways. Those numbers are multiplied to give eight different outcomes:

$$(\_\_, \_\_) = (4, 2) = 4 \cdot 2 = 8$$

EXAMPLE 2   Forming a Committee   A committee of three individuals, Abe, Bertha, and Chia, must pick one of them to be chair and a different one to be secretary. How many ways can this be done? What is the set of all possible outcomes?

Chair Sec. Outcome

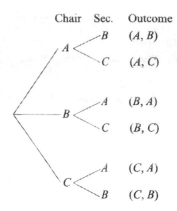

Figure 5.42

Solution The tree diagram in Figure 5.42 breaks this problem into an operation of first picking a chair and then picking a secretary. Notice that there are three choices for chair and, no matter who is picked for chair, there are always two choices for secretary. Thus there are three groups of two each or $3 \times 2 = 6$ possible outcomes. The set of all possible outcomes can be read from the tree diagrams as

$$S = \{(A,B), (A,C), (B,A), (B,C), (C,A), (C,B)\} \qquad \blacklozenge$$

If the set of all possible outcomes was not needed, the number of outcomes could be found by

$$\frac{}{\text{chair}} \times \frac{}{\text{secretary}} = \frac{3}{\text{chair}} \times \frac{2}{\text{secretary}} = 6$$

Or simply $(\underline{}, \underline{}) = (3, 2) = 3 \times 2 = 6$

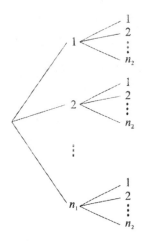

Figure 5.43

Now suppose there is an operation that consists of a sequence of two tasks with n_1 possible choices for the first task and no matter how the first task was completed, there are always n_2 possible choices for the second task. Figure 5.43 indicates a tree diagram for these two tasks. From this figure we see that there are n_1 groups, each with n_2 elements. Thus there is a total of $n_1 \cdot n_2$ possible outcomes in our sequence of two tasks. This is the multiplication principle.

> **Multiplication Principle**
> Suppose there is an operation that consists of making a sequence of two tasks with n_1 choices for the first task and, no matter how the first task was completed, there are always n_2 possible choices for the second task. Then there are $n_1 \cdot n_2$ possible ways in which the sequence of two task can be completed.

EXAMPLE 3   Picking Two Horses   Ten horses are running in the first race at Aqueduct. You wish to buy a Perfecta ticket, which requires picking the first and second finishers in order. How many possible tickets are there?

Solution You have two tasks: choose the first place horse and choose the second place horse. There are 10 choices for the first task as any of the 10 horses could come in first. Once the horse places first, it is not available to place second, so we have only 9 horses to choose from when we pick a horse for second place. The tasks can be shown as

$$\frac{}{1^{\text{st}}\text{place}} \times \frac{}{2^{\text{nd}}\text{place}} = \frac{10}{1^{\text{st}}\text{place}} \times \frac{9}{2^{\text{nd}}\text{place}} = 90$$

Or, this can be summarized as $(\underline{}, \underline{}) = (10, 9) = 10 \cdot 9 = 90$. Thus, by the multiplication principle, there are 90 possible tickets. $\qquad \blacklozenge$

We now can see in the same way the general multiplication principle.

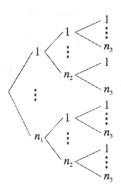

Figure 5.44

> **General Multiplication Principle**
> Suppose there is an operation that consists of making a sequence of k tasks with n_1 possible choices for the first task and, no matter what choice was made for the first task, there are always n_2 possible choices for the second task, and, no matter what choices were made for the first two tasks, there are always n_3 possible choices for the third task, and so on. Then there are $n_1 \cdot n_2 \cdots n_k$ possible ways in which the sequence of k tasks can be made.

For example, in Figure 5.44 , there are $n_1 \cdot n_2$ elements in the second column, as we noted in Figure 5.43. Emanating from each one of these elements there are n_3 "branches" in the third column. Thus there are $n_1 \cdot n_2 \cdot n_3$ elements in the third column.

EXAMPLE 4   Picking Three Horses   Ten horses are running in the first race at Aqueduct. You wish to buy a Trifecta ticket that requires picking the first three finishers in order. How many possible tickets are there?

Solution   You must make a choice: (first, second, third). Thus we have a sequence of three blanks (___, ___, ___), and we must fill in the blanks. There are 10 choices for first. No matter what horse you pick for first there are always 9 left for second, and no matter which horses you pick for the first and second choices, there are always 8 left for the third. This can be summarized as $(10, 9, 8)$. By the general multiplication principle there are $10 \times 9 \times 8 = 720$ possible tickets.   ◆

REMARK: Often the application of the multiplication principle requires some care due to restrictions. Perhaps when you are seating children you wish to have boys and girls alternate. Or when you choose a PIN code you cannot have three of the same digits in the code. Or your computer password must end in two digits. These restrictions require extra care when determining the number of ways a task can be completed.

EXAMPLE 5   Picking Horses   In the seventh race at Aqueduct, which is running 10 horses, you have learned through impeccable sources that the overwhelming favorite will be held back from winning. You wish to be assured of having a winning Trifecta ticket. How many must you buy?

Solution   Again you must make a choice for each of your three tasks: choose the first, second, and third place horses. This time, from your inside knowledge, you know that there are only nine choices for first, and, given any of these nine choices, there remain nine horses to pick for second. No matter what the first and second picks are, there remains eight choices for the third place horse. This can be summarized as $(9, 9, 8)$. Thus, by the multiplication principle, there are $9 \times 9 \times 8 = 648$ possible choices. Therefore you must buy 648 different tickets to be assured of a winning ticket.   ◆

EXAMPLE 6   Forming Words   How many three-letter words that all begin with consonants and have exactly one vowel can be made using the first seven letters of the alphabet where using a letter twice is permitted but having two consonants next to each other is not?

Solution Since two consonants cannot be next to each other, one must make the choice (consonant, vowel, consonant). There are five choices for the first consonant in the set $\{b,c,d,f,g\}$. No matter what the first choice there are two choices for vowels $\{a,e\}$, and no matter what the first two choices, there remain the same five consonants to pick from. This can be summarized as (5, 2, 5). Thus the multiplication principle gives $5 \times 2 \times 5 = 50$ possible words. ◆

✧ Factorials

We will be encountering expressions such as $6 \cdot 5 \cdot 4 \cdot 3 \cdot 2 \cdot 1$ and it will useful to have a symbol to denote this product. We have the following definition.

Factorials
For any natural number n

$$n! = n(n-1)(n-2)\cdots 3 \cdot 2 \cdot 1$$
$$0! = 1$$

Technology Option

See Technology Note 1 on page 261 for details on finding factorials using a graphing calculator or a spreadsheet.
Quick Fact: Factorials can be found on the TI graphing calculator by entering the number and then going pressing MATH and choosing the PRB menu. The factorial function is fourth option, 4:!. Select this and then ENTER as shown below.

```
4!
              24
5!
             120
6!
             720
■
```

EXAMPLE 7   Calculating Some Factorials Find 4!, 5!, and 6!.

Solution

$$4! = 4 \cdot 3 \cdot 2 \cdot 1 = 24$$
$$5! = 5 \cdot 4 \cdot 3 \cdot 2 \cdot 1 = 120$$
$$6! = 6 \cdot 5 \cdot 4 \cdot 3 \cdot 2 \cdot 1 = 720$$

◆

✧ Permutations

The set of digits $\{1,2,3,4\}$ can be arranged in various orders. For example, they can be listed as $(1,3,4,2)$ or perhaps $(4,3,1,2)$. Each of these ordered arrangements differ and we call these different arrangements a permutation of the set of digits $\{1,2,3,4\}$. We have the following definition.

Permutations
A permutation of a set of elements is an ordered arrangement of all the elements.

By "arrangement" it is understood that elements can be used only once and the order that the elements are in matters. That is the arrangement $\{1,2\}$ is a different arrangement than $\{2,1\}$.

EXAMPLE 8   Counting the Number of Permutations Find all permutations of the set $\{a,b,c\}$ and count the total number.

Solution Given the set $\{a,b,c\}$, we can use a tree diagram to find all possible permutations. See Figure 5.45. The set of all possible permutations is

$$S = \{(a,b,c),(a,c,b),(b,a,c),(b,c,a),(c,a,b),(c,b,a)\}$$

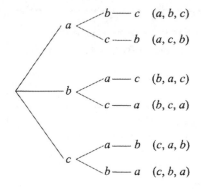

Figure 5.45

There are six possibilities, and these can be seen also by the multiplication principle to be $3 \cdot 2 \cdot 1 = 3!$.   ◆

Suppose a set of n distinct objects is given and we wish to find the number of permutations that are possible. We denote this number by $P(n,n)$. There are n choices for the task of choosing which of the n objects is in the first position. No matter which one is chosen first, there always remains $(n-1)$ objects for the second position. No matter how the first two have been chosen, there remains $(n-2)$ for the third position, and so on. By the multiplication principle, we then have the total number of possibilities to be

$$P(n,n) = n(n-1)(n-2) \cdots 3 \cdot 2 \cdot 1 = n!$$

We thus have the following.

Number of Permutations of *n* Objects
The number of permutations of n distinct objects is given by

$$P(n,n) = n(n-1)(n-2) \cdots 3 \cdot 2 \cdot 1 = n!$$

EXAMPLE 9   Counting the Number of Permutations   In how many ways can a football team of 11 players arrange themselves to trot onto the football field one at a time?

Solution   Think of this as arranging 11 different items and then the answer is given by

$$P(11,11) = 11! = 39,916,800$$

To use the multiplication principle, we have 11 ways to pick which player goes first. He is not available to go second, so there are 10 players (so 10 ways) to complete the task of choosing who runs out second. This continues as follows:

$$\underset{\text{1st player}}{11} \times \underset{\text{2nd}}{10} \cdots \underset{\text{10th}}{2} \times \underset{\text{11th player}}{1} = 11! = 39,916,800 \qquad ◆$$

There are situations in which we have a set of n distinct objects and wish to select an ordered arrangement of r of them. The total number of such arrangements is denoted by $P(n,r)$. We also refer to this as the **number of permutations of *r* objects taken from a set of size *n* objects**. Example 4 was such a case where you selected a first, second, and third place from a set of 10 horses running in a race. Recall from the multiplication principle that we have $P(10,3) = 10 \cdot 9 \cdot 8$.

We would now like to get a formula for the general case of choosing r items from a set of n items and arranging them. Let's begin by writing our result for $P(10,3)$ in a different form.

$$P(10,3) = 10 \cdot 9 \cdot 8 = 10 \cdot 9 \cdot 8 \cdot \frac{7 \cdot 6 \cdot 5 \cdot 4 \cdot 3 \cdot 2 \cdot 1}{7 \cdot 6 \cdot 5 \cdot 4 \cdot 3 \cdot 2 \cdot 1}$$

$$= \frac{10!}{7!} = \frac{10!}{(10-3)!}$$

The generalization of this is left as Exercise 43. We have below the formula for a permutation of r objects taken from a set of n objects.

Technology Option

See Technology Note 2 on page 262 for details on finding permutations using a graphing calculator or a spreadsheet. Quick Fact: permutations can be found on the TI graphing calculator by entering the number n and then going pressing MATH and choosing the PRB menu. The permutation function is second option, 2:nPr. Select this and then ENTER and then the number n and ENTER again.

```
11 nPr 11
            39916800
10 nPr 3
                 720
■
```

Number of Permutations of r Objects Taken from a Set of Size n

The number of permutations of r distinct objects taken from a set of size n is given by

$$P(n,r) = n(n-1)(n-2)\cdots(n-r+1) = \frac{n!}{(n-r)!}$$

Since $0! = 1$,

$$P(n,n) = \frac{n!}{(n-n)!} = \frac{n!}{1} = n!$$

which is what we obtained earlier.

EXAMPLE 10   License Plates   A certain state uses license plates with three letters followed by three digits with no repeats of letters or digits. How many such license plates can be made?

Solution   This problem can be done directly from the multiplication principle with six different tasks or as a permutation. Using the multiplication principle we have the following tasks:

$$\underset{\text{letter}}{26} \times \underset{\text{letter}}{25} \times \underset{\text{letter}}{24} \times \underset{\text{digit}}{10} \times \underset{\text{digit}}{9} \times \underset{\text{digit}}{8} = 11,232,000$$

If we use our knowledge of permutations, we can think of deciding on a license plate as a two-task process. The first task is to choose the three letters and then the second task is to choose the three numbers. The number of ways of arranging the three letters without repetitions and when order is important is the number of permutations of 26 letters taken 3 at a time or $P(26,3)$. The number of ways of arranging the digits without repetitions and when order is important is the number of permutations of 10 digits taken 3 at a time or $P(10,3)$. By the multiplication principle (when there are two tasks), the total number of different license plates will be

$$P(26,3)P(10,3) = (26 \cdot 25 \cdot 24)(10 \cdot 9 \cdot 8) = 11,232,000 \qquad \blacklozenge$$

REMARK: If we were not restricted to "no repeats," there would be $26 \cdot 26 \cdot 26 \cdot 10 \cdot 10 \cdot 10 = 17,576,000$ different license plates. But, for some states, such as California, that is not enough for each car to have a unique license plate. The current California plates have a digit followed by three letters and three digits which brings the total number of different plates to $175,760,000$. States such as Wyoming have a county code (from 1 to 23) followed by three letters. There are $23 \cdot 26 \cdot 26 \cdot 26 = 404,248$ possible plates using that pattern.

EXAMPLE 11   Movie Seatings   Matthew and Jennifer go to the movies with four of their friends. How many ways can these six children be seated if
a. there are no restrictions?
b. Matthew and Jennifer are seated next to each other?
c. Matthew and Jennifer are not next to each other?

Solution

a. There are six children to be seated, so we can look at this as a sequence of six tasks, (first, second, third, fourth, fifth, sixth) = (6, 5, 4, 3, 2, 1) = 6! or we can recognize this as a permutation of six objects taken 6 at a time to find $P(6,6) = 6!$. Either way the number of ways for the children to be seated is 720.

b. There is more than one way to assure that Matthew and Jennifer are seated together. One way is to "glue" Matthew and Jennifer together. That is, we will treat them as a single object in the initial seating arrangement. Then we will have two tasks. The first task will be to arrange the five objects (four children and the object that is Matthew and Jennifer glued together). The next task is to "un-glue" Matthew and Jennifer and determine how many ways those two objects can be arranged.

$$\underbrace{}_{\text{arrange 5 objects}} \times \underbrace{}_{\text{arrange M and J}} = \frac{5! \times 2!}{} = 120 \cdot 2 = 240$$

Or, we could think of it as a series of three tasks where we begin by finding how many pairs of seats Matthew and Jennifer could sit in. The next task is to determine how many ways Matthew and Jennifer could sit in their pair of seats and the last task is to seat the rest of the children. If we look at Figure 5.46, we see there are five pairs of seats for Matthew and Jennifer. There will be 2! ways that Matthew and Jennifer can sit in the pair of seats. For the third task there are four empty seats and four children to be seated, so there will be 4! ways to complete this task. In all we have

$$\underbrace{5}_{\text{choose pair of seats}} \times \underbrace{2!}_{\text{arrange M and J}} \times \underbrace{4!}_{\text{arrange remaining children}}$$
$$= 5 \cdot 2 \cdot 24 = 240$$

c. In the 720 ways to seat the children found in the first part, Matthew and Jennifer are seated together or they are not seated together. These are mutually exclusive events as they can't be seated together and not seated together at the same time. So, since there are 240 ways they are seated together, there must be $720 - 240 = 480$ ways they are not seated together. ✦

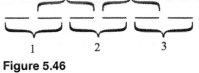

Figure 5.46

✧ Technology Corner

⑨Technology Note 1   Factorials

The commands for many counting operations are found by pressing the [MATH] button and arrowing over to the PRB menu as shown in Screen 1. To evaluate a factorial, enter the number first and then [MATH] then PRB and finally 4:!. This returns you to the homepage where [ENTER] will evaluate the factorial. See the note on page 258 to see this function in use.

To find factorials using a spreadsheet such as Excel, place your cursor in a cell and type =FACT(followed by the value and a closing). Enter and the factorial will be evaluated. See Worksheet 1. Alternatively, you can put the number to be evaluated in a cell and then refer to that cell in the FACT function.

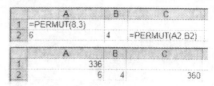

```
MATH NUM CPX PRB
1:rand
2:nPr
3:nCr
4:!
5:randInt(
6:randNorm(
7:randBin(
```
Screen 1

Worksheet 1

Worksheet 2

🖉 **Technology Note 2   Permutations**

The calculator command for permutations is accessed via the PRB menu shown in Screen 1. To use it, enter then number of objects, n then press **MATH**, then arrow over to PRB and select 2:nPr. Press **ENTER** then the number selected, r and then **ENTER**. See the note on page 260 to see this function in use.

To find permutations using a spreadsheet such as Excel, place your cursor in a cell and enter =PERMUT(. Then enter the number of objects followed by a comma and the number selected. Close with a) and enter. See Worksheet 2. Alternatively, enter the number of objects and the number chosen in two cells and refer to these cells in the PERMUT command.

Self-Help Exercises 5.1

1. A restaurant serves 3 soups, 4 salads, 10 main dishes, and 6 desserts. How many different meals can be served if one of each category is chosen?

2. Six junior executives and three senior executives are to line up for a picture. The senior executives must all be lined up together on the left and the junior executives must be all together on the right. In how many ways can this be done?

3. Four couples are going to the movie together. How many ways can these eight people be seated if couples sit together?

5.1 Exercises

In Exercises 1 through 12, evaluate the given expression.

1. $P(5,3)$ **2.** $P(5,2)$ **3.** $P(8,5)$

4. $P(8,3)$ **5.** $P(7,7)$ **6.** $P(7,1)$

7. $P(9,9)$ **8.** $P(9,1)$ **9.** $P(9,2)$

10. $P(n,0)$ **11.** $P(n,1)$ **12.** $P(n,2)$

13. A manufacturer offers 4 styles of sofas with 30 fabrics for each sofa. How many different sofas are there?

14. A manufacturer offers 3 grades of carpet with 10 colors for each grade. How many different carpets are there?

15. A restaurant offers 4 types of salads, 10 main dishes, and 5 desserts. How many different complete meals are there?

16. A card is picked from a standard deck of 52, and then a coin is flipped twice. How many possible outcomes are there?

17. A state's license plates have six digits with repetitions permitted. How many possible license plates of such type are there?

18. A state's license plates have five letters with repetitions not permitted. How many possible license plates of such type are there?

19. An automobile manufacturer offers a certain style car with two types of radios, 10 choices of exterior colors, 5 different interior colors, and 3 types of engines. How many different automobiles are offered?

20. A contractor has four styles of homes, each with three styles of garages, four styles of decks, and five styles of carpeting. How many possibilities are there?

21. A state makes license plates with three letters followed by three digits with repetitions permitted. How many possibilities are there?

22. A state makes license plates with three letters followed by three numbers with no repetitions of letters permitted. How many possibilities are there?

23. How many three-letter words can be made from the first eight letters of the alphabet if consonants cannot be next to each other and letters cannot be repeated?

24. How many five-letter words can be made from the first eight letters of the alphabet if consonants cannot be next to each other, vowels cannot be next to each other, and vowels cannot be repeated but consonants can be?

25. At an awards ceremony, five men and four women are to be called one at a time to receive an award. In how many ways can this be done if men and women must alternate?

26. At an awards ceremony, five women and four men are each to receive one award and are to be presented their award one at a time. Two of the awards are to be first given to two of the women, and then the remaining awards will alternate between men and women. How many ways can this be done?

27. In how many ways can the five members of a basketball team line up in a row for a picture?

28. In how many ways can the individuals in a foursome of golfers tee off in succession?

29. An executive is scheduling meetings with 12 people in succession. The first two meetings must be with two directors on the board, the second four with four vice presidents, and the last six with six junior executives. How many ways can this schedule be made out?

30. An executive is scheduling trips to the company's European plants. First the four French plants will be visited, followed by the three Italian plants, and then the five German ones. How many ways can this schedule be made out?

31. The starting nine players on the school baseball team and the starting five players on the basketball team are to line up for a picture with all members of the baseball team together on the left. How many ways can this be done?

32. The seven starting offensive linemen and four starting offensive backs of the New York Giants are to line up for a picture with the seven linemen in the middle. How many ways can this be done?

33. On a baseball team, the three outfielders can play any of the three outfield positions, and the four infielders can play any of the four infield positions. How many different arrangements of these seven players can be made?

34. On a football team, the seven linemen can play any of the seven linemen positions and the four backs can play any of the backfield positions. How many different arrangements of these 11 players can be made?

35. A group of 12 must select a president, a vice president, a treasurer, and a secretary. How many ways can this be done?

36. In the Superfecta, one must pick the first four finishers of a horse race in correct order. If there are 10 horses running in a race, how many different tickets are there?

37. A buyer for a furniture store selects 8 different style sofas from a group of 10 and has each style shipped on successive weeks. How many ways can this be done?

38. A chef can make 12 main courses. Every day a menu is formed by selecting 7 of the main courses and listing them in order. How many different such menus can be made?

39. Two groups are formed with 10 in the first group and 8 different people in the second. A president, vice president, and a secretary/treasurer is to be chosen in each group. How many ways can this be done?

40. At a race track you have the opportunity to buy a ticket that requires you to pick the first and second place horse in the first two races. If the first race runs 8 horses and the second runs 10, how many different tickets are possible?

41. A picture is to be taken by lining up 4 of the 11 players from the football team on the left, then 3 of the 9 players from the baseball team in the center, and finally 2 of the 5 players from the basketball team on the right. How many ways can this arrangement be done?

42. A tourist has eight cities in Great Britain, six in France, five in Italy, and seven in Germany on a list she would like to visit. She decides that she will first go to Great Britain and visit four of the cities on her list, then on to France to visit three cities on the list, then on to Italy for two cities, and then on to Germany to visit four on the list. How many ways can her itinerary be made out?

Extensions

43. Prove the general case that $P(n, r) = \dfrac{n!}{(n-r)!}$

44. How many different ways can seven people be seated at a round table with seven seats?

45. How many different ways can five condiments be placed along the edge of a lazy susan (a round tray that spins)?

Solutions to Self-Help Exercises 5.1

1. A restaurant that serves 3 soups, 4 salads, 10 main dishes, and 6 desserts can by the multiplication principle serve $3 \times 4 \times 10 \times 6 = 720$ different meals.

2. Six junior executives can line up in 6! ways on the right. For each of these ways the three senior executives can line up in 3! ways on the left. Thus by the multiplication principle, the two groups can line up in $3! \times 6! = 4320$ ways.

3. Consider each couple to be a single object. We have 4! ways to arrange the four couples. Each couple can be seated in 2! ways so in all there are

$$\underset{\substack{\text{arrange} \\ \text{couples}}}{\underbrace{4!}} \times \underset{\text{couple 1}}{\underbrace{2!}} \times \underset{\text{couple 2}}{\underbrace{2!}} \times \underset{\text{couple 3}}{\underbrace{2!}} \times \underset{\text{couple 4}}{\underbrace{2!}} = 24 \cdot 2 \cdot 2 \cdot 2 \cdot 2 = 384$$

5.2   Combinations

APPLICATION
Connecticut Lotto Game

> In the state of Connecticut's lotto game, 6 numbered balls are randomly selected without replacement from a set of 44 to determine a winning set of numbers (without regard to order). If no one picks these 6 numbers, the money wagered stays in the "pot" for the next drawing. After several consecutive games with no winners, the pot gets large and attracts a lot of attention and ticket sales.
>
> When the Connecticut lotto game started, the total number of balls was 36. After a number of years when there were very few long streaks with no winners, lotto officials changed the total number of balls from 36 to 44. Suppose a number of weeks has gone by without a winner and the pot has grown very large. You wish to organize a syndicate of investors that will purchase every possible ticket to ensure obtaining a winning ticket. How many tickets will the syndicate have to buy if there are 36 balls? If there are 44? The answer can be found in the discussion before Example 1.

✧ Combinations

When a permutation of n distinct objects is taken r at a time, one selects r of the objects in a specific order. A combination of r distinct objects taken from a set of size n is merely a selection of r of the objects (without concern for order). We consider combinations in this section.

Given the set $\{a,b,c\}$ we know from the last section that there are $P(3,2) = 3 \times 2 = 6$ ways of selecting two of these at a time when order is important. The six ways are

$$(a,b), \quad (b,a), \quad (a,c), \quad (c,a), \quad (b,c), \quad (c,b)$$

If now we wish to select two at a time when order is not important, then (a,b) is the same as (b,a), and (a,c) is the same as (c,a), and (b,c) is the same as (c,b). Thus there are only three ways of selecting two objects at a time when order is not important: $\{a,b\}, \{a,c\}, \{b,c\}$. These are referred to as combinations.

> **Combinations**
>
> A combination of r distinct objects taken from a set of size n is a selection of r of the objects (without concern for order).

For example, if from a group of four people, we wish to select a president, a vice president, and a secretary/treasurer, then order is important. If, on the other hand, we wish to select a committee of three people from a set of four, then order is not important since the duties and title of each committee member is the same no matter in what order they are selected.

We know from the last section that the number of permutations of r objects taken from a set of size n is given by $P(n,r)$. We denote the number of combinations of r objects taken from a set of size n by $C(n,r)$. We wish to find a formula for $C(n,r)$.

We can see this by viewing the process of selecting all permutations of r objects taken from a set of size n as a sequence of two tasks.

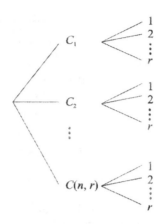

Figure 5.47

1. The first task is to select r distinct objects where the order that the objects are chosen doesn't matter. The number of ways to complete this task will be $C(n,r)$ as this is the definition of what we mean by combination.

2. In the second task the r objects selected in the combination are arranged in some order. The number of ways to complete this task is $r!$, as we learned in the last section. Notice that no matter what combination we take, we then always permute by the same number, $(r!)$.

That is, first select a combination of r distinct objects and then order them. By the multiplication principle we have

$$P(n,r) = C(n,r)r! \qquad \rightarrow \qquad C(n,r) = \frac{1}{r!}P(n,r) = \frac{n!}{(r!)(n-r)!}$$

See Figure 5.47 where the distinct combinations are listed as $C_1, C_2, \ldots, C(n,r)$. We have proven the following.

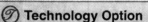
> **Number of Combinations of r Objects taken from a Set of Size n**
> The number of combinations of r distinct objects taken from a set of size n, denoted by $C(n,r)$, is given by
> $$C(n,r) = \frac{n!}{(r!)(n-r)!}$$

We now solve the problem posed at the beginning of this chapter. Since the order in which the numbers are selected is of no consequence, we are looking for $C(36,6)$ in the first case and $C(44,6)$ in the second case. These are

$$C(36,6) = \frac{36!}{6!(36-6)!} = \frac{36 \cdot 35 \cdot 34 \cdot 33 \cdot 32 \cdot 31 \cdot (30!)}{6!(30!)}$$

$$= \frac{36 \cdot 35 \cdot 34 \cdot 33 \cdot 32 \cdot 31}{6!} = 1,947,792$$

and

$$C(44,6) = \frac{44!}{6!(44-6)!} = \frac{44 \cdot 43 \cdot 42 \cdot 41 \cdot 40 \cdot 39 \cdot (38!)}{6!(38!)}$$

$$= \frac{44 \cdot 43 \cdot 42 \cdot 41 \cdot 40 \cdot 39}{6!} = 7,059,053$$

Thus with 36 balls, the syndicate must buy about 2 million tickets. If there are 44 balls, then about 7 million tickets must be bought to guarantee a winning ticket.

EXAMPLE 1   Calculating the Number of Different Poker Hands   How many different 5-card poker hands can be dealt from a standard deck of 52 cards?

Solution   Refer to Figure 5.48 for a standard deck of cards. Since the order in which the cards in a poker hand are dealt is of no consequence, we are looking for $C(52,5)$ which is

Figure 5.48

$$C(52,5) = \frac{52!}{5!(52-5)!} = \frac{52 \cdot 51 \cdot 50 \cdot 49 \cdot 48 \cdot (47!)}{5!(47!)} = \frac{52 \cdot 51 \cdot 50 \cdot 49 \cdot 48}{5!}$$
$$= 2,598,960$$

◆

EXAMPLE 2   A Counting Problem in Poker   Find the number of poker hands with three queens and two jacks.

Solution   View this as a sequence of two tasks. In the first task, select three queens from a deck with four queens. In the second task, select two jacks from a deck with four jacks. Since order is not important in either case, the first task can be done in $C(4,3)$ ways and the second task can be done in $C(4,2)$ ways. No matter how the first task is completed, the second task can always be made in $C(4,2)$ ways, the multiplication principle then indicates that the number of hands with three queens and two jacks is given by

$$C(4,3)C(4,2) = \left(\frac{4!}{3!(4-3)!} \right) \left(\frac{4!}{2!(4-2)!} \right) = \left(\frac{4(3!)}{3!} \right) \left(\frac{4 \cdot 3 \cdot 2}{2 \cdot 2} \right)$$
$$= (4)(6) = 24$$

◆

EXAMPLE 3   Counting Using Both Combinations and Permutations   In how many ways can a committee be formed with a chair, a vice chair, a secretary/treasurer, and 4 additional people all chosen from a group of 10 people?

Solution   This example, like many other counting problems, can be solved in more than one way. We illustrate four ways this question can be solved. Of course all of them lead to the same correct value!

1. Using the multiplication principle we have a series of tasks. Our first task is to choose a chair of the committee. We will have 10 choices for this task. The person chosen cannot be chosen again for vice chair, so we will have 9 ways to complete the task of choosing the vice chair. That leaves us with 8 ways to choose the secretary/treasurer. Now there are 7 people available to be put in the remaining spots on the committee and the order that these are chosen doesn't matter. Therefore there will be $C(7,4)$ ways to complete the task of choosing the rest of the committee. This is summarized below:

$$\underbrace{10}_{\text{chair}} \times \underbrace{9}_{\text{vicechair}} \times \underbrace{8}_{\text{S/T}} \times \underbrace{C(7,4)}_{\text{rest}} = 10 \cdot 9 \cdot 8 \cdot 35 = 25,200$$

2. Another way of doing this problem is to see the process as a sequence of two selections. The first is to pick the chair, vice chair, and secretary/treasurer from the set of 10. Since order is important, this can be done in $P(10,3)$ ways. The second selection is to then pick the other 4 members of the committee from the remaining 7 people. This can done in $C(7,4)$ ways since the order is not important. Furthermore, since the second selection can always be made in $C(7,4)$ ways no matter how the first selection was made, the multiplication principle indicates that the total number of ways of selecting the committee is

$$P(10,3)C(7,4) = 10 \cdot 9 \cdot 8 \frac{7 \cdot 6 \cdot 5 \cdot 4}{4 \cdot 3 \cdot 2} = 25,200$$

3. Yet another way of viewing this is to select four of the committee members from the group of 10 and then select the chair, vice chair, and secretary/treasurer from the remaining six. This gives

$$C(10,4)P(6,3) = \frac{10 \cdot 9 \cdot 8 \cdot 7}{4 \cdot 3 \cdot 2} 6 \cdot 5 \cdot 4 = 25,200$$

4. Finally, another way of looking at this is to select the committee of seven from the group of 10 and then select the chair, vice chair, and the secretary/treasurer from the committee of seven. This gives

$$C(10,7)P(7,3) = \frac{10 \cdot 9 \cdot 8}{3\cdot} 7 \cdot 6 \cdot 5 = 25,200 \qquad \blacklozenge$$

EXAMPLE 4 A Counting Problem Using Combinations A committee of 15 people consists of eight men and seven women. In how many ways can a subcommittee of five be formed if the subcommittee consists of
a. any five committee members?
b. all men?
c. at least three men?

Solution

a. Since the order of selection is of no consequence, the answer is

$$C(15,5) = \frac{15!}{5!(15-5)!} = \frac{15 \cdot 14 \cdot 13 \cdot 12 \cdot 11 \cdot (10!)}{5!(10!)} = \frac{15 \cdot 14 \cdot 13 \cdot 12 \cdot 11}{5!}$$
$$= 3003$$

b. Here we must pick five men out of eight possible men. This can be done in $C(8,5)$ ways since again order is not important. Thus

$$C(8,5) = \frac{8!}{5!(8-5)!} = \frac{8 \cdot 7 \cdot 6 \cdot (5!)}{5!(3 \cdot 2)} = 56$$

c. At least three men means all subcommittees with three men and two women, plus all subcommittees with four men and one women, plus all with five men. This is

$$C(8,3)\ C(7,2) + C(8,4)C(7,1) + C(8,5)C(7,0)$$
$$= \frac{8 \cdot 7 \cdot 6}{3 \cdot 2} \left(\frac{7 \cdot 6}{2} \right) + \frac{8 \cdot 7 \cdot 6 \cdot 5}{4 \cdot 3 \cdot 2}(7) + \frac{8 \cdot 7 \cdot 6 \cdot 5 \cdot 4}{5 \cdot 4 \cdot 3 \cdot 2}(1)$$
$$= (56)(21) + (70)(7) + (56)(1) = 1722 \qquad \blacklozenge$$

✧ Additional Applications of Combinations

EXAMPLE 5 A Counting Problem Involving a Sequence An investor has selected a growth mutual fund from a large set of growth funds and will consider any of the next 10 years a success (S) if this mutual fund performs above average in the set of funds and a failure (F) otherwise.
a. How many different outcomes are possible?

b. How many different outcomes have exactly sic successes?

c. How many different outcomes have at least three successes?

Solution

a. An outcome consists of 10 operations in sequence. Each operation assigns a S or F. One such example is

$$(S,S,F,S,S,F,F,F,S,S)$$

No matter what the assignments of S's and F's in any of the prior years, there are always two possibilities for the current year: S or F. Using the multiplication principle with $k = 10$ and $n_1 = n_2 = \ldots = n_{10} = 2$ yields $2^{10} = 1024$ as the total number of possible outcomes.

b. An outcome with exactly 6 S's was given in the first part. Notice that this amounts to filling in six years with S's and four years with F's. A particular outcome will be determined once we fill in 6 S's in six of the years. This can be done in $C(10,6)$ ways. This is

$$C(10,6) = \frac{10!}{6!(10-6)!} = \frac{10 \cdot 9 \cdot 8 \cdot 7}{4 \cdot 3 \cdot 2} = 210$$

c. The answer to this is the number with exactly 3 S's plus the number with exactly 4 S's plus ... the number with exactly 10 S's, or

$$C(10,3) + C(10,4) + \ldots + C(10,10).$$

A shorter way can be given by noticing that this is just the total number less the number with at most 2 S's. This is

$$1024 - [C(10,0) + C(10,1) + C(10,2)] = 1024 - [1 + 10 + 45] = 968. \quad \blacklozenge$$

EXAMPLE 6   Selecting a Jury   Twenty people are called for jury duty. A jury of 12 will be selected at random followed by the selection of two alternate jurors. How many ways can this be done?

Solution   This is a two-step process. We begin by selecting the jury where 12 are chosen from 20 and order does not matter. This can be done $C(20,12)$ ways. The second task is to choose the alternate jurors from the remaining $20 - 12 = 8$ people. This can be done $C(8,2)$ ways. In all

$$\underbrace{C(20,12)}_{\text{jury}} \times \underbrace{C(8,2)}_{\text{alternates}} = 125970 \cdot 28 = 35,271,600$$

There are 35,271,600 different ways that the jury and the alternates can be chosen. $\blacklozenge$

✧ Technology Corner

⑦Technology Note 1   **Combinations**

To find combinations using a spreadsheet such as Excel, place your cursor in a cell and enter =COMBIN(. Then enter the number of objects followed by a

	A	B	C
1	1947792		
2	44	6	7059052

	A	B	C
1	=COMBIN(36,6)		
2	44	6	=COMBIN(A2,B2)

comma and the number selected. Close with a) and enter. See Worksheet 3. Alternatively, enter the number of objects and the number chosen in two cells and refer to these cells in the COMBIN command.

Worksheet 3

Self-Help Exercises 5.2

1. A quinella ticket at a race track allows one to pick the first two finishers without regard to order. How many different tickets are possible in a race with 10 horses?

2. A company wishes to select 4 junior executives from the San Francisco office, 5 from the Dallas office, and 5 from the Miami office to bring to the New York City headquarters. In how many ways can this be done if there are 10 junior executives in San Francisco, 12 in Dallas, and 15 in Miami?

5.2 Exercises

In Exercises 1 through 12, calculate the indicated quantity.

1. $C(8,3)$ **2.** $C(8,4)$ **3.** $C(8,5)$

4. $C(12,12)$ **5.** $C(12,1)$ **6.** $C(12,0)$

7. $C(7,4)$ **8.** $C(7,3)$ **9.** $C(15,2)$

10. $C(n,0)$ **11.** $C(n,1)$ **12.** $C(n,2)$

13. Find all permutations of $\{a,b,c\}$ taken two at a time by first finding all combinations of the set taken two at a time and then permuting each combination. Construct a tree similar to Figure 5.47 in the text.

14. Find all permutations of $\{a,b,c,d\}$ taken three at a time by first finding all combinations of the set taken three at a time and then permuting each combination. Construct a tree similar to Figure 5.47 in the text.

15. If you have a penny, a nickel, a dime, a quarter, and a half-dollar in your pocket or purse, how many different tips can you leave using 3 coins?

16. From a list of 40 captains, 5 are to be promoted to major. In how many ways can this be done?

17. In a certain lotto game, six numbered balls are randomly selected without replacement from a set of balls numbered from 1 to 46 to determine a winning set of numbers (without regard to order). Find the number of possible outcomes.

18. A boxed Trifecta ticket at a horse track allows you to pick the first three finishers without regard to order. How many different tickets are possible in a race with 10 horses?

19. From a list of 20 recommended stocks from your brokerage firm, you wish to select 5 of them for purchase. In how many ways can you do this?

20. A restaurant offers eight toppings on its pizza. In how many ways can you select three of them?

21. If you join a book club, you can purchase 4 books at a sharp discount from a list of 20. In how many ways can you do this?

22. A firm is considering expanding into four of nine possible cities. In how many ways can this be done?

23. In how many ways can an inspector select 5 bolts from a batch of 40 for inspection?

24. A chef has 20 dinners that she can make. In how many ways can she select 6 of them for the menu for today?

25. In her last semester, a student must pick 3 mathematics courses and 2 computer science courses to graduate with a degree in mathematics with a minor in computer science. If there are 11 mathematics courses and 7 computer science courses available to take, how many different ways can this be done?

26. A committee of 12 U.S. senators is to be formed with 7 Democrats and 5 Republicans. In how many ways can this be done if there are 53 Democratic senators and 47 Republican senators?

27. A chef has 20 main courses and six soups that he can prepare. How many different menus could he require if he always has seven main courses and three soups on each menu?

28. A firm must select 4 out of a possible 10 sites on the East Coast and 3 out of a possible 8 sites on the West Coast for expansion. In how many ways can this be done?

29. A firm has 12 junior executives. Three are to be sent to Pittsburgh, one to Houston, one to Atlanta, and one to Boston. In how many ways can this be done?

30. Six prizes are to be given to six different people in a group of nine. In how many ways can a first prize, a second prize, a third prize, and three fourth prizes be given?

31. In a new group of 11 employees 4 are to be assigned to production, 1 to sales, and 1 to advertising. In how many ways can this be done?

32. A parent of seven children wants two children to make dinner, one to dust, and one to vacuum. In how many ways can this be done?

33. In how many ways can the nine member Supreme Court give a five-to-four decision upholding a lower court?

34. In how many ways can a committee of five reach a majority decision if there are no abstentions?

35. A coin is flipped eight times in succession. In how many ways can exactly five heads occur?

36. A coin is flipped eight times in succession. In how many ways can at least six heads occur?

37. A coin is flipped eight times in succession. In how many ways can at least two heads occur?

38. A baseball team takes a road trip and plays 12 games. In how many ways could they win 7 and lose 5?

39. A banana split is made with 3 scoops of ice cream, three different flavors of ice cream, three different syrups, two different types of nuts, and with or without whipped cream. How many different banana splits can be made if there are twelve flavors of ice cream, eight syrups, and four types of nuts to choose from?

40. A salesman has 10 customers in New York City, 8 in Dallas, and 6 in Denver. In how many ways can he see 4 customers in New York City, 3 in Dallas, and 4 in Denver?

41. Find the number of different poker hands that contain exactly three aces, while the remaining two cards do not form a pair.

42. Find the number of full houses in a poker hand, that is, the number of poker hands with three of a kind and two of a kind.

43. Find the number of poker hands with two pairs, that is, two different two of a kinds with the fifth card a third different kind.

44. In how many ways can a doubles game of tennis be arranged from eight boys and four girls if each side must have one boy and one girl?

45. Show that $C(n, r) = C(n, (n - r))$.

Solutions to Self-Help Exercises 5.2

⑦ Technology Option

```
10 nCr 2
                  45
(10 nCr 4)*(12 n
Cr 5)*(15 nCr 5)
        499458960
```

1. The number of tickets is the same as the number of ways of selecting 2 objects from 10 when order is not important. That is

$$C(10, 2) = \frac{10 \cdot 9}{2} = 45$$

2. The number of ways that junior executives can be selected from San Francisco, Dallas, and Miami, is respectively, $C(10, 4)$, $C(12, 5)$, and $C(15, 5)$. By the multiplication principle the total number of ways this can be done is

$$C(10,4)C(12,5)C(15,5) = \frac{10!}{4!(10-4)!} \frac{12!}{5!(12-5)!} \frac{15!}{5!(15-5)!}$$

$$= \frac{10 \cdot 9 \cdot 8 \cdot 7}{4 \cdot 3 \cdot 2} \cdot \frac{12 \cdot 11 \cdot 10 \cdot 9 \cdot 8}{5 \cdot 4 \cdot 3 \cdot 2} \cdot \frac{15 \cdot 14 \cdot 13 \cdot 12 \cdot 11}{5 \cdot 4 \cdot 3 \cdot 2}$$

$$= (10 \cdot 3 \cdot 7)(11 \cdot 9 \cdot 8)(7 \cdot 13 \cdot 3 \cdot 11)$$

$$= 499{,}458{,}960$$

5.3   Probability Applications of Counting Principles

APPLICATION
Probability in Games

> Find the probability of drawing a flush, but not a straight flush, in a poker game, assuming that any 5-card hand is just as likely as any other. For the answer see Example 4.

Recall from the previous chapter that the probability of an event E is given by

$$P(E) = \frac{n(E)}{n(S)}$$

where $n(E)$ is the number of outcomes in event E and $n(S)$ is the number of outcomes in the uniform sample space for this experiment. Up to this point, $n(S)$ was found using a tree diagram or simply listing the outcomes of the experiment. In this section the sample spaces will be found using the counting techniques learned in this chapter.

EXAMPLE 1   Two Defective Transistors   A bin contains 15 identical (to the eye) transistors except that 6 are defective and 9 are not. Suppose a transistor is selected from the bin and then another is selected without replacing the first. What is the probability that both transistors are defective?

Solution   First note that we wish to select 2 transistors from 15 with order not important. The number of ways to do this is

$$C(15,2) = \frac{15 \cdot 14}{2} = 105$$

The number of ways we can select 2 defective transistors from a set of 6 is

$$C(6,2) = \frac{6 \cdot 5}{2} = 15$$

If the event E is "both transistors are defective," then

$$P(E) = \frac{C(6,2)}{C(15,2)} = \frac{15}{105} = \frac{1}{7} \qquad \blacklozenge$$

EXAMPLE 2   Defective Transistors Again   What is the probability of selecting 5 transistors from the bin in Example 1 with 2 defective and 3 not defective?

Solution   The number of ways of selecting 5 from the 15 is

$$C(15,5) = \frac{15 \cdot 14 \cdot 13 \cdot 12 \cdot 11}{5 \cdot 4 \cdot 3 \cdot 2} = 3003$$

The number of ways of selecting 2 defectives from 6 is $C(6,2)$, while the number of ways of selecting 3 non-defective ones from 9 is $C(9,3)$. Thus by the multiplication principle, the number of ways of doing both is

$$C(6,2) \cdot C(9,3) = \frac{6 \cdot 5}{2} \cdot \frac{9 \cdot 8 \cdot 7}{3 \cdot 2} = 1260$$

If E is the probability of selecting 2 defective transistors and 3 non-defective ones, then

$$P(E) = \frac{1260}{3003} \approx 0.420 \qquad \blacklozenge$$

EXAMPLE 3   Coin Tosses A fair coin is tossed six times. Assuming that any outcome is as likely as any other, find the probability of obtaining exactly three heads.

Solution   By the multiplication principle, there are $2^6 = 64$ possible outcomes. The number of ways of obtaining exactly three heads is the number of ways of selecting three slots from among six to place the heads. This is

$$C(6,3) = \frac{6 \cdot 5 \cdot 4}{3 \cdot 2} = 20$$

Thus if E is the event that exactly three heads occur, then

$$P(E) = \frac{20}{64} = \frac{5}{16} \qquad \blacklozenge$$

EXAMPLE 4   A Poker Hand Find the probability of drawing a flush, but not a straight flush, in a poker game, assuming that any 5-card hand is just as likely as any other.

Solution   A deck in poker has 52 cards. Thus there are

$$C(52,5) = \frac{52 \cdot 51 \cdot 50 \cdot 49 \cdot 48}{5 \cdot 4 \cdot 3 \cdot 2} = 2,598,960$$

possible hands.

A flush consists of 5 cards in a single suit. There are four suits, each of 13 cards. Thus the number of ways of obtaining a flush in a particular suit is

$$C(13,5) = \frac{13 \cdot 12 \cdot 11 \cdot 10 \cdot 9}{5 \cdot 4 \cdot 3 \cdot 2} = 1287$$

A straight consists of 5 cards in sequence. There are 10 such straight flushes in each suit:

$$\{1,2,3,4,5\}, \ldots, \{10, J, Q, K, A\}$$

Thus the number of flushes that are not straights is $4(1287 - 10) = 5108$. Therefore if E is the event of drawing a flush, but not a straight flush, then

$$P(E) = \frac{5108}{2,598,960} \approx 0.0020 \qquad \blacklozenge$$

REMARK: The ranking of poker hands depends on the difficulty (probability) of obtaining that hand. In the exercises the probabilities are calculated and this will demonstrate why, for example, a straight flush is a higher ranked hand than four-of-a-kind.

✧ Distinguishable Permutations

In our previous counting problems we have only arranged items that were different. That is, if we arranged the letters in the word *ERG* we would have six ways to arrange them and they are all different:

ERG   EGR   REG   GER   GRE   RGE

If we try to do the same with the word *EGG* notice what happens

EGG   EGG   GEG   GEG   GGE   GGE

It appears there are duplicate arrangements. This is because while there are two *G*'s, they are identical. So if we want to only count those arrangements that look different, it seems we must take into account the fact that some of the items we are arranging are identical. A similar case occurs when partitioning items into multiple groups. The general formula for dealing with these cases will be developed in the following examples.

EXAMPLE 5   Dividing a Committee to Perform Tasks   In how many ways can a group of 14 people be divided into three committees, each assigned a different task, the first committee consisting of 8 people, the second 4 people, and the third 2 people?

Solution   We can select 8 people for the first committee in $C(14,8)$ ways and then select 4 people for the second committee from among the remaining 6 people in $C(6,4)$ ways. The remaining 2 people can then go into the third committee in only one way. By the multiplication principle, the total number of ways this can be done is

$$C(14,8) \cdot C(6,4) = \frac{14!}{8!6!} \frac{6!}{4!2!} = \frac{14!}{8!4!2!}$$

We leave the answer in this form in view of what we are about to do. However, the actual value is 45,045. $\qquad \blacklozenge$

We can think of the three committees in the previous problem as a division of the set of $n = 14$ people into three groups. We select n_1 elements from the set of n . Now select n_2 elements from the remaining $n - n_1$ elements. Finally, place the remaining n_3 elements in the third group. The total number of ways this can be done is then, in analogy with the committee of 14 discussed above,

$$\frac{n!}{n_1!n_2!n_3!}$$

where $n_1 + n_2 + n_3 = n$.

REMARK: You can do this as an exercise by realizing that the answer should be $C(n, n_1)C(n - n_1, n_2)$. Now compute this and obtain the answer given above.

Distinguishable Permutations
A set of size n is divided into k groups of sizes $n_1, n_2, \ldots, n_k$, with all elements in each group being identical. Then the number of distinguishable permutations is

$$\frac{n!}{n_1! n_2! \cdots n_k!}$$

where $n_1 + n_2 + \cdots + n_k = n$.

EXAMPLE 6   Arrangements of Letters Find the number of arrangements of the word MISSISSIPPI.

Solution   We can think of this as forming the S-committee (or S-group), the I-committee (or I-group), the P-committee, and the M-committee. The word MISSISSIPPI has 11 letters, so we then have

$$\frac{11!}{4! 4! 2! 1!} = 34,650 \qquad \blacklozenge$$

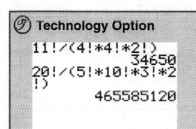
EXAMPLE 7   Arrangement of Books A shelf in the book room of a math department has 20 books for its teachers. There are of the same algebra books, 10 of the same finite math books, 3 of the same geometry books, and 2 of the same calculus books. How many distinguishable ways can these 20 books be arranged on the shelf?

Solution   From the set of 20 elements we have

$$\frac{20!}{5! 10! 3! 2!} = 465,585,120 \qquad \blacklozenge$$

✧ Optional: A Nonintuitive Example

We now calculate the probability of a certain event and obtain a very surprising (nonintuitive) result.

EXAMPLE 8   The Birthday Problem Suppose there are 50 people in a room with you. What is the probability that at least 2 of these people will have the same birthday?

Solution   Suppose more generally there are n people in the room. Let E be the event that at least 2 of these people will have the same birthday. We will ignore leap years and assume that every one of the 365 days of the year is just as likely to be a birthday as any other. It is much easier to first find $P(E^c)$, the probability that no two have the same birthday.

First notice that there are 365 possible birthdays for each individual. Thus, by the multiplication principle, there are 365^n possible birthdays for the n individuals. This is the total number in the sample space. To find $P(E^c)$ notice that there are 365 possible birthdays for the first individual and since the second individual cannot have the same birthday as the first, there are 364 possible birthdays for the second, and then 363 for the third, and so on. We have

n	$P(E)$
15	0.25
20	0.41
23	0.51
30	0.71
50	0.97

$$P(E) = 1 - P(E^c) = \frac{(365)(364)\cdots(365-n+1)}{365^n}$$

The table on the left gives this for several values of n. Notice the very surprising result that for n equal to only 23 the probability is about 0.51. With 50 people in the room the probability is approximately 0.97 that 2 or more of these people will have the same birthday.   ◆

Self-Help Exercises 5.3

1. A lotto game consists of picking (in any order) the correct 6 numbers drawn from 1 to 42 without replacement.

   a. What is the probability of any 1 pick winning?

   b. What is the probability of a winning pick being all consecutive numbers?

2. A group of five boys and five girls are lining up for lunch. What is the probability that boys and girls alternate?

5.3 Exercises

In Exercises 1 and 2, let an urn have 10 balls, identical except that 4 are white and 6 are red.

1. If 3 are selected randomly without replacement, what is the probability that 2 are white and 1 is red? At least 2 are white?

2. If 5 are selected randomly without replacement, what is the probability that 3 are white and 2 are red? At least 3 are white?

In Exercises 3 through 6, let an urn have 21 identical balls except that 6 are white, 7 are red, and 8 are blue.

3. What is the probability that there is one of each color if 3 are selected randomly without replacement?

4. What is the probability that all are white if 3 are selected randomly without replacement?

5. What is the probability that 3 are white, 2 are red, and 1 is blue if 6 are selected randomly without replacement?

6. What is the probability that at least 5 are white if 6 are selected randomly without replacement?

In Exercises 7 through 12 a 2-card hand is drawn from a standard deck of 52 cards. Find the probability that the hand contains the given cards.

7. two kings

8. two spades

9. a pair

10. two of the same suit

11. two consecutive cards

12. no face card

In Exercises 13 through 20, find the probability of obtaining each of the given in a 5-card poker hand. Hint: The probabilities increase.

13. royal flush: ace, king, queen, jack, ten in the same suit

14. straight flush: five cards in sequence in the same suit but not a royal flush

15. four of a kind: four queens, four sevens, etc.

16. full house: three of a kind together with a pair

17. straight: five cards in sequence not all in the same suit

18. three of a kind

19. two pairs

20. one pair

21. Assume that the probability of an individual being born in any month is the same and that there are n individuals in a room. Find the probability that at least two individuals have their birthdays in the same month when $n = 2, 3, 4, 5$.

22. Suppose n different letters have been written with n corresponding addressed envelopes, and the letters are inserted *randomly* into the envelope. What is the probability that no letter gets into its correct envelope for $n = 2, 3, 4, 5$?

23. What is the probability that at least two members of the 434-member United States House of Representatives have their birthdays on the same day?

24. What is the probability that at least 2 of the 100 Senators of the U.S. Congress have the same birthday?

Applications

25. **Quality Control** A bin has four defective transistors and six non-defective ones. If two are picked randomly from the bin, what is the probability that both are defective?

26. **Stock Selection** Among a group of 20 stocks, suppose that 10 stocks will perform above average and the other 10 below average. If you pick 3 stocks from this group, what is the probability that all 3 will be above average in performance?

27. **Mutual Funds** Suppose in any year a certain mutual fund is just as likely to perform above average as not. Find the probability that this fund will perform above average in at least 8 of the next 10 years.

28. **Committees** A committee of three is to be selected at random from a group of three senior and four junior executives. What is the probability that the committee will have more senior than junior executives?

29. **Testing** A company places a dozen of the same product in one box. Before sealing, three of the product are tested. If any of the three is defective, the entire box will be rejected. Suppose a box has two defective products. What is the probability the box will be rejected?

30. **Awarding of Contracts** Suppose that there are three corporations competing for four different government contracts. If the contracts are awarded randomly, what is the probability that each corporation will get a contract?

31. A manufacturing company buys a certain component from three different vendors. In how many ways can the company order eight components with four from the first vendor and two each from the other vendors?

32. A mutual fund has 20 stocks in its portfolio. On a given day 3 stocks move up, 15 stay the same, and 2 move down. In how many ways could this happen?

33. An advertising firm has 12 potential clients and three different salesmen. In how many ways can it divide the potential clients equally among the three salesmen?

34. In how many ways can a class of 10 students be assigned 1 A, 2 B's, 4 C's, 2 D's, and 1 F?

35. Two scholarships of $10,000 each, three of $5000 each, and five of $2000 each are to be awarded to 10 finalists. In how many ways can this be done?

36. The 12 directors of a company are to be divided equally into three separate committees to study sales, recent products, and labor relations. In how many ways can this be done?

37. Find the number of arrangements of each of the following words that can be distinguished.
    a. $a_1 a_2 b$ **b.** *aab* **c.** $a_1 a_2 b_1 b_2$ **d.** $aab_1 b_2$
    e. *aabb*

38. Find the number of arrangements of each of the following words that can be distinguished.
    a. $a_1 a_2 b_1 b_2 b_3$ **b.** $aab_1 b_2 b_3$ **c.** *aabbb*

39. Find the number of arrangements of the word TENNESSEE that can be distinguished.

40. Suppose a word has n symbols made from k distinct elements, with n_1 of the first element, n_2 of the second element, $\dots$, n_k of the kth element. If $n_1 + n_2 + \cdots n_k = n$, show that the number of distinguishable arrangements of the n symbol word is

$$\frac{n!}{n_1!n_2!\cdots n_k!}$$

Verify that this works for the previous exercise.

Solutions to Self-Help Exercises 5.3

1. Since the numbers can be drawn in any order, we will use combinations to find the probability.

   a. The number in the sample space S is the number of ways of selecting 6 objects (without replacement) from a set of 42 where order is not important. This is

   $$C(42,6) = \frac{42\cdot 41\cdot 40\cdot 39\cdot 38\cdot 37}{6\cdot 5\cdot 4\cdot 3\cdot 2} = 5,245,786$$

   Thus the probability of any one pick is $\dfrac{1}{5,245,786}$.

   b. The picks in which the numbers are consecutive are

   $$\{1,2,3,4,5,6\}, \cdots, \{37,38,39,40,41,42\}$$

   There are 37 such selections. Thus the probability of any one of these being the winning number is $\dfrac{37}{5,245,786}$.

2. The number in the sample space is the number of ways that these 10 children can line up without any restrictions, so $n(S) = 10! = 3,628,800$. $n(E)$ will be the number of ways the children can line up with boys and girls alternating. This can be found using the multiplication principle and realizing that a boy or girl can be first in line so that there are 10 ways to complete the task of choosing who is first in line. The next person has to be a boy, if a girl was first or a girl, if a boy was first, so there will be 5 ways to complete the task of choosing who is second in line. This gives us $10\cdot 5\cdot 4\cdot 4\cdot 3\cdot 3\cdot 2\cdot 2\cdot 1\cdot 1) = 28,800$. Therefore the probability that boys and girls alternate is

   $$P(E) = \frac{n(E)}{n(S)} = \frac{28,800}{3,628,800} = \frac{1}{26} \approx 0.008$$

5.4 Bernoulli Trials

APPLICATION
Finding Probabilities of
Non-defective Microchips

A computer manufacturer uses eight microchips in each of its computers. It knows that 5% of these chips are defective. What is the probability that at least six are good? See Example 3 for the answer.

✧ Bernoulli Trials

In this section we consider the simplest possible experiments: those with just two outcomes. We refer to experiments in which there are just two outcomes as Bernoulli trials. Some examples are as follows.

- Flip a coin and see if heads or tails turns up.

- Test a transistor to see if it is defective or not.

- Examine a patient to see if a particular disease is present or not.

- Take a free throw in basketball and make the basket or not.

We commonly refer to the two outcomes of a Bernoulli trial as "success" (S) or "failure" (F). We agree always to write p for the probability of "success" and q for the probability of "failure." Naturally, $q = 1 - p$.

In this section we are actually not so much interested in performing an experiment with two outcomes once, but rather many times. We refer to this as a repeated Bernoulli trial. We make the following very fundamental assumption.

Fundamental Assumption for Bernoulli Trials
Successive Bernoulli trials are independent of one another.

Thus, for example, flipping a coin 10 times is a repeated Bernoulli trial. Tossing a die 20 times and seeing if an even number or an odd number occurs each time is another example. Consider randomly selecting a card from a standard deck and noting if it is an ace. If we repeat this experiment, but always first replace any card drawn, then the trials are independent and the probability of selecting an ace stays the same. But if we do not replace any card drawn, then the probability of selecting an ace changes, and the trials are not independent of each other.

Given a Bernoulli trial repeated n times, we are interested in determining the probability that a specific number of successes occurs. We will often shorten this to $P(k = x)$.

EXAMPLE 1   Making Free Throws Suppose a basketball player makes on average 2 free throws of every 3 attempted and that success and failure on any 1 free throw does not depend on the outcomes of the other shots. If the player shoots 10 free throws, find the probability of making exactly 6 of them.

Solution   We let S designate "making the basket" and F "not making the basket." A typical sequence of exactly six successes looks like

$$SSFSFSSFFS$$

Now the product rule indicates that the probability of this occurring is

$$\left(\frac{2}{3}\right)\left(\frac{2}{3}\right)\left(\frac{1}{3}\right)\left(\frac{2}{3}\right)\left(\frac{1}{3}\right)\left(\frac{2}{3}\right)\left(\frac{2}{3}\right)\left(\frac{1}{3}\right)\left(\frac{1}{3}\right)\left(\frac{2}{3}\right) = \left(\frac{2}{3}\right)^6 \left(\frac{1}{3}\right)^4$$

We might think of the process of obtaining exactly six successes as lining up 10 boxes in a row and picking exactly 6 of them in which to place an S. Thus the previous sequence of successes and failures would be

S	S		S		S	S			S

Since every such sequence must contain exactly six S's and four F's, the probability of any one of these occurring is always $(2/3)^6(1/3)^4$. We then must count the number of ways there can be exactly six successes. But this is the number of ways of selecting six of the boxes to place an S inside. This can be done in $C(10,6)$ ways. Thus

$$C(10,6)\left(\frac{2}{3}\right)^6\left(\frac{1}{3}\right)^4 = \frac{10\cdot9\cdot8\cdot7\cdot6\cdot5}{6\cdot5\cdot4\cdot3\cdot2}\left(\frac{2}{3}\right)^6\left(\frac{1}{3}\right)^4$$
$$= 210\left(\frac{2}{3}\right)^6\left(\frac{1}{3}\right)^4$$
$$\approx 0.228 \qquad \blacklozenge$$

In general, to find the probability of exactly k successes in n repeated Bernoulli trials, first notice that any particular sequence with exactly k successes have exactly, $n-k$ failures. Thus by the product rule, the probability of any one of these occurring is

$$p^k q^{n-k}$$

The number of ways of obtaining exactly k successes in n trials is the number of ways of selecting k objects (the boxes with S inside a box in the above discussion) from a total of n. This is $C(n,k)$. The probability of obtaining exactly k successes in n trials is then

$$C(n,k)p^k q^{n-k}$$

REMARK: Be careful to clearly designate which of the outcomes is success and which is failure. Confusing the two will result in using the above formula incorrectly.

(⑦) **Technology Option**

See Technology Note 1 on page 281 for details on finding probabilities in repeated Bernoulli trials using a graphing calculator or a spreadsheet.

Quick Fact: the probability can be found on the TI graphing calculator by going to DISTR which is above the VARS button and scrolling down the A:binompdf(option. Select this and then enter the number number of trials, n, a comma then p followed by another comma and finally k, the number of successes. Close the parentheses and press ENTER.

```
binompdf(10,2/3,
6)
        .2276075801
```

✧ Applications

EXAMPLE 2   Baseball Hits   What was the probability of a baseball player who has a 0.300 batting average getting at least two hits in a game if we assume that he came to bat four official times in that game and if we assume coming to bat each time is an independent trial.

Solution   If we designate success as a hit, then $p = 0.300$ and $q = 1 - p = 0.700$. The probability $P(k)$, where k is the number of successes, is then

$$P(k) = C(n,k)p^k q^{n-k} = C(4,k)(0.300)^k(0.700)^{4-k}$$

We then are looking for $P(2) + P(3) + P(4)$. We have

$$P(2) = C(4,2)(0.3)^2(0.7)^2 = 6(0.09)(0.49) = 0.2646$$
$$P(3) = C(4,3)(0.3)^3(0.7)^1 = 4(0.027)(0.7) = 0.0756$$
$$P(4) = C(4,4)(0.3)^4(0.7)^0 = 1(0.0081)(1) = 0.0081$$

Then
$$P(2) + P(3) + P(4) = 0.2646 + 0.0756 + 0.0081 = 0.3483$$

So about 35% of the time the player should have obtained at least two hits out of four times-at-bat. ◆

EXAMPLE 3 **Defective Microchips** A computer manufacturer uses eight microchips in each of its computers. It knows that 5% of these chips are defective. What is the probability that

a. all eight chips are good?

b. the first three chips are good and one of the last five is defective?

Solution If we let S be the event "not defective," then $p = 0.95$ and $q = 0.05$.

a. We have exactly eight successes, so $k = 8$ and the answer is

$$C(8,8)(0.95)^8(0.05)^0 = (0.95)^8 \approx 0.66342$$

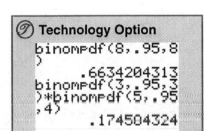

Technology Option
binompdf(8,.95,8)
          .6634204313
binompdf(3,.95,3
)*binompdf(5,.95
,4)
          .174504324

b. There are two events here. The first event is to find the probability that the first three chips are all good and the second event is to find the probability that exactly one of the last five is defective. These probabilities are independent of each other, so we can multiply them to find the probability that they both occur. That is

$$P = C(3,3)(0.95)^3(0.05)^0 \times C(5,4)(0.95)^4(0.05)^1$$
$$= 0.85738 \times 0.20363 \approx 0.17458$$
◆

✧ Technology Corner

⑨Technology Note 1 Binomials

The TI-83/84 calculators have built-in functions for many probability distributions, including the binomial distribution. To access the distribution functions, press the **2ND** and **VARS** buttons to access the DISTR menu. Scroll down until the A:binomialpdf(is shown. See Screen 1.

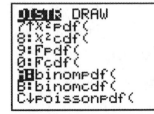

DRAW
7↑X²pdf(
8:X²cdf(
9:Fpdf(
0:Fcdf(
A:binompdf(
B:binomcdf(
C↓poissonpdf(

Screen 1

binompdf(4,.25)
{.31640625 :421…
binompdf(4,.25,0
)
          .31640625

Screen 2

binomcdf(4,.25,1
)
          .73828125
binompdf(4,.25,0
)+binompdf(4,.25
,1)
          .73828125

Screen 3

The binomialpdf command has two required values and one optional value. The first value is the number of trials and the second value is the probability of success in a single trial. If the optional third value with the number of successes is not entered, all the values are calculated. See Screen 2 for an experiment with 4 trials and probability of success $p = 0.25$ in each trial. The first value shown in the row under the command is the probability of 0 successes. The left and right arrows will let you view all the results. If a third value, the number of success, is entered in the binomialpdf command, then only that probability is calculated. This is also shown on Screen 2.

To find the cumulative probability, use the `binomcdf` command. This function finds the probability of at most k successes. The number of trials is entered first followed by the probability of success in a single trial and then the maximum number of successes. Screen 3 shows the probability of at most one success in a binomial experiment with 4 trials and probability of success 0.25 in a single trial. This value is verified in Screen 3 by explicitly adding the probability of 0 and 1 successes.

A spreadsheet such as Excel can also calculate binomial probability. In Excel the command is BINOMDIST. This function requires the number of successes first, followed by the number of trials, the probability of success in a single trial, and finally if the cumulative probability is to be calculated or not. This is shown in Worksheet 1.

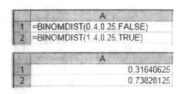

Worksheet 1

Self-Help Exercises 5.4

1. If a repeated Bernoulli trial is performed six times, find the probability of obtaining two successes and four failures if $p = 0.20$.

2. A retail store sells two brands of TVs, with the first brand comprising 60% of these sales. What is the probability that the next five sales of TVs will consist of at most one of the first brand?

5.4 Exercises

For Exercises 1 through 6, a repeated Bernoulli trial is performed. Find the probability of obtaining the indicated number of successes and failures for the indicated value of p.

1. 4 S's, 1 F, $p = 0.2$

2. 4 S's, 3 F's, $p = 0.3$

3. 3 S's, 4 F's, $p = 0.5$

4. 4 S's, 4 F's, $p = 0.5$

5. 4 S's, 4 F's, $p = 0.25$

6. 2 S's, 2 F's, $p = 0.1$

In Exercises 7 through 12, find the probability of exactly k successes in n repeated Bernoulli trials where the probability of success is p.

7. $n = 6, k = 3, p = 0.5$

8. $n = 6, k = 4, p = 0.5$

9. $n = 7, k = 4, p = 0.1$

10. $n = 4, k = 3, p = 0.2$

11. $n = 5, k = 3, p = 0.1$

12. $n = 8, k = 3, p = 0.2$

In Exercises 13 through 18, flip a fair coin 10 times. Find the probability of getting the following outcomes.

13. exactly eight heads

14. exactly three heads

15. at least eight heads

16. at least seven heads

17. at most one head

18. at most two heads

In Exercises 19 through 23, an event E has probability $p = p(E) = 0.6$ in some sample space. Suppose the experiment that yields this sample space is repeated seven times and the outcomes are independent. Find the probability of getting the following outcomes.

19. E exactly six times

20. E exactly three times

21. *E* at least six times

22. *E* at least five times

23. *E* at most two times

24. Show that the probability of exactly $n - k$ successes in n repeated Bernoulli trials where the probability of success is $1 - p$ is the same as the probability of exactly n successes in n repeated Bernoulli trials where the probability of success is p. Hint: Use the formula $C(n,k) = C(n, n - k)$.

Ty Cobb has the highest lifetime batting average of any big league baseball player with a remarkable average of .367. Assume in Exercises 25 through 28 that Cobb came to bat officially four times in every game played.

25. What would be Cobb's probability of getting at least one hit in a game?

26. What would be Cobb's probability of getting at least three hits in a game?

27. What would be Cobb's probability of getting at least one hit in 10 successive games? (Use the result in Exercise 25.)

28. What would be Cobb's probability of getting at least one hit in 20 successive games? (Use the result in Exercise 25.)

Babe Ruth holds the record for the highest lifetime percent (8.5%) of home runs per times-at-bat. Assume in Exercises 29 through 32 that Ruth came to bat officially four times in every game played.

29. What would be Ruth's probability of getting at least two home runs in a game?

30. What would be Ruth's probability of getting at least one home run in a game?

31. What would be Ruth's probability of getting at least two home runs in three successive games? (Use the result in Exercise 29.)

32. What would be Ruth's probability of getting four home runs in a game?

Applications

Oil Drilling. An oil company estimates that only 1 oil well in 20 will yield commercial quantities of oil. Assume that successful drilled wells represent independent event. If 12 wells are drilled, find the probability of obtaining a commercially successful well for the following number of times.

33. exactly 1

34. none

35. at most 2

36. exactly 4

Personnel. A company finds that one out of five workers it hires turns out to be unsatisfactory. Assume that the satisfactory performance of any hired worker is independent of that of any other hired workers. If the company hires 20 people, what is the probability that the following number of people will turn out satisfactory?

37. exactly 10

38. at most 2

39. at least 18

40. exactly 20

Medicine. A certain type of heart surgery in a certain hospital results in mortality in 5% of the cases. Assume that the death of a person undergoing this surgery is independent from the death of any others who have undergone this same surgery. If 20 people have this heart surgery at this hospital, find the probability that the following number of people will not survive the operation.

41. exactly 2

42. at most 2

43. at most 3

44. exactly 10

Solutions to Self-Help Exercises 5.4

1. In a repeated Bernoulli trial the probability of obtaining 2 successes and 4 failures if $p = 0.20$ is

$$C(n,k)p^k q^{n-k} = C(6,2)(0.20)^2(0.80)^4$$
$$= \frac{6 \cdot 5}{2}(0.20)^2(0.80)^4$$
$$\approx 0.246$$

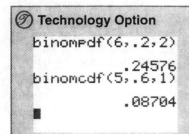

Technology Option

binompdf(6,.2,2)
                .24576
binomcdf(5,.6,1)
                .08704

2. If a retail store sells two brands of TVs, with the first brand comprising 60% of these sales, then the probability that the next five sales of TVs will consist of at most one of the first brand is the probability that the next five sales will consist of exactly zero of the first brand plus exactly one. This is

$$C(5,0)(0.60)^0(0.40)^5 + C(5,1)(0.60)^1(0.40)^4$$
$$= (0.40)^5 + 5(0.60)(0.40)^4$$
$$= 0.01024 + 0.0768 + 0.08704$$
$$= 0.08704$$

5.5   Binomial Theorem

APPLICATION

Number of Ways of Dividing a Committee

> A study committee reports to an executive that to solve a particular problem any number of four different actions can be taken, including doing nothing. How many options does the executive have? See Example 3 for the answer.

✧ The Binomial Theorem

The expansion of $(x+y)^2$ is familiar,

$$(x+y)^2 = x^2 + 2xy + y^2$$

In this section formulas for the expansion of $(x+y)^n$ where n is any integer will be given.

We wish to develop a systemic way of writing the expansion of expressions of the form $(x+y)^n$ where n is a positive integer.

First calculating by direct multiplication we can obtain

$$(x+y)^0 = 1$$
$$(x+y)^1 = x+y$$
$$(x+y)^2 = x^2 + 2xy + y^2$$
$$(x+y)^3 = x^3 + 3x^2y + 3xy^2 + y^3$$
$$(x+y)^4 = x^4 + 4x^3y + 6x^2y^2 + 4xy^3 + y^4$$
$$(x+y)^5 = x^5 + 5x^4y + 10x^3y^2 + 10x^2y^3 + 5xy^4 + y^5$$
$$(x+y)^6 = x^6 + 6x^5y + 15x^4y^2 + 20x^3y^3 + 15x^2y^4 + 6xy^5 + y^6$$

Notice that in the expression $(x+y)^n$ the powers of x decrease by one and the powers of y increase by one as we move to the next term. Also notice that for the expression $x^a y^b$, we have $a + b = n$.

How can we predict the coefficients of such terms? Take $(x+y)^5$ as an example. Write

$$(x+y)^5 = (x+y)(x+y)(x+y)(x+y)(x+y) \tag{1}$$

as the product of five factors. We can obtain an x^2y^3 term in the product by selecting y from exactly three of the factors on the right of (1). We can think of this as filling in the blanks of

$$\{\underline{}, \underline{}, \underline{}, \underline{}, \underline{}\}$$

with exactly three y's. (The other blanks then must be x.) For example, $\{y,x,y,y,x\}$ indicates that we have selected y from only the first, third, and fourth factors on the right of (1). The number of ways we can select exactly three blanks to put a y in from the five possible blanks is $C(5,3)$. This is

$$C(5,3) = \frac{5 \cdot 4 \cdot 3}{3 \cdot 2} = 10$$

which agrees with the coefficient of x^2y^3 in the above expression of $(x+y)^5$.

In general, when looking at the expansion

$$(x+y)^n = (x+y)(x+y) \cdots (x+y)$$

we will obtain an $x^{n-k}y^k$ term by selecting y from exactly k of the n factors. This can be done in $C(n,k)$ ways. Thus the coefficient of the $x^{n-k}y^k$ term must be $C(n,k)$. We have proven the following theorem.

The Binomial Theorem
The coefficient of $x^{n-k}y^k$ in the expansion of $(x+y)^n$ is $C(n,k)$.

EXAMPLE 1   Using the Binomial Theorem   Find the coefficient of x^7y^3 in the expansion $(x+y)^{10}$.

Solution   According to the binomial theorem this must be

$$C(10,3) = \frac{10 \cdot 9 \cdot 8}{3 \cdot 2} = 120 \qquad \blacklozenge$$

It is common to use the notation

$$\binom{n}{k} = C(n,k)$$

With this notation we then have

$$(x+y)^n = \binom{n}{n}x^n + \binom{n}{n-1}x^{n-1}y + \binom{n}{n-2}x^{n-2}y^2 + \cdots$$

$$+ \binom{n}{2}x^2y^{n-2} + \binom{n}{1}xy^{n-1} + \binom{n}{0}y^n$$

As an exercise you can show that the coefficient of x^n and y^n are both 1 and that the coefficient of $x^{n-1}y$ and xy^{n-1} are both n.

EXAMPLE 2 Using the Binomial Theorem Write out the expansion of $(a - 2b)^4$.

Solution By setting $x = a$ and $y = -2b$ in the binomial theorem and using the above notation, we have

$$
\begin{aligned}
(a - 2b)^4 &= (a + (-2b))^4 \\
&= \binom{4}{0}a^4 + \binom{4}{1}a^3(-2b) + \binom{4}{2}a^2(-2b)^2 \\
&\quad + \binom{4}{3}a(-2b)^3 + \binom{4}{4}(-2b)^4 \\
&= a^4 + 4a^3(-2b) + 6a^2(-2b)^2 + 4a(-2b)^3 + (-2b)^4 \\
&= a^4 - 8a^3b + 24a^2b^2 - 32ab^3 + 16b^4
\end{aligned}
$$

$\blacklozenge$

A consequence of the binomial theorem is the following.

The Number of Subsets of a Set
A set with n distinct elements has 2^n distinct subsets.

Before giving a proof, let us list all the subsets of $\{a, b, c\}$ by listing all subsets with three elements, all with two elements, all with one element, and all with no elements. We have 8, which is $8 = 2^3$.

$$
\begin{aligned}
&\{a,b,c\} \\
&\{a,b\}, \{a,c\}, \{b,c\} \\
&\{a\}, \{b\}, \{c\} \\
&\emptyset
\end{aligned}
$$

To establish the theorem, the total number of subsets of a set with n distinct elements is the number of subsets with n elements, plus the number of subsets with $(n-1)$ elements, plus the number with $(n-2)$ elements, and so on. This is just

$$
\binom{n}{n} + \binom{n}{n-1} + \binom{n}{n-2} + \cdots + \binom{n}{1} + \binom{n}{0}
$$

Now setting $x = y = 1$ in the binomial theorem gives

$$
\begin{aligned}
2^n &= (1 + 1)^n \\
&= \binom{n}{n}(1)^n + \binom{n}{n-1}(1)^{n-1}(1) + \binom{n}{n-2}(1)^{n-2}(1)^2 + \cdots \\
&\quad + \binom{n}{2}(1)^2(1)^{n-2} + \binom{n}{1}(1)(1)^{n-1} + \binom{n}{0}(1)^n \\
&= \binom{n}{n} + \binom{n}{n-1} + \binom{n}{n-2} + \cdots + \binom{n}{1} + \binom{n}{0}
\end{aligned}
$$

which, as we have just seen, is the total number of subsets we are seeking.

EXAMPLE 3   The Number of Ways of Dividing a Committee   A study committee reports to an executive that to solve a particular problem any number of four different actions can be taken, including doing nothing. How many options does the executive have?

Solution   The executive has the option of selecting any subset from a set with 4 elements in it. This can be done in $2^4 = 16$ ways.   ◆

```
            1
          1  2  1
        1  3  3  1
      1  4  6  4  1
    1  5  10  10  5  1
  1  6  15  20  15  6  1
```

Figure 5.49

✧ Pascal's Triangle

Figure 5.49 lists the coefficients from the expression of $(x + y)^n$ given at the beginning of this section. This is called Pascal's Triangle, named after its discoverer, Blaise Pascal (1623–1662). Notice that there are always 1's at the two sides and that any coefficient inside the triangle can be obtained by adding the coefficient above and to the left with the coefficient above and to the right. This is another way the coefficients can be obtained.

Self-Help Exercise 5.5

1. Find the coefficient of $x^4 y^5$ in the expansion of $(x + y)^9$.

5.5 Exercises

In Exercises 1 through 10, expand using the binomial theorem.

1. $(a - b)^5$
2. $(2a + b)^4$
3. $(2x + 3y)^5$
4. $(3x - 2y)^4$
5. $(1 - x)^5$
6. $(2 + x)^6$
7. $(2 - x^2)^4$
8. $(1 + 2x)^6$
9. $(s^2 + t^2)^6$
10. $(s^2 - 1)^5$
11. $(x^2 + y^3)^5$
12. $(2x - y^2)^5$

In Exercises 13 through 22, determine the first three and last three terms in the expansion of each of the expressions.

13. $(a - b)^{10}$
14. $(a + b)^{12}$
15. $(x + y)^{11}$
16. $(x - y)^8$
17. $(1 - z)^{12}$
18. $(1 + x)^{10}$
19. $(1 - x^3)^{12}$
20. $(x^2 - 1)^{10}$
21. $(2a + b)^{10}$
22. $(a - 2b)^{12}$

23. Determine the next row (row 7) in Pascal's Triangle in Figure 5.49.

24. Find the coefficient of $x^4 y^4$ in the expansion of $(x + y)^8$ using Pascal's Triangle.

Applications

25. A restaurant offers a sundae to which any number of four possible toppings can be added. How many different sundaes can be ordered?

26. A restaurant offers a pizza to which any number of six possible toppings can be added. How many different pizzas can be ordered?

27. A class ring can be ordered in white or yellow gold, in men's or women's style, with or without a diamond and with or without engraving on the inside and a dark or light finish. How many different class rings are possible?

28. A letter jacket has the following options that can be included or not with the jacket: name, class year, academic patch, fine arts patch, athletics patch, student council patch, and FFA patch. How many different letter jackets are possible?

Solution to Self-Help Exercise 5.5

1. Using the binomial theorem, we find the coefficient of $x^4 y^5$ in the expansion of $(x+y)^9$ is

$$C(9,5) = \frac{9!}{5!(9-5)!} = \frac{9 \cdot 8 \cdot 7 \cdot 6 \cdot 5}{5 \cdot 4 \cdot 3 \cdot 2} = 126$$

Review

✧ Summary Outline

- **General Multiplication Principle.** Suppose there is an operation that consists of making a sequence of k choices with n_1 possible outcomes for the first choice, and, no matter what the first choice, there are always n_2 possible outcomes for the second choice, and, no matter what the first two choices, there are always n_3 possible outcomes for the third choice, and so on. Then there are $n_1 \cdot n_2 \cdots n_k$ possible ways in which the sequence of k choices can be made.

- For any natural number n

$$n! = n(n-1)(n-2) \cdots 3 \cdot 2 \cdot 1$$
$$0! = 1$$

- A *permutation* of a set of elements is an ordered arrangement of all the elements.

- A *permutation of r objects taken from a set of size n* is a selection of r of the objects with order being important.

- The number of permutations of n distinct objects is given by

$$P(n,n) = n(n-1)(n-2) \cdots 3 \cdot 2 \cdot 1 = n!$$

- The number of permutations of r distinct objects taken from a set of size n is given by

$$P(n,r) = n(n-1)(n-2) \cdots (n-r+1) = \frac{n!}{(n-r)!}$$

- A *combination* of r distinct objects taken from a set of size n is a selection of r of the objects (without concern for order).

- The number of combinations of r distinct objects taken from a set of size n, denoted by $C(n,r)$, is given by

$$C(n,r) = \frac{n!}{(r!)(n-r)!}$$

- The **Binomial Theorem.** The coefficient of $x^{n-k}y^k$ in the expansion of $(x+y)^n$ is $C(n,k)$.

- Given a set S of n elements, an ordered partition of S of type $(n_1, n_2, \ldots, n_k)$ is a division of S into k subsets, $S_1, S_2, \ldots, S_k$, with order being important and where $n_1 = n(S_1)$, $n_2 = n(S_2)$, $\ldots$, $n_k = n(S_k)$. The number of such ordered partitions is

$$\frac{n!}{n_1! n_2! \cdots n_k!}$$

- The probability of exactly k successes in n repeated Bernoulli trials where the probability of success is p and failure is q is given by $C(n,k)p^k q^{n-k}$

✧ Review Exercises

1. Find $P(10,4)$ and $C(10,4)$.

2. If instead of a social security *number*, we had a social security *word* where letters could be repeated, what would be the length of the words needed to have at least 250 million different words?

3. Before five labor leaders and six management personnel begin negotiating a new labor contract, they decided to first take a picture with the five labor leaders together on the left. In how many different ways can such a picture be taken?

4. In the previous exercise suppose a picture is to be taken of three of the labor leaders and three of the management personnel with the labor leaders grouped together on the right. In how many ways can this be done?

5. Refer to Exercise 3. Suppose a committee of three labor leaders and four management personnel is formed to study the issue of pensions. In how many ways can this be done?

6. Refer to Exercise 3. In a straw vote on a proposal from the labor leaders, the six management personnel each cast a vote with no abstentions. In how many ways can these six individuals come to a majority decision?

7. An investor decides that her investment year is a success if her portfolio of stocks beats the S&P 500. In how many ways can her next 10 years have exactly seven successes?

8. Expand $(2-x)^5$ using the binomial theorem.

9. Find the last three terms in the expansion of $(1-x)^9$.

10. In how many ways can a laboratory divide 12 union tists into four groups of equal size in order to perform four different experiments?

11. An urn has 10 white, 5 red, and 15 blue balls. What is the probability that there is one of each color if 3 are selected randomly without replacement? With replacement?

12. For the urn in the previous exercise, what is the probability that 3 are white, 4 are red, and 2 are blue, if 9 are selected randomly without replacement? With replacement?

13. **Assembly Line** A machine on an assembly line is malfunctioning randomly and produces defective parts 30% of the time. What is the probability that this machine will produce exactly three defective parts among the next six?

14. **Teaching Methods** An instructor finds that only 55% of her college algebra students pass the course. She then tries a new teaching method and finds that 85% of the 20 students in the first class with the new method pass. Assuming that the probability at this school of passing college algebra is 0.55 and that any one student passing is independent of any other student passing, what is the probability that at least 85% of a college algebra class of 20 will pass this course? Is the instructor justified in claiming that the new method is superior to the old method?

CHAPTER 6

Probability Distributions and Statistics

CONNECTION

Casino Games

If a casino game such as craps or roulette is played many times, how much money would you expect to win or lose? Is a ticket for a lottery a "good" bet if the jackpot is large? What will happen if you play a slot machine with a 90% payoff many times?

In this chapter we will learn how to associate a value with the outcomes of a probability distribution. With this knowledge, the "expected" value of an experiment can be found. So the "expected" value of playing a game such as roulette or purchasing a lottery ticket can be computed.

6.1 Random Variables and Histograms

In this section we wish to see how to present numerical data in a manner that will permit making interpretations and comparisons. First, we define the important idea of a "random variable."

✧ Random Variables

The outcomes of many experiments are numbers. For example, the number shown uppermost on a six-sided dice that has been tossed is $\{1, 2, 3, 4, 5, 6\}$. But outcomes of experiments are not always real numbers. The outcomes of experiments can be "an even number," "heads," "above average," or "defective," none of which are real numbers. However, it is often useful to assign a real number to each outcome of an experiment. For example, the outcome of the experiment "your grade in math" is a letter. But for purposes that you are well aware of, each letter is assigned a real number. Typically 4 is assigned to an A, 3 to a B, 2 to a C, 1 to a D, and 0 to an F.

Usually there is some rational basis on which the assignment of a real number to an outcome is made. For example, since a grade of A is "better" than a grade of B, it makes sense to assign a higher number to the grade A than to B. Also the assignment of the numbers to each letter is done in such a manner that the numerical difference between two successive letters will be equal. Assigning zero to F makes sense since no credit is given for a grade of F. Finally, using the numbers 0, 1, 2, 3, and 4 makes it easy to calculate the "average" grade and for this number to have a readily understood meaning.

When numbers are assigned to the outcomes of experiments according to some rule or function, we refer to the function as a random variable. As we have seen in assigning numbers to letter grades, the assignments of numbers to the outcomes of experiments are normally done in a manner that is reasonable and, most importantly, in a manner that permits these numbers to be used for interpretation and comparison.

Random Variables
A random variable is a rule that assigns precisely one real number to each outcome of an experiment.

REMARK: Unless otherwise specified, when the outcomes of an experiment are themselves numbers, the random variable is the rule that simply assigns each number to itself.

EXAMPLE 1 Random Variables A fair coin is flipped three times. We want to determine the probability of the events "3 heads have appeared," "exactly 2 heads have appeared," and so on. Associate a random variable with the outcomes and determine a probability distribution for the random variable.

Solution First list all the eight possible sequences of heads (H) and tails (T).

$$\{(HHH), (HHT), (HTH), (HTT), (TTT), (TTH), (THT), (THH)\}$$

From this list we note how many times heads appear.

3: (HHH)

2: (HHT),(HTH),(THH)

1: (HTT),(TTH),(THT)

0: (TTT)

It would be natural to assign the number 3 to the event "heads appear three times," the number 2 to the event "heads appear exactly two times," and so on. We then have the following table that shows the probability distribution where the random variable X is the number of heads and $P(X)$ is the probability of the event associated with the random variable X.

X	0	1	2	3
$P(X)$	$1/8$	$3/8$	$3/8$	$1/8$

◆

There are three types of random variables, as we now indicate.

Types of Random Variables

1. A random variable is **finite discrete** if it assumes only a finite number of values.

2. A random variable is **infinite discrete** if it takes on an infinite number of values that can be listed in a sequence, so that there is a first one, a second one, a third one, and so on.

3. A random variable is said to be **continuous** if it can take any of the infinite number of values in some interval of real numbers.

EXAMPLE 2   Classifying Random Variables   Classify the following experiments as finite discrete, infinite discrete, or continuous. List the values of the random variable X.

a. Flip a fair coin. Assign the random variables 1 to head and 2 to tail.

b. Flip a fair coin until a head is obtained. Assign the random variable X to the number of flips until a head is shown.

c. Measure the height of adult men in this country. Assign the random variable X to the height measured in feet.

Solution

a. The random variable can take on either value in the set $S = \{1,2\}$ and so it is a finite discrete random variable.

b. The random variable can take on any value in the set $S = \{1, 2, \ldots\}$ and so it is an infinite discrete random variable.

c. The random variable can take on any value in the set $S = [2, 8]$ or $S = \{X | 2 \leq X \leq 8\}$ and thus is continuous.   ◆

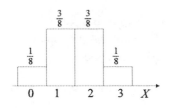

Figure 6.50

⑦ **Technology Option**

See Technology Note 1 on page 298 for information on graphing histograms on a graphing calculator.

✧ Histograms

We can further present the data in graphical form. In Example 1 the random variables 0, 1, 2, 3 represent the possible outcomes. These numbers are located on the horizontal axis as in Figure 6.50. Above each number a rectangle is drawn with base equal to one unit and height equal to the probability of that value of X. For example, above the number 0 is a rectangle with height $1/8$ and above the number 1 is a rectangle with height $3/8$. Such graphs are called histograms; they give a vivid description of how the probability is distributed. As a consequence, comparison can be made more easily between two histograms than between the two tables of probability.

EXAMPLE 3   Finding a Probability Distribution and Corresponding Histogram   Suppose a pair of fair dice is tossed. Let X denote the random variable that gives the sum of the top faces. Find the probability distribution and draw a histogram.

Solution   We first list all the 36 possible outcomes of each pair of dice.

$$S = \{ (1,1),(1,2),(1,3),(1,4),(1,5),(1,6),$$
$$(2,1),(2,2),(2,3),(2,4),(2,5),(2,6),$$
$$(3,1),(3,2),(3,3),(3,4),(3,5),(3,6),$$
$$(4,1),(4,2),(4,3),(4,4),(4,5),(4,6),$$
$$(5,1),(5,2),(5,3),(5,4),(5,5),(5,6),$$
$$(6,1),(6,2),(6,3),(6,4),(6,5),(6,6)\}$$

Actually we found the probability distribution in a previous chapter. But we will repeat the work with the new interpretation that the outcomes can be associated with a random variable. We define the random variable X as the number that can take any of the values $S = \{2,3,\ldots,12\}$. We first note that a sum of 2 can only be taken by $(1,1)$. So the probability of a sum of 2 is just $1/36$, since the probability of any of the 36 pairs of numbers is equally likely. Using the new notation we have $P(X = 2) = 1/36$. We also note that a sum of 3 can only be taken by $(2,1)$ and $(1,2)$ and so the probability of a sum of 3 is just $2/36$. Using the new notation we also have $P(X = 3) = 2/36$. Doing this then yields the probability distribution given in the following table. The histogram is drawn in Figure 6.51.   ◆

x	2	3	4	5	6	7	8	9	10	11	12
$P(X = x)$	$1/36$	$2/36$	$3/36$	$4/36$	$5/36$	$6/36$	$5/36$	$4/36$	$3/36$	$2/36$	$1/36$

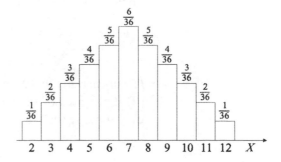

Figure 6.51

EXAMPLE 4 **Finding a Probability Distribution** Suppose a pair of fair dice is tossed. Let X be the random variable given by 1 if the sum of the top two faces is a prime number and 0 otherwise. Find the probability distribution.

Solution Since the primes are 2, 3, 5, 7, and 11, the table in the previous example indicates that

$$P(X = x) = \frac{1+2+4+6+2}{36} = \frac{15}{36}$$

The probability distribution table, including the random variable X, is in the table on the left. ◆

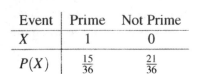

Event	Prime	Not Prime
X	1	0
$P(X)$	$\frac{15}{36}$	$\frac{21}{36}$

REMARK: Note how the probability distribution table has the event listed. This is particularly helpful when the outcome of the experiment is not the value of the random variable.

EXAMPLE 5 **Finding a Probability Distribution and Corresponding Histogram** Ted Williams had a batting average of .406 in 1941. During that year he had 112 singles, 33 doubles, 3 triples, and 37 home runs in 456 (official) times-at-bat. Let the random variable X be 0 for no hit, 1 for a single, 2 for a double, 3 for a triple, and 4 for a home run. Find a probability distribution for Ted Williams obtaining a 0, 1, 2, 3, or 4 for each time-at-bat during 1941. Draw a histogram.

Solution The probability of each event is the relative frequency of the event. Therefore the probability of hitting a home run is $37/456 \approx 0.081$, for a triple is $3/456 \approx 0.007$, for a double is $33/456 \approx 0.072$, and for a single is $112/456 \approx 0.246$. For no hit, we have $[456 - (37 + 3 + 33 + 112)]/456 = 271/456 \approx 0.594$.

Event	No Hit	Single	Double	Triple	Home Run
X	0	1	2	3	4
Frequency	271	112	33	3	37
$P(X = x)$	$\frac{271}{456}$	$\frac{112}{456}$	$\frac{33}{456}$	$\frac{3}{456}$	$\frac{37}{456}$

The histogram is drawn in Figure 6.52 ◆

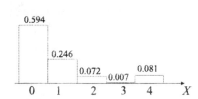

Figure 6.52

We will now use histograms to find the probability of events by measuring the areas under appropriate rectangles.

EXAMPLE 6 **Finding Probability Using Histograms** Use the histogram in Figure 6.51 to find the probability that the sum of the top faces of two fair die when tossed will be at least 9 and less than 12.

Solution We are seeking

$$P(9 \leq X < 12) = P(X = 9) + P(X = 10) + P(X = 11)$$

The probability that $X = 9$, $P(X = 9)$, is the area of the rectangle above 9, $P(X = 10)$ is the area of the rectangle above 10, and so on. Thus, we are seeking the area of the shaded region in Figure 6.53. This is

$$\frac{4}{36} + \frac{3}{36} + \frac{2}{36} = \frac{1}{4}$$
◆

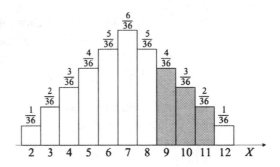

Figure 6.53

Area and Probability

The area of a region of a histogram associated with the random variable X is equal to $P(X)$, the probability that X occurs. Furthermore the probability that X takes on the values in the range $X_i \leq X \leq X_j$ is the sum of the areas of the histogram from X_i to X_j.

✧ Binomial Distribution

We now wish to consider a probability distribution that we will refer to as a binomial distribution. Recall that we discussed Bernoulli trials in a previous chapter and that Bernoulli trials were experiments in which there are just two outcomes. When such an experiment is repeated many times, we refer to this as a repeated Bernoulli trial. We always made the assumption that successive Bernoulli trials are independent of one another. We commonly refer to the two outcomes of a Bernoulli trial as "success" or "failure." We agree always to write p for the probability of "success" and q for the probability of "failure." Naturally, $p + q = 1$.

Given a Bernoulli trial repeated n times with k the number of successes, we found that the probability of exactly k successes in n repeated Bernoulli trials was

$$C(n,k)p^k q^{n-k}$$

where $C(n,k)$ is the number of combinations of k distinct objects from a set of size n, without concern for order.

You may recall from the binomial theorem that the coefficients $x^{n-k}y^k$ in the expansion of $(x+y)^n$ is $C(n,k)$. This is where the term "binomial distribution" comes from. With this review, we now give the following definition.

Binomial Distribution

Given a sequence of n Bernoulli trials with the probability of success p and the probability of failure q, the binomial distribution is given by

$$P(X = k) = C(n,k)p^k q^{n-k}$$

for $k = 0 \ldots n$.

EXAMPLE 7   A Binomial Distribution   Suppose a fair coin is flipped six times. Let X denote the random variable that gives the number of "heads." Find the probability distribution for X and graph this in a histogram. Use the histogram to find the probability of at most two heads and the probability of four or five heads.

Solution   Define "heads" to be "success." We use the formula for the binomial distribution with $k = x$,

$$P(X = x) = C(6,x)p^x q^{n-x} = C(6,x)(0.5)^x(0.5)^{6-x} = C(6,x)(0.5)^6$$
$$= \frac{C(6,x)}{64}$$

Then calculating $C(6,x)$ for $x = 0, 1, \ldots 6$ yields the probability distribution in the following table.

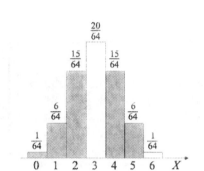

Figure 6.54

Number of Successes, x	0	1	2	3	4	5	6
$P(X = x)$	$1/64$	$6/64$	$15/64$	$20/64$	$15/64$	$6/64$	$1/64$

The histogram is shown in Figure 6.54. The probability of at most two heads is

$$P(X \le 2) = P(X = 0) + P(X = 1) + P(x = 2) = \frac{1}{64} + \frac{6}{64} + \frac{15}{64} = \frac{22}{64}$$

This is the same as the area shaded in blue on the histogram. The probability of four or five heads is

$$P(X = 4) + P(X = 5) = \frac{15}{64} + \frac{6}{64} = \frac{21}{64}$$

which is shaded in pink on the histogram.   ◆

✧ Applications

When working with real data it will often be important to decide what values are associated with the random variable, X, and which values are associated with the frequency. Only after this determination has been made can the probability distribution table be created and the histogram drawn. It can be useful to remember that the random variable is the outcome that is counted and the frequency is how often the outcome is observed.

EXAMPLE 8   Quality Control   Blue Baker prides itself on having the best chocolate chip cookies in town. To be sure each cookie has the right number of chocolate chips, a few cookies are selected from each batch and the number of chocolate chips in each cookie is counted. This is done for several days and the following results were found:

Number of Cookies	2	4	5	6	8
Number of Chocolate Chips	8	11	12	13	14

Identify the random variable in this experiment and display the data in a histogram.

Solution   In this experiment the number of chocolate chips is counted and is therefore the random variable X. The number of cookies is how often that X value

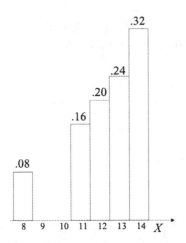

occurred which is the frequency. There were a total of $2 + 4 + 5 + 6 + 8 = 25$ cookies examined and so we can create a probability distribution table for the number of chocolate chips per cookie.

Number of Chocolate Chips, X	8	11	12	13	14
Number of Cookies, Frequency	2	4	5	6	8
Relative Frequency, $P(X)$	$2/25$	$4/25$	$5/25$	$6/25$	$8/25$

The histogram is displayed in the figure on the left. ◆

✧ Optional: Grouped Data

A teacher has the results of her latest exam. There are 100 students in the class and the exam grades ranged from 99 to 18. The scores are listed below in descending numerical order.

99 98 94 94 92 92 92 92 92 90 90

89 89 87 87 86 84 84 83 83 83 82 82 82 82 80 80

79 79 79 79 79 79 79 78 78 78 78 78 78 77 77 77 76 76
75 75 75 74 74 72 72 72 72 72 72 71 70 70 70

69 69 69 69 68 67 65 65 64 64 64 64 64 64 62

59 58 57 57 56 56 55 54 52 52 52 51 51 50 50

49 49 49 48 45 45 44 43

34

18

She wishes to view the results in a histogram. It is possible to do this letting X be the score on each exam and then there would be 82 rectangles to draw. Some of the rectangles may have a height of 0 if no students got a particular score. See Figure 6.55.

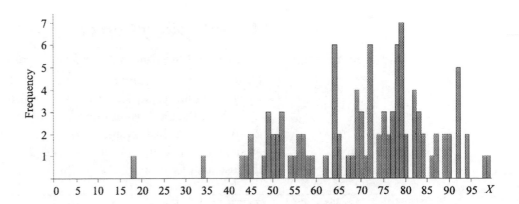

Figure 6.55

 Technology Option

See Technology Note 2 on page 299 for information on graphing histograms using a spreadsheet.

Note that any patterns in the data are not particularly clear. This leads us to the idea of grouped data. We can divide the data into a series of "bins." The size of each bin will depend on the amount of data you have and the range of the data, but it is typically good to have 8 to 16 bins and the size of each bin should be a simple multiple of 2, 3, 5, 10, 25, 50, 100 and so on. Here we shall have our bins of size 10 as shown in the table below. Note that we have the empirical probability as the relative frequency.

Grade	$10 \le X \le 19$	$20 \le X \le 29$	$30 \le X \le 39$	$40 \le X \le 49$	$50 \le X \le 59$
Frequency	1	0	1	8	15
Probability	0.01	0	0.01	0.08	0.15

Grade	$60 \le X \le 69$	$70 \le X \le 79$	$80 \le X \le 89$	$90 \le X \le 99$
Frequency	15	33	16	11
Probability	0.15	0.33	0.16	0.11

Notice how each of the bins holds 10 values. For example, the bin $40 \le X \le 49$ has the outcomes $X = 40, 41, 42, 43, 44, 45, 46, 47, 48, 49$, a total of 10 values. Do not find the width of the interval by simply subtracting $49 - 40$. When we represent the grouped data in a histogram, the rectangle is the width of the bin and the height is the total probability of a value of X being in that range. So the rectangle representing $40 \le X \le 49$ is drawn from 39.5 to 49.5 and a tick mark is placed at the center of the rectangle, 44.5. The center of the rectangle is found by dividing the width by 2 and adding that to the lower value. So in this case the width is 10 and half of the width is 5. So the center of the rectangle for $40 \le X \le 49$ is $39.5 + 5 = 44.5$. See Figure 6.56.

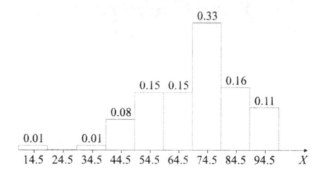

Figure 6.56

✧ Technology Corner

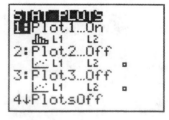 Technology Note 1   Using a Graphing Calculator for Histograms

Histograms can be quickly and accurately drawn on a graphing calculator. Begin by pressing the STAT as shown in Screen 1. Then press ENTER to Edit the lists L1 and L2. Put the X values into L1 and the probabilities in L2 as shown in Screen 2. To enable the histogram, go to the STAT PLOT menu by pressing 2ND and Y= as shown in Screen 3. Your STAT PLOT menu may look different depending on the last stat plot used.

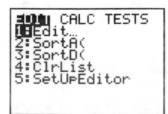

Screen 1

Screen 2

Screen 3

Choose `Plot 1` by pressing `Enter` to access the stat plot menu shown in Screen 4. Set the plot to be On, the `Type:` to a histogram, the `Xlist:` to L1 and the `Ylist:` to L2 as shown in Screen 4. Note that the list names are found above the buttons for the numbers 1 and 2. Finally a window must be chosen. If the settings are not correct, the histogram will not display in the desired manner (that is, each rectangle is one unit wide and centered on the X it represents). Set `Xmin` to half a unit below the lowest value of the random variable X. In this case $Xmin = 0 - 0.5 = -0.5$. Set `Xmax` to a value greater than the largest value of X and set `Xscl = 1`. This is shown in Screen 5. Press `GRAPH` to see the histogram displayed as shown in Screen 6.

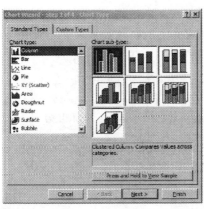

Screen 4

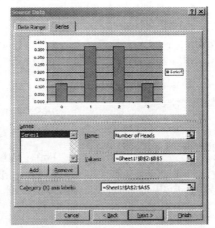

Screen 5

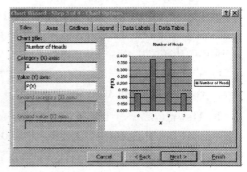

Screen 6

⑰Technology Note 2   **Using a Spreadsheet for Histograms**

The Chart Wizard in the Excel spreadsheet program allows the creation of colorful and interesting histograms with a few simple steps. Begin by entering the X and $P(X)$ values in columns A and B as shown in Worksheet 1. If the data does not display as a number, highlight the cells that contain the data and click Format and choose Cells and set the data to be numeric data.

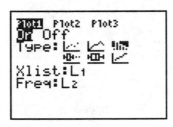

Worksheet 1

Click the Chart Wizard and choose the Column type as shown in Worksheet 2. Press the Next button and choose the Series tab. Then add the X values as the Catagory (X) axis labels and the $P(X)$ values as the Values as shown in Worksheet 3. A title may be added in the Name box. Press Next. The third step in the Chart Wizard is shown in Worksheet 4.

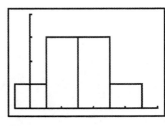

Worksheet 4

Worksheet 2

Worksheet 3

The titles and labels are added here. Press Next to go to Step 4 of 4 and choose the chart location. Press Finish and the histogram will be displayed as it looked in Worksheet 4. To produce the histogram shown in Worksheet 5, several settings were changed after the chart was created.

• Right click the legend and choose Clear.

- Right click the background and choose Format Plot Area. Then choose None for the area.

- Right click inside a bar and choose Format Data Series. On the Options tab set the Gap width to 0.

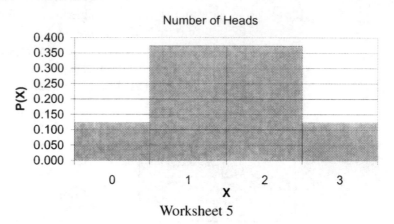

Worksheet 5

Self-Help Exercises 6.1

1. Use the histogram in Figure 6.52 to find the probability that Ted Williams obtained an extra-base hit (double, triple, or home run) during 1941.

2. Find the probability distribution of a binomial experiment with 6 trials and a probability of success $p = 0.75$ in each trial and draw a histogram.

6.1 Exercises

In Exercises 1 through 8, determine the possible values of the given random variable and indicate as your answer whether the random variable is finite discrete, infinite discrete, or continuous.

1. The number of times a coin must be flipped before two heads appear in succession.

2. The number of times two heads appear in succession when a coin is flipped 1,000,000 times.

3. The number of hours spent studying math each week.

4. The number of rotten eggs in a dozen eggs.

5. A card is drawn at random and without replacement from a well-shuffled standard deck of 52 cards until the queen of spades is picked.

6. A card is drawn at random and with replacement from a well-shuffled standard deck of 52 cards until the king of hearts is picked.

7. A marble is drawn at random with replacement from a bowl containing four red and six green marbles until a red marble is picked.

8. A marble is drawn at random and without replacement from a bowl containing four red and six green marbles until a green marble is picked.

9. The grade distribution in a certain math class is given in the following table.

	A	B	C	D	F
Random Variable, x	4	3	2	1	0
Frequency	6	10	19	11	4
$P(X = x)$					

Fill in the last row. Draw a histogram.

10. In 1961 Roger Maris set the record for most home runs in a season that lasted until recent years. Com-

plete the following table, where 0 is associated with no hit, 1 with a single, and so on.

Random Variable, x	0	1	2	3	4
Frequency	431	78	16	4	61
$P(X = x)$					

11. The student ratings of a particular mathematics professor are given in the following table. Complete the last line and draw a histogram.

Event	1	2	3	4	5	6	7	8	9	10
Frequency	5	2	3	0	4	10	10	11	3	2
$P(X = x)$										

12. A basketball player has a probability of 0.8 of sinking a free throw. Assume that sinking a shot is independent of what occurred before. Let X be the random variable given by the number of foul shots sunk by this player in five successive shots. Find the probability distribution. Draw a histogram.

13. A pair of fair dice is tossed. Let X be the random variable given by the absolute value of the difference of the numbers on the top faces of the dice. Find the probability distribution. Draw a histogram.

14. On a true-false test with five questions, let X denote the random variable given by the total number of questions correctly answered by guessing. Find the probability distribution. Draw a histogram.

15. In the previous problem let X denote the random variable given by twice the total number of correct answers minus the number of incorrect answers. Find the probability distribution. Draw a histogram.

16. Let X denote the random variable given by the number of girls in a family of four children. Find the probability distribution if a girl is as likely as a boy. Draw a histogram.

17. Two balls are selected at random from an urn that contains three white and seven red balls. Let the random variable X denote the number of white balls drawn. Find the probability distribution. Draw a histogram.

18. In the previous problem let the random variable X denote the number of white balls times the number of red balls drawn. Find the probability distribution.

19. The probability distribution of the random variable X is given in the following table. What must z be?

Random Variable, x	0	1	2	3	4
$P(X = x)$	0.2	0.1	0.1	z	0.3

20. The probability distribution of the random variable (r. v.) X is given in the following table.

r. v. x	-2	-1	0	1	2	3
$P(X = x)$	.20	.15	.05	.35	.15	.10

Draw a histogram. Find the following probabilities and identify each of the probabilities as an area on the histogram.

a. $P(X = 0)$ **b.** $P(X \leq 0)$ **c.** $P(-1 < X \leq 4)$
d. $P(X \geq 1)$

21. The probability distribution of the random variable (r. v.) X is given in the following table.

r. v. x	4	5	6	7	8	9
$P(X = x)$	0.15	0.26	0.14	0.22	0.18	0.05

Draw a histogram. Find the following probabilities and identify each of the probabilities as an area on the histogram.

a. $P(X = 4)$ **b.** $P(X \leq 2)$ **c.** $P(5 \leq X \leq 6)$
d. $P(X \geq 8)$.

22. Let Y be the random variable given by X^2 where X is given in Exercise 20. Find the probability distribution of Y by completing the following table.

Random Variable, y	0	1	4	9
$P(X^2 = y)$				

23. Let Y be the random variable given by $X + 2$ where X is given in Exercise 20. Find the probability distribution of Y.

Applications

In Exercises 24 through 27, use a histogram to represent the requested data for the percent distribution of population by height.

Height	Males 25 – 34 yrs	Males 35 – 44 yrs	Females 25 – 34 yrs	Females 35 – 44 yrs
< 5′2″	0.42	0.87	19.11	18.24
5′2″ − 5′4″	1.13	2.81	28.32	31.66
5′4″ − 5′6″	7.96	8.79	27.49	28.17
5′6″ − 5′8″	17.18	14.01	18.56	15.36
5′8″ − 5′10″	28.66	30.61	6.21	5.76
5′10″ − 6′	26.23	24.14	0.31	0.81
> 6′	18.42	18.77	0.00	0.00

24. **Height Distribution** Males ages 25-34

25. **Height Distribution** Males ages 35-44

26. **Height Distribution** Females ages 25-34

27. **Height Distribution** Females ages 35-44

28. **Sales of Cars** A car dealership tracks the number of cars sold each week. During the past year they sold from zero to six cars per week with the frequencies indicated in the following table. Find the probability distribution.

Sold/Week	0	1	2	3	4	5	6
No. of Weeks	4	11	8	10	10	5	2

29. **Quality Control** Suppose two light bulbs are chosen at random from an assembly line that has 5% defective light bulbs. Let X denote the random variable that gives the number of defective light bulbs chosen. Find the probability distribution of X. Draw a histogram.

30. **Sales of Veggie Wraps** A sandwich shop tracks the number of veggie wraps sold each day. During the past month they sold from zero to eight wraps per day with the frequencies indicated in the following table. Find the probability distribution.

Sold/Day	0	1	2	3	4	5	6	7	8
No. of Days	2	0	5	6	10	1	0	3	2

Solutions to Self-Help Exercises 6.1

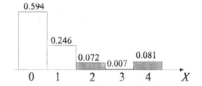

1. The appropriate area in the accompanying histogram has been shaded. The area and thus the probability that Ted Williams obtained an extra-base hit in 1941 is then

$$P(X > 1) = 0.072 + 0.007 + 0.081 = 0.160$$

2. Using our formula for binomial probability, we have

$$P(X = k) = C(6, k)\left(\frac{3}{4}\right)^k \left(\frac{1}{4}\right)^{6-k} = C(6, k)3^k \left(\frac{1}{4}\right)^6$$

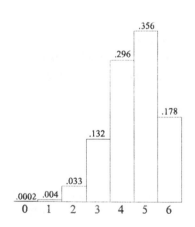

Let $h = (0.25)^6 \approx 0.000244$. Then for $k = 0, 1, \ldots, 6$, $P(X = k)$ are successively $1 \cdot 3^0 h, 6 \cdot 3^1 h, 15 \cdot 3^2 h, 20 \cdot 3^3 h, 15 \cdot 3^4 h, 6 \cdot 3^5 h, 1 \cdot 3^6 h$, or $h, 18h, 135h, 540h, 1215h, 1458h, 729h$. The histogram is shown in the figure. Notice how the probability distribution is skewed to the right with $p > 0.5$.

6.2 Measures of Central Tendency

APPLICATION
Expected Profit of an Insurance Policy

An insurance company sells a newlywed couple a l-year insurance policy on an engagement ring. The policy, which costs $100, pays $5000 in the event the ring is lost during the next year. Suppose there is a 1% chance that the ring will be lost in the next year. If the insurance company were to sell a large number of the same insurance policies under the same conditions, what should they expect for an average profit per such policy? See Example 5 for the answer.

✧ Expected Value

In this section we introduce several statistics that will be used to measure the "center" of the data. Loosely these are called the "average" of the data. We shall be more precise when finding these measures of central tendency.

We have studied probability distributions, that is, how probability was distributed over the various outcomes. We also saw the need for comparing two probability distributions. The expected value will now be discussed. We will see that this number is a generalization of the average and conveys certain very useful information about the data. The expected value will be seen to be one way of locating the "center" of the data. In another typical application, we will use the expected value to compare two investments in order to determine which will be more profitable.

We begin with a discussion of one kind of average which is familiar to most. If you have three test grades of 95, 85, and 93, the mean test grade is the sum of all the numbers divided by the total number of tests or

$$\frac{95 + 85 + 93}{3} = \frac{273}{3} = 91$$

There are two symbols used for the average or mean of a data set. One is $\bar{x}$ which is pronounced "x-bar." The other is the Greek letter μ which is pronounced $m\bar{u}$ (rhymes with who). Roughly speaking we will use μ when we have all the data values in our set and use $\bar{x}$ when we have a sample of the data values in our set (such as only two of the three test scores). More discussion about when each symbol is appropriate is found at the end of this section. For now we will assume we have all the values and use μ for the mean. In general we have the following definition of average or mean.

Average or Mean
The average or Mean of the n numbers $x_1, x_2, \cdots , x_n$, denoted by μ, is given by

$$\mu = \frac{x_1 + x_2 + \cdots + x_n}{n}$$

EXAMPLE 1   Calculating the Mean   You are thinking of buying a small manufacturer of quality yachts and have obtained the following data from the owners that give how often various numbers of yacht sales occur per quarter.

Number Sold in One Quarter	1	2	3	4	5
Number of Quarters	10	15	16	7	2

Find the average or mean number sold per quarter.

Solution   We first need to determine which row represents our random variable X and which row represents the frequency. From the chart we see that the number of yachts sold is our random variable X and the number of quarters is the frequency. The probability will be the relative frequency so next we find the total number of quarters. This is

$$10 + 15 + 16 + 7 + 2 = 50$$

Now we need to find the total number of yachts sold and divide by 50. To find the total sold, notice that on 10 occasions exactly 1 was sold, on 15 occasions 2 were sold, and so on. Thus we must sum up the number one 10 times plus sum up the number two 15 times and so on. Then divide by 50, that is, we have

$$\frac{\overbrace{1 + \cdots + 1}^{10 \text{ times}} + \overbrace{2 + \cdots + 2}^{15 \text{ times}} + \overbrace{3 + \cdots + 3}^{16 \text{ times}} + \overbrace{4 + \cdots + 4}^{7 \text{ times}} + \overbrace{5 + 5}^{2 \text{ times}}}{50}$$

or

$$\mu = \frac{1 \cdot 10 + 2 \cdot 15 + 3 \cdot 16 + 4 \cdot 7 + 5 \cdot 2}{50} = 2.52$$

There was an average of 2.52 yachts sold per quarter.   ◆

We can gain considerable insight into this mean if we write the above fraction in a different form. We can write

$$\mu = \frac{1 \cdot 10 + 2 \cdot 15 + 3 \cdot 16 + 4 \cdot 7 + 5 \cdot 2}{50}$$

$$= 1 \cdot \frac{10}{50} + 2 \cdot \frac{15}{50} + 3 \cdot \frac{16}{50} + 4 \cdot \frac{7}{50} + 5 \cdot \frac{2}{50}$$

$$= 1 \cdot p_1 + 2 \cdot p_2 + 3 \cdot p_3 + 4 \cdot p_4 + 5 \cdot p_5$$

where p_1, p_2, p_3, p_4, and p_5, are, respectively, the (empirical) probabilities of the five possible outcomes 1, 2, 3, 4, and 5. If we now let $x_1 = 1$, $x_2 = 2$, $x_3 = 3$, $x_4 = 4$, and $x_5 = 5$, then this can be written as

$$\mu = x_1 p_1 + x_2 p_2 + x_3 p_3 + x_4 p_4 + x_5 p_5$$

This is the form we are seeking. Notice that each term is the product of an outcome with the probability of that outcome. We call it the expected value. In general we have the following, using the language of random variables.

Expected Value or Mean
Let X denote the random variable that has values $x_1, x_2, \ldots, x_n$, and let the associated probabilities be $p_1, p_2, \ldots, p_n$. The expected value or mean of the random variable X, denoted by $E(X)$, is

$$E(X) = x_1 p_1 + x_2 p_2 \cdots + x_n p_n$$

$E(X)$ is what we "expect" over the long term. But we must realize that $E(X)$ need not be an actual outcome. In Example 1, the expected value of sales per quarter was 2.52. We cannot sell 2.52 yachts. Nonetheless, it is extremely useful to think as though we could. (Actually, if the yacht manufacturer were incorporated with 100 shares outstanding and you owned one of these shares, it would make a great deal of sense to say you sold 2.52 yachts.)

In the case that all the n outcomes are equally likely, the probabilities are just $1/n$ and then

$$E(X) = x_1\frac{1}{n} + x_2\frac{1}{n} + \cdots + x_n\frac{1}{n} = \frac{x_1 + x_2 + \cdots + x_n}{n}$$

which is the mean.

EXAMPLE 2   Calculating the Expected Value   Redo Example 1 using the formula for $E(X)$.

Solution   Recall that we found the empirical probabilities to be $p_1 = 10/50 = 0.20$, $p_2 = 15/50 = 0.30$, $p_3 = 16/50 = 0.32$, $p_4 = 7/50 = 0.14$, and $p_5 = 10/50 = 0.04$. Then

$$\begin{aligned} E(X) &= x_1p_1 + x_2p_2 \cdots + x_np_n \\ &= (1)(0.20) + (2)(0.30) + (3)(0.32) + (4)(0.14) + (5)(0.04) \\ &= 2.52 \end{aligned}$$

Which is, of course, the same result as Example 1.   ◆

✧ Applications

Suppose in considering buying the yacht manufacturer in Example 1, you wish to take into account a principal competitor who also manufactures yachts. Knowledge of the competitor's profits would be useful in determining how competitive the two manufacturers are and would heavily influence whether you actually make the purchase. It would be convenient to know the details of the competitor's operations, but this is privileged information you are not likely to obtain. You then hire some analysts who have considerable knowledge of the yacht business and ask them to prepare a table like the one in the previous example that you can use as a comparison. Naturally they are unable to give you exact figures, but they give you the data in the table below.

Number Sold in One Quarter	0	1	2	3	4	5
Probability of Occurrence	0.10	0.20	0.30	0.25	0.10	0.05

Notice that they have assessed from their collective knowledge a probability that the various outcomes will occur.

EXAMPLE 3   Calculating the Expected Value   Suppose in Example 1 you are told that the average profit per yacht is $20,000 and for the competitor, is $21,000. Can you decide which company will have the higher profits per quarter?

Solution   For Example 1, the average quarterly sales are 2.52 and the average profit per yacht is $20,000, thus the average quarterly profit is

$$(2.52)(\$20,000) = \$50,400$$

Looking now at the competitor the "expected" quarterly sales is

$$E(X) = (0)(0.10) + (1)(0.20) + (2)(0.30) + (3)(0.25) + (4)(0.10) + (5)(0.05) = 2.2$$

Thus you expect the competitor to sell 2.2 yachts per quarter. Their quarterly profit is then expected to be

$$(2.2)(\$21,000) = \$46,200$$

The profits of the competitor are less, so you feel more comfortable about the purchase. ✦

There are two common versions of roulette: American and European. In the European version of roulette the numbers from 0 to 36 are located at 37 equally spaced slots on the wheel. Half of the numbers from 1 to 36 are red and the other half are black. The zero slot is green. You place a bet on one or more numbers. The wheel spins, and a ball falls randomly into one of the 37 slots.

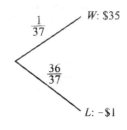

Figure 6.57

EXAMPLE 4   Expected Value of a Bet   In this bet select any of the 37 numbers. Making a $1 bet results in winning back $36 if your number occurs and, of course, you lose your $1 if your number does not occur. Find the expected return.

Solution   A tree diagram is shown in Figure 6.57. There is a probability of $1/37$ of winning and of $36/37$ of losing. Let the random variable X be $35 if you win and $-$1 if you lose. Then the expected return is

$$E(X) = (35)\frac{1}{37} - (1)\frac{36}{37} = -\frac{1}{37} \approx -0.027$$

On this bet you expect to lose about $.03 per $1 bet or 2.7% in the long run. ✦

EXAMPLE 5   Calculating the Expected Value   An insurance company sells a newlywed couple a 1-year replacement insurance policy on an engagement ring. The policy, which costs $100, pays $5000 in the event that the ring is lost during the next year. If there is a 1% chance that the ring will be lost in the next year, find the probability distribution for this financial transaction for the insurance company and find their expected return. What meaning does this expected value have to the insurance company?

Solution   If the ring is not lost during the next year, $100 is made by the insurance company. If the ring is lost the next year, $5000 - $100 = $4900 is lost by the company. The random variable and the associated probability is described in the following table.

Event	Not Lost	Lost
X	100	−4900
$P(X)$	0.99	0.01

Thus

$$E(X) = 100(0.99) - -4900(0.01) = 50$$

which is $50. If the insurance company were to sell a large number of the same insurance policies under the same conditions, they would expect a $50 return per policy. ✦

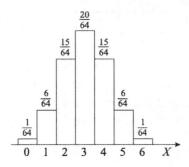

✧ Mean of the Binomial Distribution

Figure 6.54 of the last section gives the histogram for the binomial distribution $P(X = k)$, where $n = 6$ and $p = 0.50$. Notice the perfect symmetry about the point $x = 3$. By inspection we should have $E(X) = 3$. This is indeed the case. Notice that we can obtain $E(X) = 3$ by multiplying $n = 6$ by $p = 0.50$. This is not an accident. The following is true in general.

Expected Value of Binomial Distribution
The expected value of the binomial distribution with n trials and probability of success p in a single trial and $q = 1 - p$ is

$$E(X) = np$$

EXAMPLE 6   Finding the Expected Value of a Binomial Distribution   Find the expected value of the binomial distribution $P(X = k)$, where $n = 6$ and $p = 0.75$. Is it to the right of 3?

Solution   We obtain

$$E(X) = np = 6(0.75) = 4.5$$

which is greater than 3 and therefore to the right of 3.   ✦

EXAMPLE 7   Finding the Expected Value of a Binomial Distribution   A manufacturer of light bulbs produces 1% of them with defects. In a case of 100 bulbs, what will be the mean number of defective bulbs?

Solution   If $p = 0.01$, then choosing a defective light bulb is a binomial distribution where "success" is picking a defective light bulb. We have

$$E(X) = np = 100(0.01) = 1$$

And so the mean or expected number of defective light bulbs is 1.   ✦

✧ Median and Mode

Suppose 10 families live on Millionaire Avenue. One family has an annual income of $10 million, while the other 9 have annual incomes of $20,000 each. The mean annual income is $(10,000,000 + 9 \times 20,000)/10 = 1,018,000$ or over $1 million. Does this number convey what we would like the "average" to convey? Hardly. This simple example illustrates what happens to the mean when one or a few extreme values exist in a set of numbers.

Two other measures of the center of a set of numbers are the median and the mode. Roughly speaking, the median of a collection of numbers is the middle number when arranged in increasing (or decreasing order), while the mode is the value that occurs most often. A more precise definition, covering all possible cases, is given in the following.

> **Median and Mode**
>
> 1. The median of a set of numerical data is the middle number when the numbers are arranged in order of size and there is an odd number of entries in the set. In the case that the number of entries in the set is even, the median is the mean of the two middle numbers.
>
> 2. The mode of a set of observations is the observation that occurs more frequently than the others. If the frequency of occurrence of two observations is the same and also greater than the frequency of occurrence of all the other observations, then we say the set is bimodal and has two modes. If no one or two observations occurs more frequently than the others, we say that the set has no mode.

EXAMPLE 8   Finding the Mean, Median, and the Mode   Find the mean, median, and the mode of the set of data $\{1, 1, 1, 2, 3, 6, 6, 6\}$.

Solution   The mean is

$$\frac{1+1+1+2+3+6+6+6}{8} = 3.25$$

Since there is an even number in the collection, the median is the mean of the middle two numbers 2 and 3. This is 2.5. The set is bimodal with modes of 1 and 6. ◆

> **Technology Option**
>
> A graphing calculator or spreadsheet can also find the mean and median. See Technology Note 1 on page 311

The following example illustrates that the mean is very sensitive to extreme values whereas the median and mode are not.

EXAMPLE 9   Finding the Mean, Median, and the Mode   Find the mean, median, and the mode of the set of data $\{1, 1, 1, 2, 3, 6, 6, 6, 8974\}$ and compare your answers to the answers in the previous example.

Solution   The mean is

$$\frac{1+1+1+2+3+6+6+6+8974}{9} = 1000$$

which is considerably different from the mean in the previous example. Since there is an odd number in the collection, the median is the middle number 3. This has changed only slightly. The set is still bimodal with the modes still 1 and 6. ◆

REMARK: There can be a mode for non-numerical data. If we ask a group of people "What is your favorite color?" we cannot find a mean or median favorite color. However, we can say the most popular color (or colors) is the average favorite color as the mode is a kind of average.

There is a physical interpretation of our measures of central tendency that can be useful in understanding what they represent.   Draw a histogram of the probability distribution as indicated in Figure 6.58.   Turn the rectangle above x_1, the area of which is the probability p_1 of x_1 occurring, into a thin rectangle with

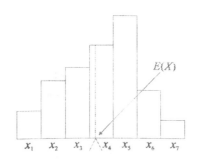

$E(X)$

$x_1 \quad x_2 \quad x_3 \quad x_4 \quad x_5 \quad x_6 \quad x_7$

Figure 6.58

uniform thickness with weight equal to p_1. Do the same for each of the points x_i. Then the point $\mu = E(X)$ is the point at which the histogram will be balanced.

The median of a data set is the place where the area is cut in half. That is, half of the values are above the median and half are below. Finally, the mode is the value that occurs the most often, so that will be the tallest rectangle (or rectangles) on the histogram.

✦ Optional: Mean of Grouped Data

Consider the list of 100 exam grades in the previous section. The teacher found it preferable to graph the histogram with the data in groups. If she has the original data, the mean is 70.79. However, if you only have the grouped data, the mean can be calculated in a straightforward manner. Simply multiply the mid-point of the interval by the probability of that interval and sum these products. In this case we would have

$$\bar{x} = 14.5 \times 0.01 + 24.5 \times 0 + 34.5 \times 0.01 + 44.5 \times 0.08 + 54.5 \times 0.15$$
$$+ 64.5 \times 0.15 + 74.5 \times 0.33 + 84.5 \times 0.16 + 94.5 \times 0.11$$
$$= 70.4$$

This is a slightly different result from the original data, but still a reasonable measure of central tendency.

EXAMPLE 10   Raisins in a Box   A large number of boxes of snack sized boxes of raisins is opened and the number of raisins in each is counted. Find the mean for the number of raisins in a box.

Number of Raisins	12 – 14	15 – 17	18 – 20	21 – 23	24 – 26
Number of Boxes	4	12	20	24	15

Solution   The number of raisins was counted. We let the random variable X be the mid-points of the intervals. The frequency is the number of boxes and a total of $N = 4 + 12 + 20 + 24 + 15 = 75$. The mid-points of the intervals and the relative frequency of the interval is then

X (mid-point)	13	16	19	22	25
Relative Frequency	4/75	12/75	20/75	24/75	15/75

Now the mean can be found using the expected value formula,

$$E(X) = 13 \cdot \frac{4}{75} + 14 \cdot \frac{12}{75} + 19 \cdot \frac{20}{75} + 22 \cdot \frac{24}{75} + 25 \cdot \frac{15}{75} = 20.36$$

or a mean of 20.36 raisins.   ✦

✦ Optional: Samples vs. Populations

When every piece of data for a population is counted, we call our statistics population statistics. There are no numbers missing and so the mean we find is the true mean and we represent it with the symbol μ. However, if we only have a sample of the data from our population, the mean we calculate may or may not be close to the true mean. We call the sample mean $\bar{x}$. Both values are calculated by the methods discussed at the beginning of the section. However, the interpretation is quite different.

Refer again to our 100 test scores. If there are exactly 100 students in the class and we use the 100 scores to find the mean of 70.79, this is the true mean, $\mu = 70.79$. But, if the instructor just wanted a rough estimate of the mean and used the first 20 scores of papers that were graded, she may have had

92, 92, 89, 83, 79, 78, 71, 70, 69, 64, 64, 64, 64, 62, 59, 55, 54, 50, 45, 44

and the mean of this data is $\bar{x} = 67.4$. A different sample would likely produce a different mean. The topic of determining if a sample is a "good" sample or not is beyond the scope of this text, but it is a very important concept in statistics. It effects many things such as polls (after all, they don't poll all voters, just a sample of them) and the interpretation of the census data (since not everyone returns their census, and the return rate varies in some interesting ways).

EXAMPLE 11   Sample Mean   Find the mean of the 20 values given below. Then find the mean of every other value starting with the first value, the mean of the first 10, and the mean of the last ten. Compare these sample means with the true mean.

0 10, 2, 2, 14, 4, 14, 12, 16, 6, 2, 16, 14, 18, 11, 16, 5, 12, 5, 19, 13

Solution   The mean of all 20 numbers is

$$\mu = \frac{10+2+2+14+4+14+12+16+6+\ldots 12+5+19+13}{20}$$

$$= \frac{211}{20} = 10.55$$

Using every other value we find

$$\bar{x} = \frac{10+2+4+12+6+16+18+16+12+19}{10} = \frac{115}{10} = 11.5$$

Using the first 10 values we find

$$\bar{x} = \frac{10+2+2+14+4+14+12+16+6+2}{20} = \frac{82}{10} = 8.2$$

Using the last 10 values we find

$$\bar{x} = \frac{16+14+18+11+16+5+12+5+19+13}{20} = \frac{129}{10} = 12.9$$

Comparing the values $\mu = 10.55$ to $\bar{x} = 11.5$, 8.2 and 12.9 we find quite a difference between the true mean and our sample means.   ◆

The importance of knowing if the data is a sample or population is clear from the example above. The 20 data values were generated using the random number function in Excel and should not have any bias. Yet we find great differences in the mean when a sample of the data is chosen.

✧ Technology Corner

Using Technology for Averages

When a TI-83/84 calculator is used to compute the mean or median, the data must be entered into a list. Consider Example 8 in this section. To computer the averages, press ▥STAT▥ and then choose Edit and then ▥ENTER▥ to enter the 7 data values into list L1 as shown in Screen 1 (note the last value of 6 is not visible). Then press ▥STAT▥ again and right arrow over to the CALC menu. Choose 1: 1-Var Stats shown in Screen 2. Press ▥ENTER▥ to return to the home page with the 1:1-Var Stats command appearing. Press ▥2ND▥ and ▥1▥ to paste L1 next to the 1-Var Stats command as shown in Screen 3.

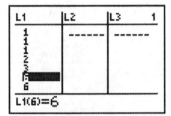

Screen 1

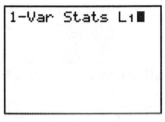

Screen 2

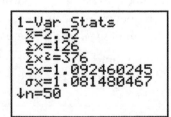

Screen 3

Now press ▥ENTER▥ and the results are displayed in Screens 4 and 5. The down arrow must be pressed to see the data in Screen 5. The mean is displayed as $\bar{x}$ and the median is displayed at Med. To find the mode, plot the data in a histogram as described in the Technology Corner in the previous section. The histogram in Screen 6 shows two highest points at $X = 1$ and $X = 6$ and so these are the modes.

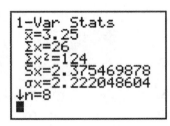

Screen 4

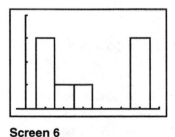

Screen 5

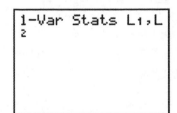

Screen 6

[-.5, 7]x[0, 4]

If the data is in the form of a probability or frequency distribution, the X values are entered into list L1 and the probability or frequency into list L2. The data for Example 1 is shown in Screen 7. When the 1-Var Stats command is called, the arguments are L1, L2 as shown in Screen 8. The result is shown in Screen 9.

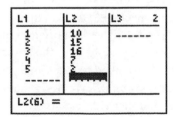

Screen 7

Screen 8

Screen 9

When a spreadsheet such as Microsoft Excel is used to find averages, the data is entered cells as shown in Worksheet 1. Then in the cell to hold the mean or median, type =AVERAGE(or =MEDIAN(, respectively. Then highlight the cells to be evaluated and then press ENTER. The result is show in Worksheet 2.

	A	B	C
1	1		
2	1	mean=	=AVERAGE(A1:A8)
3	1	median=	=MEDIAN(A1:A8)
4	2		
5	3		
6	6		
7	6		
8	6		

	A	B	C
1	1		
2	1	mean=	3.25
3	1	median=	2.5
4	2		
5	3		
6	6		
7	6		
8	6		

Worksheet 1   Worksheet 2

Self-Help Exercises 6.2

1. Find the expected value of the random variable (rv) having the probability distribution given in the following table.

rv x	-2	-1	0	1	3	5
$P(X = x)$	0.20	0.15	0.30	0.05	0.20	0.10

2. In European roulette you can bet on a color, say red. If red occurs, you win back twice your bet. If black occurs, you lose your stake. If 0 occurs, the wheel is spun again until 0 does not occur. If red occurs, then you win the original stake back. If black comes up, you lose your original stake. Find the expected return.

6.2 Exercises

1. If the random variable X denotes the real valued outcomes given in the following table with the given frequency of occurrence of each of the outcomes, fill in the last line of the table and find $E(X)$.

Outcome	0	2	4	6	8	10
Frequency	50	5	10	5	20	10
$P(X)$						

2. If the random variable X denotes the real valued outcomes given in the following table with the given frequency of occurrence of each of the outcomes, fill in the last line of the table and find $E(X)$.

Outcome	-2	-1	0	1	2	10
Frequency	10	11	9	9	5	6
$P(X)$						

3. Find the expected value of the random variable X having the probability distribution given in the following table.

X	-30	-10	0	5	10	20
$P(X)$	0.15	0.25	0.05	0.10	0.25	0.20

4. Find the expected value of the random variable X having the probability distribution given in the following table.

X	-4	-1	0	1	2	3
$P(X)$	0.10	0.10	0.40	0.10	0.10	0.20

5. Babe Ruth established the all-time highest "slugging average" for a single season in 1920. With the random variable X assigned as indicated in the following table with the associated probability, find $E(X)$ rounded to 3 decimal places. This is the "slugging average." We designated no hit by 0, single by 1, double by 2, and so on.

X	0	1	2	3	4
$P(X)$	.6245	.1594	.0786	.0197	.1179

6. A student takes a single course during summer school and decides that the probability of obtaining each grade is as shown in the following table. Find the expected grade point average for this summer; that is, find the expected value of the random variable X.

Outcome	A	B	C	D	F
X	4	3	2	1	0
$P(X)$	0.6	0.2	0.1	0.05	0.05

7. The annual returns for an investment over the last three years are 50%, 0%, −50%. Find the average annual return. Find the actual return over the three-year period.

8. A two-year investment breaks even at the end of two years but yielded a 50% loss in the first year. Find the average annual rate of return for this investment.

9. For an advertising promotion a company is giving away $10,000. All you have to do to enter is submit a letter with your address on the entry form. The winning entry will then be randomly selected, your chance of winning being the same as anyone else's. If 100,000 people enter this contest and your only cost is a 32-cent stamp, what is your expected return (to the nearest cent)?

10. In the daily numbers game, a person picks any of the 1000 numbers from 0 to 999. A $1 wager on one number will return $600 if that number hits; otherwise nothing is returned. If the probability of any one number is the same as that of any other, find the expected return of this wager.

11. One version of roulette has a wheel with 38 numbers (1 through 36 plus 0 and 00) in 38 equally spaced slots. Half of the numbers from 1 to 36 are red, and the other half are black. The numbers 0 and 00 are green. Consider a $1 bet on red. If red comes up, you are returned $2; otherwise, you lose the $1 wagered. Find the expected return for this bet.

12. In the version of roulette in the previous exercise, consider a $1 bet on a number from 1 to 36. If your number hits, you have $36 returned to you; otherwise, you lose your $1 bet. Find the expected return for this bet.

13. In the version of roulette in the previous exercise, consider a $1 bet that can be made on two adjacent numbers. If one of the numbers comes up, the player wins back $18; otherwise, nothing is won. What is the expected value of this bet?

14. A fair die is tossed. If X denotes the random variable giving the number of the top face of the die, find $E(X)$.

15. A lottery has a grand prize of $500,000, two runner-up prizes of $100,000 each, and 100 consolation prizes of $1000 each. If 1 million tickets are sold for $1 each and the probability of any ticket winning is the same as that of any other winning, find the expected return on a $1 ticket.

16. A lottery has a grand prize of $50,000, five runner-up prizes of $5,000 each, 10 third-place prizes of $1000, and 100 consolation prizes of $10 each. If 100,000 tickets are sold for $1 each and the probability of any ticket winning is the same as that of any other winning, find the expected return on a $1 ticket.

17. Two fair dice are tossed. If you roll a total of 7, you win $6; otherwise you lose $1. What is the expected return of this game?

18. Two coins are taken at random (without replacement) from a bag containing five nickels, four dimes, and one quarter. Let X denote the random variable given by the total value of the two coins. Find $E(X)$.

19. Two people are asked to find the average of 200 numbers. They decide that one will find the average of the first 100 and the other will find the average of the second 100. They will then take the average of these two averages. Is this the average of the 200 numbers? Why or why not?

20. A person is asked to find the average of the 100 numbers 1234(1), 1234(2), ... , 1234(100). They decide to factor out the number 1234, then find the average of the integers from 1 to 100, and then multiply this last average by 1234. Are they obtaining the correct average? Why or why not?

21. A person is asked to find the average of the 100 integers from 1234 to 1333. They decide to "move each data point 1234 units to the left, find the average of the resulting data, then move the average over 1234." In other words, they find the average of all the integers from 0 to 99, and then add 1234 to this average. Is this the correct average? Why or why not?

22. Let X be a discrete random variable and c a constant. Define Y to be the random variable given by $Y = cX$.

a. Show $E(Y) = cE(X)$, that is, show $E(cX) = cE(X)$.

b. Given the random variable X with the probability distribution shown in the following table, find $E(X)$.

X	12	24	36
$P(X)$	0.1	0.6	0.3

c. Now using the fact that the probability distribution for $\frac{1}{12}X$ must be the same as that for X, find $E(\frac{1}{12}X)$. Verify that $E(X) = 12E(\frac{1}{12}X)$.

23. Let X be a discrete random variable and c a constant. Define Y to be the random variable given by $Y = X - c$.

a. Show $E(Y) = E(X) - c$, that is, show $E(X - c) = E(X) - c$, or $E(X) = E(X - c) + c$.

b. Given the random variable X with the probability distribution shown in the following table, find $E(X)$.

X	12	13	14
$P(X)$	0.2	0.5	0.3

c. Now find the probability distribution for $X - 13$ and then find $E(X - 13)$. Verify that $E(X) = E(X - 13) + 13$.

24. Let X and Y be two discrete random variables associated with the outcomes of the same experiment. Define the random variable Z by $Z = X + Y$. Show $E(Z) = E(X) + E(Y)$, that is, show $E(X + Y) = E(X) + E(Y)$.

25. If the mean for a binomial distribution is 0.9 and there were 10 trials, find p.

26. If the mean for a binomial distribution is 1.2 and there were six trials, find p.

In Exercises 27 through 31, find the mean, median, and mode of the given data sets.

27. $S = \{1, 2, 2, 3, 5, 7\}$

28. $S = \{1, 2, 3, 5, 5, 100\}$

29. $S = \{12, 18, 18, 20, 29, 29, 310\}$

30. $S = \{55, 55, 60, 70, 75, 75, 80\}$

31. $S = \{3, 5, 8, 9, 12, 14\}$

Applications

32. Insurance An insurance company sells a $10,000, five-year term life insurance policy to an individual for $700. Find the expected return for the company if the probability that the individual will live for the next five years is 0.95.

33. Sales The number of sales per week and the associated probabilities of a car salesman are given in the following table. Find the expected number of sales per week.

Number	0	1	2	3	4
Probability	0.50	0.30	0.10	0.07	.03

34. Employee Attendance A bank has four tellers. The following table gives the probabilities that a given number will be at work on any given day.

Number	4	3	2	1	0
Probability	0.80	0.10	0.07	0.02	.01

35. Investment Returns The following tables give all the possible returns and the associated probabilities of two investments, A and B. Find the expected value of each investment and compare the two.

	Investment A		
Outcome	$1000	$2000	$1000
Probability	0.1	0.8	0.1

	Investment B		
Outcome	-$1000	$0	$9000
Probability	0.8	0.1	0.1

36. Investment Adviser An investment adviser informs you that his average annual return for the last 3 years is 100%. Furthermore, he says his annual return during each of the first 2 years of this 3-year period was 200%. Find how the people did who followed his advice by finding the return for the third year of this 3-year period.

37. Quality Control Electrical switches are manufactured with the probability of 5% that any one is defective. If 50 are chosen at random, what is the expected number of defective switches in this batch?

38. Medicine For a certain heart operation, the probability of survival is .95. If 10 of these operations are performed every week, what is the expected number of deaths due to this operation?

39. Comparing Investments Two car dealerships are up for sale. The following two tables give the number of cars sold per day together with the associated probabilities.

	First Dealership			
Number	0	1	2	3
Probability	.50	.30	.15	.05

	Second Dealership				
Number	0	1	2	3	4
Probability	.60	.20	.05	.05	.10

The average profit per car at the first dealership is $400, and that at the second is $300. Which dealership will yield the higher daily profit?

40. Comparing Investments Two motels are up for sale. The following two tables give the number (No.) of rooms rented per day together with the associated probabilities (*P*).

	Motel 1					
No. rooms	5	6	7	8	9	10
P	.10	.30	.40	.10	.05	.05

	Motel 2				
No. rooms	3	4	5	6	7
P	.05	.05	.10	.20	.60

The average profit per room rented at the first motel is $20, and that at the second is $21. Which motel will yield the higher daily profit?

41. Cases Argued Before Supreme Court Given below is the number of cases argued before the U.S. Supreme Court for five selected years. Find the mean, the median, and the mode of these five numbers. Cases argued: 151, 179, 154, 171, 125.

42. Voter Turnout The following list gives the voter turnout as a percentage of the voting-age population in five recent presidential elections in selected years. Find the mean, the median, and the mode percentage turnout for these five presidential elections. Percentage: 55, 54, 53, 53, 50.

43. Number of Federal Employees The following list gives the number of federal employees as a percentage of the population in some recent selected years. Find the mean, the median, and the mode of these percentages. Percentage: 1.32 1.28 1.44 1.32 1.23 1.24 1.20

44. Oil Pollution The number of oil polluting incidents in and around U.S. waters for recent selected years is given. Find the average number per year of such incidents. Number: 6539, 6352, 6791, 8225, 7114.

45. Oil Pollution The number of millions of gallons of oil polluted in and around U.S. waters for recent selected years is given. Find the average amount per year. Amount: 4.6, 3.9, 6.6, 13.6, 4.3.

46. Health Care Unit Location A state government is trying to locate a new health care unit to serve the needs of the city of Adams and the four smaller cities indicated in the figure.

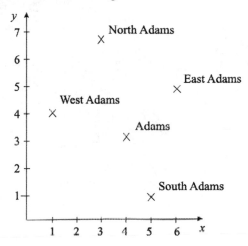

The table gives the population and coordinates of the centers of the five cities. For computational purposes we assume that all residents of a city are located precisely at the center of each city and that there are no residents between cities. The health care unit should be located at the population "center" of these five cities. The probability that a randomly selected individual in this community is in North Adams is just the population of North Adams divided by the total population of this community of five cities. Similarly, for the other four cities. If X and Y are the random variables that take on the values of x_i and y_i, respectively, then the population "center" and therefore the location of the health unit should be at the coordinate $(E(X), E(Y))$. Find this point.

City	Population	Location	
		x_i	y_i
North Adams	11,000	3	7
West Adams	12,000	1	4
Adams	42,000	4	3
East Adams	17,000	6	5
South Adams	18,000	5	1

47. Find the mean for the following grouped data

X	$0-9$	$10-19$	$20-29$	$30-39$	$40-49$
Freq	6	9	15	7	3

X	$1-7$	$8-14$	$15-21$	$22-28$	$29-35$
Freq	15	18	4	10	13

48. Find the mean for the following grouped data

Solutions to Self-Help Exercises 6.2

1. $E(X) = -2(0.20) - 1(0.15) + 0(0.30) + 1(0.05) + 3(0.20) + 5(0.10) = 0.6$.

2. A tree diagram is shown in the figure. On a $1 bet there is a probability on the first spin of $18/37$ of red occurring and of winning $1 ($2 less $1 bet). There is a probability of $18/37$ of black occurring and of losing $1. Then there is a probability of $(1/2) \cdot (1/37)$ of 0 and then red, which results in breaking even and a probability of $(1/2) \cdot (1/37)$ of 0 and then black with a subsequent loss of $1. The expected value is

$$1 \cdot \left(\frac{18}{37}\right) - 1 \cdot \left(\frac{18}{37}\right) + 0 \cdot \left(\frac{1}{2}\right) \cdot \left(\frac{18}{37}\right) - 1 \cdot \left(\frac{1}{2}\right) \cdot \left(\frac{18}{37}\right) \approx -0.0135$$

On this bet you expect to lose about 1.35% per bet in the long run.

Clearly then, in general, this bet will permit one to play twice as long as the bet in Example 4 with the same stake. Many people will play the first bet because of the excitement of occasionally obtaining a substantially larger winning amount. But notice that the casino makes the customer pay for this excitement by taking a bigger cut of the money bet.

6.3 Measures of Spread

APPLICATION
Probability Estimation

> When cereal is packaged, the actual amount of cereal varies from box to box. Suppose a sample indicates that the average in a 16-ounce box is 16.0 ounces with a standard deviation of 0.5. Find the minimum percent of boxes that will have 15 to 17 ounces of cereal. For the answer see Example 4.

✦ Variance and Standard Deviation

In the last section we saw that the mean or the expected value is one measure of the "center" of the data. It is often helpful to not only know the central tendency of a probability distribution, but also the extent of its spread or dispersion.

In this section, we will use the variance and the standard deviation to measure the extent of the dispersion of the data from the mean. We will then use Chebyshev's inequality to give crude estimates of any probability distribution, knowing only the mean and variance.

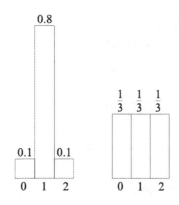

Figure 6.59

Figure 6.59 shows the histograms of two probability distributions. We can readily see, without a calculation, that the means of both are $\mu = 1$. However, notice that the first is concentrated about its mean, whereas the second one is widely spread or dispersed about its mean. We will see that the variance will give us a measure of this dispersion.

Consider a manufacturer of ball bearings that measure the diameters of the first four ball bearings coming off the assembly. They are $x_1 = 1.02$, $x_2 = 0.98$, $x_3 = 1.03$, and $x_4 = 0.97$ in cm. We readily calculate the mean to be

$$\mu = \frac{1.02 + 0.98 + 1.03 + 0.97}{4} = 1.00$$

It is tempting to measure the dispersion by taking the average of all the differences

$$x_1 - \mu, \quad x_2 - \mu, \quad x_3 - \mu, \quad x_4 - \mu$$

But as a simple calculation will show the answer is 0! It turns out that this will always happen for any data set. You might think that a good idea would be to take the average of the absolute value of the differences; however, this leads to algebraic difficulties. Instead, we get around the sign problem by taking the average of the squares of the differences and call this number the variance. We then have

$$\text{Var} = \frac{(x_1 - \mu)^2 + (x_2 - \mu)^2 + (x_3 - \mu)^2 + (x_4 - \mu)^2}{4}$$

$$= \frac{(1.020 - 1)^2 + (0.980 - 1)^2 + (1.030 - 1)^2 + (0.970 - 1)^2}{4}$$

$$= \frac{0.0004 + 0.0004 + 0.0009 + 0.0009}{4}$$

$$= 0.00065$$

There is one unsettling aspect of the variance we just found. The units are squared. The variance is 0.00065 and is given in cm^2 and thus is difficult to relate back to the original problem, which is in cm. To remedy this we define the standard deviation to be the square root of the variance and denote it by σ. Thus $\sigma = \sqrt{\text{Var}}$. We have

$$\sigma = \sqrt{0.00065} \approx 0.025$$

We will now find a more general and useful definition of variance. After all, we must be able to find the variance of probability distributions such as those found in Figure 6.59.

Suppose we have a data set of N outcomes with the distinct outcomes x_1, x_2, ..., x_n, where x_1 is observed to occur a frequency of f_1 times, x_2 is observed f_2 times, and so on. (We must have $f_1 + f_2 + \ldots + f_n = N$.) Then if the mean is μ, the variance is

$$\text{Var} = \frac{\overbrace{(x_1 - \mu)^2 + \ldots + (x_1 - \mu)^2}^{f_1 \text{ times}} + \ldots + \overbrace{(x_n - \mu)^2 + \ldots + (x_n - \mu)^2}^{f_n \text{ times}}}{N}$$

$$= \frac{(x_1 - \mu)^2 f_1 + (x_2 - \mu)^2 f_2 + \ldots + (x_n - \mu)^2 f_n}{N}$$

$$= (x_1 - \mu)^2 \frac{f_1}{N} + (x_2 - \mu)^2 \frac{f_2}{N} + \ldots + (x_n - \mu)^2 \frac{f_n}{N}$$

⑦ Technology Option

See Technology Note 1 on page 323 for details on finding the standard deviation and variance using a graphing calculator or a spreadsheet. The technology option boxes in the remainder of the section will show the results of following the directions in the technology note for the graphing calculator for each example.

The empirical probability p_1 of the event x_1 is f_1/N, and similarly for the other empirical probabilities. Thus, the right-hand side of the last displayed line becomes

$$(x_1 - \mu)^2 p_1 + (x_2 - \mu)^2 p_2 + \ldots + (x_n - \mu)^2 p_n$$

We call this term the variance. In the language of random variables we then have the following.

Variance and Standard Deviation
Let X denote the random variable that takes on the values $x_1, x_2, \ldots, x_n$, and let the associated probabilities be $p_1, p_2, \ldots, p_n$. Then if $\mu = E(X)$, the variance of the random variable X, denoted by $\text{Var}(X)$, is

$$\text{Var}(X) = (x_1 - \mu)^2 p_1 + (x_2 - \mu)^2 p_2 + \ldots + (x_n - \mu)^2 p_n$$

The standard deviation, denoted by $\sigma(X)$ is

$$\sigma(X) = \sqrt{\text{Var}(X)}$$

EXAMPLE 1   Comparing Variances of Two Probability Distributions   Figure 6.59 shows the histograms of two probability distributions both with means equal to 1. Find the variance of each, and compare the two.

Solution   The variance of the first probability distribution shown in Figure 6.59 is

$$
\begin{aligned}
\text{Var} &= (x_1 - \mu)^2 p_1 + (x_2 - \mu)^2 p_2 + (x_3 - \mu)^2 p_3 \\
&= (0 - 1)^2 (0.10) + (1 - 1)^2 (0.80) + (2 - 1)^2 (0.10) \\
&= 0.20
\end{aligned}
$$

The variance of the second probability distribution shown in Figure 6.59 is

$$
\begin{aligned}
\text{Var} &= (x_1 - \mu)^2 p_1 + (x_2 - \mu)^2 p_2 + (x_3 - \mu)^2 p_3 \\
&= (0 - 1)^2 \tfrac{1}{3} + (1 - 1)^2 \tfrac{1}{3} + (2 - 1)^2 \tfrac{1}{3} \\
&= \tfrac{2}{3}
\end{aligned}
$$

much larger than the variance of the first. This just reflects the fact, seen from Figure 6.59, that the second probability distribution is more dispersed from the mean than the first one.   ✦

Often the probabilities are not known, but an experiment has been performed giving the empirical probabilities $p_1, p_2, \cdots, p_n$. This is illustrated in the next example.

EXAMPLE 2   Finding the Standard Deviation   You have completed 40 courses, each with the same number of credits, with the frequency of each grade given in the following table.

Outcome	A	B	C	D	F
Random Variable, X	4	3	2	1	0
Frequency	25	11	3	1	0

Find the expected value of the random variable X; that is, find the grade point average, and then find Var(X).

Solution   We first notice that the total number is given by

$$f_1 + f_2 + f_3 + f_4 + f_5 = 25 + 11 + 3 + 1 + 0 = 40$$

Dividing each of the frequencies by 40 gives the relative frequencies or the empirical probability. Doing this gives the following table.

Outcome	A	B	C	D	F
Random Variable, X	4	3	2	1	0
Frequency	25	11	3	1	0
Relative Frequency	$\frac{25}{40}$	$\frac{11}{40}$	$\frac{3}{40}$	$\frac{1}{40}$	$\frac{0}{40}$

The expected value and variance are

$$\mu = x_1 p_1 + x_2 p_2 + x_3 p_3 + x_4 p_4 + x_5 p_5$$

$$= 4 \cdot \frac{25}{40} + 3 \cdot \frac{11}{40} + 2 \cdot \frac{3}{40} + 1 \cdot \frac{1}{40} + 0 \cdot \frac{0}{40}$$

$$= 3.5$$

$$\text{Var}(X) = (x_1 - \mu)^2 p_1 + (x_2 - \mu)^2 p_2 + (x_3 - \mu)^2 p_3 + (x_4 - \mu)^2 p_4 + (x_5 - \mu)^2 p_5$$

$$= (4 - 3.5)^2 \frac{25}{40} + (3 - 3.5)^2 \frac{11}{40} + (2 - 3.5)^2 \frac{3}{40} + (1 - 3.5)^2 \frac{1}{40} + (0 - 3.5)^2 \frac{0}{40}$$

$$= 0.55$$

◆

✧ Chebyshev's Inequality

Knowing only the mean and variance of a probability law is not sufficient in general to determine the probability law. However, crude estimates of the probability law can be made, which suffice for many purposes, from a knowledge of just the mean and variance. One such estimate is Chebyshev's inequality.

Chebyshev's Inequality

Let X be a random variable with expected value μ and standard deviation σ. Then the probability that the random variable associated with a random outcome lies between $\mu - h\sigma$ and $\mu + h\sigma$ is at least $1 - \frac{1}{h^2}$, that is

$$P(\mu - h\sigma \leq X \leq \mu + h\sigma) \geq 1 - \frac{1}{h^2}$$

For Chebyshev's inequality to give new information, clearly we must have $h \geq 1$.

EXAMPLE 3 **Using Chebyshev's Inequality** A probability distribution of a random variable X has mean $\mu = 14$ and standard deviation $\sigma = 4$. Use Chebyshev's inequality to give a lower bound for the probability that X is within 12 units of μ.

Solution Setting $12 = h\sigma = h \cdot 4$, yields $h = 3$. Then $\mu - h\sigma = 2$ and $\mu + h\sigma = 26$ and

$$P(2 \leq X \leq 26) \geq 1 - \frac{1}{3^2} \approx 0.89$$

Thus there is at least an 89% chance that the random variable lies on the interval $[2, 26]$. ◆

EXAMPLE 4 **Using Chebyshev's Inequality** When cereal is packaged, the actual amount of cereal varies from box to box. Suppose a sample indicates that the average in a 16-ounce box is 16.0 ounces with a standard deviation of 0.5 ounces. Using Chebyshev's inequality, find the minimum percent of boxes that will have 15 to 17 ounces of cereal.

Solution Let X be the random variable equal to the number of ounces in a box of cereal. We are given $\mu = 16$ and $\sigma = 0.5$. We are seeking an estimate of $P(15 \leq X \leq 17)$ or in terms of $\mu = 16$, $P(\mu - 1 \leq X \leq \mu + 1)$. In the terminology of Chebyshev's inequality, we then must have $1 = h\sigma = h(0.5)$. This implies $h = 2$. Thus

$$P(15 \leq X \leq 17) \geq 1 - \frac{1}{4} = 0.75$$

At least 75% of these boxes will have between 15 and 17 ounces of cereal. ◆

✧ Variance of the Binomial Distribution

We give without proof the following additional useful fact about binomial distributions.

Variance of the Binomial Distribution
The variance of the binomial distribution with n trials and the probability of "success" equal to p and of "failure" equal to q is

$$\mathrm{Var}(X) = npq$$

✧ Optional: An Alternative Form of the Variance

If you are using a calculator or computer that computes variance, then you need not to bother with this subsection. Otherwise, the computation of

$$\mathrm{Var}(X) = (x_1 - \mu)^2 p_1 + (x_2 - \mu)^2 p_2 + \ldots + (x_n - \mu)^2 p_n$$

can be simplified by using an alternative form. To see how, write the terms on the right-hand side as

$$(x_1 - \mu)^2 p_1 = x_1^2 p_1 - 2x_1\mu p_1 + \mu^2 p_1$$
$$\cdots$$
$$(x_n - \mu)^2 p_n = x_n^2 p_n - 2x_n\mu p_n + \mu^2 p_n$$

Summing up the left-hand sides of these equations gives $\mathrm{Var}(X)$. Doing this and rearranging the sum of the right-hand sides gives

$$\mathrm{Var}(X) = (x_1^2 p_1 + \cdots + x_n^2 p_n) - 2\mu(x_1 p_1 + \cdots + x_n p_n) + \mu^2(p_1 + \cdots + p_n)$$

But recall that $\mu = x_1 p_1 + \cdots + x_n p_n$ while $p_1 + \cdots + p_n = 1$. Using these last two facts then yields

$$\mathrm{Var}(X) = (x_1^2 p_1 + \cdots + x_n^2 p_n) - 2\mu\mu + \mu^2$$
$$= (x_1^2 p_1 + \cdots + x_n^2 p_n) - \mu^2$$

This will save a substantial amount of work, if you are doing your calculations by hand. We have the following:

Alternate Form of Variance

An alternate form of the variance is given by

$$\mathrm{Var}(X) = (x_1^2 p_1 + \cdots + x_n^2 p_n) - \mu^2$$

EXAMPLE 5   Using the Alternate Form of the Variance   Use this last form to find $\mathrm{Var}(X)$ in the last example.

Solution   Create the following table.

x_i	p_i	$x_i p_i$	$x_i^2 p_i$
4	25/40	2.500	10.000
3	11/40	0.825	2.475
2	3/40	0.150	0.300
1	1/40	0.025	0.025
0	0/40	0.000	0.000
Sum		3.5	12.8

Then $\mathrm{Var}(X) = (x_1^2 p_1 + \cdots + x_n^2 p_n) - \mu^2 = 12.8 - (3.5)^2 = 0.55$.   ◆

✦ Optional: Variance as a Measure of Risk

It is a basic tenet in the modern theory of finance that the amount that the value of an asset varies over time is a measure of the risk of the asset. The standard measure of this variability is the standard deviation.

If everyone has a great deal of confidence what the future value of an investment is, then the value of the investment should vary little. For example, everyone has essentially complete confidence what the future performance of money in the bank will be. Thus the value of this asset (the principal) does not vary in time. This reflects the fact that this investment is (essentially) risk-free. Everyone has very high confidence in the future performance of a high quality bond. However, there is some variability in price as investors change somewhat from week to week their assessment of the economy, inflation, and other factors that may affect the price of the bond. This reflects the fact that a bond does have some risk.

Moving on to stocks, the future earnings and dividend performance of a very large company such as General Electric (GE) is estimated by many analysts with reasonable confidence and so the price of this security does not vary significantly. However, the future earnings of a small bio-tech firm is likely to be very unpredictable. Will it be able to come up with new products? Will it be able to fend off competitors? Will some key personnel leave? Thus the weekly assessment of such a firm is likely to change substantially more than that of GE. As a consequence, the weekly price changes of this company will vary significantly more, reflecting the fact that an investment in the small company is more risky.

Therefore the risk of a security is defined as the standard deviation of the daily (or perhaps weekly) prices of the security.

The table below gives the weekly price changes in percent of four assets: money in the bank, a bond, a blue chip stock, and a tech stock.

Principle in Bank	Bond	Blue Chip Stock	Tech Stock
0.0	0.0	0.3	4.6
0.0	−0.2	0.0	4.7
0.0	−0.1	3.1	0.0
0.0	0.0	−2.0	8.7
0.0	−0.5	2.1	−4.2

According to Exercises 17 and 18 at the end of this section, the standard deviation of the four assets over this period of time was 0, 0.19, 1.77, and 4.44, respectively. This reflects the fact that these assets are increasingly risky in the order listed.

✦ Optional: Sample vs. Population Standard Deviation

In the previous section there was a discussion about sample and population means. Remember that μ is the true mean of the entire population and $\bar{x}$ is the sample mean. Both quantities are calculated the same way, add all the data values and divide by the number of data values. The variance and standard deviation calculated this section has been the population variance, σ^2, and population standard deviation, σ. When we have a sample of our data, then the sample standard deviation, S, should be used. The formula for sample standard deviation is

$$S = \sqrt{\frac{(x_1 - \bar{x})^2 + (x_2 - \bar{x})^2 + \ldots (x_n - \bar{x})^2}{n-1}}$$

where the denominator is $n-1$ rather than n to account for the fact that the data is only a sample.

EXAMPLE 6 **Sample Standard Deviation** Find the population standard deviation of the 20 values given below. Then find the sample standard deviation of every other value starting with the first value, the sample standard deviation of the first 10, and the sample standard deviation of the last 10 values.

10, 2, 2, 14, 4, 14, 12, 16, 6, 2, 16, 14, 18, 11, 16, 5, 12, 5, 19, 13

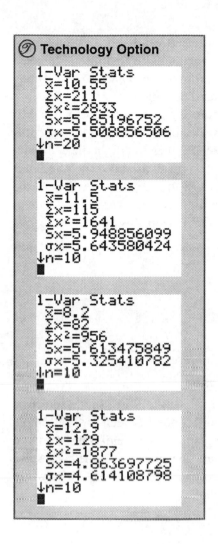

Technology Option

Solution   In the previous section we found $\mu = 10.55$, so

$$\sigma = \sqrt{\frac{(10-10.55)^2 + (2-10.55)^2 + \ldots + (13-10.55)^2}{20}} = \sqrt{\frac{606.95}{20}}$$

$$\approx 5.5089$$

When every other value is used, $\bar{x} = 11.5$ and the sample standard deviation is

$$S = \sqrt{\frac{(10-11.5)^2 + (2-11.5)^2 + \ldots + (19-11.5)^2}{9}} = \sqrt{\frac{318.5}{9}}$$

$$\approx 5.9489$$

Using the first 10 values we found $\bar{x} = 8.2$ and the sample standard deviation is

$$S = \sqrt{\frac{(10-8.2)^2 + (2-8.2)^2 + \ldots + (2-8.2)^2}{9}} = \sqrt{\frac{283.6}{9}}$$

$$\approx 5.6135$$

Using the last 10 values we found $x = 12.9$ and the sample standard deviation is

$$S = \sqrt{\frac{(16-12.9)^2 + (14-12.9)^2 + \ldots + (13-12.9)^2}{9}} = \sqrt{\frac{212.9}{9}}$$

$$\approx 4.8637$$

◆

✧ Technology Corner

⑨Technology Note 1   Using Technology for Standard Deviation

To find the standard deviation using a graphing calculator, the data for the ball bearings, 1.02, 0.98, 1.03, and 0.97 is entered into list L1. Then as in the last section, press STAT then right arrow to CALC and choose 1: 1-Var Stats and ENTER. Then L1 (by pressing 2ND and then 1) and ENTER. The result is shown in Screen 1.

The standard deviation is shown on line 5 as σx=0.0254950976. To find the variance, the standard deviation must be squared. To do this, press VARS (see Screen 2) and choose 5: Statistics... (see Screen 3). Then choose 4: σx which will return you to the home screen and then press x² and ENTER to find the variance as shown in Screen 4.

Screen 1

Screen 2   **Screen 3**   **Screen 4**

If the data is in the form of a probability distribution table or a frequency table, the X values are entered in list L1 and the probability or frequency is entered into list L2 as was done in the previous section for the mean and median. Doing 1-Var Stats L1, L2 will calculate the standard deviation σ.

To find the variance and standard deviation using a spreadsheet such as Microsoft Excel, begin by entering the data in a worksheet as shown in Worksheet 1. In the cell that will have the variance, type =VARP(, then highlight the cells with the data. Press Enter to evaluate the variance command as shown in Worksheet 2. To find the standard deviation, type =STDEVP(in the cell that will hold the answer, then highlight the cells with the data as shown in Worksheet 3. Press Enter to evaluate the standard deviation as shown in Worksheet 4.

	A	E
1	1.02	
2	0.98	
3	1.03	
4	0.97	
5		
6	=VARP(A1.A4)	

Worksheet 1

	A	E
1	1.02	
2	0.98	
3	1.03	
4	0.97	
5		
6	0.00065	

Worksheet 2

	A	B	C
1	1.02		
2	0.98		
3	1.03		
4	0.97		
5			
6	0.00065	=STDEVP(A1.A4)	

Worksheet 3

	A	B	C
1	1.02		
2	0.98		
3	1.03		
4	0.97		
5			
6	0.00065	0.025495	

Worksheet 4

⑦Technology Note 2   Using Technology for Sample Standard Deviation

The sample standard deviation, S, is found on the same 1-Var Stats screen as the population standard deviation. See the fourth line of Screen 1. The sample variance is found in the same way as the population variance except when you are on Screen 3, choose 3: Sx and square that. The spreadsheet method is also very similar. The sample commands are VAR(and STDEV(. This is shown in Worksheets 5 and 6.

	A	B
1	1.02	
2	0.98	
3	1.03	
4	0.97	
5		
6	0.000866667	0.029439203

Worksheet 5

	A	B
1	1.02	
2	0.98	
3	1.03	
4	0.97	
5		
6	=VAR(A1.A4)	=STDEV(A1.A4)

Worksheet 6

Self-Help Exercises 6.3

1. The following table gives two probability distributions associated with the same outcomes.

Outcome	1	2	3	4	5
a. Probability	0.1	0.2	0.4	0.2	0.1
b. Probability	0.4	0.1	0.0	0.1	0.4

Draw a histogram of each probability distribution. By inspecting these histograms (making no calcula-

tions), determine the means and determine which one has the largest variance. Now calculate the means, variances, and standard deviations.

2. Use Chebyshev's inequality to estimate the minimum probability that the outcome is between 2 and 4 for a probability distribution with $\mu = 3$ and $\sigma = 0.25$.

6.3 Exercises

In Exercises 1 through 2, you are given a table with two probability distributions associated with the same outcomes. For each exercise draw a histogram of each probability distribution. Using only these histograms and making no calculations, determine the means and determine which one has the largest variance. Now calculate the means, variances, and standard deviations.

1.
Outcome	1	2	3	4	5
a. Probability	0.2	0.2	0.2	0.2	0.2
b. Probability	0.1	0.2	0.4	0.2	0.1

2.
Outcome	1	2	3	4	5
a. Probability	0.1	0.1	0.6	0.1	0.1
b. Probability	0.3	0.1	0.2	0.1	0.3

3. In the recent Atlantic City Golf Classic, the top three finishers had the following scores for the three rounds of the tournament.

Jane	71	68	69
Cindy	70	70	69
Amy	69	68	72

Find the mean, variance, and standard deviation for the three rounds for each of the players. Which one had the lowest average? Which one was the most consistent?

4. In the recent McDonald's Golf Championship, the top five finishers had the following scores for the four rounds of the tournament.

Beth	67	71	67	68
Pat	69	67	70	71
Sally	67	69	67	74
Mary	70	66	72	70
Auro	70	65	73	70

Find the mean, variance, and standard deviation for the three rounds for each of the players. Which one had the lowest average? Which one was the most consistent? Least consistent?

5. Find the mean, variance, and standard deviation of the random variable having the probability distribution given in the following table.

Random Variable, x	−3	0	1
$P(X = x)$	0.2	0.5	0.3

6. Find the mean, variance, and standard deviation of the random variable having the probability distribution given in the following table.

Random Variable, x	−2	1	3
$P(X = x)$	0.1	0.3	.06

7. Find the mean, variance, and standard deviation of the random variable (r.v.) having the probability distribution given in the following table.

r.v., x	−2	0	1	2	4
$P(X = x)$	0.1	0.3	0.1	0.2	0.3

8. Find the mean, variance, and standard deviation of the random variable (r.v.) having the probability distribution given in the following table.

r.v., x	−2	-1	1	2	5
$P(X = x)$	0.2	0.1	0.25	0.25	0.2

9. By inspection of the following two histograms (and making no calculations), determine the means and determine which has the largest variance.

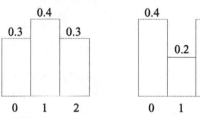

10. By inspection of the following two histograms (and making no calculations), determine the means and determine which has the largest variance.

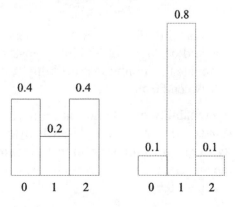

11. Let X be a discrete random variable and c a constant. Define Y to be the random variable given by $Y = cX$.

 a. Show $\text{Var}(Y) = c^2\text{Var}(X)$. That is, show that $\text{Var}(cX) = c^2\text{Var}(X)$. *Hint:* Use the fact given in Exercise 22 of the last section that $E(cX) = cE(X)$, or $\mu(cX) = c\mu(X)$, and the second form of variance.

 b. Given the random variable X with the probability distribution shown in the following table, find $\text{var}(X)$.

Random Variable, x	3	6	9
$P(X = x)$	0.1	0.6	0.3

 c. Now using the fact that the probability distribution for $\frac{1}{3}X$ must be the same as for X, find $\text{Var}(\frac{1}{3}X)$. Verify that $\text{Var}(X) = 9\text{Var}(\frac{1}{3}X)$.

12. Let X be a discrete random variable and c a constant. Define Y to be the random variable given by $Y = X - c$.

 a. Show $\text{Var}(Y) = \text{Var}(X)$, that is, show $\text{Var}(X - c) = \text{Var}(X)$. *Hint:* Use the fact given in Exercise 23 of the last section that $E(X) - c = E(X - c)$, or $\mu(X - c) = \mu(X) - c$, and the first form of the variance.

 b. Given the random variable X with the probability distribution shown in the following table, find $\text{Var}(X)$.

Random Variable, x	12	13	14
$P(X = x)$	0.2	0.5	0.3

 c. Now find the probability distribution for $X - 13$ and then find $\text{Var}(X - 13)$. Verify that $\text{Var}(X) = \text{Var}(X - 13)$.

13. A probability distribution has a mean of 30 and a standard deviation of 2. Use Chebyshev's inequality to find the minimum probability that an outcome is between 20 and 40.

14. A probability distribution has a mean of 90 and a standard deviation of 3. Use Chebyshev's inequality to find the minimum probability that an outcome is between 60 and 120.

15. A probability distribution has a mean of 60 and a standard deviation of 1. Use Chebyshev's inequality to find the number c so that the probability that the numerical outcome is between $60 - c$ and $60 + c$ is at least 0.99.

16. A probability distribution has a mean of μ and a standard deviation of σ. Use Chebyshev's inequality to find a lower bound for the percentage of outcomes between $\mu - 5\sigma$ and $\mu + 5\sigma$.

Applications

17. **Finance** Find the mean, variance, and standard deviation of the weekly percentage change in the value of the principal in the bank account and for the bond in the table in the subsection of the measure of risk. Which is varying the most? How do you correlate your answer with the risk of each investment?

18. **Finance** Find the mean, variance, and standard deviation of the weekly percentage change in the values of the two stocks given in table in the subsection of the measure of risk. Which is varying the most? How do you correlate your answer with the risk of each investment?

19. **Finance** During a 5-week period in 2007, the stock of a utility company and the stock of a small technology company showed the following weekly percentage changes.

Company	Weekly Price Change (%)				
Utility Stock	−1.1	0.4	1.5	−2.5	−2.2
Tech Stock	5.4	−1.2	5.9	1.0	−3.2

Find the variance of the weekly price changes of each. Relate the two variances found to the riskiness of the two stocks.

20. **Finance** During a 5-week period in 2007, the stock of an insurance company and the stock of a small tech company showed the following weekly percentage changes.

Company	Weekly Price Change (%)				
Insur. Stock	−0.3	−2.8	1.2	1.8	0.0
Tech Stock	2.9	−5.9	6.3	−11.8	−3.2

Find the variance of the weekly price changes of each. Relate the two variances found to the riskiness of the two stocks.

21. **Sales** The number of sales per week and the associated probabilities of two car salespeople, A and B, are given in the following table. Find the mean, variance, and standard deviation for the sales per week of each. Which one will sell more cars? Which one is more consistent?

Number	0	1	2	3	4
Probability A	0.50	0.30	0.10	0.07	0.03
Probability B	0.40	0.20	0.20	0.1	0.1

22. **Employee Absences** The following table gives the probabilities that two employees, A and B, will have the given number of absences from work per month. Find the mean, variance, and standard deviation for each. Which attendance is the best? Which attendance is the most consistent?

Number	0	1	2	3	4
Probability A	0.90	0.04	0.03	0.02	0.01
Probability B	0.85	0.05	0.05	0.05	0

23. **Two Diseases** The following table gives the number of thousands of reported cases of two diseases in the United States. Find the average, variance, and standard deviation of each. Which is varying the most?

G	911	901	781	720	733	690
S	68	68	87	103	111	134

24. **Mortality Rates from Legal Abortions and Child-birth** The following table gives the mortality rates in numbers per 100,000 from legal abortions and childbirth in the United States. Find the average, variance, and standard deviation of each. Which is varying the most?

Abortion	0.4	0.8	0.7	0.7	0.4
Childbirth	7.2	7.9	8.0	7.9	7.8

25. **Temperatures.** The following table gives the average monthly temperatures for two cities for four selected months. Find the average, variance, and standard deviation of each. Which is varying the most?

Month	Jan	Apr	Jul	Oct
San Diego	65	68	76	75
Chicago	29	59	83	64

26. **Health** The following table gives the number of reported cases of plague and polio in the United States for some recent selected years. Find the average, variance, and standard deviation of each. Which is varying the most?

Plague	17	10	12	15	4	2
Polio, Acute	7	8	6	9	5	7

27. **Drug Use** The following table gives the percentage of current users of marijuana and cocaine in the 18 to 25-year-old age group in the United States for some recent selected years. Find the average, variance, and standard deviation of each. Which group of users is varying more?

Marihuana	25	35	27	22	16	13
Cocaine	3	9	7	8	5	2

28. **Drug Use** The following table gives the percentage of current users of alcohol and cigarettes in the 18 to 25-year-old age group in the United States for some recent selected years. Find the average, variance, and standard deviation of each. Which group of users is varying more?

Alcohol	69	76	71	71	65	64
Cigarettes	49	43	40	37	35	32

29. **Scholastic Aptitude Test Scores** The following table gives the verbal SAT scores for some recent selected years. Find the average, variance, and standard deviation of each. Which is varying the most?

Males	435	435	434	429	426
Females	425	422	421	419	418

30. **Scholastic Aptitude Test Scores** The following table gives the math SAT scores for some recent selected years. Find the average, variance, and standard deviation of each. Which is varying the most?

Males	500	498	500	499	497
Females	453	455	454	455	453

31. **Air Pollutant Concentration** The following table gives the concentration of two pollutants, carbon monoxide (CO) and ozone (O_3) in appropriate units, for some recent selected years. Find the average, variance, and standard deviation of each. Which is varying the most?

CO	7.1	6.7	6.4	6.3	5.9
O_3	0.12	0.13	0.14	0.12	0.11

32. **Air Pollutant Concentration** The following table gives the concentration of two pollutants, in appropriate units, for some recent selected years. Find the average, variance, and standard deviation of each. Which is varying the most?

Sulfur Dioxide	9	9	9	8	8
Nitrogen Dioxide	24	24	24	23	22

33. **Death Rates by Causes** The death rate per 100,000 in the United States for viral hepatitis and meningitis for some recent selected years is given in the following table. Find the average, variance, and standard deviation of each. Which is varying the most?

Viral Hepatitis	0.5	0.4	0.4	0.7
Meningitis	0.8	0.6	0.5	0.5

34. **Death Rates by Causes** The death rate per 100,000 in the United States for accidents from automobiles and for all other accidents for some recent selected years is given in the following table. Find the average, variance, and standard deviation of each. Which is varying the most?

Automobiles	27	24	19	19
All Others	30	23	20	18

35. **Sales** The expected amount of sales for each person on a sales force of a company is $100,000 per month with a standard deviation of $20,000. Find the minimum probability using Chebyshev's inequality that

a salesman will sell between $70,000 and $130,000 in a particular month.

36. **Quality Control** The expected number of defective parts produced on an assembly line per shift is 40 with a standard deviation of 10. Find the minimum probability using Chebyshev's inequality that the number of defective parts on a particular shift will be between 20 and 60.

37. **Useful Life of a Product** The expected useful life of a certain brand of VCR is 5 years with standard deviation equal to 1 year. Find the minimum probability using Chebyshev's inequality that the useful life of one of these VCRs will be between 3 and 7 years.

38. **Weights** If the mean weight of a delivered ton of top soil is 2000 pounds with a standard deviation 200 pounds, find the minimum probability using Chebyshev's inequality that the weight of a delivered "ton" is between 1700 and 2300 pounds.

Solutions to Self-Help Exercises 6.3

1. The figure shows the histograms.

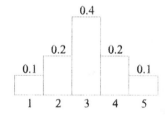 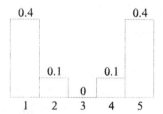

From the histograms one sees that the probability is evenly distributed about 3 in each case. Thus the mean should be 3. In the first case the probability is clustered about the mean, whereas in the second case the probability is more dispersed away from the mean. Thus the variance in the second case should be larger. To calculate the mean and variance, make the following table.

	Probability (a)			Probability (b)		
x_i	p_i	$x_i p_i$	$x_i^2 p_i$	p_i	$x_i p_i$	$x_i^2 p_i$
1	0.1	0.1	0.1	0.4	0.4	0.4
2	0.2	0.4	0.8	0.1	0.2	0.4
3	0.4	1.2	3.6	0.0	0.0	0.0
4	0.2	0.8	3.2	0.1	0.4	1.6
5	0.1	0.5	2.5	0.4	2.0	10.0
	Sum = 3.0	Sum = 10.2		Sum = 3.0	Sum = 12.4	

a. Thus from the table $\mu = 3$ and using the second form for variance gives

$$\text{Var} = 10.2 - 3^2 = 1.2$$
$$\sigma = \sqrt{1.2} \approx 1.095$$

b. From the table $\mu = 3$ and using the second form for variance gives

$$\text{Var} = 12.4 - 3^2 = 3.4$$
$$\sigma = \sqrt{3.4} \approx 1.84$$

As we see, the means are the same, and the variance (and standard deviation) of the second distribution is larger.

2. If X is the random variable equal to the outcome, then we are seeking an estimate of $P(2 \leq X \leq 4)$. Since $\mu = 3$, this can be written as $P(\mu - 1 \leq X \leq \mu + 1)$. This implies that $1 = h\sigma = h(0.25)$. Thus $h = 4$ and, from Chebyshev's inequality,

$$P(\mu - h\sigma \leq X \leq \mu + h\sigma) \geq 1 - \frac{1}{h^2} = 1 - \frac{1}{(4)^2} = 0.9375$$

Thus there is a probability of at least 0.9375 that the outcome will lie between 2 and 4.

Technology Option

```
1-Var Stats
x̄=3
Σx=3
Σx²=10.2
Sx=
σx=1.095445115
↓n=1
■
```

```
1-Var Stats
x̄=3
Σx=3
Σx²=12.4
Sx=
σx=1.843908891
↓n=1
■
```

6.4   The Normal Distribution

APPLICATION

Determination of Warranty Periods

A manufacturer of washing machines has collected data indicating that the time before one of its washers needs its first repair is normally distributed with mean 2 years and standard deviation 0.608 years. What length of time should the manufacturer set for the warranty period so that at least 95% of the machines will get through the warranty period without the need of a repair. See Example 5 for the answer.

✦ Continuous Probability Distributions

In the first section of this chapter we learned to distinguish discrete and continuous random variables. After that our focus turned to discrete variables that could be represented in a histogram. Continuous variables cannot be displayed in a histogram as we cannot have an infinite number of rectangles to represent the infinite number of values that the random variable can assume. We will need to have a different approach if we want to represent the probability distribution for a continuous random variable.

To understand this better, consider the spinner shown in Figure 6.60. The tip of the spinner is infinitely sharp so that the value the spinner lands on can be any value in the range $0 \leq X < 1$. We can assume that the spinner is on a flat surface

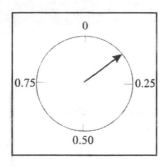

Figure 6.60

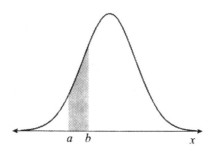

Figure 6.61

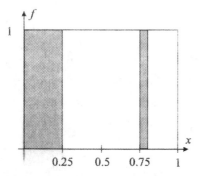

Figure 6.62

and is fair so that any point on the spinner has the same chance as any other point. We then ask, "What is the probability the spinner lands on $X = 0.25$?" If all points have the same probability and there are an infinite number of points, the probability of landing on a single point will be zero. That is, $P(X = 0.25) = 0$.

So, let us ask a different question: "What is the probability the spinner lands on a value between 0 and 0.25?" Well, this represents $^1/_4$ of the circle so we can say $P(0 < X < 0.25) = 0.25$. Additionally, since $P(X = 0) = 0$ and $P(X = 0.25) = 0$ as they are single points, we can also say

$$P(0 \leq X \leq 0.25) = 0.25$$

We can now conclude that for a continuous random variable we can't find the probability of a single value, but we can find the probability for a range of values. To represent this graphically we will use a probability density function or PDF. For our spinner, the PDF is shown in Figure 6.61. The region $0 \leq X \leq 0.25$ is shaded in and has an area of base $\times$ height $= 0.25 \times 1 = 0.25$, the same value we found earlier. Therefore the area under the PDF will correspond to the probability the X value lies in that range.

There are many kinds of PDF functions corresponding to different types of continuous random variables. Most do not have the simple shape of our spinner's PDF. In this section we will study the bell curve which is more properly called the normal distribution. This is arguably the most important probability distribution. One reason for its importance is that many natural phenomena obey a normal distribution or at least have a probability distribution that closely approximates a normal distribution. Examples of such random variables are: the weights of house cats, the heights of women in Spain, the waiting time in a line at a bank, the diameter of a ball bearing coming off an assembly line, the pounds of fertilizer in a 100-pound bag.

A normally distributed random variable has the property that it can take any value in the interval $(-\infty, \infty)$ and thus is a continuous random variable. We are familiar with viewing probabilities associated with a discrete random variable as areas in a histogram. In a similar fashion we can view probabilities associated with a continuous random variable that is normally distributed as areas under a normal curve. Figure 6.62 shows a typical normal curve. The probability $P(a \leq X \leq b)$ that the random variable X is between a and b is the area under the normal curve on the interval $[a, b]$. The area under the entire curve is 1. This is merely due to the fact that the probability that the random variable X takes some value is 1.

Another reason for the importance of the normal distribution, is the "central limit theorem of probability theory." This theorem can be stated approximately as follows. Suppose X is a random variable with an unknown probability distribution. Given a random sample of n observations with n large, the means

$$\bar{x} = \frac{x_1 + x_2 + \cdots + x_n}{n}$$

have a distribution that is approximately normal. An important consequence of this theorem is that, under various conditions, the normal probability distribution closely approximates many other probability distributions. For example, we shall see in the next section how to approximate a binomial distribution with a normal distribution.

◇ Standard Normal Distribution

We now consider the standard normal distribution. As we shall see later in this section, to find the probability for a normally distributed random variable we find the probability of a certain standard normally distributed random variable. We thus need to work first with the standard normal distribution. We state the following definition:

Technology Option

See Technology Note 1 on page 336 for details on finding the probability of a normal distribution using a graphing calculator or a spreadsheet. Note that the remaining Technology Options boxes will show the calculations on a graphing calculator following the directions given in the Technology Note.

Standard Normal Distribution

The random variable X has a **standard normal distribution** on the interval $(-\infty, \infty)$ if the probability $P(a \leq X \leq b)$ that X is between a and b is the area under the standard normal curve given by

$$y = \frac{1}{\sqrt{2\pi}} e^{-0.5x^2}$$

on the interval $[a, b]$, where $\pi \approx 3.14159$ and $e \approx 2.71828$.

REMARK: We will not use this formula in our calculations. Rather, we shall rely on tables or technology to find the area under this interesting and complex curve.

A graph of this curve is shown in Figure 6.63. The curve has a number of important characteristics.

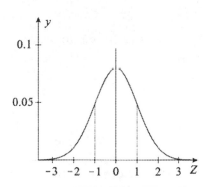

Figure 6.63

Characteristics of the Standard Normal Curve

The graph of the normal curve shown in Figure 6.63 has the following characteristics.

1. It is bell shaped.

2. It is symmetric about $x = 0$.

3. It lies above the x-axis.

4. It approaches but is never equal to 0 on both the positive and negative x-axis.

5. The curve "bends downward" on the interval $(-1, 1)$ and "bends upward" outside this interval.

6. The area under the entire curve is exactly 1.

From the symmetry, it appears that the mean is 0. In fact, it can be shown that for the standard normal distribution, $\mu = 0$. It can also be shown that the standard deviation $\sigma = 1$.

Since the normal distribution is so extraordinarily important, a table has been constructed that gives the area under the standard normal curve. Given any value b, the table gives the area under the curve to the left of b, shown as the shaded region in Figure 6.64. We designated this area as $\mathscr{A}(b)$. There is a table on page 390 that can be used to find this number.

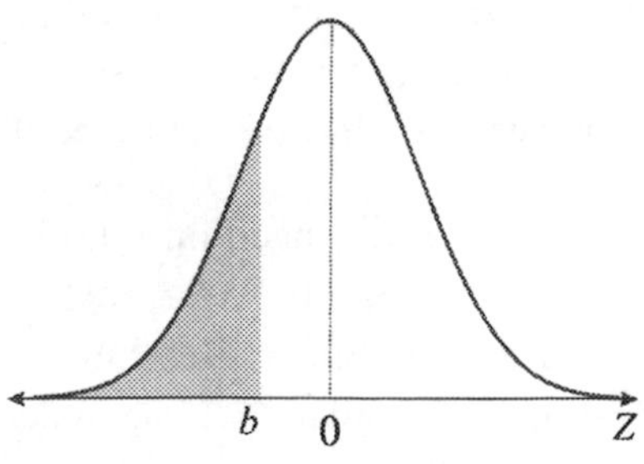

Figure 6.64

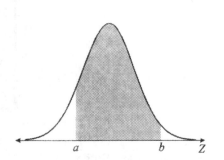

Figure 6.65

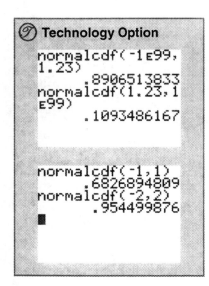

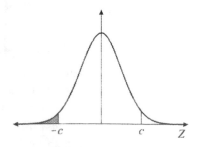

Figure 6.66

> **CONVENTION**
> The random variable associated with the standard normal distribution is designated by Z.

If we are asked for $P(Z \leq b)$, this is just $\mathscr{A}(b)$. Thus

$$P(Z \leq b) = \mathscr{A}(b)$$

where we can find $\mathscr{A}(b)$ in the table on page 390.

The probability $P(b \leq Z)$ is the area under the normal curve to the right of b, which is also the unshaded area under the curve in Figure 6.64. This area is also the entire area under the curve (which is 1) less the area under the curve to the left of b. Thus

$$P(b \leq Z) = 1 - \mathscr{A}(b)$$

Finally, $P(a \leq Z \leq b)$ is the area under the normal curve from a to b shown in Figure 6.65. This can be obtained as the area to the left of b, $\mathscr{A}(b)$, less the area to the left of a, $\mathscr{A}(a)$. Thus

$$P(a \leq Z \leq b) = \mathscr{A}(b) - \mathscr{A}(a)$$

where both the numbers $\mathscr{A}(b)$ and $\mathscr{A}(a)$ are obtained in the table on page 390.

EXAMPLE 1   Finding Probabilities for the Standard Normal Distribution
Let Z be a random variable with a standard normal distribution. Use the table on page 390 for the standard normal distribution to find

a. $P(Z \leq 1.23)$ **b.** $P(Z \geq 1.23)$ **c.** $P(-1 \leq Z \leq 1)$ **d.** $P(-2 \leq Z \leq 2)$

Solution   The table gives the following results:
a. $P(Z \leq 1.23) = \mathscr{A}(1.23) = 0.8907$
b. $P(Z \geq 1.23) = 1 - \mathscr{A}(1.23) = 1 - 0.8907 = 0.1093$
c. $P(-1 \leq Z \leq 1) = \mathscr{A}(1) - \mathscr{A}(-1) = 0.8413 - 0.1587 = 0.6826$
d. $P(-2 \leq Z \leq 2) = \mathscr{A}(2) - \mathscr{A}(-2) = 0.9772 - 0.0028 = 0.9544$ ◆

It is instructive to notice that the answer to (c) is approximately two-thirds and to (d) is approximately 0.95. That is, if the random variable is normally distributed with $\mu = 0$ and $\sigma = 1$, the probability that the random variable is within one standard deviation of the mean is about two-thirds, and the probability that the random variable is within two standard deviations of the mean is about 0.95.

EXAMPLE 2   Finding a Symmetric Interval About the Mean With Given Probability   Let Z be a random variable with a standard normal distribution. Using the table of the standard normal distribution, find the interval $[-c, c]$ so that the probability that the random variable is in this interval is 0.99. See Figure 6.66

Solution   Given the symmetry of the normal distribution, we need only find c such that the probability that the random variable is less than c is 0.995, that is, $P(Z \leq c) = 0.995$. The area of the "tail" is then 0.005. Symmetry then implies that the area of the "tail" to the left of $-c$ is also 0.005. Thus since the area under

```
invNorm(.005)
       -2.575829303
■
```

the entire curve is 1, the area under the curve from $-c$ to $+c$ is then $1 - 0.005 - 0.005 = 0.99$.

If we look up the value of c in the table for which $\mathscr{A}(c) = 0.995$, we obtain 2.575 after extrapolation. Thus $c = 2.575$, that is, $P(-2.575 \le Z \le 2.575) = 0.99$. This also says that there is a 99% chance that the random variable Z is within about 2.5 standard deviations of the mean. ◆

This gives a good indication of just how fast the standard normal curve is approaching the x-axis. The area under the curve on the interval $[-2.575, 2.575]$ is 0.99, so that the remaining area under all the rest of the curve is just 0.01.

✧ Normal distribution

We now consider the general normal distribution.

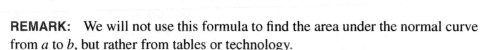

> **The Normal Probability Distribution**
> The random variable X has a normal probability distribution with mean μ and standard deviation σ on $(-\infty, \infty)$ if the probability $P(a < X \le b)$ that X is between a and b is the area under the normal curve given by
> $$y = \frac{1}{\sigma\sqrt{2\pi}}e^{-0.5[(x-\mu)/\sigma]^2}$$
> on the interval $[a, b]$.

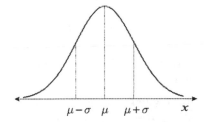

Figure 6.67

REMARK: We will not use this formula to find the area under the normal curve from a to b, but rather from tables or technology.

Figure 6.67 indicates a typical such curve. The curve has a number of important characteristics.

> **Characteristics of the Normal Curve**
> The graph of the normal curve in Figure 6.67 has the following characteristics.
>
> 1. It is bell shaped.
>
> 2. It is symmetric about $x = \mu$.
>
> 3. It lies above the x-axis.
>
> 4. It approaches but is never equal to 0 on both the positive and negative x-axis.
>
> 5. The curve "bends downward" on the interval $(\mu - \sigma, \mu + \sigma)$ and "bends upward" outside this interval.
>
> 6. The area under the entire curve is exactly 1.

Figure 6.68 indicates three such curves with the same standard deviation $\sigma = 1$ but different means. The curves with $\mu = -2$ and 2 are identical to the one with $\mu = 0$, except that they have been shifted over by an amount equal to μ.

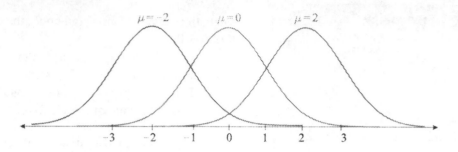

Figure 6.68

Figure 6.69 indicates three normal curves all with $\mu = 0$ and different standard deviations. Notice that the larger σ is the more spread out the curve is.

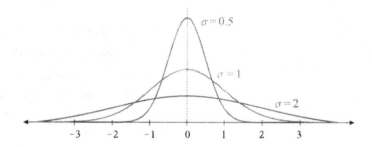

Figure 6.69

One might think that finding the area under a normal curve with mean μ and standard deviation σ would require a different table for different values of μ and σ. Fortunately this is not the case. We can readily find $P(a \leq X \leq b)$ in terms of certain probabilities of the standard normal distribution.

It turns out that if X is normally distributed with mean μ and standard deviation σ, and

$$Z = \frac{X - \mu}{\sigma}$$

then Z is normally distributed with mean $\mu = 0$ and $\sigma = 1$. The situation is summarized as follows.

Finding the Probability of a Normal Distribution
Let X be a random variable with mean μ and standard deviation σ. Then

$$P(a \leq X \leq b) = P\left(\frac{a - \mu}{\sigma} \leq Z \leq \frac{b - \mu}{\sigma}\right)$$

$$= \mathscr{A}\left(\frac{b - \mu}{\sigma}\right) - \mathscr{A}\left(\frac{a - \mu}{\sigma}\right)$$

EXAMPLE 3 **Finding the Probability for a Normal Distribution** Suppose that the number of pounds in 100-pound bags of fertilizer is normally distributed with a mean of 100 and a standard deviation of 4. What is the probability that the bag will contain less than 95 pounds?

Solution We are being asked for $P(X \leq 95)$ for a random variable that is normally distributed with mean $\mu = 100$ and standard deviation $\sigma = 4$. We form

Technology Option

```
normalcdf(-1E99,
95,100,4)
        .105649839
```

the Z variable as

$$Z = \frac{95 - \mu}{\sigma} = \frac{95 - 100}{4} = -1.25$$

Then

$$P(X \leq 95) = P(Z \leq -1.25) = 0.1056$$

from the table. Thus we expect about 10.56% of the bags to have less than 95 pounds of fertilizer in them. ✦

EXAMPLE 4 **Quality Control Using the Normal Distribution** The diameters of ball bearings produced at a plant are normally distributed with a mean of 1 cm and standard deviation of 0.004 cm. A ball bearing is acceptable if the diameter lies in the interval $[0.99, 1.01]$. What percentage of ball bearings will be rejected?

Solution We will first find the probability that one will be accepted. If X is the random variable that denotes the diameters of the ball bearings, then this probability is $P(0.99 \leq X \leq 1.01)$. Then

Technology Option

```
normalcdf(.99,1.
01,1,.004)
        .9875806403
1-Ans
        .0124193597
```

$$
\begin{aligned}
P(0.99 \leq X \leq 1.01) &= P\left(\frac{a - \mu}{\sigma} \leq Z \leq \frac{b - \mu}{\sigma}\right) \\
&= \mathscr{A}\left(\frac{b - \mu}{\sigma}\right) - \mathscr{A}\left(\frac{a - \mu}{\sigma}\right) \\
&= \mathscr{A}\left(\frac{1.01 - 1.00}{0.004}\right) - \mathscr{A}\left(\frac{0.99 - 1.00}{0.004}\right) \\
&= \mathscr{A}(2.5) - \mathscr{A}(-2.5) \\
&= 0.9938 - 0.0062 = 0.9876
\end{aligned}
$$

These numbers come from the standard normal table. To find the probability that one will be rejected is $1 - 0.9876 = 0.0124$. So about 1.24% of these ball bearings will be rejected. ✦

EXAMPLE 5 **Determining a Warranty Period** A manufacturer of washing machines has collected data indicating that the time before one of its washers needs its first repair is normally distributed with mean 2 years and standard deviation 0.608 years. What length of time should the manufacturer set for the warranty period so that at least 95% of the machines will get through the warranty period without need of a repair?

Solution If X denotes the life of a washer and L denotes the length of the warranty period, we are asking that the probability that $X \leq L$ should be 0.95; that is, $P(X \leq L) = 0.95$. Since X is normally distributed with mean $\mu = 2$ and standard deviation $\sigma = 0.608$, using the Z statistic, this is the same as

Technology Option

```
invNorm(.95,2,.6
08)
        3.000071005
```

$$P\left(Z \leq \frac{L - \mu}{\sigma}\right)$$

We wish this probability to be 0.95. Using the normal table, we see that this will occur if

$$\frac{L - \mu}{\sigma} = 1.645$$

Solving for L, we obtain

$$L = 1.645\sigma + \mu = 1.645(0.608) + 2 \approx 3$$

The manufacturer should have a 3-year warranty period since 95% of the washers will go through a 3-year period without any need for repairs.　◆

✦ Technology Corner

⑨ **Technology Note 1**　**Using Technology for Normal Probability Calculations**

The TI-83/84 family of calculators have three functions that are used for normal probability calculations. Access the Distributions menu by pressing 2ND and then VARS as shown in Screen 1. The 1:normalpdf(command will find the normal probability density function for a given value of Z. This is shown in Screen 2. It is important to realize that this does not give the probability - the probability is the area under this curve. The 2:normalcdf(command finds area under the normal probability density function. The first value entered is the left endpoint and the second value entered is the right endpoint. So to find the probability $P(-1 \leq Z \leq 1)$, enter normalcdf(-1,1) and press ENTER as shown in Screen 3.

Screen 1

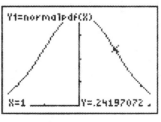
Screen 2
[-2,2]x[0,.4]

Screen 3

While the TI-83/84 calculators do not have an $\pm\infty$ button, the value $\pm 1 \times 10^{99}$ will function effectively as $\pm\infty$. To find $P(Z \leq 1.5)$, the left endpoint is -1×10^{99}. This is entered as (-)1 2ND , 99 as the EE above the comma button acts as the 10^. See Screen 4 and note that on the screen the EE appears as E. If the TI-83/84 functions are used, it will not be necessary to convert from X to Z when the normal distribution is not standard. Entering the mean and standard deviation after the left and right endpoints will result in finding the probability using a distribution with the given mean and standard deviation. If a normal probability distribution has a mean of 100 and a standard deviation of 15, the probability that $X \geq 80$ is simply normalcdf(80, 1E99, 100, 15) as shown in Screen 5.

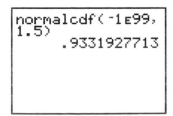
Screen 4

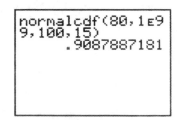
Screen 5

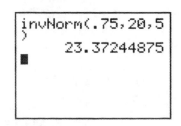
Screen 6

Finally, when the probability (area to the left) is known, the invNorm(function will find the corresponding Z or X value. The function requires the area to the left of the unknown X or Z value along with the mean and standard deviation if it is not a standard normal probability distribution. To find c where

$P(X \leq c) = 0.75$ on a normal probability distribution with a mean of 20 and standard deviation of 5, enter `invNorm(.75,20,5)` to find $c = 23.3724$ as shown in Screen 6. These functions are summarized in the table below. The distribution has a mean μ and standard deviation σ.

`normalpdf(x, μ, σ)`	The value of the normal probability density function at x
`normalcdf(left, right, μ, σ)`	The probability that a value of x is between *left* and *right*
`invNorm(p, μ, σ)`	Finds the value of x that has area p to the left of that x.

A spreadsheet such as Microsoft Excel can find the area under the normal curve. The function NORMDIST(x, mean, standard deviation, TRUE) finds the area to the left of x for a normal probability distribution with the given mean and standard deviation. The last value is set to TRUE or just the value (not the area to the left) of the normal probability density function is returned. See Worksheets 1 and 2 for examples that correspond to Screens 3 - 6. Note that Worksheet 1 shows the formulas and Worksheet 2 shows the values of the formulas.

	A
1	=NORMDIST(1,0,1,TRUE)-NORMDIST(-1,0,1,TRUE)
2	=NORMDIST(1.5,0,1,TRUE)
3	=1-NORMDIST(80,100,15,TRUE)
4	=NORMINV(0.75,20,5)

	A
1	0.682689492
2	0.933192799
3	0.90878878
4	23.37244875

Worksheet 1   Worksheet 2

Self-Help Exercises 6.4

1. Let X be a normally distributed random variable with mean $\mu = 4$ and standard deviation $\sigma = 2$. Find
   a. $P(X \leq 3)$ **b.** $P(X \geq 3)$ **c.** $P(1 \leq X \leq 3)$

2. Let Z be a random variable with a standard normal distribution. Find the value Z_0, such that $P(Z \geq Z_0) = 0.10$.

3. Suppose the daily production X, in tons, of a steel manufacturer is normally distributed with $\mu = 100$ tons and $\sigma = 10$ tons. Management decides to offer the employees a bonus whenever the daily production level is in the top 10% of the daily production distribution. What is the level of production that will produce the bonus?

6.4 Exercises

In Exercises 1 through 12, find the indicated probabilities given that Z is a random variable with a standard normal distribution.

1. $P(Z \leq 0.5)$

2. $P(Z \leq 0.75)$

3. $P(Z \leq -0.3)$

4. $P(Z \leq -1.5)$

5. $P(Z \geq 1.5)$

6. $P(Z \geq 0.6)$

7. $P(Z \geq -0.8)$

8. $P(Z \geq -1.42)$

9. $P(1.0 \leq Z \leq 1.5)$

10. $P(0 \leq Z \leq 1.5)$

11. $P(-1.0 \leq Z \leq -0.5)$

12. $P(-0.5 \leq Z \leq 1.0)$

In Exercises 13 through 20, find the indicated probabilities assuming that x is a random variable with a normal distribution with the given mean and standard deviation.

13. $P(x \leq 50), \mu = 38, \sigma = 8$

14. $P(x \leq 200), \mu = 100, \sigma = 50$

15. $P(x \geq 0.01), \mu = 0.006, \sigma = 0.002$

16. $P(x \geq -10), \mu = 20, \sigma = 30$

17. $P(100 \leq x \leq 150), \mu = 20, \sigma = 100$

18. $P(10 \leq x \leq 20), \mu = 5, \sigma = 10$

19. $P(0.01 \leq x \leq 0.02), \mu = 0.005, \sigma = 0.01$

20. $P(-3 \leq x \leq 10), \mu = 4, \sigma = 10$

21. Find the area under the standard normal curve on the interval $[-2, 2]$.

22. Find the area under the standard normal curve on the interval $[-3, 3]$.

Applications

23. Quality Control A machine produces ball bearings with diameters normally distributed. The mean diameter is 3.50 cm and the standard deviation is 0.02 cm. Quality requirements demand a ball bearing to be rejected if the diameter is more than 0.05 cm different from the mean. What percentage of bearings will be rejected?

24. Quality Control The length, in feet, of a certain structural steel beam is normally distributed with a mean of 10 feet and a standard deviation of 1 inch. Quality requirements demand a beam to be rejected if the length is more than 2 inches different from the mean. What percentage of beams will be rejected?

25. Revenue The weekly revenue, in thousands of dollars, of a certain retail store is normally distributed with a mean of 1000 and a standard deviation of 600. What percentage of weeks will revenue
a. exceed 1600
b. be less than 600
c. be between 800 and 1200?

26. Sales The number of a particular item sold in a week is normally distributed with a mean of 1000 and a standard deviation of 400. What percentage of weeks will sales
a. exceed 1500
b. be less than 600
c. be between 800 and 1200?

27. Manufacturing The number of ounces of detergent in an advertised one-pound box is normally distributed with a mean of 16.1 ounces and a standard deviation of 0.3. What percentage of boxes have at least 1 pound of detergent in them?

28. Manufacturing A company regularly orders 2000 copies of a newsletter from a printer. The number of copies delivered is normally distributed with a mean of 2000 and a standard deviation of 100. The delivery is not acceptable if the number delivered is less than 90% of the original order. What percentage of deliveries is not acceptable?

29. Manufacturing The amount of tape on a roll is normally distributed with a mean of 30 feet and a standard deviation of 2 feet. What percentage of rolls will have less than 27 feet?

30. Manufacturing The amount of soda in a 16-ounce can is normally distributed with a mean of 16 ounces and a standard deviation of 0.50 ounce. What percentage of these cans will have less than 15 ounces?

31. Medicine The time, in hours, to perform a certain operation is normally distributed with a mean of 3 hours and a standard deviation of 1 hour. What percentage of times will this operation be
a. less than 1
b. more than 3 hours
c. between 1 and 3 hours?

32. Biology The weight, in pounds, of a certain type of adult squirrel is normally distributed with a mean of 3 pounds and a standard deviation of 0.50 pound. What percentage of these squirrels have weight
a. less than 2 pounds
b. greater than 4 pounds
c. between 2 and 4 pounds?

33. Learning Time The learning time for a particular task on an assembly line is normally distributed with a mean of 5 hours and a standard deviation of 2 hours. If an employee is given an 8-hour shift in which to learn the task, what is the probability that the task will be learned before the shift ends?

34. Testing A corporation notes that scores on an intelligence test for newly hired employees is normally distributed with mean 100 and standard deviation 20. What percentage of new employees should score
a. above 110
b. below 80
c. between 95 and 105.

Solutions to Self-Help Exercises 6.4

1. If X is a normally distributed random variable with mean $\mu = 4$ and standard deviation $\sigma = 2$, then if Z is the random variable for the standard normal distribution,

   a. $P(X \le 3) = P\left(Z \le \dfrac{3-\mu}{\sigma}\right) = P\left(Z \le \dfrac{3-4}{2}\right)$

   $\qquad\qquad\;\; = \mathscr{A}(-0.5) = 0.3085$

   b. $P(X \ge 3) = 1 - P(X \le 3) = 1 - 0.3085 = 0.6915$

   c. $P(1 \le X \le 3) = \mathscr{A}\left(\dfrac{3-4}{2}\right) - \mathscr{A}\left(\dfrac{1-4}{2}\right) 0.3085 - 0.0668 = 0.2417$

2. Let Z be a random variable with standard normal distribution. The value Z_0, such that $P(Z \ge Z_0) = 0.10$, is given by the value Z_0 such that $\mathscr{A}(Z_0) = 0.90$. Looking through the normal table for this Z_0, we find that $Z_0 = 1.28$.

3. With the daily production, X, in tons of a steel manufacturer normally distributed with $\mu = 100$ tons and $\sigma = 10$ tons, the Z statistic is given by

$$Z = \frac{X - \mu}{\sigma}$$

We know from the previous example that $\mathscr{A}(1.28) = 0.90$. Thus we have

$$X = \mu + Z\sigma = 100 + 1.28(10) = 112.8$$

Thus when the daily production is 112.8 tons, 90% of the time the daily production is less than this number.

6.5 Normal Approximation to the Binomial Distribution

APPLICATION
Lot Acceptance Sampling

An electronics manufacturer randomly selects 200 stamped circuits from the production line for one day where a 5% rate of defectives is acceptable. Determine approximately the probability that 18 or more defectives are discovered in this sample. Is this alarming? The answer is given in Example 4.

✧ Normal Approximation to the Binomial Distribution

Finding probabilities that arise using the binomial distribution can be extremely tedious. In this section we will see how, under certain conditions, the normal distribution can be used as an effective approximation to the binomial distribution.

According to the National Cancer Institute, the 5-year survival rate for cancer of the cervix diagnosed in a recent period was approximately 66%. Suppose at a particular hospital, 15 patients were diagnosed for cancer of the cervix. What is the probability that at least 10 of these patients will survive for 5 years using the above probability of survival?

If success for a patient diagnosed as having cervical cancer is survival for 5 years, then the situation above can be described as a repeated Bernoulli trial with $n = 15$, $p = 0.66$, and $q = 0.34$. The answer can readily be written down in terms of the binomial distribution as

$$C(15, 10)(.66)^{10}(.34)^5 + C(15, 11)(.66)^{11}(.34)^4 + \cdots$$
$$+ C(15, 15)(.66)^{15}(.34)^0$$

Unfortunately, this will be a lengthy calculation. Figure 6.70 shows a histogram of the probability of the number of successes for 15 repeated Bernoulli trials with the probability of success equal to 0.66.

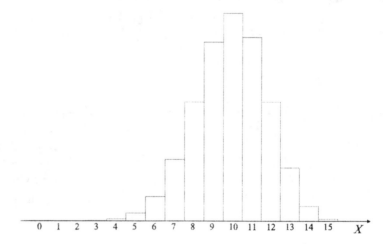

Figure 6.70

As we have noted in a previous section, the answer to the question posed above is the area of the shaded rectangles shown in the histogram of Figure 6.70. In this section we will see that this area is very close to a certain area under a certain normal curve, which will be easy to find using tables or technology. We will now see how to do this.

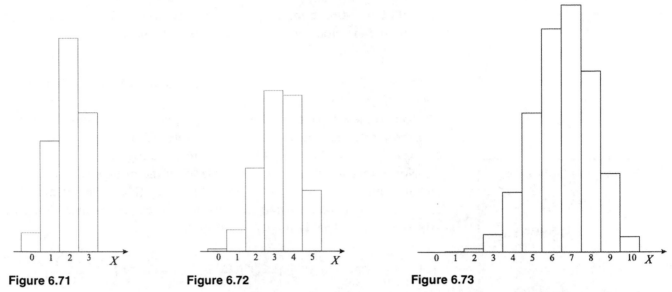

Figure 6.71   **Figure 6.72**   **Figure 6.73**

Figure 6.71, Figure 6.72, and Figure 6.73 show histograms of the binomial distributions for $p = 0.66$ and $n = 3$, 5, and 10, respectively. Notice how as n increases, the histograms are more bell shaped and appear more similar to a normal curve. This is indeed the case. Figure 6.74 shows the binomial distribution of Figure 6.70 overlaid with the normal distribution with the same mean $\mu = np = 15(0.66) = 9.9$ and the same standard deviation $\sigma = \sqrt{npq} = \sqrt{15(0.66)(0.34)} \approx 1.835$ as the binomial distribution shown.

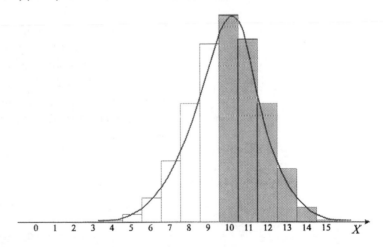

Figure 6.74

Notice how good an approximation the normal curve is to the histogram for the binomial distribution. This is true under a wide set of conditions, as the following theorem indicates.

Normal Approximation to the Binomial Distribution

In a sequence of n repeated (independent) Bernoulli trials with probability of success equal to p and probability of failure equal to q, let the random variable X denote the number of successes. Then the histogram for the probability distribution of X is approximated by the normal curve with mean $\mu = np$ and standard deviation $\sigma = \sqrt{npq}$. This is a particularly close approximation when $np \geq 5$ and $nq \geq 5$.

EXAMPLE 1 Using the Normal Approximation Using the normal approximation, find the probability that at least 10 of the patients mentioned above will survive for 5 years.

Solution First notice that $np = 9.9 \geq 5$ and $nq = 5.1 \geq 5$. Thus the normal approximation should be excellent.

To find the area of the shaded rectangles, we use the normal approximation with the normal curve with mean $\mu = np = 15(0.66) = 9.9$ and standard deviation $\sigma = \sqrt{npq} = \sqrt{15(0.66)(0.34)} \approx 1.835$. Refer to Figure 6.74.

Notice that since we want to include all of the histogram to the right of 10 and including 10, we must include the entire rectangle corresponding to 10. Thus to use the approximating normal curve we must take the area to the right of $10 - 0.50 = 9.5$. That is, use the Z substitution,

$$P(X \geq 9.5) = 1 - \mathscr{A}\left(\frac{9.5 - \mu}{\sigma}\right) = 1 - \mathscr{A}\left(\frac{9.5 - 9.9}{1.835}\right)$$
$$= 1 - \mathscr{A}(-0.22) = 1 - 0.4129$$
$$= 0.5871$$

Technology Option

```
normalcdf(9.5,15
.5,9.9,√(15*.66*
.34))
          .5851590482
■
```

using the normal tables. This compares with the actual value of 0.5968. ◆

EXAMPLE 2 Using the Normal Approximation A coin has been flipped 900 times and heads has been observed 496 times. Is there some justification in claiming that this is an unfair coin?

Solution First notice that $np = nq = 450 \geq 5$ so the normal approximation can be used. If we assume the coin is fair, then we have 900 repeated Bernoulli trials with $p = 0.5 = q$. The mean is $\mu = np = 450$. We will calculate the probability that the number of heads of a fair coin could deviate by more than 45 from the mean. This is one less the probability that it could deviate by as much as 46 from the mean. If X is the random variable that denotes the number of heads, then this latter probability is

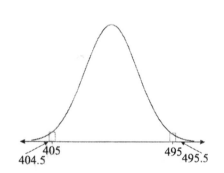

Figure 6.75

$$P(405 \leq X \leq 495) = C(900,405)(0.5)^{405}(0.5)^{495} + C(900,406)(0.5)^{406}(0.5)^{494}$$
$$+ \cdots + C(900,495)(0.5)^{495}(0.5)^{405}$$

The need for approximating this by the area under a normal curve is apparent. We use the normal curve with $\mu = 450$ and $\sigma = \sqrt{npq} = \sqrt{900(0.5)(0.5)} = 15$ and let the random variable Y denote the continuous random value associated with this. From Figure 6.75 we see that we must include the rectangles corresponding to 405 and 495. Then $P(405 \leq X \leq 495)$ is approximately the area under this normal curve from $405 - 0.50 = 404.5$ to $495 + 0.50 = 495.5$ and is denoted by $P(404.5 \leq Y \leq 495.5)$. Then

$$P(404.5 \leq Y \leq 495.5) = \mathscr{A}\left(\frac{495.5 - 450}{15}\right) - \mathscr{A}\left(\frac{404.5 - 450}{15}\right)$$
$$= \mathscr{A}(3.03) - \mathscr{A}(-3.03)$$
$$\approx 0.9987 - 0.0013 = 0.9974$$

Technology Option

```
normalcdf(404.5,
495.5,450,√(900*
.5*.5)
          .997581179
■
```

using the tables. One less this is 0.0026 and is the probability that the number of heads can deviate by more than 45 from the mean when a fair coin is flipped 900 times. Since this is so low, we can conclude that the coin is likely not a fair coin. ✦

We saw in the last example that a fair coin has a very small probability of deviating very far from the mean. We now examine how likely it is for the number of heads to be very close to the mean.

EXAMPLE 3   Using the Normal Approximation   For the experiment in the previous example, find the probability that the number of heads varies at most by 1 from the mean.

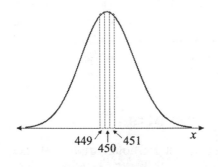

Figure 6.76

Solution   With X denoting the number of heads in 900 flips of the fair coin, the mean is 450, and we are seeking the probability $P(449 \leq X \leq 451)$, which is the area under the three rectangles shown in Figure 6.76. If Y is the same as in the previous example, we see from Figure 6.76 that we approximate this by $P(448.5 \leq Y \leq 451.5)$, the area under the approximating normal curve from 448.5 to 451.5. We then obtain

$$P(448.5 \leq Y \leq 451.5) = \mathscr{A}\left(\frac{451.5 - 450}{15}\right) - \mathscr{A}\left(\frac{448.5 - 450}{15}\right)$$
$$= \mathscr{A}(0.10) - \mathscr{A}(-0.10)$$
$$\approx 0.5398 - 0.4602 = 0.0796$$

using the table on page 390. So there is about an 8% chance of the number of heads being within 1 of the mean. Thus we see that just as there is a small probability of the number of heads deviating far from the mean, so too is the probability that the number of heads will be very close to the mean. ✦

Many electronic items can be mass produced cheaply because the solid-state circuitry used can be stamped by a machine. Controlling the quality of the items is a serious problem and is often handled by using lot acceptance sampling. In this method a sample is taken from a large lot of items and inspected. The entire lot will be accepted or rejected on the basis of the number of defective items in the sample.

EXAMPLE 4   Lot Acceptance Sampling   An electronics manufacturer randomly selects 200 stamped circuits from the production line for one day where a 5% rate of defectives is acceptable. Determine approximately the probability that 18 or more defectives are discovered in this sample. Should this discovery be cause for concern?

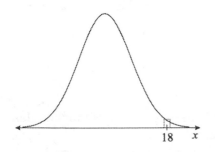

Figure 6.77

Solution   First, suppose that the defective rate is 5%. Then the random variable that gives the number of defective circuits is binomially distributed with $n = 200$, $p = 0.05$, and $q = 0.95$. Since $np = 10 \geq 5$ and $nq = 190 \geq 5$, we expect the normal approximation with mean $\mu = np = 10$ and standard deviation $\sigma = \sqrt{npq} = \sqrt{200(0.05)(0.95)} \approx 3.1$ to be a good approximation for the binomial distribution.

To find the approximating area corresponding to $X \leq 18$, refer to Figure 6.77. Since we must include the rectangle that corresponds to 18, we take the area under the approximating curve to start at $18 - 0.50 = 17.5$. Then

$$
\begin{aligned}
P(X \geq 17.5) &= 1 - \mathscr{A}\left(\frac{17.5 - 10}{3.1}\right) \\
&\approx 1 - 0.9922 = 0.0078
\end{aligned}
$$

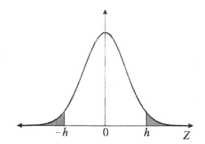

Technology Option

```
normalcdf(17.5,2
00.5,10,√(200*.0
5*.95))
        .0074805091
■
```

using tables. Thus the approximate probability that at least 18 defective circuits are in the sample of 200 is 0.0078 *if in fact the true defective rate is 5%*. Since the probability of 0.0075 is extremely small, the manufacturer should be concerned that the defective rate of the sample is, in fact, much higher than 5%.   ◆

✧ Enrichment: The Law of Large Numbers

Assume an experiment with n repeated independent Bernoulli trials with the probability of success p equal to the probability of failure q. Then $p = q = 0.5$. Let X denote the random variable given by the number of successes. We seek an estimate of the probability that X differs from the mean $\mu = np = 0.5n$ by at most h standard deviations.

Since the standard deviation is $\sigma = \sqrt{npq} = 0.5\sqrt{n}$, we are seeking a good estimate of

$$
P(|X - 0.5n| \leq 0.5h\sqrt{n}) = P(|X - \mu| \leq h\sigma) = P\left(-h \leq \frac{X - \mu}{\sigma} \leq h\right)
$$

If Y is the random variable given by the normal distribution with mean $\mu = 0.5n$ and standard deviation $\sigma = 0.5\sqrt{n}$, then by the normal approximation, this probability is approximated by $P\left(-h \leq \dfrac{Y - \mu}{\sigma} \leq h\right)$. But using the Z statistic for the standard normal distribution, this is $P(-h \leq Z \leq h)$. From Figure 6.78 we note that the area under the entire standard normal curve is 1 and that by symmetry the area under each "tail" is the same. Thus

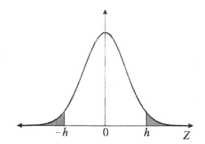

Figure 6.78

$$
P(-h \leq Z \leq h) = 1 - 2P(Z \leq -h)
$$

Thus we have established the important estimate that

$$
P\left(|X - 0.5n| \leq 0.5h\sqrt{n}\right) \approx 1 - 2P(Z \leq -h) = 1 - 2\mathscr{A}(-h) \qquad (1)
$$

Now if we are given a specific value of h, we can look up $P(Z \leq -h) = \mathscr{A}(-h)$ in the normal table. For example, if $h = 2$, then looking in this table, we have

$$
P(-2 \leq Z \leq 2) = 1 - 2P(Z \leq -2) = 1 - 2(0.0228) = 0.9544
$$

Thus we can say that there is about a 95% chance that the number of successes will be within $2\sigma = \sqrt{n}$ of $\mu = 0.5n$.

EXAMPLE 5 **The Law of Large Numbers** In the experiment of flipping a fair coin let H be the event that a head occurs. Estimate how large n must be so that there is a probability of 0.95 that the relative frequency of the number of heads to n is within 0.01 of 0.50. Within 0.001.

Solution Let $f(H)$ be the frequency that heads occurs. If we let the random variable be $X = f(H)$, then we can use the estimate given by equation (1). We already noticed above that if $h = 2$, then $1 - 2\mathscr{A}(-h) \approx 0.95$. Thus with $h = 2$ equation (1) becomes

$$P\left(|X - 0.5n| \le \sqrt{n}\right) \approx 0.95$$

Setting $X = f(H)$ and dividing by n, this can be rewritten as

$$P\left(\left|\frac{f(H)}{n} - \frac{1}{2}\right|\right) \approx 0.95 \tag{2}$$

If we want the relative frequency $f(H)/n$ to be within ε of $\frac{1}{2}$, we want

$$\left|\frac{f(H)}{n} - \frac{1}{2}\right| \le \varepsilon$$

Looking at equation (2), we then want

$$\varepsilon = \frac{1}{\sqrt{n}} \qquad \text{or} \qquad n = \frac{1}{\varepsilon^2} \tag{3}$$

Now using equation (3) if $\varepsilon = 0.01$, then $n = 10,000$. If $\varepsilon = 0.001$, then $n = 1,000,000$. This means, for example, that if $n = 10,000$, the relative frequency $f(H)/n$ will be within the interval $(0.49, 0.51)$ with a probability of 0.95. More precisely, this means that 95% of the time that a fair coin is flipped 10,000 times, the relative frequency will be within the interval $(0.49, 0.51)$. The answer means that 95% of the time that a fair coin is flipped 1,000,000 times, the relative frequency will be within the interval $(0.499, 0.501)$. ✦

Self-Help Exercises 6.5

1. About 3% of the flashlights produced by a manufacturer are defective. Using the normal curve approximation, find the probability that in a shipment of 1000 to a distributor, at least 35 will be defective.

2. (Optional) Assume an experiment with n repeated independent Bernoulli trials with the probability of success equal to p and the probability of failure equal to $q = 1 - p$. Let X denote the random variable given by the number of successes. Find the value of h so that the probability is about 0.99 that X differs from the mean $\mu = np$ by at most $h\sigma = h\sqrt{npq}$.

6.5 Exercises

1. A fair coin has been tossed 1600 times. Use the normal approximation to find the probability that

   a. the number of heads is at least 825
   b. the number of heads is between 775 and 825.

2. A fair die has been tossed 180 times. Use the normal approximation to find the probability that

   a. the number 1 appears at most 35 times
   b. the number 3 appears between 25 and 35 times.

3. A baseball player has a batting average of .300. What is the probability that he will have a batting average of at least .400 over the next 100 official times at bat?

4. A basketball player hits 80% of her free throws.

What is the probability that she will hit 90% of her next 50 free throws?

Applications

5. **Bladder Cancer** According to the National Cancer Institute, the 5-year survival rate for cancer of the bladder diagnosed in a recent period was 78%. Among 1000 such diagnosed cases, find the probability that

   a. 750 or more survived 5 years,

   b. between 750 and 500 survived 5 years.

6. **Thyroid Cancer** Repeat the previous exercise for cancer of the thyroid with a 5-year survival rate of 93%.

7. **Heart Disease** Approximately 43% of deaths in this country are attributed to heart disease. Among 1000 randomly chosen deaths, what is the probability that heart disease was the cause in at least 300 instances? Between 400 and 450?

8. **Accidental Deaths** About 4.5% of deaths in this country are attributed to accidents. Among 1000 randomly chosen deaths, what is the probability that an accident was the cause in at most 50 instances? Between 30 and 60?

9. **Use of Marihuana** It was reported that 37% of a certain group of college students reported using marihuana during the previous year. What is the probability that, among 300 randomly chosen college students that

   a. at least 120 used marijuana during the previous year?

   b. between 100 and 120?

10. **Use of Cocaine** It was reported that 8% of a certain group of adults reported using cocaine during the last year. What is the probability that among 300 randomly chosen of these people

    a. at least 30 used cocaine during the previous year?

    b. between 20 and 40?

11. **Immigration** In a recent year about 41% of legal immigrants admitted to this country were Asian. Among 100 randomly selected of these immigrants to this country, what is the probability that

    a. at least 30 were Asian?

    b. between 30 and 50 were Asian?

12. **Arrests** Approximately 82% of those arrested each year in this country are males. Given 100 randomly chosen arrests, what is the probability that

    a. at least 10 were female?

    b. between 10 and 20 were female?

13. **Heart Disease** In Exercise 7 find the probability that the number of deaths due to heart disease differs from the mean by at most 2.5 standard deviations.

14. **Accidental Deaths** In Exercise 8 find the probability that the number of deaths due to accidents differs from the mean by at most 3 standard deviations.

15. **Quality Control** About 3% of a certain product of a manufacturer has been found to be defective. A new system of quality control has been introduced with 18 defective products found in the first 1000 after the new system went into effect. Is the new system effective? *Hint*: Find the probability of at most 18 defectives under the old system.

16. **Safety** In a certain plant about 5% of the workers were suffering an accident each year. New safety procedures were instituted that resulted in 30 accidents among 1000 workers during the next year. Are the safety procedures working?

17. **Advertising** A company received a 15% response to its mail advertisements. After changing to a new advertisement, it noticed a 20% response among the next 1000 mailings. Is the new advertisement effective?

18. **Drug Effectiveness** For a certain disease, 20% of individuals with the disease will recover without any treatment. A new experiment drug is administered to 40 individuals with the disease and 16 recover. Is this drug promising? *Hint*: Find the probability that at least 16 patients would recover without the drug.

19. **The Law of Large Numbers** In the experiment of flipping a fair coin, let H be the event that a head occurs. Estimate how large n must be so that there is a probability of 0.50 that the relative frequency $f(H)/n$ is within 0.01 of 0.50. Within 0.001.

20. **The Law of Large Numbers** In the experiment of flipping a fair coin, let H be the event that a head occurs. Estimate how large n must be so that there is a probability of 0.50 that the relative frequency $f(H)/n$ is within 0.0001 of 0.50. Within 0.00001.

21. The Law of Large Numbers In the experiment of flipping a fair coin, let H be the event that a head occurs. Estimate how large n must be so that there is a probability of 0.90 that the relative frequency $f(H)/n$ is within 0.01 of 0.50. Within 0.001.

22. The Law of Large Numbers In the experiment of flipping a unfair coin, let H be the event that a head occurs and $p = p(H) = 0.60$. Estimate how large n must be so that there is a probability of 0.95 that the relative frequency $f(H)/n$ is within 0.01 of $p = 0.60$. Within 0.001.

Solutions to Self-Help Exercises 6.5

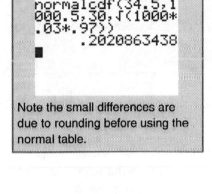

Technology Option

normalcdf(34.5,1
000.5,30,√(1000*
.03*.97))
               .2020863438

Note the small differences are due to rounding before using the normal table.

1. The situation is a repeated Bernoulli trial with $n = 1000$ and $p = 0.03$. If X denotes the number of defective flashlights, then we are seeking $P(X \geq 35)$. If Y denotes the random variable associated with the normal distribution with mean $\mu = np = 1000(0.03) = 30$ and standard deviation $\sigma = \sqrt{npq} = \sqrt{1000(0.03)(0.97)} \approx 5.3944$, then

$$
\begin{aligned}
P(X \geq 35) &\approx P(Y \geq 34.5) = P\left(Z \geq \frac{34.5 - 30}{5.3944}\right) \\
&= P(Z \geq 0.83) = 1 - \mathscr{A}(0.83) \\
&= 1 - 0.7967 = 0.2033
\end{aligned}
$$

Thus there is about a 20% chance that at least 35 flashlights will be defective in a shipment of 1000.

2. Equation (1) says that

$$P(|X - np| \leq h\sqrt{npq}) \approx 1 - 2P(Z \leq -h) = 1 - 2\mathscr{A}(-h)$$

Thus we are seeking the value of h for which

$$0.99 = 1 - 2\mathscr{A}(-h)$$

This can be written as

$$\mathscr{A}(-h) = 0.005$$

Looking for an h in the normal table for which this is true, we find that $h = 2.575$. Thus we can say that X differs from the mean $\mu = np$ by $2.575\sigma = 2.575\sqrt{npq}$ with probability of 0.99.

Technology Option

invNorm(.005)
        -2.575829303

Review

✧ Summary Outline

- A **random variable** is a rule that assigns precisely one real number to each outcome of an experiment.

- A random variable is finite discrete if it assumes only a finite number of values. A random variable is infinite discrete if it takes on an infinite number of values that can be listed in a sequence, so that, there is a first one, a second one, a third one, and so on. A random variable is said to be continuous if it can take any of the infinite number of values in some interval of real numbers.

- Suppose the random variable X can take the values $x_1, \ldots, x_n$. The probability distribution of the random variable X is a listing of all the probabilities associated with all possible values of the random variable, that is, $p_1, \ldots, p_n$, where $p_1 = P(x_1), \ldots p_n = P(x_n)$.

- Given a sequence of n Bernoulli trials with the probability of success p and the probability of failure q, the binomial distribution is given by

$$P(X = k) = C(n, k) p^k q^{n-k}$$

- The average or mean of the n numbers $x_1, x_2, \ldots, x_n$, denoted by the Greek letter μ, is given by

$$\mu = \frac{x_1 + x_2 + \cdots + x_n}{n}$$

- If there is only a sample of the data, the mean that is computed is the sample mean and it is denoted by $\bar{x}$.

- Let X denote the random variable that takes on the values $x_1, x_2, \ldots, x_n$ and let the associated probabilities be $p_1, p_2, \ldots, p_n$, then the expected value or mean of the random variable X, denoted by $E(X)$ or by μ, is

$$E(X) = x_1 p_1 + x_2 p_2 + \cdots + x_n p_n$$

- The expected value of the random variable X associated with a binomial distribution having n trials and probability of success p in a single trial is $E(X) = np$.

- The median of a set of numerical data is the middle number when the numbers are arranged in order of size and there is an odd number of entries in the set. In the case that the number of entries in the set is even, the median is the mean of the two middle numbers.

- The mode of a set of numbers is the number that occurs more frequently than the others. If the frequency of occurrence of two numbers is the same and also greater than the frequency of occurrence of all the other numbers, then we say the set is bimodal and has two modes. If no one or two numbers occur more frequently than the others, we say that the set has no mode.

- Let X denote the random variable that takes on the values $x_1, x_2, \ldots, x_n$, and let the associated probabilities be $p_1, p_2, \ldots, p_n$. Then if $\mu = E(X)$, the variance of the random variable X, denoted by $\mathrm{Var}(X)$, is

$$\mathrm{Var}(X) = (x_1 - \mu)^2 p_1 + (x_2 - \mu)^2 p_2 + \cdots + (x_n - \mu)^2 p_n$$

- The standard deviation, denoted by $\sigma(X)$ is

$$\sigma(X) = \sqrt{\text{Var}(X)}$$

- An alternate form of the variance is given by

$$\text{Var}(X) = (x_1^2 p_1 + x_2^2 p_2 + \cdots + x_n^2 p_n) - \mu^2$$

- If there is only a sample of the data, the standard deviation is the sample standard deviation and it is

$$S = \sqrt{\frac{(x_1 - \bar{x})^2 + (x_2 - \bar{x})^2 + \ldots (x_n - \bar{x})^2}{n-1}}$$

- Chebyshev's Inequality. Let X be a random variable with expected value μ and standard deviation σ. Then the probability that the random variable associated with a random outcome lies between $\mu - h\sigma$ and $\mu + h\sigma$ is at least $1 - 1/h^2$, that is

$$P(\mu - h\sigma \leq X \leq \mu + h\sigma) \geq 1 - \frac{1}{h^2}$$

- The variance of the binomial distribution with n trials and the probability of "success" equal to p and of "failure" equal to q is $\text{Var}(X) = npq$.

- The random variable X has a standard normal distribution on the interval $(-\infty, \infty)$ if the probability $P(a \leq X \leq b)$ that X is between a and b is the area under the normal curve given by

$$y = \frac{1}{\sqrt{2\pi}} e^{-0.5x^2}$$

on the interval $[a, b]$, where $\pi \approx 3.14159$ and $e \approx 2.71828$.

- The random variable X has a normal probability distribution with mean μ and standard deviation σ on the interval $(-\infty, \infty)$ if the probability $P(a \leq X \leq b)$ that X is between a and b is the area under the normal curve given by

$$y = \frac{1}{\sigma\sqrt{2\pi}} e^{-0.5[(x-\mu)/\sigma]^2}$$

on the interval $[a, b]$, where $\pi \approx 3.14159$ and $e \approx 2.71828$.

- Let X be a normal random variable with mean μ and standard deviation σ. Then

$$P(a \leq X \leq b) = P\left(\frac{a - \mu}{\sigma} \leq Z \leq \frac{b - \mu}{\sigma}\right) = \mathscr{A}\left(\frac{b - \mu}{\sigma}\right) - \mathscr{A}\left(\frac{a - \mu}{\sigma}\right)$$

where $\mathscr{A}(b)$ is the area under the standard normal curve to the left of b, which can be found in the normal tables.

- In a sequence of n repeated (independent) Bernoulli trials with probability of success equal to p and probability of failure to q, let the random variable X denote the number of successes. Then the histogram for the probability distribution of X is approximated by the normal curve with mean $\mu = np$ and standard deviation $\sigma = \sqrt{npq}$. This is a particularly close approximation when $np \geq 5$ and $nq \geq 5$.

- If $p_\lambda(X = x) = p_\lambda(x)$ is the probability of x number of occurrences per unit of measure, then the Poisson distribution with mean λ is given by

$$p_\lambda(X = x) = \frac{\lambda^x}{x!}e^{-\lambda} \qquad\qquad \pi \approx 2.7182818$$

The mean is $\mu = \lambda$ and the standard deviation is $\sigma = \sqrt{\lambda}$.

- As a rule of thumb, if $p \leq 0.10$, the Poisson distribution $\dfrac{\lambda^x}{x!}e^{-\lambda}$ will be approximately equal to the binomial distribution $C(n,x)p^x q^{n-x}$.

Review Exercises

1. A baseball player has a batting average of .300. Let X be the number of hits in the next five official times at bat. Find the probability distribution.

2. The probability distribution of the random variable X is given in the following table.

x	0	1	2	3	4	5
$P(X = x)$	.20	.10	.05	.15	.18	.32

Draw a histogram and find $P(X = 0)$, $P(X \leq 2)$, $P(0 \leq X \leq 3)$, and $P(X \geq 2)$. Identify $P(X \leq 2)$ as an area on the histogram.

3. Find the expected value of the random variable given in the previous exercise.

4. Lottery A lottery has a grand prize of $1,000,000, a second prize of $100,000, and 10 consolation prizes of $2000 each. If 1 million tickets are sold and the probability of any ticket winning is the same as any other, find the expected return on a $1 ticket.

5. Life Insurance An insurance company sells a $10,000, 5-year term life insurance policy to an individual for $800. Find the expected return for the company if the probability that the individual will live for the next 5 years is 0.96.

6. The pitcher Cy Young holds the all-time record for the most wins in a lifetime with 511, a record that is unlikely to be matched. The following table gives his number of wins (W) and number of losses (L) for the 5-year period beginning with 1900.

Year	1900	1901	1902	1903	1904
W	20	33	32	28	27
L	18	10	10	9	16

Find the mean, variance, and standard deviation for his wins and also for is losses for this 5-year period. Which is varying the most?

7. AIDS The following table gives the number of deaths due to acquired immunodeficiency syndrome (AIDS) for some recent selected years in the U.S. by two age groups. Find the average, variance, and standard deviation of each. Which is varying the most?

Year	1	2	3	4	5
13-29	2864	3531	4598	4745	3574
30-39	6535	8091	11308	11927	8830

8. Find the variance and the standard deviation of the random variable given in Exercise 2 above.

9. A probability distribution has a mean of 20 and a standard deviation of 2. Use Chebyshev's inequality to find the minimum probability that an outcome is between 10 and 30.

10. Let Z be a random variable with a standard normal distribution. Find
  a. $P(Z \leq 0.87)$ **b.** $P(Z \geq 0.87)$
  c. $P(-0.50 \leq Z \leq 0.87)$

11. Let Z be a random variable with a standard normal distribution. Find the interval $[-c, c]$ so that the probability that the random variable is in this interval is 0.98.

12. Manufacturing Suppose that in a production run of 100 twelve-ounce sodas the mean number of ounces in these cans was 12 and the standard deviation was 0.25 ounces. What is the probability that a can will have less than 11.5 ounces if the number of ounces in the cans is normally distributed?

13. The heights of professional soccer players are normally distributed with a mean of 71 inches and a standard deviation of 2 inches. What percentage of players are within 1 inch of the mean?

14. A coin has been flipped 900 times and heads has been observed 485 times. What is the probability of obtaining at least 485 heads if the coin were fair?

15. Quality Control About 2% of a certain product is found to be defective. What is the probability that in a shipment of 1000 of these products at least 25 will be defective?

16. Crime If the probability is 0.001 that any one passenger on a subway in a large city will be robbed, what is the probability that at least 10 of the next 5000 passengers will be robbed? Use the Poisson approximation to the binomial distribution.

17. Pollution The amount of plant emissions of a certain pollutant is limited to 2 parts per million by the EPA. Suppose a particular plant emits 1 part per million on an average day. What is the probability on a given day that this plant will exceed the EPA emissions standard?

Finance

CONNECTION

The Value of Manhattan

Suppose that after the Lenape Indians sold Manhattan for $24 in 1626, the money was deposited into a Dutch guilder account that yielded an annual rate of 6% compounded quarterly. In 2008 this account would be worth $182,000,000,000. In Section F.2 the "wonders of compounding" are explored and discussed.

F.1   Simple Interest and Discount

APPLICATION
Simple Interest Rates

A person deposits $1000 into an account earning simple interest. What simple interest rate is being obtained if the amount at the end of eight months is $1060? See Example 3 for the answer.

APPLICATION
Discounted Notes

A borrower signs a note and agrees to pay $20,000 to a bank in nine months at 10% simple discount. What is the discount and what does the borrower actually receive from the bank? See Example 5 for the answer.

✧ Simple Interest

If you lend someone a sum of money, the sum of money is called the principal or present value. You then charge for the use of this money. This charge is called interest. Thus the future amount F of money at any time is given as the principal P plus the interest I or

$$\text{future amount} = \text{principal} + \text{interest}$$
$$F = P + I$$

Normally, the interest paid is given in terms of some interest rate expressed as a percent. To calculate the interest, this percent must be converted to a decimal. For example, if the account pays 5% interest per year, and the principal (present value) at the beginning of the year is $1000, then the interest rate is $r = 0.05$, and the interest is

$$I = Pr = \$1000(0.05) = \$50$$

The simple interest after three years in the previous example is just 3 times $50 or $150. The simple interest for half a year is one-half of $50 or $25. In general, we have the following.

Simple Interest

Suppose a sum of money P, called the principal or present value, is invested for t years at an annual simple interest rate of r, where r is given as a decimal. Then the interest I at the end of t years is given by

$$I = Prt$$

The future value F at the end of t years is

$$F = P + I = P + Prt = P(1 + rt)$$

EXAMPLE 1   Monthly Interest on Credit Card Account   Suppose you have borrowed $1000 on a credit card that charges simple interest at an annual rate of 18%. What is your interest for the first month?

Solution Here $r = 0.18$. $P = \$1000$, and $t = 1/12$. Thus the interest for the first month is

$$I = Prt = \$1000(0.18)\frac{1}{12} = \$1000(0.015) = \$15 \qquad \blacklozenge$$

EXAMPLE 2   The Future Value in an Account Paying Simple Interest An account with an initial amount of $1000 earns simple interest of 9% annually. How much is in the account after four years? After t years?

Solution After four years we have $P = \$1000$, $i = 0.09$, and $t = 4$. Thus the amount in this account is

$$F = P(1 + rt) = \$1000[1 + (0.09)(4)] = \$1360$$

After t years $P = \$1000$, $i = 0.09$, and $t = t$. Thus the dollar amount in this account is

$$F = P(1 + rt) = 1000[1 + (0.09)(t)] = 1000 + 90t \qquad \blacklozenge$$

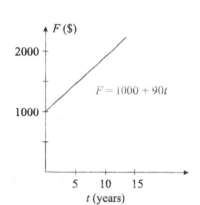

Figure F.1

REMARK: We saw that the amount in the account in Example 2 after t years was $1000 + 90t$. The equation $F = 1000 + 90t$ is the equation of a straight line with F-intercept 1000 and slope 90. See Figure F.1.

EXAMPLE 3   Determining the Annual Rate A person deposits $1000 into an account earning simple interest. What simple interest rate is being obtained if the amount F at the end of eight months is $1060?

Solution We substitute $P = 1000$, $F = 1060$, and $t = \frac{8}{12} = \frac{2}{3}$ into the equation $F = P + Prt$ and obtain

$$F = P + Prt$$
$$1060 = 1000 + 1000r\tfrac{2}{3}$$
$$60 = 1000 \cdot r \cdot \tfrac{2}{3}$$
$$1000r = \tfrac{3}{2} \cdot 60 = 90$$
$$r = 0.09$$

which is an annual rate of 9%. $\qquad \blacklozenge$

◇ Present Value

Very often we find ourselves needing a certain amount of money at a specific time in the future. We will now consider how to determine the present amount or present value of money needed to deposit into an account earning simple interest in order to attain this future need. Suppose we need the future amount F at the end of t years where money is deposited at a simple annual rate of r, expressed as a decimal. Then to find the present amount needed to be deposited into this account, we solve for P in the equation

$$F = P(1 + rt) \qquad \rightarrow \qquad P = \frac{F}{1 + rt}$$

We then have the following.

> **Present Value**
> The present value needed to deposit into an account earning a simple annual rate of r, expressed as a decimal, in order to have a future amount F after t years is
> $$P = \frac{F}{1+rt}$$

When asked how to amass $1 million the easy way, the banker quipped "start with $950,000."

EXAMPLE 4   **Present Value**   How much should be placed into an account paying simple interest of 8% so that after six months the future value of the account will be $1,000,000?

Solution   We have $F = \$1,000,000$, $r = 0.08$, and $t = \frac{6}{12} = 0.5$. Thus

$$P = \frac{F}{1+rt} = \frac{\$1,000,000}{1+(0.08)(0.5)} = \$961,538.46$$

Thus you can have $1 million in this account in six months if you deposit $961,538.46 now.   ◆

✧ Discounts

Often when a bank loans money for some specific length of time, the bank will deduct interest when the loan is made. Such a loan or note is said to be discounted. The interest discounted from the loan is referred to as the simple discount or just discount. The amount that the borrower actually receives is called the proceeds, and the amount to be repaid is called the maturity value. Keep in mind that the bank gives the borrower the maturity value less the discount. We can use the simple interest formula to obtain the discount for a simple discounted loan.

> **Discount and Proceeds**
> The discount D on a discounted loan of M dollars at a simple annual interest rate of r for t years is
> $$D = Mrt$$
> where
> $D =$ discount (interest paid at time of loan)
> $M =$ maturity value (amount borrowed)
> $r =$ discount rate (annual simple interest rate)
> $t =$ length of loan.
> The proceeds P of the loan is the actual amount the borrower receives when the loan is made and is given by
> $$P = M - D$$

EXAMPLE 5   **Determining Discounts and Proceeds**   A borrower signs a note and agrees to pay $20,000 to a bank in nine months at 10% simple discount. What is the discount and what does the borrower actually receive from the bank?

Solution   We have $M = \$20,000$, $r = 0.10$, and $t = 9/12 = 0.75$. The discount is

$$D = Mrt = \$20,000(0.10)(0.75) = \$1500$$

The proceeds are

$$P = M - D = \$20,000 - \$1500 = \$18,500$$

Thus the borrower will receive $18,500 at the time of the loan and pay the bank $20,000 in nine months.   ✦

EXAMPLE 6   Discounted Loan with Given Proceeds   Suppose the borrower in the previous example wanted to receive $20,000. What should the maturity value be?

Solution   We need to solve for the maturity value M in the equation

$$P = M - D = M - Mrt = M(1 - rt)$$

We have the proceeds $P = \$20,000$, $r = 0.10$, and $t = 9/12 = 0.75$. Thus

$$M = \frac{P}{1 - rt} = \frac{\$20,000}{1 - (0.10)(0.75)} = \$21,621.62$$

Thus the borrower will receive the proceeds of $20,000 at the time of the loan and must pay the bank $21,621.62 after 9 months.   ✦

In Example 5 the bank quoted an annual interest rate of 10%. But the rate of interest actually paid is called the effective rate.

EXAMPLE 7   Effective Rate of Interest   What is the effective rate of interest for the borrower in Example 5?

Solution   The borrower must pay the bank $20,000 in 9 months after receiving $18,500. The discount or interest was $1500. We can calculate the effective interest rate r_{eff} by using the formula $D = I = Pr_{eff}t$ and solving for r_{eff}, where $D = I = \$1500$, $P = \$18,500$, and $t = 9/12 = 0.75$. We have

$$D = Pr_{eff}t$$
$$r_{eff} = \frac{D}{Pt}$$
$$= \frac{1500}{18,500(0.75)}$$
$$= 0.1081$$

Thus the effective annual interest is 10.81%, whereas the advertised discount rate r was 10%.   ✦

We can calculate the effective interest rate using only the discount rate r and the length t of the loan. We know from Example 7 that

$$r_{eff} = \frac{D}{Pt} = \frac{Mrt}{(M - Mrt)t} = \frac{r}{1 - rt}$$

> **Effective Rate of a Discounted Loan**
> The effective interest rate given on a discounted loan of length t years with a discount rate of r is
> $$r_{eff} = \frac{r}{1 - rt}$$

EXAMPLE 8 Effective Rate on a Discounted Loan Use the above formula to find the effective rate of the discounted loan in Example 5.

Solution We have $r = 0.10$ and $t = 0.75$. Thus

$$r_{eff} = \frac{r}{1 - rt} = \frac{0.10}{1 - 0.10(0.75)} = 0.1081$$

As a percentage, this is 10.81%. ◆

Self-Help Exercises F.1

1. A bank borrows $100,000 for three months at a simple interest rate of 6% per year. How much must be repaid at the end of the three months?

2. The United States government borrows substantial sums of money by issuing treasury bills (T-bills). T-bills do not specify an interest rate, but rather are sold at public auction. A bank wishes to purchase a 6-month $1 million T-bill. For such a T-bill the bank will receive $1 million at the end of six months. If the bank wishes to earn 5% simple discount interest on this T-bill, what should the bank bid?

3. If the bank obtains a 6-month T-bill at a discount rate of 5%, what is the effective yield?

F.1 Exercises

In Exercises 1 through 4, an amount of P dollars is borrowed for the given length of time at an annual interest rate of r. Find the simple interest that is owed.

1. $P = \$1000$, $r = 8.0\%$, 4 months

2. $P = \$2000$, $r = 6.0\%$, 3 months

3. $P = \$6000$, $r = 4.0\%$, 2 years

4. $P = \$5000$, $r = 7.0\%$, 3 years

In Exercises 5 through 8, an amount of P dollars is borrowed for the given length of time at an annual simple interest rate of r. Find the amount due at the end of the given length of time.

5. $P = \$2000$, $r = 4.0\%$, 7 months

6. $P = \$5000$, $r = 5.0\%$, 4 months

7. $P = \$1000$, $r = 6.0\%$, 2 years

8. $P = \$8000$, $r = 7.0\%$, 3 years

In Exercises 9 through 12, an amount of P dollars is borrowed for the given length of time with the amount F due at the end of the given length of time. Find the annual simple interest rate r.

9. $P = \$2000$, $F = \$2100$, 7 months

10. $P = \$5000$, $F = \$5200$, 4 months

11. $P = \$1000$, $F = \$1070$, 2 years

12. $P = \$8000$, $F = \$9200$, 3 years

In Exercises 13 through 16, find the present amount needed to attain a future amount of F dollars in the given time using an annual simple interest rate of r.

13. $F = \$2000$, $r = 4.0\%$, 3 months

14. $F = \$5000$, $r = 5.0\%$, 8 months

15. $F = \$6000$, $r = 6.0\%$, 2 years

16. $F = \$8000$, $r = 7.0\%$, 3 years

In Exercises 17 through 20, find the effective yield on a discount loan with the given discount rate r and the time.

17. $r = 5\%$, 5 months

18. $r = 6\%$, 9 months

19. $r = 7\%$, 3 months

20. $r = 8\%$, 10 months

In Exercises 21 through 24, find the simple discount and the proceeds for the simple discounted loans.

21. $M = \$1000$, 5 months, $r = 0.04$

22. $M = \$3000$, 8 months, $r = 0.05$

23. $M = \$5000$, 20 months, $r = 0.06$

24. $M = \$7000$, 2 years, $r = 0.08$

Applications

25. **Future Value** A principal of $5000 earns 8% per year simple interest. How long will it take for the future value to become $6000?

26. **Future Value** A principal of $2000 earns 6% per year simple interest. How long will it take for the future value to become $2300?

27. **Doubling Time** A principal earns 8% per year simple interest. How long will it take for the future value to double?

28. **Tripling Time** A principal earns 6% per year simple interest. How long will it take for the future value to triple?

29. **Simple Discount** A borrower signs a note and agrees to pay $50,000 to a bank in five months at 8% simple discount. What is the discount and what does the borrower actually receive from the bank?

30. **Simple Discount** A borrower signs a note and agrees to pay $40,000 to a bank in seven months at 6% simple discount. What is the discount and what does the borrower actually receive from the bank?

Solutions to Self-Help Exercises F.1

1. Since $P = \$100,000$, $r = 0.06$, and $t = 3/12 = 0.25$,

$$F = P(1 + rt) = \$100,000[1 + (0.06)(0.25)] = \$101,500$$

2. Since $M = \$1,000,000$, $r = 0.05$, and $t = 6/12 = 0.50$,

$$\begin{aligned}
P &= M - D \\
&= M - Mrt \\
&= M(1 - rt) \\
&= \$1,000,000[1 - (0.05)(0.50)] \\
&= \$975,000
\end{aligned}$$

3. Since $r = 0.05$ and $t = 0.50$.

$$r_{eff} = \frac{r}{1 - rt} = \frac{0.05}{1 - 0.05(0.50)} = 0.0513$$

or 5.13%.

F.2 Compound Interest

APPLICATION
Calculating Interest Over a Long Period of Time

Suppose that after the Lenape Indians sold Manhattan for $24 in 1626, the money was deposited into a Dutch guilder account that yielded an annual rate of 6% compounded quarterly. How much money would be in this account in 2008? See Example 3 on page 361 for the answer.

✧ A Mathematical Model of Compound Interest

We first consider how to calculate the most common type of interest, compound interest.

If the principal is invested for a period of time at an interest rate of i, where i is given as a decimal, then the amount at the end of the first period is

$$\text{principal} + \text{interest} = P + Pi = P(1+i)$$

The interest i is called the interest per period.

If, for example, the annual interest for a bank account is 6% and the time period is one month, then $i = \frac{0.06}{12} = 0.005$ is the interest per month.

If the interest and principal are left in the account for more than one period and interest is calculated not only on the principal but also on the previous interest earned, we say that the interest is being compounded.

If $1000 is deposited in a bank account earning interest at 6% a year and compounding monthly, then, as we saw above, the interest is 0.5% per month, or 0.005 as a decimal. The amount in the account at the end of any month is then always $1 + 0.005 = 1.005$ times the amount at the beginning of the month.

$$\text{amount at end of month} = [\text{amount at beginning of month}] \times (1.005)$$

If we let the amount at the beginning of any month be inside square brackets, then we have the following:

$$
\begin{aligned}
\text{amount at end of month 1} &= [\text{amount at beginning of month 1}] \times (1.005) \\
&= \$1000(1.005) \\
\text{amount at end of month 2} &= [\text{amount at beginning of month 2}] \times (1.005) \\
&= [\$1000(1.005)](1.005) \\
&= \$1000(1.005)^2 \\
\text{amount at end of month 3} &= [\text{amount at beginning of month 3}] \times (1.005) \\
&= [\$1000(1.005)^2](1.005) \\
&= \$1000(1.005)^3
\end{aligned}
$$

If we continue in this manner, the future amount of money F in the account at the end of n months will be

$$F = \$1000(1.005)^n$$

In the same way, if a principal P earns interest at the rate per period of i, expressed as a decimal, and interest is compounded, then the amount F after n

periods is

$$F = P(1 + i)^n$$

Exploration: Importance of Interest Rate

It is important to understand the relationship between the amount in a compounding account and the interest rate per period. Suppose you invest $1000 and leave your investment for 20 years. Write an equation that gives the amount in the account in terms of the interest rate x, where x is a decimal. Graph on your computer or graphing calculator, using a window with dimensions $[0, 0.15]$ by $[0, 20,000]$. What do you observe?

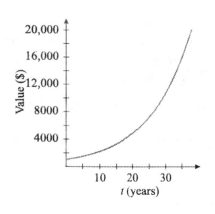

Figure F.2

⊘ Technology Option

See Technology Note 1 on page 365 for detailed directions on using a TI calculator to find compound interest.

EXAMPLE 1   Finding Compound Interest   Suppose $1000 is deposited into an account with an annual yield of 8% compounded quarterly. Find the amount in the account at the end of 5 years, 10 years, 20 years, 30 years, and 40 years.

Solution   We have $P = \$1000$. Since the compounding is quarterly, there are 4 periods per year. We calculate the interest rate per quarter by simply dividing the annual rate 0.08 by 4 and obtain $i = {}^{0.08}\!/_4 = 0.02$. Thus, $F = \$1000(1 + 0.02)^n$. We obtain the following result.

Years (t)	Periods $(n = 4t)$	Future Value
5	20	$\$1000(1 + 0.02)^{20} = \$1485.95$
10	40	$\$1000(1 + 0.02)^{40} = \$2208.04$
20	80	$\$1000(1 + 0.02)^{80} = \$4875.44$
30	120	$\$1000(1 + 0.02)^{120} = \$10,765.16$
40	160	$\$1000(1 + 0.02)^{160} = \$23,769.91$

Notice that during the first 10 years the account grows by about $1200, but during the last 10 years, it grows by about $13,000. In fact, each year the account grows by more than in the previous year. See Figure F.2   ◆

REMARK: We will use the letter i to designate the interest rate for any period, whether annual or not. But we reserve the letter r to always designate an annual rate.

Suppose r is the annual interest rate expressed as a decimal and interest is compounded m times a year. See the table on the left for the most common compounding types. The interest rate per time period is $i = {}^r\!/_m$. If the compounding goes on for t years, then there are $n = mt$ time periods, and the amount F after t years is

Compounding	m
Annually	1
Semiannually	2
Quarterly	4
Monthly	12
Weekly	52
Daily	365

$$F = P(1 + i)^n = P\left(1 + \frac{r}{m}\right)^{mt}$$

Compound Interest

Suppose a principal P earns interest at the annual rate of r, expressed as a decimal, and interest is compounded m times a year. Then the amount F after t years is

$$F = P(1+i)^n = P\left(1+\frac{r}{m}\right)^{mt}$$

where $n = mt$ is the number of time periods and $i = \dfrac{r}{m}$ is the interest per period.

EXAMPLE 2 **Finding Compound Interest** Suppose $1000 is deposited into an account that pays 9% annual interest. Find the amount in the account at the end of the fifth year if the compounding is quarterly and if the compounding is monthly.

Solution Here $P = \$1000$, $r = 0.09$, $m = 4$, and $t = 5$:

$$F = P\left(1+\frac{r}{m}\right)^{mt}$$
$$= \$1000\left(1+\frac{0.09}{4}\right)^{4\cdot 5}$$
$$= \$1560.51$$

Here $P = \$1000$, $r = 0.09$, $m = 12$, and $t = 5$:
$$F = P\left(1+\frac{r}{m}\right)^{mt}$$
$$= \$1000\left(1+\frac{0.09}{12}\right)^{12\cdot 5}$$
$$= \$1565.68 \qquad \blacklozenge$$

REMARK: Notice that the amount at the end of the time period is larger if the compounding is done more often.

EXAMPLE 3 **Calculating Interest Over a Very Long Period of Time** Suppose that after the Lenape Indians sold Manhattan for $24 in 1626, the money was deposited into a Dutch guilder account that yielded an annual rate of 6% compounded quarterly. How much money would be in this account in 2008?

Solution Since $2008 - 1626 = 382$, we have

$$F = P\left(1+\frac{r}{m}\right)^{mt}$$
$$= \$24\left(1+\frac{0.06}{4}\right)^{382\cdot 4}$$
$$\approx \$182 \text{ billion}$$

The table below indicates what the value of this account would have been at some intermediate times. $\qquad \blacklozenge$

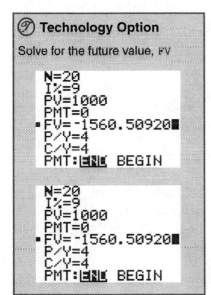

Technology Option

Solve for the future value, FV

```
N=20
I%=9
PV=1000
PMT=0
▪FV=-1560.50920▪
P/Y=4
C/Y=4
PMT:END BEGIN
```

```
N=20
I%=9
PV=1000
PMT=0
▪FV=-1560.50920▪
P/Y=4
C/Y=4
PMT:END BEGIN
```

Year			Future Value
1626			$24
1650	$24\left(1+\frac{0.06}{4}\right)^{4\cdot24}$	$\approx$	$100
1700	$24\left(1+\frac{0.06}{4}\right)^{4\cdot74}$	$\approx$	$2,000
1750	$24\left(1+\frac{0.06}{4}\right)^{4\cdot124}$	$\approx$	$39,000
1800	$24\left(1+\frac{0.06}{4}\right)^{4\cdot174}$	$\approx$	$760,000
1850	$24\left(1+\frac{0.06}{4}\right)^{4\cdot224}$	$\approx$	$15,000,000
1900	$24\left(1+\frac{0.06}{4}\right)^{4\cdot274}$	$\approx$	$293,000,000
1950	$24\left(1+\frac{0.06}{4}\right)^{4\cdot324}$	$\approx$	$6,000,000,000
2008	$24\left(1+\frac{0.06}{4}\right)^{4\cdot382}$	$\approx$	$182,000,000,000

REMARK: It is, of course, very unlikely that any investment could have survived through the upheavals of wars and financial crises that occurred during this 382-year span of time. Nonetheless, it is examples such as this one that inspire some to use the phrase "the wonders of compounding."

✧ Effective Yield

If $1000 is invested at an annual rate of 9% compounded monthly, then at the end of a year there is

$$F = \$1000\left(1+\frac{0.09}{12}\right)^{12} = \$1093.81$$

in the account. This is the same amount that is obtainable if the same principal of $1000 is invested for one year at an annual rate of 9.381% (or 0.09381 expressed as a decimal). We call the rate 9.381% the effective annual yield. The 9% annual rate is often referred to as the nominal rate.

Suppose r is the annual interest rate expressed as a decimal and interest is compounded m times a year. If the compounding goes on for one year, then the amount F after one year is

$$F = P\left(1+\frac{r}{m}\right)^{m}$$

If we let r_{eff} be the effective annual yield, then r_{eff} must satisfy

$$P\left(1+\frac{r}{m}\right)^{m} = P(1+r_{eff})$$

Solving for r_{eff}, we obtain

$$r_{eff} = \left(1+\frac{r}{m}\right)^{m} - 1$$

Effective Yield

Suppose a sum of money is invested at an annual rate of r expressed as a decimal and is compounded m times a year. The effective yield r_{eff} is

$$r_{eff} = \left(1+\frac{r}{m}\right)^{m} - 1$$

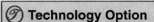

Technology Option

The Finance application has an effective rate finder. Go to Finance and scroll down to C: Eff and press ENTER . Then enter the annual rate followed by a comma and the number of compounding periods per year. Then ENTER again.

```
▸Eff(7.1,2)
            7.226025
▸Eff(7,365)
         7.250098317
■
```

EXAMPLE 4   Comparing Investments   One bank advertises a nominal rate of 7.1% compounded semiannually. A second bank advertises a nominal rate of 7% compounded daily. What are the effective yields? In which bank would you deposit your money?

Solution   For the first bank $r = 0.071$ and $m = 2$. Then

$$r_{eff} = \left(1 + \frac{0.071}{2}\right)^2 - 1 = .0723$$

or as a percent, 7.23%.
 For the second bank $r = 0.07$ and $m = 365$. Then

$$r_{eff} = \left(1 + \frac{0.07}{365}\right)^{365} - 1 = 0.0725$$

or as a percent, 7.25%.   ◆

REMARK: Despite the higher nominal rate given by the first bank, the effective yield for the second bank is higher than that for the first. Thus, money deposited in the second bank will grow faster than money deposited in the first bank.

✧ Present Value

If we have an account initially with P earning interest at an annual rate of r expressed as a decimal and interest is compounded m times a year, then the amount F in the account after t years is

$$F = P\left(1 + \frac{r}{m}\right)^{mt}$$

 If we wish to know how many dollars P to set aside now in this account so that we will have a future amount of F dollars after t years, we simply solve the above expression for P. Thus,

$$P = \frac{F}{\left(1 + \frac{r}{m}\right)^{mt}}$$

This is called the present value.

> **Present Value**
> Suppose an account earns an annual rate of r expressed as a decimal and compounds m times a year. Then the amount P, called the present value, needed currently in this account so that a future amount of F will be attained in t years is given by
>
> $$P = \frac{F}{\left(1 + \frac{r}{m}\right)^{mt}}$$

EXAMPLE 5   Finding the Present Value of a Future Balance   How much money must grandparents set aside at the birth of their grandchild if they wish

Technology Option

While $4 \cdot 18 = 72$ can be worked before entering the TVM Solver, you can also enter 4*18 in the N= place and the calculator will find the value when you move to the next place.

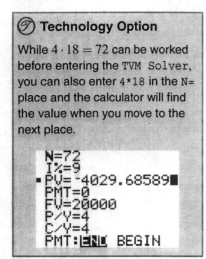

```
N=72
I%=9
•PV=-4029.68589█
PMT=0
FV=20000
P/Y=4
C/Y=4
PMT:END BEGIN
```

Technology Option

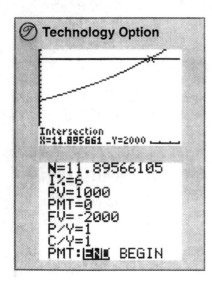

```
Intersection
X=11.895661 _Y=2000
```
```
N=11.89566105
I%=6
PV=1000
PMT=0
FV=-2000
P/Y=1
C/Y=1
PMT:END BEGIN
```

Table 1

Interest Rate	Doubling Times (Years)
4	17.67
5	14.21
6	11.90
7	10.24
8	9.01
9	8.04
10	7.27
15	4.96
20	3.80

to have \$20,000 when the grandchild reaches his or her 18th birthday. They can earn 9% compounded quarterly.

Solution Here $r = 0.09$, $m = 4$, $t = 18$, and $F = \$20,000$. Thus,

$$P = \frac{F}{\left(1 + \dfrac{r}{m}\right)^{mt}}$$

$$= \frac{\$20,000}{\left(1 + \dfrac{0.09}{4}\right)^{4(18)}} \approx \$4029.69$$

Thus, their investment of \$4029.69 will become \$20,000 in 18 years.   ◆

✧ Doubling Times

We may wish to find how long it takes for an investment to double or triple in value. We can do this easily with the help of technology.

EXAMPLE 6 Solving for Time Find the time for a \$1000 investment compounding at an annual rate of 6% to double.

Solution In t years the value of our investment will be $F = 1000(1 + .06)^t = 1000(1.06)^t$. We want to find the time for our investment to become \$2000, so we need to solve the equation

$$2000 = 1000(1.06)^t$$

or dividing each side of the equation by 1000,

$$2 = (1.06)^t$$

By trying different values of t we see that $t \approx 12$ works.

We can also use a graphical way of finding t. We graph $y_1 = 1000(1.06)^t$ together with $y_2 = 2000$. We see in the figure that the two graphs intersect at about $t \approx 11.90$. We can also use the TVM Solver to find the time to double the investment. Finally, we could use logarithms to quickly solve the equation $2 = 1.06^t$ for t, but this is beyond the scope of this text.

Thus, our investment will double in about 12 years.   ◆

Table 1 shows various interest rates and the corresponding doubling times in years.

REMARK: Start with the number 72. If you want to know the number of years it takes to double an investment, just divide the number of years into 72, and you obtain a good estimate. For example, divide 10 into 72 and you obtain 7.2, which is very close to the number (7.27) found in Table 1. Divide 8 into 72 and you obtain 9, which again is very close to the number (9.01) found in Table 1. Divide 4 into 72 and you obtain 18, which again is very close to the number (17.67) found in Table 1.

✧ Technology Corner

⑦Technology Note 1   **Compound Interest on the Calculator**

The TI calculators have an application called TVM Solver that is able to do many of the financial calculations for this chapter. To access this application, press the APPS button and select the Finance option. The TVM Solver will be at the top of the list of options. Selecting the TVM Solver will show you a screen like Screen 1. There are 8 fields to enter values.

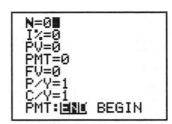

Screen 1

- N is the number of compounding periods.
- I% is the annual interest rate as a percent.
- PV is the present value.
- PMT is the payment amount.
- FV is the future value.
- P/Y is the payments per year.
- C/Y is the compounding periods per year.
- PMT:END BEGIN is when in the period the payments are made.

To do Example 1, we would use the following values in the TVM Solver. See Screen 2.

Screen 2

- N = 20 for the 5 years of quarterly compounding.
- I% = 8.
- PV = 1000.
- PMT = 0.
- FV this will be solved for.
- P/Y = 4
- C/Y = 4
- PMT:END BEGIN set to END

REMARK: For all TVM Solver calculations the calculations are done at the end of the period, so the setting PMT:END BEGIN will always be END and will not be listed in later lists. Also, in our calculations P/Y = C/Y so only the P/Y value will be listed. Finally, while no payments are made in this section, we still assume P/Y is 4 for the quarterly compounding.

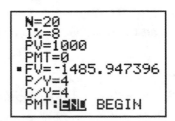

Screen 3

To find the amount in the account after five years, FV, put the cursor on the FV spot and SOLVE by pressing the ALPHA button and then the ENTER . The result is $1485.95 as shown in Screen 3.

REMARK: The FV value has a negative sign. This is due to how the TI calculators handle money flow. See your calculator manual for details. Also note that there is a black square next to the FV amount. This indicates the quantity that was solved for.

Self-Help Exercises F.2

1. An account with $1000 earns interest at an annual rate of 8%. Find the amount in this account after 10 years if the compounding is
   a. monthly   **b.** daily.

2. Find the effective yield if the annual rate is 8% and the compounding is weekly.

3. How much money should be deposited in a bank account earning an annual interest rate of 8% compounded quarterly so that there will be $10,000 in the account at the end of 10 years?

F.2 Exercises

In Exercises 1 through 10, determine how much is in each account on the basis of the indicated compounding after the specified years have passed; P is the initial principal, and r is the annual rate given as a percent.

1. $P = \$1000$, $r = 10\%$, compounded annually for 1 year.

2. $P = \$2000$, $r = 9\%$, compounded annually for 1 year.

3. After one year with, $P = \$1000$ and $r = 8\%$, compounded
   a. annually   **b.** quarterly   **c.** monthly
   d. weekly   **e.** daily

4. After one year where $P = \$1000$ and $r = 10\%$, compounded
   a. annually   **b.** quarterly   **c.** monthly
   d. weekly   **e.** daily

5. After 40 years where $P = \$1000$ and $r = 8\%$, compounded
   a. annually   **b.** quarterly   **c.** monthly
   d. weekly   **e.** daily

6. After 40 years where $P = \$1000$ and $r = 10\%$, compounded
   a. annually   **b.** quarterly   **c.** monthly
   d. weekly   **e.** daily

7. After 40 years where $P = \$1000$, compounded annually, and r is
   a. 3%   **b.** 5%   **c.** 7%   **d.** 9%   **e.** 12%   **f.** 15%

8. After 40 years where $P = \$1000$, compounded annually, and r is
   a. 4%   **b.** 6%   **c.** 8%   **d.** 10%   **e.** 20%   **f.** 25%

9. $P = \$1000$ and $r = 9\%$, compounded annually, after
   a. 5 years   **b.** 10 years   **c.** 15 years   **d.** 30 years

10. $P = \$1000$ and $r = 7\%$, compounded annually, after
    a. 5 years   **b.** 10 years   **c.** 15 years   **d.** 30 years

In Exercises 11 and 12, find the effective yield given the annual rate r and the indicated compounding.

11. $r = 8\%$, compounded
    a. semiannually   **b.** quarterly
    c. monthly   **d.** weekly
    e. daily

12. $r = 10\%$, compounded
    a. semiannually   **b.** quarterly
    c. monthly   **d.** weekly
    e. daily

In Exercises 13 through 16, find the present value of the given amounts F with the indicated annual rate of return r, the number of years t, and the indicated compounding.

13. $F = \$10,000$, $r = 9\%$, $t = 20$, compounded
    a. annually   **b.** monthly   **c.** weekly

14. $F = \$10,000$, $r = 10\%$, $t = 20$, compounded
    a. annually   **b.** monthly   **c.** weekly

15. $F = \$10,000$, $r = 9\%$, $t = 40$, compounded
    a. annually   **b.** monthly   **c.** weekly

16. $F = \$10,000$, $r = 10\%$, $t = 40$, compounded
    a. annually   **b.** quarterly   **c.** daily

17. Your rich uncle has just given you a high school graduation present of $1 million. The present, however, is in the form of a 40-year bond with an annual interest rate of 9% compounded annually. The bond says that it will be worth $1 million in 40 years. What is this million-dollar gift worth at the present time?

18. Redo Exercise 17 if the annual interest rate is 6%.

19. Your rich aunt gives you a high school graduation present of $2 million. Her present is in the form of a 50-year bond with an annual interest rate of 9%. The bond says that it will be worth $2 million in 50 years. What is this gift worth at the present time? Compare your answer to that in Exercise 17.

20. Redo Exercise 19 if the annual interest rate is 6%.

21. Using Example 3 in this section, find the amount in 2008 if the annual interest was 7% compounded quarterly. Compare your answer to that of Example 3.

22. In Example 3 in this section, find the amount in 2008 if the annual interest was 5% compounded quarterly. Compare your answer to that of Example 3 in the text.

Applications

23. Doubling Times Suppose you knew of an investment that quadrupled in value in 18 years. Using Table 1, without using a calculator, find what the approximate annual rate was. Explain how you obtain your answer.

24. Doubling Times Suppose you knew of an investment that went from $1000 to $8000 in 24 years. Using Table 1, without using a calculator, find what the approximate annual rate was. Explain how you obtained your answer.

In Exercises 25 and 26, use the ideas in Table 1 to find the doubling time in years for the given annual interest rates.

25. 2%

26. 3%

27. Use the ideas in Example 6 to find the time for an account earning interest at the annual rate of 6% to grow from $1000 to $1500.

28. Use the ideas in Example 6 to find the time for an account earning interest at the annual rate of 5% to grow from $1000 to $1600.

29. Real Estate Appreciation The United States paid about 4 cents an acre for the Louisiana Purchase in 1803. Suppose the value of this property grew at an annual rate of 5.5% compounded annually. What would an acre be worth in 2010? Does this seem realistic?

30. Real Estate Appreciation Redo previous exercise using a rate of 6% instead of 5.5%. Compare your answer with the answer to the previous exercise.

31. Appreciation Nancy's $1000 investment grew at 8% a year for about 9 years and then grew at 9% for an additional 8 years. Without using a calculator, but rather using Table 1, find approximately the value of her investment after 17 years. Explain how you obtained your answer.

32. Comparing Rates at Banks One bank advertises a nominal rate of 6.5% compounded quarterly. A second bank advertises a nominal rate of 6.6% compounded daily. What are the effective yields? In which bank would you deposit your money?

33. Comparing Rates at Banks One bank advertises a nominal rate of 8.1% compounded semiannually. A second bank advertises a nominal rate of 8% compounded weekly. What are the effective yields? In which bank would you deposit your money?

34. Saving for Machinery How much money should a company deposit in an account with a nominal rate of 8% compounded quarterly in order to have $100,000 for a certain piece of machinery in five years?

35. Saving for Machinery Repeat the previous exercise with the annual rate at 7% and compounding monthly.

Solutions to Self-Help Exercises F.2

1. We have $P = \$1000$, $r = 0.08$, $t = 10$, and $m = 12$. Thus,

$$F = P\left(1 + \frac{r}{m}\right)^{mt} = 1000\left(1 + \frac{0.08}{12}\right)^{12 \cdot 10} = 2219.64$$

2. If the annual rate is 8%, the effective yield is given by

$$r_{eff} = \left(1 + \frac{r}{m}\right)^{m} - 1 = \left(1 + \frac{0.08}{52}\right)^{52} - 1 \approx 0.0832$$

3. The present value of $10,000 if the annual interest rate is 8% compounded quarterly for 10 years is

$$P = \frac{F}{\left(1 + \frac{r}{m}\right)^{mt}} = \frac{10,000}{\left(1 + \frac{0.08}{4}\right)^{4 \cdot 10}} = 4528.90$$

Thus, a person must deposit $4528.90 in an account earning 8% compounded quarterly so that there will be $10,000 in the account after 10 years.

F.3 Annuities and Sinking Funds

APPLICATION
Future Balance in an Annuity

An individual is trying to save money for a down payment on a house purchased in five years. She can deposit $100 at the end of each month into an account that pays interest at an annual rate of 9% compounded monthly. How much is this account after five years? (The answer can be found in Example 1.)

APPLICATION
A Sinking Fund

A corporation wishes to set up a fund in order to have the money necessary to replace a current machine. It is estimated that the machine will need to be replaced in 10 years and will cost $100,000. How much per quarter should be deposited into an account with an annual interest rate of 8% compounded quarterly to meet this future obligation? (The answer can be found in Example 2.)

✧ Annuities

We have previously studied lump sum payments. We now wish to study periodic payments.

An annuity is a sequence of equal payments made at equal time periods. An ordinary annuity is one in which the payments are made at the *end* of the time periods of compounding. The term of an annuity is the time from the beginning of the first period to the end of the last period. The total amount in the account, including interest, at the end of the term of an annuity is called the future value of the annuity. Examples of annuities are regular deposits into a savings account, monthly home mortgage payments, and monthly insurance payments.

We begin with an example of regular deposits into a savings account. Suppose we make deposits of $1000 at the end of each year into a savings account that earns 8% per year. We want to determine how much is in the account at the end of the sixth year. Notice that the first payment is made at the end of the first year and we want the total in the account immediately after the last deposit is made.

Figure F.3. shows what happens to each deposit. For example, the first deposit of $1000 is in the account for five years and becomes $1000(1.08)^5$ at the end of the sixth year. The second deposit of $1000 is in the account for four years and becomes $1000(1.08)^4$ at the end of the sixth year, and so on. The amount in the account at the end of the sixth year is the sum of these six numbers or

$$S = 1000 + 1000(1.08) + 1000(1.08)^2 + 1000(1.08)^3 \\ + 1000(1.08)^4 + 1000(1.08)^5 \tag{1}$$

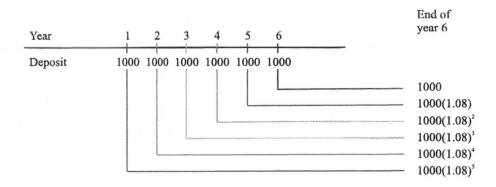

Figure F.3

It is possible to greatly simplify this quantity. First notice that this quantity is in the form of

$$S = a + ab + ab^2 + \cdots + ab^{n-2} + ab^{n-1} \tag{2}$$

where $a = 1000$, $b = 1.08$, and $n = 6$.

We now see how to find a simplified expression for any sum in the equation (2). If $b = 1$, then $S = na$. If $b \neq 1$, then multiply S by b and obtain

$$bS = ab + ab^2 + ab^3 + \cdots + ab^{n-1} + ab^n$$

If we now subtract S from bS, notice that all but two of the terms cancel and we have

$$bS - S = ab^n - a$$
$$(b-1)S = a(b^n - 1)$$
$$S = a\,\frac{b^n - 1}{b - 1}$$

Thus we have the following.

> **Summation Formula**
> For any positive integer n and any real numbers a and b, with $b \neq 1$,
>
> $$S = a + ab + ab^2 + ab^3 + \cdots + ab^{n-1} = a\,\frac{b^n - 1}{b - 1} \qquad (3)$$

Using formula (3) with $a = 1000$, $b = 1.08$, and $n = 6$, the sum of the six terms in (1) is

$$S = a\,\frac{b^n - 1}{b - 1} = 1000\,\frac{(1.08)^6 - 1}{1.08 - 1} \approx 7335.93$$

Thus there will be $7335.93 in this account at the end of the sixth year.

Now more generally, suppose that R dollars is deposited into an account at the end of each of n periods with an interest rate of i per period. We wish to know the amount at the end of the nth period. Figure F.4. indicates what each of the deposits become by the end of the nth period. The value of the account at the end of the nth period is the sum of these n values, denoted by S, and is given by

$$S = R + R(1 + i) + R(1 + i)^2 + \cdots + R(1 + i)^{n-1}$$

We can now use the summation formula with $a = R$ and $b = (1 + i)$ and obtain

$$S = a\,\frac{b^b - 1}{b - 1} = R\,\frac{[(1 + i)^n - 1]}{1 + i - 1} = R\,\frac{[(1 + i)^n - 1]}{i}$$

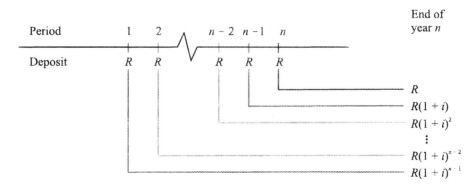

Figure F.4

It is common to write

$$s_{n\rceil i} = \frac{[(1 + i)^n - 1]}{i}$$

The symbol $s_{n\rceil i}$ is read "s angle n at i" and can be found in tables. It is also common to use the symbol FV (future value) for S and to use the symbol PMT (payment) for R. We thus have the following.

> **Future Value of an Ordinary Annuity**
> The future value FV of an ordinary annuity of n payments of PMT dollars paid at the end of each period into an account that earns interest at the rate of i per period is
>
> $$FV = PMT\,\frac{[(1 + i)^n - 1]}{i} = PMT\,s_{n\rceil i} \qquad (4)$$

REMARK: When the periodic payment PMT, is \$1, the future value FT is just $s_{n\rceil i}$. Thus we have that $s_{n\rceil i}$ is the future value of an annuity after n payments of \$1 have been made, where i is the interest rate per period and the compounding is per the same period.

EXAMPLE 1   Calculating the Future Value of an Ordinary Annuity   An individual is trying to save money for a down payment on a house to be purchased in five years. She can deposit \$100 at the end of each month into an account that pays interest at an annual rate of 9% compounded monthly. How much is in this account after five years? Also find the amount of interest that has been earned.

Solution   To use the above formula for FV, we need to find PMT, i, and n. The monthly payment is \$100, so $PMT = 100$. The interest rate per month is $0.09/12 = 0.0075$. The number of periods is $n = 12(5) = 60$. Thus

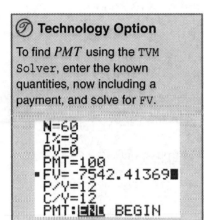
$$FV = PMT \frac{[(1+i)^n - 1]}{i} \qquad \text{or} \quad PMT\,s_{n\rceil i}$$

$$= \$100 \frac{[(1.0075)^{60} - 1]}{0.0075} \qquad \text{or} \quad \$100 s_{60\rceil 0.0075}$$

$$= \$100(75.4241)$$

$$= \$7542.41$$

To find the interest, subtract the total deposits from FV. Total deposits are equal to the number of payments times the amount of each deposit or 60(\$100). Thus

$$\text{interest} = FV - nPMT = \$7542.41 - 60(\$100) = \$1542.41 \qquad \blacklozenge$$

✧ Sinking Funds

Often an individual or corporation knows that at some future date a certain amount FV of money will be needed. Any account that is established for accumulating funds to meet a future need is called a sinking fund. The question is how much money PMT should be put away periodically so that the deposits plus interest will be FV at the needed point in time. In such a case, FV, n, and i are known and one wishes to calculate the periodic payment PMT.

To find PMT start with the formula

$$FV = PMT \frac{[(1+i)^n - 1]}{i} = PMT\,s_{n\rceil i}$$

and solve for PMT. Thus

$$PMT = FV \frac{i}{[(1+i)^n - 1]} = \frac{FV}{s_{n\rceil i}}$$

We have the following.

Sinking Fund Payment
The periodic payment PMT that is required to accumulate the sum FV over n periods of time with interest at the rate of i per period is

$$PMT = FV \frac{i}{[(1+i)^n - 1]} = \frac{FV}{s_{n\rceil i}} \qquad (5)$$

EXAMPLE 2   Calculating a Sinking Fund Payment   A corporation wishes to set up a sinking fund in order to have the funds necessary to replace a current machine. It is estimated that the machine will need to be replaced in 10 years and cost $100,000. How much per quarter should be deposited into an account with an annual rate of 8% compounded quarterly to meet this future obligation? What will be the total amount of the payments and what will be the interest earned?

Solution   We have $FV = 100,000$. Also $i = \dfrac{0.08}{4} = 0.02$. The number of periods is $n = 4(10) = 40$. Thus

$$PMT = FV \frac{i}{[(1+i)^n - 1]} \qquad \text{or} \qquad \frac{FV}{s_{n]i}}$$

$$= \$100,000 \frac{0.02}{[(1.02)^{40} - 1]} \qquad \text{or} \qquad \frac{\$100,000}{s_{40]0.02}}$$

$$= \$100,000(0.016557) \qquad \text{or} \qquad \frac{\$100,000}{62.610023}$$

$$= \$1655.57$$

Thus if $1655.57 is placed into this sinking fund at the end of every quarter, there will be $100,000 in the fund at the end of 10 years.

Since there are 40 payments, the total amount of payments is

$$\$1655.57(40) = \$66,222.80$$

The total interest earned is then $100,000 less the payments or $100,000 − $66,222.80 = $33,777.20. ◆

EXAMPLE 3   Equity in a Sinking Fund   Just four years after making the sinking fund payment in Example 2 the corporation decides to use the accumulated money (equity) for another purpose. Determine the equity.

Solution   We need to find the future value of an annuity with a quarterly payment of $1655.57 and an annual interest rate of 8% compounded quarterly at the end of four years. The number of periods is $n = 4(4) = 16$. We use formula (4).

$$FV = PMT \frac{[(1+i)^n - 1]}{i} \qquad \text{or} \qquad PMT s_{n]i}$$

$$= \$1655.57 \frac{[(1.02)^{16} - 1]}{0.02} \qquad \text{or} \qquad \$1655.57 s_{16]0.02}$$

$$\approx \$1655.57(18.6393)$$

$$= \$30,858.64$$

Thus after four years this fund has grown to $30,858.64. ◆

The following table indicates the equity in this sinking fund for selected times. The values can be found in the same way as in Example 3. The total interest is found as in Example 2, that is, by subtracting the total payments from the future value.

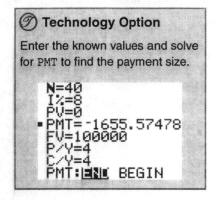

End of Year	Number of $1655.57 Payments	Total Payments	Interest Earned (Equity less total payments)	Equity
2	8	$13,244.56	$965.15	$14,209.71
4	16	26,489.12	4369.52	30,858.64
6	24	39,733.68	10,631.84	50,365.52
8	32	52,978.24	20,242.70	73,220.94
10	40	66,222.80	33,777.20	100,000.00

The above corporation with a sinking fund will need to know the interest per quarter since this interest contributes to profits. To determine the interest for any period, we note that the value of the sinking fund increases in any one period due to one payment into the fund and the interest earned during that period. Thus we have

$$\text{Interest in } m\text{th period} = \begin{array}{l} \text{value at end of } m\text{th period} \\ \text{less value at end of previous period} \\ \text{less payment} \end{array}$$

or

$$\text{Interest in } m\text{th period} = PMT\, s_{m\rceil i} - PMT\, s_{m-1\rceil i} - PMT$$
$$= PMT\, (s_{m\rceil i} - s_{m-1\rceil i}) - PMT$$

> **Interest per Period in a Sinking Fund**
> The interest earned during the mth period of a sinking fund with payments of PMT and earning interest at a rate of i per period is
>
> $$\text{interest in } m\text{th period} \quad PMT\,(s_{m\rceil i} - s_{m-1\rceil i}) - PMT$$
> $$= PMT\,(s_{m\rceil i} - s_{m-1\rceil i} - 1)$$

Technology Option

Enter the known information and solve for the future value, FV after both 16 and 17 quarters. The difference minus the $1655.57 will be the interest earned.

```
N=16
I%=8
PV=0
PMT=1655.57
•FV=-30858.64149
P/Y=4
C/Y=4
PMT:END BEGIN
```

```
N=17
I%=8
PV=0
PMT=1655.57
•FV=-33131.3843■
P/Y=4
C/Y=4
PMT:END BEGIN
```

EXAMPLE 4 Interest per Period in a Sinking Fund Find the interest earned by the sinking fund in Example 2 during the first quarter of the fifth year.

Solution The first quarter of the fifth year is the 17th period. Taking $m = 17$ in the above formula gives

$$= \$1655.57(s_{17\rceil 0.02} - s_{16\rceil 0.02}) - \$1655.57$$
$$= \$1655.57(20.012071 - 18.639285) - \$1655.57$$
$$= \$617.17$$

Thus $617.17 of interest was earned on this sinking fund during the first quarter of the fourth year. ✦

Self-Help Exercises F.3

1. Every six months an individual places $1000 into an account earning an annual rate of 10% compounded semiannually. Find the amount in the account at the end of 15 years.

2. A person will need $20,000 to start a small business in five years. How much should be deposited every three months into an account paying an annual rate of 9% compounded quarterly to meet this goal?

F.3 Exercises

In Exercises 1 through 6, find the future values of each of the ordinary annuities at the given annual rate r compounded as indicated. The payments are made to coincide with the periods of compounding.

1. $PMT = 1200$, $r = 0.08$, compounded annually for 10 years

2. $PMT = 600$, $r = 0.08$, compounded semiannually for 10 years

3. $PMT = 300$, $r = 0.08$, compounded quarterly for 10 years

4. $PMT = 100$, $r = 0.08$, compounded monthly for 10 years

5. $PMT = 100$, $r = 0.12$, compounded monthly for 20 years

6. $PMT = 100$, $r = 0.12$, compounded weekly for 40 years

In Exercises 7 through 10, find the future value of each of the annuities at the end of the given nth year where the payments are made at the beginning of each year and r is the annual interest rate compounded annually. Such an annuity is called an annuity due.

7. $PMT = \$1000$, $r = 0.08$, 10 years

8. $PMT = \$1000$, $r = 0.10$, 20 years

9. $PMT = \$1000$, $r = 0.15$, 40 years

10. $PMT = \$500$, $r = 0.12$, 30 years

In Exercises 11 through 16, find the periodic payment for each sinking fund that is needed to accumulate the given sum under the given conditions.

11. $FV = \$20,000$, $r = 0.09$, compounded annually for 10 years

12. $FV = \$20,000$, $r = 0.09$, compounded monthly for 20 years

13. $FV = \$10,000$, $r = 0.10$, compounded quarterly for 10 years

14. $FV = \$1,000,000$, $r = 0.09$, compounded weekly for 40 years

15. $FV = \$1,000,000$, $r = 0.15$, compounded weekly for 40 years

16. $FV = \$1,000,000$, $r = 0.12$, compounded monthly for 40 years

Applications

17. Retirement An individual earns an extra $2000 each year and places this money at the end of each year into an Individual Retirement Account (IRA) in which both the original earnings and the interest in the account are not subject to taxation. If the account has an annual interest rate of 9% compounded annually, how much is in the account at the end of 40 years?

18. Retirement Repeat the previous problem if the annual interest rate is 12% per year.

19. Retirement Suppose the personal income tax is set at $33\frac{1}{3}\%$. An individual earns an extra $2000 each year and pays income taxes on these earnings and at the end of each year places the remaining funds $\$2000(\frac{2}{3})$ into a regular savings account in which the interest in the account is subject to the personal income tax mentioned before. If the account earns an annual interest rate of 9% compounded annually

and the individual pays income taxes owed on the interest out of these funds, how much is in the account at the end of 40 years? Compare your answer to Exercise 17.

20. **Retirement** Repeat the previous problem if the annual interest rate is 12% per year. Compare your answer to Exercise 18.

21. **Education Fund** New parents wish to save for their newborn's education and wish to have $50,000 at the end of 18 years. How much should they place at the end of each year into a savings account that earns an annual rate of 9% compounded annually? How much interest would they earn over the life of this account? Determine the equity in this fund after 10 years. How much interest was earned during the 10th year?

22. **Education Fund** Repeat the previous problem if the annual interest rate is 7%.

23. **House Down Payment** A couple will need $20,000 at the end of five years for a down payment on a house. How much should they place at the end of each month into a savings account earning an annual rate of 9% compounded monthly to meet this goal? Determine the equity in this fund at the end of each year.

24. **House Down Payment** Repeat the previous problem if the annual interest rate is 7%.

25. **Equipment** A corporation creates a sinking fund in order to have $1 million to replace some machinery in 10 years. How much should be placed into this account at the end of each quarter if the annual interest rate is 10% compounded quarterly? Determine the equity in this fund at the end of every 2 years. How much interest was earned over the life of this fund? Determine the interest earned during the second quarter of the fifth year.

26. **Equipment** Repeat the previous problem if the annual interest rate is 6%.

Solutions to Self-Help Exercises F.3

1. The amount in an account at the end of 15 years into which $1000 has been placed every 6 months and that pays 10% compounded semiannually is given by

$$FV = PMT \frac{[(1+i)^n - 1]}{i}$$

where $PMT = \$1000$ and $i = \frac{0.10}{2} = .05$ and $n = 2(15) = 30$. Thus

$$FV = \$1000 \frac{[(1.05)^{30} - 1]}{0.05} = \$66,438.85$$

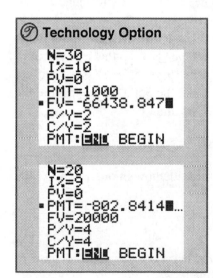

Technology Option

N=30
I%=10
PV=0
PMT=1000
• FV=-66438.847■
P/Y=2
C/Y=2
PMT:**END** BEGIN

N=20
I%=9
PV=0
• PMT=-802.8414■...
FV=20000
P/Y=4
C/Y=4
PMT:**END** BEGIN

2. The periodic payment PMT that is required to accumulate the sum of $FV = \$20,000$ over the $n = 4(5) = 20$ quarters of time with interest at the rate of $i = \frac{0.09}{4} = 0.0225$ per quarter is

$$PMT = FV \frac{i}{[(1+i)^n - 1]} = \$20,000 \frac{0.0225}{[(1.0225)^{20} - 1]} = \$802.84$$

F.4 Present Value of Annuities and Amortization

APPLICATION
Finding the Actual Value of $1,000,000 Lotto Prize

Suppose you run a lottery for your state government and you have just had a "$1 million winner." The winner is immediately given $50,000 and you must make the arrangements that will ensure that this winner will receive $50,000 at the end of each of the next 19 years. You notice that short, intermediate, and long-term interest rates are all at 8%. How much money will it presently cost your department to ensure that these 20 payments of $50,000 each will be made? In other words, how much has the "$1 million winner" really won? (The answer to this question is given below.)

APPLICATION
Finding Car Payments

You wish to borrow $12,000 from the bank to purchase a car. Interest is 12% annually, and there are to be 48 equal monthly payments with the first to begin in one month. What must the payments be so that the loan will be paid off after 48 months? (The answer is given in Example 4.)

✧ Present Value of Annuities

We now answer the question posed in the first application above.

You know that, if an amount equal to P earns interest at 8% per year, then the amount after n years is given by $F = P(1.08)^n$. Thus

$$P = \frac{F}{(1.08)^n} = F(1.08)^{-n}$$

is the present amount of money (present value) needed to attain the value F after n years if compounded annually at 8%.

After making the initial payment of $50,000, we will now see how much money must be placed into an account earning 8% per year so that a payment of $50,000 can be made at the end of each of the next 19 years. If P_1 is the present amount needed to be set aside now in order to make the $50,000 payment at the end of the first year, then, according to the above formula,

$$P_1 = 50,000(1.08)^{-1}$$

The present amount of money P_2 needed to be set aside now in order to make the $50,000 payment at the end of the second year is

$$P_2 = 50,000(1.08)^{-2}$$

And in general the present amount of money P_n, needed to be set aside now to make the $50,000 payment at the end of the nth year is

$$P_n = 50,000(1.08)^{-n}$$

See Figure F.5.

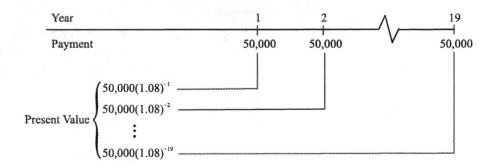

Figure F.5

The sum of these 19 payments, denoted by P, is then the amount needed.

$$P = P_1 + P_2 + \cdots + P_{19}$$
$$= 50{,}000(1.08)^{-1} + 50{,}000(1.08)^{-2} + \cdots + 50{,}000(1.08)^{-19} \tag{6}$$

Recall the summation formula mentioned in the last section.

$$S = a + ab + ab^2 + ab^3 + \cdots + ab^{n-1} = a\,\frac{b^n - 1}{b - 1}$$

The sum of the 19 numbers in (6) can be found using this last formula with $a = 50{,}000(1.08)^{-1}$, $b = (1.08)^{-1}$, and $n = 19$, to obtain

$$
\begin{aligned}
P &= a\,\frac{b^{19} - 1}{b - 1} \\[4pt]
&= 50{,}000(1.08)^{-1}\,\frac{(1.08)^{-19} - 1}{(1.08)^{-1} - 1} \\[4pt]
&= \frac{50{,}000}{(1.08)}\,\frac{1 - (1.08)^{-19}}{1 - (1.08)^{-1}} \\[4pt]
&= 50{,}000\,\frac{1 - (1.08)^{-19}}{(1.08 - 1)} \\[4pt]
&= 50{,}000\,\frac{1 - (1.08)^{-19}}{0.08} \\[4pt]
&= 50{,}000\,\frac{1 - (1.08)^{-19}}{0.08}
\end{aligned}
\tag{7}
$$

If we carry out the calculation, we obtain

$$P \approx 50{,}000(9.6036) \approx 480{,}180$$

So you need to put away into this 8% account only \$480,180 to pay out the remaining \$950,000 in 19 payments of \$50,000 each. Thus the total cost to your department for this "\$1 million" winner is just $480{,}180 + \$50{,}000 = \$530{,}180$.

In general, if R is the periodic payment, i the rate of interest per period, and n the number of periods, we can proceed as above and in analogy with formula (7) we obtain

$$P = R\,\frac{[1 - (1 + i)^{-n}]}{i}$$

It is the custom to use PV for the present value, PMT for the periodic payment and to use the notation

$$a_{\overline{n}|i} = \frac{[1 - (1 + i)^{-n}]}{i}$$

We then have the following.

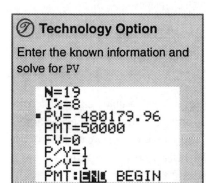

⑨ Technology Option

Enter the known information and solve for PV

```
N=19
I%=8
•PV=-480179.96
PMT=50000
FV=0
P/Y=1
C/Y=1
PMT:END BEGIN
```

> **Present Value of an Ordinary Annuity**
> The present value PV of an ordinary annuity of n payments of PMT dollars each made at the end of the period with interest compounded at the rate of i per period is
>
> $$PV = PMT\,\frac{[1-(1+i)^{-n}]}{i} = PMT\,a_{n\rceil i} \qquad (8)$$

REMARK: If the payment PMT is \$1, then the present value is just $a_{n\rceil i}$. Thus $a_{n\rceil i}$ is the value of an account needed to provide for n payments (or withdrawals) of \$1 each when interest is paid at a rate of i per period and the compounding is for the same period.

EXAMPLE 1   Calculating the Present Value of an Ordinary Annuity   You have announced to your company that you will retire in one year. Your pension plan requires the company to pay you \$25,000 in a lump sum at the end of one year and every year thereafter until your demise. The company makes the assumption that you will live to receive 15 payments. Interest rates are 7% per year compounded annually. What amount of money should the company set aside now to ensure that they can meet their pension obligations to you?

Solution   We use formula (8) with $PMT = 25,000$, $i = 0.07$, and $n = 15$, and obtain

$$PV = PMT\,\frac{[1-(1+i)^{-n}]}{i} \qquad \text{or}\quad PMT\,a_{n\rceil i}$$

$$= \$25,000\,\frac{[1-(1.07)^{-15}]}{0.07} \qquad \text{or}\quad \$25,000\,a_{15\rceil 0.07}$$

$$\approx \$25,000(9.107914)$$

$$= \$227,698$$

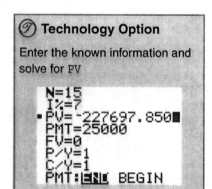

Technology Option

Enter the known information and solve for PV

```
N=15
I%=7
•PV=-227697.850■
PMT=25000
FV=0
P/Y=1
C/Y=1
PMT:END  BEGIN
```

Thus if the company now puts away \$227,698 into this account, they can make payments of \$25,000 each at the end of each of the next 15 years (with no money left in the account after the last payment).   ✦

EXAMPLE 2   Comparing Investments   You represent a bank that has \$1 million in cash to invest. An oil company seeking money to hunt for oil approaches you wishing to borrow \$1 million using one of their producing oil wells as collateral. They have the long-term oil contracts in hand and can guarantee you a payment of \$100,000 at the end of each of the next 20 years. Interest rates available to the bank on the open market are at 8% per year compounded annually. Is this a good deal?

Solution   You ask yourself how much would be needed to invest at current interest rates to guarantee a payment of \$100,000 at the end of each of the next 20 years. Use formula (8) with $PMT = 100,000$, $i = 0.08$, and $n = 20$, and obtain

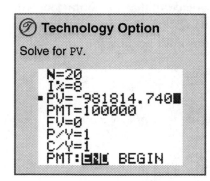

$$PV = PMT \frac{[1 - (1+i)^{-n}]}{i} \qquad \text{or} \quad PMT\, a_{n\rceil i}$$

$$= \$100,000 \frac{[1 - (1.08)^{-20}]}{0.08} \qquad \text{or} \quad \$100,000\, a_{20\rceil 0.08}$$

$$\approx \$100,000(9.818147)$$

$$= \$981,814.74$$

Thus only about $982,000 is needed at current interest rates to obtain the same cash payments as the oil company is offering for $1 million. This is not a good deal.   ◆

EXAMPLE 3   Capital Expenditure Analysis   A corporation wishes to increase productivity and thus save money by purchasing new machinery. The corporation can buy a machine for $100,000 that will save $30,000 annually and has a useful life of five years or a second machine for $160,000 that will save $35,000 annually and has a useful life of seven years. If the annual interest rate is 8% compounded annually, which machine should the corporation purchase?

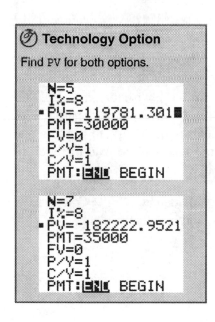

Solution   The first machine saves $30,000 annually for five years. The present value of an annuity with an annual payment of $30,000 for five years with an annual interest rate of 8% compounded annually is

$$PV = PMT\, a_{5\rceil 0.08}$$

$$= \$30,000(3.992710)$$

$$= \$119,781.30$$

This means that an annual savings of $30,000 for five years is equivalent to a lump sum of $119,781.30 now for a savings of

$$\$119,781.30 - \$100,000 = \$19,781.30$$

The second machine saves $35,000 annually for seven years. The present value of an annuity with an annual payment of $35,000 for seven years with an annual interest rate of 8% compounded annually is

$$PV = PMT\, a_{7\rceil 0.08}$$

$$= \$35,000(5.206370) \qquad \text{from tables}$$

$$= \$182,222.95$$

This means that an annual savings of $35,000 for seven years is equivalent to a lump sum of $182,222.95 now for a savings of

$$\$182,222.95 - \$160,000 = \$22,222.96$$

The second machine offers the larger savings and should be bought.   ◆

✧ Amortization

Now look again at Example 2 but this time from the perspective of the oil company, that is, from the perspective of the borrower. If the oil company wishes to borrow an amount *PV* at an interest rate of *i* with equal payments at the end of each year with interest charged on the unpaid balance so that the entire debt will be repaid after n years, what will be the payments PMT? The very same formula used by the bank that relates all of these quantities must apply, namely,

$$PV = PMT \frac{[1 - (1 + i)^{-n}]}{i}$$

Now we are interested in solving for PMT. Solving for PMT, we obtain

$$PMT = PV \frac{i}{[1 - (1 + i)^{-n}]}$$

This process of paying the debt is called amortizing (or killing) the debt. We then have

---

Amortization Formula

The periodic payment PMT to be made at the end of each period on a loan of PV dollars that is to be amortized over n periods with interest at the rate of i per period is

$$PMT = PV \frac{i}{[1 - (1 + i)^{-n}]} = \frac{PV}{a_{n|i}} \qquad (9)$$

EXAMPLE 4 Calculating Payments on a Loan You wish to borrow $12,000 from the bank to purchase a car. The bank charges interest at an annual rate of 12%. There are to be 48 equal monthly payments with the first to begin in one month. What must the payments be so that the loan will be paid off after 48 months? Find the total interest paid on this loan.

Solution The rate per month is the annual rate divided by 12 or $i = \frac{0.12}{12} = 0.01$. Using formula (9) with $PV = 12,000$, $i = 0.01$, and $n = 48$, we obtain

$$\begin{aligned} PMT &= PV \frac{i}{[1 - (1 + i)^{-n}]} && \text{or} && \frac{PV}{a_{n|i}} \\ &= \$12,000 \frac{0.01}{[1 - (1.01)^{-48}]} && \text{or} && \frac{\$12,000}{a_{48|0.01}} \\ &\approx \$12,000(0.0263338) && \text{or} && \frac{\$12,000}{37.973959} \\ &= \$316.01 \end{aligned}$$

Technology Option

Enter the known information and solve for the payment size, PMT. efgfile=xmpl4.4.eps

Thus you will have to make 48 monthly payments of $316.01 in order to pay off this loan at the given interest rate. The total interest paid is the total payments less the loan, or

$$\$316.01(48) - \$12,000 = \$15,168.48 - \$12,000 = \$3168.48 \qquad \blacklozenge$$

Amortization Schedule

We now look at what happens if you wish to make a lump-sum payment to pay off a loan. For example, it is routine for an individual to sell a house and buy another. This requires paying off the old mortgage. How much needs to be paid? To answer this we look closely at how much is owed at the end of each payment period. The next example indicates how to create such a schedule.

EXAMPLE 5   Calculating an Amortization Schedule   You agree to sell a small piece of property and grant a loan of $9000 to the buyer with annual interest at 10% compounded annually, with payments of equal amounts made at the end of each of the next six years. Construct a table that gives for each period the interest, payment toward principal, and the outstanding balance.

Solution   To find the payments we use formula (9) with $PV = 9000$, $i = 0.10$, $n = 6$ and obtain

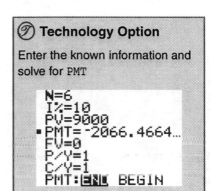

Technology Option

Enter the known information and solve for PMT

```
N=6
I%=10
PV=9000
•PMT=-2066.4664…
FV=0
P/Y=1
C/Y=1
PMT:END BEGIN
```

$$PMT = PV \frac{i}{[1-(1+i)^{-n}]} \quad \text{or} \quad \frac{PV}{a_{n|i}}$$

$$= \$9000 \frac{0.10}{[1-(1.10)^{-6}]} \quad \text{or} \quad \frac{\$9000}{a_{6|0.10}}$$

$$\approx \$9000(0.2296074) \quad \text{or} \quad \frac{\$9000}{4.355261}$$

$$= \$2066.47$$

The interest paid for the first year is $9000(0.10) = \$900$. Thus the payment on the principal is

$$\$2066.47 - \$900 = \$1166.47$$

The remaining principal is then

$$\$9000 - \$1166.47 = \$7833.53$$

The interest paid for the second year is $\$7833.53(0.10) = \$783.35$. Thus the payment on the principal is

$$\$2066.47 - \$783.35 = \$1283.12$$

The remaining principal is then

$$\$7833.53 - \$1283.12 = \$6550.41$$

The following table summarizes the remaining calculations.

End of Period	Repayment Made	Interest Charged	Payment Toward Principal	Outstanding Principal
0				9000
1	2066.47	900.00	1166.47	7833.53
2	2066.47	783.35	1283.12	6550.41
3	2066.47	655.04	1411.43	5138.98
4	2066.47	513.90	1552.57	3586.41
5	2066.47	358.64	1707.83	1878.58
6	2066.44	187.86	1878.61	0000.00

The last payment is the one that adjusts for any roundoff errors.   ◆

EXAMPLE 6 Calculating the Outstanding Principal In the loan in Example 4, suppose the individual wishes to pay off the loan after 20 payments. What is the outstanding principal or, alternatively, the *equity*?

Solution One way of finding the outstanding principal or unpaid balance is to make a table as in the previous example, but there is a less tedious way. The bank views the loan as an annuity that they purchased from the borrower. Thus the unpaid balance of a loan with $(48 - 20) = 28$ remaining payments is the present value of the annuity that can be found using formula (8). We have the payments $PMT = \$316.01$, $i = 0.01$, and $n = 28$. Thus the present value is

$$PV = PMT \, \frac{[1 - (1+i)^{-n}]}{i} \qquad \text{or} \quad PMT \, a_{n\rceil i}$$

$$= \$316.01 \, \frac{[1 - (1.01)^{-28}]}{0.01} \qquad \text{or} \quad \$316.01 \, a_{28\rceil 0.01}$$

$$= \$316.01(24.316443)$$

$$= \$7684.24$$

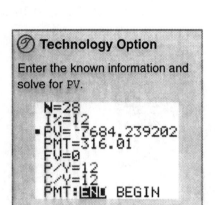
This is the outstanding balance on the loan. That is, the amount the bank will require to pay off the loan at this point. ✦

In the previous example let $n = 48$ be the total number of payments and $m = 20$ be the number of payments made, then notice that

$$PV = PMT \, a_{28\rceil 0.01} = PMT \, a_{n-m\rceil 0.01}$$

In general we have the following.

Outstanding Principal
Let n be the total number of payments required to pay off an amortized loan and let m be the number of payments of PMT made; then the outstanding principal P is given by

$$P = PMT \, a_{n-m\rceil i}$$

We can also use this formula to determine the amount of any payment that is applied to the principal. To see how to do this notice that

the amount owed after $m - 1$ payments $= PMT \, a_{n-m+1\rceil i}$
the amount owed after m payments $= PMT \, a_{n-m\rceil i}$

The difference of these two is the amount of the mth payment that is applied to the principal.

Payment Toward Principal
For an amortized loan requiring n equal payments of PMT dollars each and interest at the rate of i per period, the amount of the mth payment that is applied toward the principal is

payment toward principal $= PMT \, (a_{n-m+1\rceil i} - a_{n-m\rceil i})$

EXAMPLE 7 **Finding the Payment Toward Principal** For the amortized loan in Example 5 find the amount of the second payment R made toward the principal.

Solution Since each payment is $2066.47, $n = 6$, $m = 2$, and $i = 0.10$,

$$R = PMT(a_{n-m+1\rceil i} - a_{n-m\rceil i}) = \$2066.47(a_{5\rceil 0.10} - a_{4\rceil 0.10})$$
$$= \$2066.47(3.790787 - 3.169865)$$
$$= \$1283.12$$

This agrees with what we found in Example 5. ◆

Self-Help Exercises F.4

1. Refer to Example 2 of the text. The very next day the Federal Reserve chairman announces a concerted attempt to control inflation. The financial markets respond immediately with a 1% drop in interest rates. Do you want the deal now?

2. You borrow $100,000 to purchase a house. The bank charges interest of 9% per year (on the unpaid balance). Payments will be made every month for 30 years.

   a. What are the monthly payments to ensure that the loan is paid in full by the end of 30 years?

   b. What is the total interest paid on this mortgage?

   c. What are the amounts of the 10th and 300th payments made toward the principal?

F.4 Exercises

For Exercises 1 through 6, find the amount needed to deposit into an account today that will yield a typical pension payment of $25,000 at the end of each of the next 20 years for the given annual interest rates.

1. 4%   **2.** 5%   **3.** 6%   **4.** 7%
5. 8%   **6.** 9%

In Exercises 7 through 10, find the annual payment needed to amortize a $10,000 loan in six payments if the interest is compounded annually at the given rate. Then find the total interest paid on each loan.

7. 10%   **8.** 12%   **9.** 15%   **10.** 18%

In Exercises 11 through 14, find the monthly payment needed to amortize the following typical $100,000 mortgage loans amortized over 30 years at the given annual interest rate compounded monthly. Then find the total interest paid on each loan.

11. 7%   **12.** 8%   **13.** 9%   **14.** 10%

In Exercises 15 through 18, find the monthly payments needed to amortize the following typical $100,000 mortgage loans amortized over 15 years at the given annual interest rate compounded monthly. Then find the total interest paid on each loan and compare with your answers to Exercises 11 through 14.

15. 7%   **16.** 8%   **17.** 9%   **18.** 10%

In Exercises 19 through 22, find the monthly payment needed to amortize the following typical $10,000 automobile loans over four years at the given annual interest rate compounding monthly. Then find the total interest paid on each loan.

19. 10%   **20.** 11%   **21.** 12%   **22.** 14%

In Exercises 23 through 26, find the monthly payment needed to amortize the following typical $1000 credit card loans over three years at the given annual interest rate compounded monthly. Then find the total interest paid on each loan.

23. 14%   **24.** 16%   **25.** 18%   **26.** 20%

27. An individual wishes to pay off the mortgage in Exercise 11 after 120 payments. What amount is owed? How much of the 15th and 340th payments are applied to the principal?

28. An individual wishes to pay off the mortgage in Exercise 12 after 120 payments. What amount is owed? How much of the 15th and 340th payments are applied to the principal?

29. An individual wishes to pay off the mortgage in Exercise 15 after 60 payments. What amount is owed? How much of the 10th and 150th payments are applied to the principal?

30. An individual wishes to pay off the mortgage in Exercise 16 after 60 payments. What amount is owed? How much of the 10th and 150th payments are applied to the principal?

In Exercises 31 through 34, prepare an amortization schedule as in the table in Example 5 for each of the following loans.

31. The loan in Exercise 7

32. The loan in Exercise 8

33. The loan in Exercise 9

34. The loan in Exercise 10

35. Suppose you wish to take out a $10,000 loan at 1% a month and could make a monthly payment of $200. Use either formula (8) or (9) in the text to determine the number of payments needed to amortize this loan. Do this by trying various values of n, or by using a graphing calculator, or by using logarithms.

36. Redo the previous exercise for a monthly payment of $400.

Applications

37. **Comparing Present Values** Two oil wells are for sale. The first will yield payments of $10,000 at the end of each of the next 10 years, while the second will yield $6500 at the end of each of the next 20 years. Interest rates are assumed to hold steady at 8% per year over the next 20 years. Which has the higher present value?

38. **Comparing Present Values** Redo the previous exercise if interest rates were 6% over the next 20 years.

39. **Comparing Present Values** You are being offered a "half a million dollar" retirement package to be given in $50,000 payments at the end of each of the next 10 years. You are also given the option of accepting a $350,000 lump sum payment now. Interest rates are at 9% per year. Which looks the better to you? Why?

40. **Comparing Present Values** You are being offered a "million-dollar" retirement package to be given in $50,000 payments at the end of each of the next 20 years. You are also given the option of accepting a $500,000 lump sum payment now. Interest rates are at 9% per year. Which looks the better to you? Why?

41. **Capital Expenditures** A corporation wishes to increase productivity and thus save money by purchasing new machinery. The corporation can buy a machine for $95,000 that will save $30,000 annually and has a useful life of five years or a second machine for $160,000 that will save $35,000 annually and has a useful life of seven years. Assuming that the annual savings occurs on the last day of each year, which machine should the corporation purchase if the annual interest rate is

   a. 8% compounded annually
   b. 6% compounded annually?

42. **Leasing** A corporation can either lease a machine with a useful life of six years for $20,000 per year paid at the end of the year or buy it for $100,000. Which should the corporation do if the annual interest rate is

   a. 7% compounded annually
   b. 5% compounded annually?

43. **Car Loan** You purchase a new car for $12,000 and make a $2000 down payment. You then owe $10,000 for the car which you intend to pay off in three years. Initially, you intended to finance your car loan through your credit union that charges 9% compounded monthly for new car loans. The salesman tells you, however, that GM is having a promotion and you can finance your car through GMAC for 4% interest compounded monthly or you can receive a rebate of $800 that can be applied to the purchase price. Should you finance the full $10,000 with GMAC for the lower interest rate or take the rebate and finance $9200 with your credit union? Explain your answer.

Solutions to Self-Help Exercises F.4

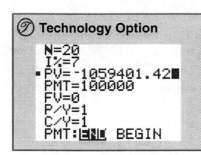

Technology Option

```
N=20
I%=7
▪PV=-1059401.42▪
PMT=100000
FV=0
P/Y=1
C/Y=1
PMT:END BEGIN
```

1. Do the same calculation as in Example 2 of the text but now use $i = 0.07$ and obtain

$$PV = PMT \frac{[1-(1+i)^{-n}]}{i} = \$100,000 \frac{[1-(1.07)^{-20}]}{0.07} = 1,059,400$$

So it will take about $1,059,400 invested at current interest rates to obtain the same cash payments as the oil company is offering for less than $1 million. The deal is now a good one (without consideration of the riskiness of the deal).

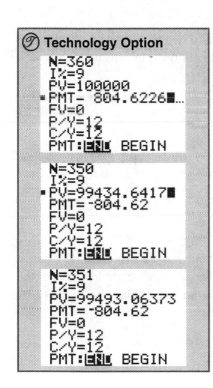

Technology Option

```
N=360
I%=9
PV=100000
▪PMT=-804.6226▪...
FV=0
P/Y=12
C/Y=12
PMT:END BEGIN
```

```
N=350
I%=9
▪PV=99434.6417▪
PMT=-804.62
FV=0
P/Y=12
C/Y=12
PMT:END BEGIN
```

```
N=351
I%=9
PV=99493.06373
PMT=-804.62
FV=0
P/Y=12
C/Y=12
PMT:END BEGIN
```

2. **a.** The monthly payment of PMT on a loan of $PV = \$100,000$ that is to amortized over $n = 12(30) = 360$ periods with interest at the rate of $i = 0.09/12 = 0.0075$ per month is, using formula (9),

$$PMT = PV \frac{i}{[1-(1+i)^{-n}]} = 100,000 \frac{0.0075}{[1-(1.0075)^{-360}]} = 804.62$$

or $804.62 as the monthly payment.

b. The interest is the total payments less the principal or
$$804.62(360) - 100,000 = 189,664.14$$

c. The amount of the 10th payment toward the principal is

$$R = \$804.62(a_{360-10+1]0.0075} - a_{360-10]0.0075})$$
$$= \$804.62(123.65224 - 123.57963)$$
$$= \$58.42$$

The amount of the 300th payment toward the principal is

$$R = \$804.62(a_{360-300+1]0.0075} - a_{360-300]0.0075})$$
$$= \$804.62(48.807318 - 48.173374)$$
$$= \$510.08$$

Review

✧ Summary Outline

- Simple Interest. Suppose a sum of money P, called the principal or present value, is invested for t years at an annual *simple* interest rate of r, where r is given as a decimal. Then the interest I at the end of t years is given by

$$I = Prt$$

The future value F at the end of t years is

$$F = P + I = P + Prt = P(1 + rt)$$

- Present Value. The present value needed to deposit into an account earning a simple annual rate of r, expressed as a decimal, in order to have a future amount F after t years is

$$P = \frac{F}{1 + rt}$$

- Discount and Proceeds. The discount D on a discounted loan of M dollars at a simple annual interest rate of r, expressed as a decimal, for t years is

$$D = Mrt$$

where D is the discount (interest paid at time of loan), M is the maturity value (amount borrowed), r is the discount rate (annual simple interest rate), and t is the length of the loan. The proceeds P of the loan is the actual amount the borrower receives when the loan is made and is given by $P = M - D$.

- Effective Rate of a Discounted Loan. The effective interest rate given on a discounted loan of length t with a discount rate of r, expressed as a decimal, is

$$r_{eff} = \frac{r}{1 - rt}$$

- Compound Interest. Suppose a principal P earns interest at the annual rate of r, expressed as a decimal, and interest is compounded m times a year. Then the amount F after t years is

$$F = P(1 + i)^n = P\left(1 + \frac{r}{m}\right)^{mt}$$

where $n = mt$ is the number of time periods and $i = \dfrac{r}{m}$ is the interest per period.

- Effective Yield. Suppose a sum of money is invested at an annual rate of r expressed as a decimal and is compounded m times a year. The effective yield r_{eff} is

$$r_{eff} = \left(1 + \frac{r}{m}\right)^m - 1$$

- Present Value. Suppose an account earns an annual rate of r expressed as a decimal and is compounded m times a year. Then the amount P, called the present value, needed presently in this account so that a future amount of F will be attained in t years is given by

$$P = \frac{F}{\left(1 + \dfrac{r}{m}\right)^{mt}}$$

- An annuity is a sequence of equal payments made at equal time periods.

- An ordinary annuity is one in which the payments are made at the *end* of the time periods and the periods of compounding are the same time periods.

- The term of an annuity is the time from the beginning of the first period to the end of the last period.

- The total amount in the account, including interest, at the end of the term of an annuity is called the future value of the annuity.

- Summation Formula. For any positive integer n and any real numbers a and b with $b \neq 1$

$$a + ab + ab^2 + ab^3 + \cdots ab^{n-1} = a\,\frac{b^n - 1}{b - 1}$$

- Future Value of an Ordinary Annuity. The future value FV of an ordinary annuity of n payments of PMT dollars paid at the end of each period into a account that earns interest at the rate of i per period is

$$FV = PMT\,\frac{[(1+i)^n - 1]}{i} = PMT\,s_{n\rceil i}$$

- Sinking Fund Payment. The periodic payment PMT that is required to accumulate the sum FV over n periods of time with interest at the rate of i per period is

$$PMT = FV\,\frac{i}{[(1+i)^n - 1]} = \frac{FV}{s_{b\rceil i}}$$

- Interest per Period in a Sinking Fund. The interest earned during the mth period of a sinking fund with payments of PMT and earning interest at a rate of i per period is

$$\text{Interest in } m\text{th period} = PMT\,(s_{m\rceil i} - s_{m-1\rceil i}) - PMT$$

- Present Value of an Ordinary Annuity. The present value PV of an ordinary annuity of n payments of PMT dollars each made at the end of the period with interest compounded at the rate of i per period is

$$PV = PMT\,\frac{[1 - (1+i)^{-n}]}{i} = PMT\,a_{n\rceil i}$$

- **Amortization Formula.** The periodic payment *PMT* to be made at the end of each period on a loan of *PV* dollars that is to be amortized over *n* periods with interest at the rate of *i* per period is

$$PMT = PV \ \frac{i}{[1 - (1+i)^{-n}]} = \frac{PV}{a_{\overline{n}|i}}$$

- **Outstanding Principal.** Let *n* be the total number of payments required to pay off an amortized loan and let *m* be the number of payments of *PMT* made; then the outstanding principal *P* is given by

$$P = PMT \ a_{\overline{n-m}|i}$$

- **Payment Toward Principal.** For an amortized loan requiring *n* equal payments of *PMT* dollars each and interest at the rate of *i* per period, the amount of the *m*th payment that is applied toward the principal is

$$\text{payment toward principal} = PMT\left(a_{\overline{n-m+1}|i} - a_{\overline{n-m}|i}\right)$$

Review Exercises

In Exercises 1 through 2, find how much is in the following accounts after the given *t* years where *P* is the initial principal, *r* is the annual rate, and the compounding is as indicated.

1. $t = 5$, $P = \$1000$, $r = 8\%$, compounded

   a. annually   **b.** quarterly

   c. monthly   **d.** weekly

   e. daily

2. $t = 5$, $P = \$1000$, $r = 10\%$, compounded

   a. annually   **b.** quarterly

   c. monthly   **d.** weekly

   e. daily

In Exercises 3 through 4 find the effective yield given the annual rate *r* and the indicated compounding.

3. $r = 9\%$, compounded

   a. semiannually   **b.** quarterly

   c. monthly   **d.** weekly

   e. daily

4. $r = 11\%$, compounded

   a. semiannually   **b.** quarterly

   c. monthly   **d.** weekly

   e. daily

In Exercises 5 through 6 find the present value of the given amounts *A* with the indicated annual rate of return *r*, the number of years *t*, and the indicated compounding.

5. $A = \$10,000$, $r = 8\%$, $t = 10$, compounded

   a. annually   **b.** monthly   **c.** weekly

6. $A = \$10,000$, $r = 9\%$, $t = 10$, compounded

   a. annually   **b.** quarterly   **c.** daily

7. You have just won a $1,000,000 lottery. Your entire prize will be given to you in 20 years in a lump sum. If current interest rates are 8% compounded annually, what is this $1,000,000 prize worth at the present?

8. How much money should you deposit now in an account earning 9% annually in order to have $10,000 in 5 years?

9. What annual rate is required for an account that is compounded annually to double in 8 years?

10. **Savings** A self-employed individual places $3000 a year into a Keogh account in which taxes are not paid on the interest. If interest rates remain at 9%, how much will be in this account after 30 years?

11. **Sinking Fund** A large corporation creates a sinking fund in order to have a $2 million cash bonus for the president of the company on his retirement in 10 years. How much should be placed into this account at the end of each quarter if the interest rate is 8% compounded quarterly? Over the life of this sinking fund how much interest accumulates? How much interest is earned in the third quarter of the fifth year?

12. **Lottery Prize** The state lottery has just had a $2 million winner and needs to pay the recipient $100,000 now and the same amount at the end of each of the next 19 years. The state does not wish to be involved in the administration of this disbursement and wishes to give this obligation together with a lump sum payment to an insurance company to handle the payments. You are an investment advisor for an insurance company. Interest rates are at 8%. What is the very least that you would accept for this obligation?

13. **Amortization** You plan to borrow $100,000 to buy a house. Interest rates are at 9% a year compounded monthly. What will be your monthly payments if the length of the mortgage is 25 years? 15 years? What will be the total interest paid in each case? In each case how much of the 10th payment will go toward the principal? The 120th?

Area Under a Normal Curve

This table gives the area under the standard normal curve to the left of $z = \dfrac{x - \mu}{\sigma}$

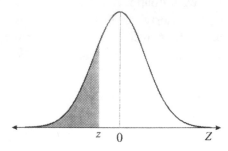

z	.00	.01	.02	.03	.04	.05	.06	.07	.08	.09
−3.4	.0003	.0003	.0003	.0003	.0003	.0003	.0003	.0003	.0003	.0002
−3.3	.0005	.0005	.0005	.0004	.0004	.0004	.0004	.0004	.0004	.0003
−3.2	.0007	.0007	.0006	.0006	.0006	.0006	.0006	.0005	.0005	.0005
−3.1	.0010	.0009	.0009	.0009	.0008	.0008	.0008	.0008	.0007	.0007
−3.0	.0013	.0013	.0013	.0012	.0012	.0011	.0011	.0011	.0010	.0010
−2.9	.0019	.0018	.0017	.0017	.0016	.0016	.0015	.0015	.0014	.0014
−2.8	.0026	.0025	.0024	.0023	.0023	.0022	.0021	.0021	.0020	.0019
−2.7	.0035	.0034	.0033	.0032	.0031	.0030	.0029	.0028	.0027	.0026
−2.6	.0047	.0045	.0044	.0043	.0041	.0040	.0039	.0038	.0037	.0036
−2.5	.0062	.0060	.0059	.0057	.0055	.0054	.0052	.0051	.0049	.0048
−2.4	.0082	.0080	.0078	.0075	.0073	.0071	.0069	.0068	.0066	.0064
−2.3	.0107	.0104	.0102	.0099	.0096	.0094	.0091	.0089	.0087	.0084
−2.2	.0139	.0136	.0132	.0129	.0125	.0122	.0119	.0116	.0113	.0110
−2.1	.0179	.0174	.0170	.0166	.0162	.0158	.0154	.0150	.0146	.0143
−2.0	.0228	.0222	.0217	.0212	.0207	.0202	.0197	.0192	.0188	.0183
−1.9	.0287	.0281	.0274	.0268	.0262	.0256	.0250	.0244	.0239	.0233
−1.8	.0359	.0352	.0344	.0336	.0329	.0322	.0314	.0307	.0301	.0294
−1.7	.0446	.0436	.0427	.0418	.0409	.0401	.0392	.0384	.0375	.0367
−1.6	.0548	.0537	.0526	.0516	.0505	.0495	.0485	.0475	.0465	.0455
−1.5	.0668	.0655	.0643	.0630	.0618	.0606	.0594	.0582	.0571	.0559
−1.4	.0808	.0793	.0778	.0764	.0749	.0735	.0722	.0708	.0694	.0681
−1.3	.0968	.0951	.0934	.0918	.0901	.0885	.0869	.0853	.0838	.0823
−1.2	.1151	.1131	.1112	.1093	.1075	.1056	.1038	.1020	.1003	.0985
−1.1	.1357	.1335	.1314	.1292	.1271	.1251	.1230	.1210	.1190	.1170
−1.0	.1587	.1562	.1539	.1515	.1492	.1469	.1446	.1423	.1401	.1379
−0.9	.1841	.1814	.1788	.1762	.1736	.1711	.1685	.1660	.1635	.1611
−0.8	.2119	.2090	.2061	.2033	.2005	.1977	.1949	.1922	.1894	.1867
−0.7	.2420	.2389	.2358	.2327	.2296	.2266	.2236	.2206	.2177	.2148
−0.6	.2743	.2709	.2676	.2643	.2611	.2578	.2546	.2514	.2483	.2451
−0.5	.3085	.3050	.3015	.2981	.2946	.2912	.2877	.2843	.2810	.2776
−0.4	.3446	.3409	.3372	.3336	.3300	.3264	.3228	.3192	.3156	.3121
−0.3	.3821	.3783	.3745	.3707	.3669	.3632	.3594	.3557	.3520	.3483
−0.2	.4207	.4168	.4129	.4090	.4052	.4013	.3974	.3936	.3897	.3859
−0.1	.4602	.4562	.4522	.4483	.4443	.4404	.4364	.4325	.4286	.4247

z	.00	.01	.02	.03	.04	.05	.06	.07	.08	.09
0.0	.5000	.5040	.5080	.5120	.5160	.5199	.5239	.5279	.5319	.5359
0.1	.5398	.5438	.5478	.5517	.5557	.5596	.5636	.5675	.5714	.5753
0.2	.5793	.5832	.5871	.5910	.5948	.5987	.6026	.6064	.6103	.6141
0.3	.6179	.6217	.6255	.6293	.6331	.6368	.6406	.6443	.6480	.6517
0.4	.6554	.6591	.6628	.6664	.6700	.6736	.6772	.6808	.6844	.6879
0.5	.6915	.6950	.6985	.7019	.7054	.7088	.7123	.7157	.7190	.7224
0.6	.7257	.7291	.7324	.7357	.7389	.7422	.7454	.7486	.7517	.7549
0.7	.7580	.7611	.7642	.7673	.7704	.7734	.7764	.7794	.7823	.7852
0.8	.7881	.7910	.7939	.7967	.7995	.8023	.8051	.8078	.8106	.8133
0.9	.8159	.8186	.8212	.8238	.8264	.8289	.8315	.8340	.8365	.8389
1.0	.8413	.8438	.8461	.8485	.8508	.8531	.8554	.8577	.8599	.8621
1.1	.8643	.8665	.8686	.8708	.8729	.8749	.8770	.8790	.8810	.8830
1.2	.8849	.8869	.8888	.8907	.8925	.8944	.8962	.8980	.8997	.9015
1.3	.9032	.9049	.9066	.9082	.9099	.9115	.9131	.9147	.9162	.9177
1.5	.9192	.9207	.9222	.9236	.9251	.9265	.9278	.9292	.9306	.9319
1.5	.9332	.9345	.9357	.9370	.9382	.9394	.9406	.9418	.9429	.9441
1.6	.9452	.9463	.9474	.9484	.9495	.9505	.9515	.9525	.9535	.9545
1.7	.9554	.9564	.9573	.9582	.9591	.9599	.9608	.9616	.9625	.9633
1.8	.9641	.9649	.9656	.9664	.9671	.9678	.9686	.9693	.9699	.9706
1.9	.9713	.9719	.9726	.9732	.9738	.9744	.9750	.9756	.9761	.9767
2.0	.9772	.9778	.9783	.9788	.9793	.9798	.9803	.9808	.9812	.9817
2.1	.9821	.9826	.9830	.9834	.9838	.9842	.9846	.9850	.9854	.9857
2.2	.9861	.9864	.9868	.9871	.9875	.9878	.9881	.9884	.9887	.9890
2.3	.9893	.9896	.9898	.9901	.9904	.9906	.9909	.9911	.9913	.9916
2.4	.9918	.9920	.9922	.9925	.9927	.9929	.9931	.9932	.9934	.9936
2.5	.9938	.9940	.9941	.9943	.9945	.9946	.9948	.9949	.9951	.9952
2.6	.9953	.9955	.9956	.9957	.9959	.9960	.9961	.9962	.9963	.9964
2.7	.9965	.9966	.9967	.9968	.9969	.9970	.9971	.9972	.9973	.9974
2.8	.9974	.9975	.9976	.9977	.9977	.9978	.9979	.9979	.9980	.9981
2.9	.9981	.9982	.9982	.9983	.9984	.9984	.9984	.9985	.9986	.9986
3.0	.9987	.9987	.9987	.9988	.9988	.9989	.9989	.9989	.9990	.9990
3.1	.9990	.9991	.9991	.9991	.9992	.9992	.9992	.9992	.9993	.9993
3.2	.9993	.9993	.9994	.9994	.9994	.9994	.9994	.9995	.9995	.9995
3.3	.9995	.9995	.9995	.9996	.9996	.9996	.9996	.9996	.9996	.9997
3.4	.9997	.9997	.9997	.9997	.9997	.9997	.9997	.9997	.9997	.9998

Answers to Selected Exercises

1.1 EXERCISES

1. $C(x) = 3x + 10,000$, x is number of items and C is the cost in dollars.

3. $R(x) = 5x$, x is number of items and R is the revenue in dollars.

5. $P(x) = 2x - 10,000$, x is number of items and P is the profit in dollars.

7. $p = D(x) = -0.4x + 12$, x is number of items and p is the price per item in dollars.

9. $p = D(x) = -0.25x + 60$, x is number of items and p is the price per item in dollars.

11. $p = S(x) = 1.6x + 15$, x is number of items and p is the price per item in dollars

13. $p = S(x) = 5x + 10$, x is number of items and p is the price per item in dollars.

15. $V(t) = -15t + 130$, $0 \le t \le 7$, t in years and V is value in dollars.

17. $V(t) = -1500t + 15,000$, $0 \le t \le 6$, t in years and V is value in dollars

19. $C(x) = 10x + 150$, x in hours and C is cost in dollars

21. $C(x) = 2x + 91,000$, x number of shirts and C is cost in dollars.

23. $C(x) = 5x + 1000$, x is number of items and C is cost in dollars

25. \$.85 per bead

27. $R(x) = 12x$, x is number of items and R is the revenue in dollars.

29. $C(x) = x + 2000$, x is number of items and C is the cost in dollars.

31. $R(x) = 11x$, x is number of items and R is the revenue in dollars.

33. $p = D(x) = -0.05x + 4.53$, x is the number of packages of blueberries and p is the price per package in dollars.

35. $p = S(x) = -0.05x + 1.25$, x is the number of packages of basil and p is the price per package in dollars.

37. $V = -5000t + 50,000$. After 1 year, $V(1) = 45,000$. After 5 year, $V(5) = 25,000$

39. Fixed costs are \$674,000. Variable costs are \$21.

41. x is the number of pairs of fenders and the cost function in dollars are:

Steel: $C(x) = 260,000 + 5.26x$
Aluminum: $C(x) = 385,000 + 12.67x$
RMP: $C(x) = 95,000 + 13.19x$
NPN: $C(x) = 95,000 + 9.53x$

43. $R = 2274x$. The independent variable is x, the tons of grapes and the dependent variable is $R(x)$, the revenue from selling the grapes.

45. $R = 40x$, 2500 visitors

47. $R(x) = 0.704x$

49. **a.** \$446   **b.** \$127

51. $C(x) = 209.03x + 447,917$, $R(x) = 266.67x$, $P(x) = 57.64x - 447,917$

53. $p = D(x) = -5.6x + 155$, \$71

55. **a.** 300,000 yen   **b.** 0.1 yen per ton

57. 11.76 months

59. Since no sales result in no revenue, we must have $R(0) = 0$.

61. The area is the base times the height. But the height is the price and the base is the number of items sold. Therefore, the area of the rectangle is the price times the number sold, which is the revenue.

63. $c(x) = -6x + 12$

65. Let x be the number of cows, then the cost $C(x)$ in dollars is $C(x) = 13,386 + 393x$. The revenue function in dollars is $R(x) = 470x$. The profit function in dollars is $P(x) = 77x - 13,386$. The profit for an average of 97 cows is $P(97) = -5917$, that is a loss of \$5917. For many such farms the property and buildings have already been paid off. Thus, the fixed costs for these farms are lower than stated in the table.

67. Let the cost revenue, and profits be given in thousands of dollars. We have $C(x) = 3.84x + 300,000$, $R(x) = 4.8x$, $P(x) = 0.96x - 300,000$

Number	200,000	300,000	400,000
Cost	1068	1452	1836
Revenue	960	1440	1920
Profit	−108	−12	84

1.2 EXERCISES

1. 2 items   3. 20 items   5. $(1.5, 4.5)$

7. $(1, 15)$ 9. 2000 purses

11. **a.** Rental: $C_R = 320d$ **b.** Buy: $C_B = 28,000 + 40d$ **c.** buy   **d.** 100 days

13. **a.** $C(x) = 5000x$ **b.** $C(x) = 1000x + 40000$ **c.** 10 years

15. Acme: $C_A = 75 + 0.40x$, Bell: $C_B = 105 + 0.25x$
a. 200 miles   **b.** Acme

17. 40,000 manuals, In-house

19. 20 bunches at \$4 per bunch

21. \$446

23. 3925 tons   25. 174 cows

27. 65,000 miles, steel   29. 40,000 miles, steel

31. **a.** Houston, Boston   **b.** 7,000,000 items

33. 557,692 pairs of fenders   35. 22,634 pairs of fenders

37. **a.** Manual is \$17,000. Automatic is \$8200.
b. 4430 plates.

1.3 EXERCISES

1. $(x, y) = (2, 5)$ 3. $(x, y) = (1, -2)$

5. $(x, y) = (-1, -1)$ 7. $(x, y) = (-2, 1)$

9. $(x, y) = (1, 2)$ 11. $(x, y, z) = (1, 2, 0)$

13. $(x, y, z) = (5, 0, 5)$ 15. $(x, y, z) = (1, 2, 3)$

17. $(x, y, z) = (1.5, 1.5, -0.5)$ 19. $(x, y, z) = (-1, 1, 1)$

21. $(x, y, z, u) = (2, 1, 1, 2)$

23. $(x,y,z,u) = (1,-1,2,3)$
25. 5 quarters and 20 dimes
27. 10 nickels, 20 dimes, 6 quarters
29. 8 contracts and 6 leases
31. $700 in the first bank, $300 in second
33. 160 Pathfinder shirts and 300 Trekking shirts
35. Three appeals, five claims, four enrollment forms
37. 100 shares of MathOne, 20 shares of NewModule, 50 shares of JavaTime
39. 10 of Frame A, 40 of Frame B, and 20 of Frame C
41. 30 muffins (5 batches), 20 scones (2 batches), and 36 croissants (3 batches)
43. 5 oz. of food I, 2 oz. of Food II, and 8 oz. of Food III
45. Three oranges, two cups of strawberries, one cup of blackberries
47. Since $x = -11$, there is no solution for the dietitian.
49. 1200 of the first species could be added.

1.4 EXERCISES

1. Yes   3. Yes
5. No, the second row should be at the bottom.
7. $x = 2$ and $y = 3$
9. $(x,y) = (4 - 2t, t)$, where t is any number.
11. $(x,y,z,u) = (4 - 2s - 3t, 5 - 2s - 3t, s, t)$, where s and t are any numbers.
13. $(x,y,z,u) = (6 - 2s - 4t, 1 - 2s - 3t, s, t)$, where s and t are any numbers.
15. $(x,y,z,u,v,w) = (r, 1 - 2s - 2t, s, 2 - t, t, 3)$, where r, s, and t are any numbers.
17. no solution   19. $(2t + 4, t)$ 21. $(3t - 7, t)$
23. no solution   25. $(6 - \frac{7}{3}t, 10 - \frac{8}{3}t, t)$
27. $(3s + 2t - 6, s, t)$
29. $(5t - 7, t, 0)$ 31. $(1.5, -t - 0.5, t)$
33. no solution   35. $(1, t, t)$
37. $(x,y) = (1,3)$ 39. no solution   41. no solution
43. $(5, 10, 8)$
45. no solution   47. no solution
49. nickels, dimes, quarters $= (3t - 8, 44 - 4t, t)$, where t is any natural number such that $3 \le t \le 11$
51. (Moon,Spoon,Loon) $= (15 - 5t, 3t, t)$, $t = 0, 1, 2,$ or 3.
53. 100 Tiderunner, 150 of Sport, 50 of Stone Harbor
55. The production manager cannot meet the demands of his boss.
57. There are exactly two solutions: 9 appeals, 4 claims, and no enrollment forms, and 3 appeals, 5 claims, and 4 enrollment forms.
59. $([2c - 5a]t - 2d + 5b, [2a - c]t + d - 2b, t)$
61. $(x_1, x_2, x_3, x_4) = (700 - t, t - 100, 900 - t, t)$, where t is any number so that $100 \le t \le 700$.
63. The equilibrium is $(x,y,p,q) = (2,3,5,6)$.
65. Not possible since some of the amounts are negative.
67. The method in the text uses one less multiplication

1.5 EXERCISES

A TI-84 was used to obtain all of the following answers. See the Technology Corner for details.

1. $y = 0.50x + 0.50$, $r = 0.5000$.

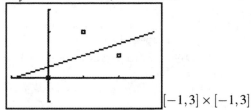
$[-1,3] \times [-1,3]$

3. $y = 1.1x + 0.1$, $r = 0.9467$.

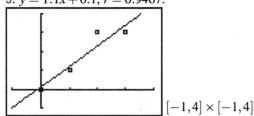
$[-1,4] \times [-1,4]$

5. $y = -0.9x + 4.5$, $r = -0.9234$.

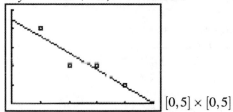
$[0,5] \times [0,5]$

7. $y = -0.7x + 3.4$, $r = -0.9037$.

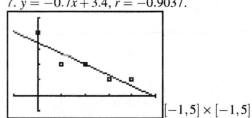
$[-1,5] \times [-1,5]$

9. $y = D(x) = -0.394x + 8.489$, $4.55
11. $V = -3.617t + 26.147$, where $t = 0$ corresponds to the year 1998. So, $V(0) = 26.147$, or $26,147
13. **a.** $y = 0.213x + 12.454$ **b.** An increase of the deer population by one, results, on average, of an increase of 0.213 collisions with vehicles on roads.
15. **a.** Linear regression gives $y = 2.0768x + 1.4086$, $r = 0.9961$. **b.** Using the value operation gives $y \approx 209$, when $x = 100$. Thus, the total cost is $209,000. **c.** Inputting $y_2 = 125$ and using the intersect operation gives $x \approx 59.511$, which gives 59,511 dozen.
17. **a.** $y = 0.8605x + 0.5638$, $r = 0.9703$. **b.** $y \approx 6.6$ when $x = 7$, giving GNP growth of 6.6%. **c.** $y_2 = 7$ yields $x \approx 7.5$, giving a productivity growth of 7.5%.
19. $y = -87.16x + 1343$, $r = -0.8216$.
21. **a.** $y = 3.4505x + 14.4455$, $r = 0.9706$ and $z = 2.0446x + 1.0990$, $r = 0.9413$.
b. For each additional aphid per plant the percentage of times the virus is transmitted to the fruit increases by about 3.5% for the brown aphid and about 2% for the melon aphid.
c. The brown aphid is more destructive since the brown aphid transmits the virus more often than the melon aphid.
23. **a.** $y = 1.75x + 0.140$, $x = 0$ corresponds to the year 2000. **b.** 2.59 **c.** $r = 0.9944$

25. a. $y = 0.35x + 67.29$, $x = 0$ corresponds the year 2000
b. 69.4%   **c.** $r = 0.9737$
27. a. $y = 411.9x + 5359.1$, $x = 1$ corresponds for the year
1990   **b.** 12,361.4   **c.** $r = 0.9984$
29. a. $y = 100.5x + 1609.8$, $x = 1$ corresponds to the year
2000   **b.** 2313.3   **c.** $r = 0.9987$
31. a. $y = 0.63x + 60.1$, $x = 1$ corresponds to the year 1990
b. 70.81   **c.** $r = 0.9559$

REVIEW EXERCISES

1. $C = 2000 + 6x$ 2. $R = 10x$ 3. $P = 4x - 2000$, 500
4. 150
5. 1000   6. $p = -0.000005x + 1.5$ 7. 12,000
8. $P = 12,000t - 70,000$ 9. $P = 2000t - 20,000$
10. **a.** $C_R = 150x$ **b.** $C_O = 1400 + 10x$ **c.** He should buy.
d. 10 days
11. $(x, y) = (1, 2)$ 12. no solution
13. $(x, y) = (1 - 3t, t)$ 14. $(x, y) = (3, 4)$
15. $(x, y, z) = (1.6 - 0.2t, 0.4t + 0.8, t)$
16. $(x, y, z) = (10 - t, t, 0)$ 17. $(x, y, z) = (1, 3, 1)$
18. $(x, y, z) = (2t - 2, 7 - 3t, t)$
19. (3 par, 4 par, 5 par) $= (t + 1, 8 - 2t, t)$, $0 \le t \le 4$
20. Seven standard sweepers, five deluxe sweepers
21. 8 of the first and 6 of the second
22. 20 ham specials, 30 beef specials
23. 90 liters of first solution, 60 of second, 150 of third
24. Plants 1, 2, and 3 should produce 100, 200, and 50, respectively.
25. $y = (5x + 1)/7$
26. **a.** $y = 4x + 45$, $x = 1$ corresponds to the year 1999   **b.**
77%   **c.** $r = 0.9759$

2.1 EXERCISES

1. 4×2 3. 1×2 5. 1   7. 8   9. -2 11. 6

13. 2   15. $A = \begin{bmatrix} 5 & 5 & 5 \\ 5 & 5 & 5 \end{bmatrix}$ 17. $\begin{bmatrix} 1 & 0 & 0 \\ 0 & 1 & 0 \\ 0 & 0 & 1 \end{bmatrix}$

19. $\begin{bmatrix} 0 & 0 & 0 \\ 0 & 0 & 0 \\ 0 & 0 & 0 \end{bmatrix}$ 21. $x = 3$, $y = 0$, $z = 4$

23. $\begin{bmatrix} 4 & 5 \\ 1 & 10 \\ -3 & 10 \\ 5 & 6 \end{bmatrix}$ 25. $\begin{bmatrix} 0 & 6 \end{bmatrix}$ 27. $\begin{bmatrix} 2 & -3 \\ -5 & -2 \\ 3 & -4 \\ -1 & 10 \end{bmatrix}$

29. $\begin{bmatrix} -2 & -2 \end{bmatrix}$ 31. $\begin{bmatrix} 2 & 6 & -6 & 6 \\ 8 & 12 & 14 & -4 \end{bmatrix}$

33. $\begin{bmatrix} 4 & 16 \end{bmatrix}$ 35. $\begin{bmatrix} 7 & 6 \\ -1 & 14 \\ -3 & 13 \\ 7 & 14 \end{bmatrix}$ 37. $\begin{bmatrix} 1 & 16 \end{bmatrix}$

39. Not defined
41. **a.** not defined   **b.** 3×2 **c.** $F + K$ **d.** 2×3
43. $a = 1$, $b = 2$, $c = 6$, $d = -2$

45. $A + M = \begin{bmatrix} 520 & 310 & 100 \\ 365 & 420 & 730 \end{bmatrix}$

47. $0.9 \begin{bmatrix} 300 & 200 & 100 \\ 200 & 200 & 400 \end{bmatrix} = \begin{bmatrix} 270 & 180 & 90 \\ 180 & 180 & 360 \end{bmatrix}$

49. **a.**

	Army	Navy
Officers	37,615	18,596
W. Officers	2682	190
Enlisted	171,593	69,369

b.

	Army	Navy
Officers	19,211	13,617
W. Officers	1774	6
Enlisted	96,420	51,074

c.

	Army	Navy
Officers	56,826	32,213
W. Officers	4456	196
Enlisted	268,013	120,443

51. $\begin{bmatrix} 4 & 5 \\ 3 & 3 \\ 4 & -1 \end{bmatrix}$, \$3000, $-$\$1000

53. $Q = $

	Atlanta	Chicago
Blouses	18.7	18.7
Skirts	9.9	5.5
Dresses	15.4	15.4

, \$18,700

55. $N = \begin{bmatrix} 250 & 300 & 350 & 300 \\ 300 & 200 & 250 & 150 \\ 200 & 240 & 320 & 220 \end{bmatrix}$

57. $N + L = \begin{bmatrix} 550 & 650 & 800 & 700 \\ 620 & 440 & 530 & 400 \\ 450 & 500 & 740 & 500 \end{bmatrix}$

59. $1.2N = \begin{bmatrix} 300 & 360 & 420 & 360 \\ 360 & 240 & 300 & 180 \\ 240 & 288 & 384 & 264 \end{bmatrix}$

61. $A + B = \begin{bmatrix} a_{11} & a_{12} \\ a_{21} & a_{22} \end{bmatrix} + \begin{bmatrix} b_{11} & b_{12} \\ b_{21} & b_{22} \end{bmatrix}$

$= \begin{bmatrix} a_{11} + b_{11} & a_{12} + b_{12} \\ a_{21} + b_{21} & a_{22} + b_{22} \end{bmatrix}$

$= \begin{bmatrix} b_{11} + a_{11} & b_{12} + a_{12} \\ b_{21} + a_{21} & b_{22} + a_{22} \end{bmatrix}$

$= \begin{bmatrix} b_{11} & b_{12} \\ b_{21} & b_{22} \end{bmatrix} + \begin{bmatrix} a_{11} & a_{12} \\ a_{21} & a_{22} \end{bmatrix}$

$= B + A$

63. $A + O = \begin{bmatrix} a_{11} & a_{12} \\ a_{21} & a_{22} \end{bmatrix} + \begin{bmatrix} 0 & 0 \\ 0 & 0 \end{bmatrix}$

$= \begin{bmatrix} a_{11}+0 & a_{12}+0 \\ a_{21}+0 & a_{22}+0 \end{bmatrix}$

$= \begin{bmatrix} a_{11} & a_{12} \\ a_{21} & a_{22} \end{bmatrix} = A$

Thus $A + O = A$. Using the formula given in the previous problem, we then have $0 + A = A$.

65. $A - A = \begin{bmatrix} a_{11} & a_{12} \\ a_{21} & a_{22} \end{bmatrix} - \begin{bmatrix} a_{11} & a_{12} \\ a_{21} & a_{22} \end{bmatrix}$

$= \begin{bmatrix} a_{11}-a_{11} & a_{12}-a_{12} \\ a_{21}-a_{21} & a_{22}-a_{22} \end{bmatrix}$

$= \begin{bmatrix} 0 & 0 \\ 0 & 0 \end{bmatrix} = O$

67. Proof : Add $-A$ to both sides of $X + A = B$. Then we have $(X + A) - A = B - A$. Using the results established in 44 and 47, $(X + A) - A = X + (A - A) = X$. Thus $X = B - A$.

2.2 EXERCISES

1. 16   3. 23   5. Not defined
7. Order of AB is 2×4. Order of BA is undefined.
9. Order of AB is undefined. Order of BA is 5×4.
11. Order of AB is 3×5. Order of BA is undefined.
13. Order of AB and BA is 6×6.
15. Not defined. Not defined.

17. $\begin{bmatrix} 29 \\ 23 \end{bmatrix}$ 19. $\begin{bmatrix} 43 & 29 \end{bmatrix}$ 21. $\begin{bmatrix} 0.9 & 0.8 \\ 3.3 & 2.2 \end{bmatrix}$

23. $\begin{bmatrix} 36 \\ 18 \end{bmatrix}$ 25. $\begin{bmatrix} 0.8 & 2 \\ 1.3 & 2.8 \end{bmatrix}$

27. $\begin{bmatrix} 3 & 30 & 31 & 14 \\ 8 & 46 & 26 & 26 \end{bmatrix}$

29. $\begin{bmatrix} 0.07 & 0.18 & 0.05 \end{bmatrix}$ 31. $\begin{bmatrix} 26 \\ 10 \\ 12 \end{bmatrix}$

33. $\begin{bmatrix} -4 & 4 & 21 \end{bmatrix}$ 35. $= \begin{bmatrix} 5 & 10 & 21 \\ 0 & 4 & 8 \\ 16 & 5 & 15 \end{bmatrix}$

37. Not defined   39. $\begin{bmatrix} 6 & 10 \\ 15 & 25 \end{bmatrix}$ 41. Not defined   43.

$AB = \begin{bmatrix} 1 & 1 \\ 1 & 1 \end{bmatrix} \begin{bmatrix} 1 & 1 \\ -1 & -1 \end{bmatrix}$

$= \begin{bmatrix} 1(1)+1(-1) & 1(1)+1(-1) \\ 1(1)+1(-1) & 1(1)+1(-1) \end{bmatrix}$

$= \begin{bmatrix} 0 & 0 \\ 0 & 0 \end{bmatrix} = O$

45. $A^2 = AA = \begin{bmatrix} 1 & 1 \\ -1 & -1 \end{bmatrix} \begin{bmatrix} 1 & 1 \\ -1 & -1 \end{bmatrix}$

$= \begin{bmatrix} 1(1)+1(-1) & 1(1)+1(-1) \\ -1(1)-1(-1) & -1(1)+1(-1) \end{bmatrix}$

$= \begin{bmatrix} 0 & 0 \\ 0 & 0 \end{bmatrix} = O$

47. $(A+B)^2 = \begin{bmatrix} 8 & 8 \\ 32 & 40 \end{bmatrix}$

$A^2 + 2AB + B^2 = \begin{bmatrix} 13 & 13 \\ 32 & 35 \end{bmatrix}$

Thus $(A+B)^2 \neq A^2 + 2AB + B^2$.

49. $A(B+C) = AB + AC = \begin{bmatrix} 7 & 6 \\ 9 & 10 \end{bmatrix}$

$A(BC) = (AB)C = \begin{bmatrix} 1 & 1 \\ 1 & 1 \end{bmatrix}$

51. $A^2 = AA = \begin{bmatrix} 0 & 1 & 2 \\ 0 & 0 & 3 \\ 0 & 0 & 0 \end{bmatrix} \begin{bmatrix} 0 & 1 & 2 \\ 0 & 0 & 3 \\ 0 & 0 & 0 \end{bmatrix} = \begin{bmatrix} 0 & 0 & 3 \\ 0 & 0 & 0 \\ 0 & 0 & 0 \end{bmatrix}$

$A(AA) = \begin{bmatrix} 0 & 1 & 2 \\ 0 & 0 & 3 \\ 0 & 0 & 0 \end{bmatrix} \begin{bmatrix} 0 & 0 & 3 \\ 0 & 0 & 0 \\ 0 & 0 & 0 \end{bmatrix} = \begin{bmatrix} 0 & 0 & 0 \\ 0 & 0 & 0 \\ 0 & 0 & 0 \end{bmatrix}$

53. $A = \begin{bmatrix} 2 & 3 \\ 3 & -5 \end{bmatrix}, X = \begin{bmatrix} x_1 \\ x_2 \end{bmatrix}, B = \begin{bmatrix} 5 \\ 7 \end{bmatrix}$

55. $A = \begin{bmatrix} 2 & 5 & 3 \\ 4 & -7 & -2 \\ 5 & -2 & 6 \end{bmatrix}, X = \begin{bmatrix} x_1 \\ x_2 \\ x_3 \end{bmatrix}, B = \begin{bmatrix} 16 \\ 12 \\ 24 \end{bmatrix}$

57. $A = \begin{bmatrix} 2 & -3 & 3 \\ 5 & 6 & -2 \end{bmatrix}, X = \begin{bmatrix} x_1 \\ x_2 \\ x_3 \end{bmatrix}, B = \begin{bmatrix} 3 \\ 1 \end{bmatrix}$

59. $A = \begin{bmatrix} 2 & 3 \end{bmatrix}, X = \begin{bmatrix} x_1 \\ x_2 \end{bmatrix}, B = \begin{bmatrix} 7 \end{bmatrix}$

61. $H = \begin{bmatrix} 3 \\ 4.5 \\ 4 \end{bmatrix}$ 63. $N = \begin{bmatrix} 3 & 2 & 1 \end{bmatrix}$

65. MN represents the total of each vitamin the dog gets in a meal.

67. **a.** $NR = \begin{bmatrix} 27 & 5.3 & 42 \\ 25 & 4.4 & 38 \\ 21 & 3.4 & 35 \end{bmatrix}$

The number 27 in the first row and first column indicates that 27 hundred tires are needed in LA. The number 38 in the second row and third column indicates that 38 hundred plugs are needed in NYC, and so forth.

$$\begin{array}{c} \\ \text{LA} \\ \textbf{b. } QC = \text{NYC} \\ \text{SL} \end{array} \begin{bmatrix} \$ \\ 2954 \\ 2714 \\ 2271 \end{bmatrix}$$

The number 2954 in the first row and first column indicates that a total of 2954 hundred dollars is needed for replacement parts in LA. The number 2714 in the second row and first column indicates that a total of 2714 hundred dollars is needed for replacement parts in NYC. The number 2271 in the third row and first column indicates that a total of 2271 hundred dollars is needed for replacement parts in SL.

69. **a.** $B = \begin{bmatrix} 0.4 & 0 & 0 \\ 0.6 & 1 & 0.5 \\ 0 & 0 & 0.5 \end{bmatrix}$ **b.** $C = \begin{bmatrix} 1 & 0.2 & 0 \\ 0 & 0.3 & 0 \\ 0 & 0.2 & 0.4 \\ 0 & 0.3 & 0.6 \end{bmatrix}$

c. $W = CZ = C(BY) = (CB)Y = (CB)(AX) = (CBA)X$ **d.**
$w_1 = 1930, w_2 = 1695, w_3 = 2266, w_4 = 3399$

71.

x_i	y_i	x_i^2	$x_i y_i$
0	4	0	0
1	2	1	2
2	2	4	4
3	1	9	3
4	1	16	4
Sum 10	10	30	13

We then have the system of two equations in the two unknowns a and b.

$$30a + 10b = 13$$
$$10a + 5b = 10$$

These equations can be readily solved using the techniques used in Chapter 1 and obtain $y = -0.7x + 3.4$.

2.3 EXERCISES

1. Yes 3. Yes 5. Yes 7. Yes 9. Yes

11. $\begin{bmatrix} 10 & -3 \\ -3 & 1 \end{bmatrix}$ 13. $\frac{1}{7}\begin{bmatrix} 2 & 1 \\ 3 & 5 \end{bmatrix}$ 15. No inverse

17. No inverse 19. $\begin{bmatrix} 1 & -0.5 & 0 \\ -1 & 1 & -1 \\ 1 & -0.5 & 1 \end{bmatrix}$

21. $\frac{1}{3}\begin{bmatrix} 1 & 2 & 4 \\ 1 & -1 & -2 \\ -1 & 1 & -1 \end{bmatrix}$ 23. $\frac{1}{2}\begin{bmatrix} -2 & 0 & 2 \\ 7 & -1 & -3 \\ -3 & 1 & 1 \end{bmatrix}$

25. $\frac{1}{2}\begin{bmatrix} 3 & -1 & -1 & -1 \\ 1 & 1 & -1 & -1 \\ -1 & 1 & 1 & -1 \\ -1 & -1 & 1 & 3 \end{bmatrix}$

27. $A^{-1} = \frac{1}{2}\begin{bmatrix} -1 & 4 \\ -1 & 2 \end{bmatrix}$, the solution is $(-9, -7)$.

29. $A^{-1} = \begin{bmatrix} 3 & -1 \\ -2 & 1 \end{bmatrix}$, the solution is $(9, -3)$.

31. $A^{-1} = \frac{1}{2}\begin{bmatrix} -5 & 4 \\ 3 & -2 \end{bmatrix}$, the solution is $(-7, 5)$

33. $x = 11, y = -3$ 35. $x = {}^{11}/_7, y = {}^{27}/_7$
37. $x = 3, y = -1, z = -1$
39. $x = 2, y = -7/2, z = 3/2$
41. $x_1 = -1, x_2 = -1, x_3 = 0, x_4 = 3$
43. Assume $D = ad - bc \neq 0$.

$$\frac{1}{D}\begin{bmatrix} d & -b \\ -c & a \end{bmatrix}\begin{bmatrix} a & b \\ c & d \end{bmatrix}$$
$$= \frac{1}{D}\begin{bmatrix} da-bc & db-bd \\ -ca+ac & -cb+ad \end{bmatrix} = \frac{1}{D}\begin{bmatrix} D & 0 \\ 0 & D \end{bmatrix} = \begin{bmatrix} 1 & 0 \\ 0 & 1 \end{bmatrix}$$

$$\begin{bmatrix} a & b \\ c & d \end{bmatrix}\frac{1}{D}\begin{bmatrix} d & -b \\ -c & a \end{bmatrix}$$
$$= \frac{1}{D}\begin{bmatrix} ad+b(-c) & a(-b)+ba \\ cd+d(-c) & c(-b)+da \end{bmatrix} = \frac{1}{D}\begin{bmatrix} D & 0 \\ 0 & D \end{bmatrix} = \begin{bmatrix} 1 & 0 \\ 0 & 1 \end{bmatrix}$$

45. The first client should invest $75,000 in the bond fund and $25,000 in the stock fund. The second client should invest $25,000 in the bond fund and $25,000 in the stock fund.
47. **a.** 80 of style A chairs and 40 of style B chairs
b. 10 of style A and 130 of style B
49. No 51. Yes 53. No 55. Yes
57. $X = (A+I)^{-1}B$, if $(A+I)$ has an inverse.
59. $X = I + A^{-1}B$, if A has an inverse.
61. 74 127 92 54 119 62 27 64 31

2.4 EXERCISES

1. $\frac{1}{41}\begin{bmatrix} 1,100,000,000 \\ 1,800,000,000 \end{bmatrix}$ 3. $\begin{bmatrix} 375,000,000 \\ 437,500,000 \end{bmatrix}$

5. $\frac{1}{41}\begin{bmatrix} 21,000,000,000 \\ 23,000,000,000 \end{bmatrix}$

7. Produce $2000 of food, $4000 of cloth and $2000 of wood.

9. $\frac{5}{192}\begin{bmatrix} 162,000,000 \\ 139,000,000 \\ 103,000,000 \end{bmatrix}$

11. $p_1 = {}^{2t}/_7, p_2 = t$ 13. $p_1 = {}^1/_6, p_2 = t$
15. $p_1 = {}^{28t}/_{85}, p_2 = {}^{82t}/_{85}, p_3 = t$
17. $p_1 = {}^{14t}/_{39}, p_2 = {}^{20t}/_{394}, p_3 = t$

19. **a.** $\begin{bmatrix} 728/6985 & 3114/81.554 & 350/185.865 \\ 409/6985 & 7624/81.554 & 6737/185.865 \\ 1008/6985 & 9159/81.554 & 43.949/185.865 \end{bmatrix}$

b. $X = \begin{bmatrix} 6985 \\ 81,554 \\ 185,865 \end{bmatrix}$

c. X is the total output column of the table.

21. $X = \begin{bmatrix} 2000 \\ 2000 \\ 2000 \\ 1000 \end{bmatrix}$

REVIEW EXERCISES

1. $\begin{bmatrix} 3 & 9 \\ 6 & 3 \\ -3 & 9 \end{bmatrix}$ 2. $\begin{bmatrix} -4 & -10 \\ -2 & 0 \\ -6 & 4 \end{bmatrix}$ 3. $\begin{bmatrix} -1 & -1 \\ 4 & 3 \\ -9 & 13 \end{bmatrix}$

4. [14] 5. Not defined 6. Not defined

7. $\begin{bmatrix} 4 \\ 2 \end{bmatrix}$ 8. Not defined 9. $\begin{bmatrix} 11 & 3 & 5 \\ 7 & 1 & 0 \\ 7 & 3 & 7 \end{bmatrix}$

10. $\begin{bmatrix} 3 & 3 \\ 3 & 16 \end{bmatrix}$ 11. Not defined 12. [12]

13. Part (a) follows from part (b) by taking $B = A$. To show part (b) notice that

$$AB = \begin{bmatrix} a_{11} & 0 & 0 \\ 0 & a_{22} & 0 \\ 0 & 0 & a_{33} \end{bmatrix}\begin{bmatrix} b_{11} & 0 & 0 \\ 0 & b_{22} & 0 \\ 0 & 0 & b_{33} \end{bmatrix} = \begin{bmatrix} a_{11}b_{11} & 0 & 0 \\ 0 & a_{22}b_{22} & 0 \\ 0 & 0 & a_{33}b_{33} \end{bmatrix}$$

14. $\frac{1}{3}\begin{bmatrix} 1 & -1 \\ -2 & 5 \end{bmatrix}$ 15. Not defined   16. $-\frac{1}{7}\begin{bmatrix} 1 & 3 \\ 3 & 2 \end{bmatrix}$

17. $\frac{1}{3}\begin{bmatrix} -12 & 6 & -3 \\ 5 & -2 & 1 \\ -1 & 1 & 1 \end{bmatrix}$ 18. Does not exist

19. $\frac{1}{3}\begin{bmatrix} 2 & -1 & 0 \\ 6 & 0 & -3 \\ -5 & 1 & 3 \end{bmatrix}$ 20. $x - 1, y = 4$

21. $x = -17, y = -16$ 22. $x = 8, y = -3, z = 2$

23. $x = 23, y = 60, z = -53$ 24. $\frac{1}{21}\begin{bmatrix} 550,000,000 \\ 1,150,000,000 \end{bmatrix}$

25. $\frac{1}{1597}\begin{bmatrix} 42,000,000,000 \\ 68,300,000,000 \\ 76,800,000,000 \end{bmatrix}$ 26. $p_1 = {}^{3t}/8, p_2 = t$

27. $p_1 = {}^{37t}/85, p_2 = {}^{78t}/85, p_3 = t$

3.1 EXERCISES

1. $x =$ no. of tractors to St. Louis,
$y =$ no. of tractors to Minneapolis
Minimize $C = 30x + 40y$
Subject to
$x + y \leq 200$
$x \geq 100$
$y \geq 50$
$x, y \geq 0$

3. $x =$ no. of plain pen tips, $y =$ no. of fancy pen tips
Maximize $P = 4x + 5y$
Subject to
$x + 2y \leq 20$
$x + y \leq 11$
$2x + y \leq 15$
$x, y \geq 0$

5. $x =$ no. of tables, $y =$ no. of desks
Maximize $P = 4x + 3y$
Subject to
$x + 3y \leq 45$
$x + 2y \leq 35$
$2x + y \leq 55$
$x, y \geq 0$

7. $x =$ no. of smallmouth bass,
$y =$ no. of largemouth bass
Maximize $Z = x + y$
Subject to
$x + 4y \leq 800$
$x + 2y \leq 500$
$2x + y \leq 700$
$x, y \geq 0$

9. $x =$ no. acres of white corn,
$y =$ no. of acres of yellow corn
Maximize $R = 380x + 420y$
Subject to
$x + y \leq 100$
$95x - 360y \geq 0$
$x, y \geq 0$

11. $x =$ no. of oatmeal cookies, $y =$ no. of oatmeal bars
Maximize $R = x + 1.5y$
Subject to $x/18 + y/16 \leq 50$
$x - 2y \geq 0$
$x, y \geq 0$

13. $x_1 =$ amount in m.m. fund in thousands of dollars,
$x_2 =$ amount in bond fund in thousands of dollars,
$x_3 =$ amount in cons. stock fund in thousands of dollars,
$x_4 =$ amount in spec. stock fund in thousands of dollars
Maximize $z = 0.06x_1 + 0.08x_2$
$+ 0.1x_3 + 0.13x_4$
Subject to $x_1 + x_2 + x_3 + x_4 \leq 100$
$x_3 \geq 10$
$10 \leq x_1 \leq 40$
$x_2 - x_3 \geq 0$
$x_1 - x_4 \geq 0$
$x_1, x_2, x_3, x_4 \geq 0$

15. $x_1 =$ no. of screens shipped from Denver to DM
$x_2 =$ no. of screens shipped from Denver to FW
$x_3 =$ no. of screens shipped from Santa Fe to DM
$x_4 =$ no. of screens shipped from Santa Fe to FW
Minimize $C = 20x_1 + 40x_2$
$+ 50x_3 + 20x_4$
Subject to $x_1 + x_2 \leq 500$
$x_3 + x_4 \leq 100$
$x_1 + x_3 \geq 150$
$x_2 + x_4 \geq 250$
$x_1, x_2, x_3, x_4 \geq 0$

17. $x_1 =$ no. oz. of Food A, $x_2 =$ no. oz. of Food B, $x_3 =$ no. oz of Food C
Minimize $C = 4x_1 + 3x_2 + x_3$
Subject to $x_1 + x_2 + x_3 \leq 20$
$30x_1 + 30x_2 + 10x_3 \geq 500$
$20x_1 + 20x_2 + 10x_3 \geq 329$
$35x_1 + 50x_2 + 20x_3 \geq 425$
$x_1, x_2, x_3 \geq 0$

19. $x_1 =$ no. bags of fertilizer A,
$x_2 =$ no. bag of fertilizer B,
$x_3 =$ no. bag of fertilizer C
Minimize $C = 20x_1 + 30x_2 + 20x_3$
Subject to $40x_1 + 20x_2 \geq 4400$
$30x_1 + 20x_2 + 30x_3 \geq 1800$
$10x_1 + 60x_2 + 40x_3 \geq 2800$
$x_1, x_2, x_3 \geq 0$

21. $x_1 =$ no. days first plant operates,
$x_2 =$ no. days second plant operates,
$x_3 =$ no. days third plant operates
Minimize $C = 40,000x_1 + 30,000x_2$
$+ 45,000x_3$
Subject to $8000x_1 + 4000x_2 + 4500x_3 \geq 40,000$
$3000x_1 + 6000x_2 + 6500x_3 \geq 24,000$
$x_1, x_2, x_3 \geq 0$

23. $x_1 =$ no. days first mine operates,
$x_2 =$ no. days second mine operates,

$x_3 =$ no. days third mine operates

Minimize $C = 2000x_1 + 3000x_2 + 4000x_3$

Subject to

$$2x_1 + x_2 + x_3 \geq 21$$
$$x_1 + x_2 + 3x_3 \geq 19$$
$$x_1 + 4x_2 + 3x_3 \geq 25$$
$$x_1, x_2, x_3 \geq 0$$

25. $x_1 =$ no. of students bused from SW to NW

$x_2 =$ no. of students bused from SW to NE

$x_3 =$ no. of students bused from SE to NW

$x_4 =$ no. of students bused from SE to NE

Minimize $C = 4x_1 + 2x_2 + 2x_3 + 4x_4$

Subject to

$$x_1 + x_2 \geq 400$$
$$x_3 + x_4 \geq 300$$
$$x_1 + x_3 \leq 200$$
$$x_2 + x_4 \leq 600$$
$$x_1, x_2, x_3, x_4 \geq 0$$

27. $x_1 =$ no. oz. of Food A, $x_2 =$ no. oz. of Food B, $x_3 =$ no. oz of Food C, $x_4 =$ no. oz of Food D

Minimize

$$C = 0.5x_1 + 0.4x_2$$
$$+0.6x_3 + 0.75x_4$$

Subject to

$$x_1 + x_2 + x_3 + x_4 \leq 18$$
$$x_1 + 2x_2 \geq 10$$
$$100x_1 + 50x_2 + 10x_4 \geq 800$$
$$100x_1 + 200x_3 + 20x_4 \geq 500$$
$$50x_3 + 70x_4 \geq 200$$
$$200x_1 + 150x_2 + 75x_3 + 250x_4 \leq 3000$$
$$2000x_2 + 5000x_4 \leq 25,000$$
$$5x_1 + 20x_2 + 30x_3 + 70x_4 \leq 130$$
$$x_1, x_2, x_3, x_4 \geq 0$$

29. $x_1 =$ no. oz of sugar used in the first candy

$x_2 =$ no. oz of nuts used in the first candy

$x_3 =$ no. oz of chocolate used in the first candy

$y_1 =$ no. oz of sugar used in the second candy

$y_2 =$ no. oz of nuts used in the second candy

$y_3 =$ no. oz of chocolate used in the second candy

Maximize

$$R = 0.5(x_1 + x_2 + x_3)$$
$$+0.65(y_1 + y_2 + y_3)$$

Subject to

$$x_1 + y_1 \leq 200$$
$$x_2 + y_2 \leq 30$$
$$x_3 + y_3 \leq 60$$
$$-0.25x_1 + 0.75x_2 - 0.25x_3 \geq 0$$
$$-0.15y_1 + 0.85y_2 - 0.15y_3 \geq 0$$
$$-0.1y_1 - 0.1y_2 + 0.9y_3 \geq 0$$
$$x_1, x_2, x_3 \geq 0$$
$$y_1, y_2, y_3 \geq 0$$

31. $x_1 =$ no. of employees who work M – F,

$x_2 =$ no. of employees who work Tu – Sa,

$x_3 =$ no. of employees who work W – Su,

$x_4 =$ no. of employees who work Th – M,

$x_5 =$ no. of employees who work F – Tu,

$x_6 =$ no. of employees who work Sa – W,

$x_7 =$ no. of employees who work Su – Th,

Minimize $z = x_1 + x_2 + x_3 + x_4$
$$+x_5 + x_6 + x_7$$

Subject to

$$x_1 + x_4 + x_5 + x_6 + x_7 \geq 82$$
$$x_1 + x_2 + x_5 + x_6 + x_7 \geq 87$$
$$x_1 + x_2 + x_3 + x_6 + x_7 \geq 77$$
$$x_1 + x_2 + x_3 + x_4 + x_7 \geq 73$$
$$x_1 + x_2 + x_3 + x_4 + x_5 \geq 75$$
$$x_2 + x_3 + x_4 + x_5 + x_6 \geq 42$$
$$x_3 + x_4 + x_5 + x_6 + x_7 \geq 23$$
$$x_1, x_2, x_3, x_4, x_5, x_6, x_7 \geq 0$$

33. $x =$ no. of shares of KO, $y =$ no. of shares of INTC, $z =$ no. shares of MCD

Maximize $R = 1.25x + 0.40y + 0.67z$

Subject to

$$42x + 21y + 35z \leq 12,000$$
$$21y - 70z \geq 0$$
$$35z \leq 3000$$
$$x, y \geq 0$$

3.2 EXERCISES

1.

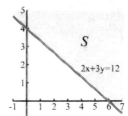

3.

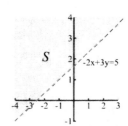

5.

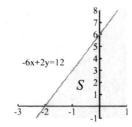

7.

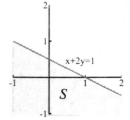

9.

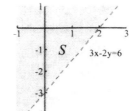

11.

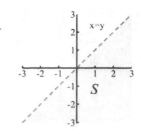

13.

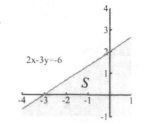

15.

17.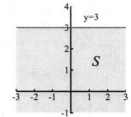

19.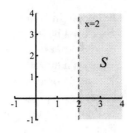

21.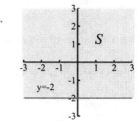

23.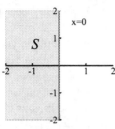

25.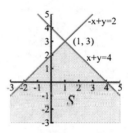

27.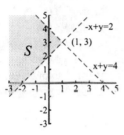

29.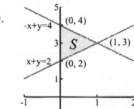

31.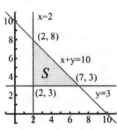

33.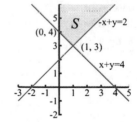

35.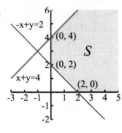

37.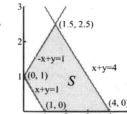

39.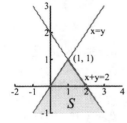

41.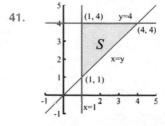

43. $2y - x \geq 0$
$12y + 5x \leq 44$
$8y + 43x \geq -16$
$(-16/47, -8/47), (4,2), (-8/7, 29/7)$

45. $y - 4x \leq 2$
$2y - x \geq 44$
$3y + 5x \leq 15$
$(-4/7, -2/7), (9/17, 70/17), (30/13, 15/13)$

47. $2y + x \leq 6$
$5y - 2x \geq -10$
$y + 2x \geq 0$
$(50/9, 2/9), (-2,4), (5/6, -10/6)$

49. $x + y \leq 200$
$x \geq 100$
$y \geq 50$
$(100,50), (150,50), (100,100)$

51. $x + 2y \leq 20$
$x + y \leq 11$
$2x + y \leq 15$
$x, y \geq 0$
$(7.5,0), (4,7), (2,9), (0,10)$

53. $x + 3y \leq 45$
$x + 2y \leq 35$
$2x + y \leq 55$
$x, y \geq 0$
$(27.5,0), (25,5), (15,10), (0,15)$

55. $x + 4y \leq 800$
$x + 2y \leq 500$
$2x + y \leq 700$
$x, y \geq 0$
$(350,0), (300,100), (200,150), (0,200)$

57. $x + y \leq 100$
$-3x + y \leq 0$
$x, y \geq 0$

59. $x/18 + y/16 \leq 50$
$x - 2y \geq 0$
$x, y \geq 0$

3.3 EXERCISES

1. Maximum is 12, minimum is 3.
3. Maximum is 16, minimum is 7.
5. No maximum, minimum is 6.
7. Maximum is 1400 at $(10,40)$
9. Maximum is 180 at $(30,40)$
11. Minimum is 7 at $(3,4)$
13. Minimum is 2 at $(1,0)$
15. Maximum is 48 at $(8,4)$
17. Minimum is 20 at $(5,0)$
19. No maximum.   21. No minimum.
23. Minimum of $5000, 100 shipped to St. Louis distributor, 50 shipped to Minneapolis distributor.
25. Maximum of $53, 2 plain tip pens, 9 fancy tip pens.

27. Maximum of $115, 25 tables, 5 desks.   29. 400
31. $390,000. 3 days for Plant A and 15 days for Plant B, or 5 days for Plant A and 12 days for Plant B
33. $1150, 200 smallmouth, 150 largemouth.
35. $20,000 for possible values of product 1 and product 2 $(5, 15), (6, 14), (7, 13), (8, 12), (9, 11),$ or $(10, 10)$
37. 16.31 at $(12.12, 6.88)$
39. $z(0, 5) = 10$, $z(1, 2) = 7$, $z(2, 1) = 8$, $z(6, 0) = 18$, $z(0, 8) = 16$, $z(8, 8) = 40$, $z(8, 0) = 24$. Since the minimum occurs at an actual corner of the feasible region, this linear programming problem has a minimum. Since the maximum occurs at a corner that is not a corner of the feasible region, this linear programming problem does not have a maximum.
41. No minimum and no maximum

REVIEW EXERCISES

1. 10 100-lb sack of sludge and 10 100-lb sack of bone meal.
2. 3 of the first type and 2 of the second
3. 26 chairs and 8 sofas.
4. **a.** The wood is in excess and by 10 feet.
b. The wood is in excess and by 90 feet. The material is in excess and by 80 square yards.
5. 3 of the first type of park benches and 6 of the second type of park benches.
6. **a.** The labor is in excess by 3 hours.
b. Wood is in excess by 6 square feet.
7. North mine 2 days and South mine 3 days, $18,000
8. 30 acres of corn and 210 acres of soybeans, $59,040.
9. 12 pounds of the first mixture and 21 pounds of the second mixture, $144
10. **a.** $(17 - h/2, 8 + h)$, $1840 + 20h$
b. $-8 \le h \le 34$ **c.** 20

4.1 EXERCISES

1. **a.** False **b.** False   3. **a.** True **b.** False
5. **a.** False **b.** True **c.** False (d) True
7. **a.** $\emptyset$, $\{3\}$ **b.** $\emptyset$, $\{3\}$, $\{4\}$, $\{3, 4\}$

9.
11. **a.** 2   **b.** 3   disjoint
13. **a.** 1, 2, 3   **b.** 1   not disjoint
15. **a.** I   **b.** V
17. **a.** VIII   **b.** IV
19. **a.** II, V, VI   **b.** III, IV, VII
21. **a.** VII   **b.** I, II, III, IV, V, VII, VIII
23. **a.** $\{4, 5, 6\}$ **b.** $\{1, 2, 3, 4, 5, 6, 7, 8\}$
25. **a.** $\{1, 2, 3\}$ **b.** $\{9, 10\}$
27. **a.** $\{5, 6\}$ **b.** $\{1, 2, 3, 4, 7, 8, 9, 10\}$
29. **a.** $\emptyset$ **b.** $\emptyset$
31. **a.** People in your state who do not own an automobile
b. People in your state who own an automobile or house
c. People in your state who own an automobile or not a house
33. **a.** People in your state who own an automobile but not a house

b. People in your state who do not own an automobile and do not own a house
c. People in your state who do not own an automobile or do not own a house
35. **a.** People in your state who own an automobile and a house and a piano
b. People in your state who own an automobile or a house or a piano
c. People in your state who own both an automobile and a house or else own a piano
37. **a.** People in your state who do not own both an automobile and a house but do own a piano
b. People in your state who do not own an automobile, nor a house, nor a piano
c. People in your state who own a piano, but do not own a car or a house
39. **a.** $N \cap F$ **b.** $N \cap H^c$ 41. **a.** $N \cup S$ **b.** $N^c \cap S^c$
43. **a.** $(N \cap H) \cup (S \cap H)$ **b.** $(N \cap F) \cap H^c$
45. **a.** $(F \cap H) \cap (N \cup S)^c$ **b.** $F \cap H^c \cap N^c \cap S^c$
47. Both expressions give U
49. Both expressions give $\{1, 2, 3, 4, 5, 6, 7\}$
51. Both expressions give $\{8, 9, 10\}$.

4.2 EXERCISES

1. 135   3. 70   5. 60   7. 150   9. 110
11. 90   13. 15   15. 7   17. 3   19. 56
21. **a.** 1100   **b.** 750   **c.** 100
23. **a.** 100   **b.** 500
25. **a.** 30   **b.** 360   **c.** 70
27. **a.** 20   **b.** 25   **c.** 345   29. 30
31. From the figure we have $n(A) - n(A \cap B) = x + w$, $n(B) - n(B \cap C) = u + y$, $n(C) - n(A \cap C) = v + z$, and $n(A \cap B \cap C) = t$. Adding these four equations gives the result since from the figure $n(A \cup B \cup C) = t + u + v + w + x + y + z$.

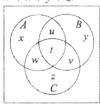

4.3 EXERCISES

1. $\emptyset$, $\{a\}$, $\{b\}$, $\{c\}$, $\{a, b\}$, $\{a, c\}$, $\{b, c\}$, $\{a, b, c\}$
3. $S = \{(H, H, H), (H, H, T), (H, T, H), (T, H, H), (H, T, T),$ $(T, H, T), (T, T, H), (T, T, T)\}$,
$E = \{(H, H, H), (H, H, T), (H, T, H), (T, H, H)\}$
5. $S = \{(1, 1, 1), (1, 1, 0), (1, 0, 1), (0, 1, 1), (0, 0, 1),$ $(0, 1, 0), (1, 0, 0), (0, 0, 0)\}$, $E = \{(1, 1, 1), (1, 1, 0), (1, 0, 1),$ $(0, 1, 1)\}$
7. **a.** $\{black, white, red\}$ **b.** $\{black, red\}$
9. $\{(A, B, C), (A, B, D), (A, B, E), (A, C, D), (A, C, E),$ $(A, D, E), (B, C, D), (B, C, E), (B, D, E), (C, D, E)\}$, $\{(A, B, C), (A, B, D), (A, B, E), (B, C, D), (B, C, E), (B, D, E)\}$
11. $S = \{1, 2, 3, 4, 6, 9\}$, $E = \{2, 4, 6\}$

13. **a.** $\{0,1,2,3,4,5,6,7,8,9,10\}$ **b.** $E = \{6,7,8,9,10\}$ **c.**
$F = \{0,1,2,3,4\}$
d. $E \cup F = \{0,1,2,3,4,6,7,8,9,10\}$. $E \cap F = \emptyset$. $E^c = \{0,1,2,3,4,5\}$. $E \cap F^c = \{6,7,8,9,10\}$. $E^c \cap F^c = \{5\}$
e. E^c and $E \cap F^c$. $E \cap F^c$ and $E^c \cap F^c$. $E \cup F$ and $E^c \cap F^c$.
15. **a.** $\{(S,S,S), (S,S,F), (S,F,S), (F,S,S), (S,F,F),$
$(F,S,F), (F,F,S), (F,F,F)\}$
b. $E = \{(S,S,S),(S,S,F),(S,F,S),(F,S,S)\}$
c. $G = \{(S,S,S),(S,S,F),(S,F,S),(S,F,F)\}$
d. $E \cup G = \{ (S,S,S), (S,S,F), (S,F,S), (S,F,F),$
$(F,S,S)\}$, $E \cap G = \{(S,S,S),(S,S,F),(S,F,S)\}$,
$G^c = \{(F,S,S),(F,S,F),(F,F,S),(F,F,F)\}$, $E^c \cap G = \{(S,F,F)\}$, $(E \cup G)^c = \{(F,F,S),(F,S,F),(F,F,F)\}$.
e. $E \cap G$ and G^c. $E \cap G$ and $E^c \cap G$. $E \cap G$ and $(E \cup G)^c$. G^c and $E^c \cap G$. $E^c \cap G$ and $(E \cup G)^c$. $E \cup G$ and $(E \cup G)^c$.
17. **a.** Pencils that are longer than 10 cm and less than 25 cm.
b. Pencils that are less than 10 cm long.
c. Pencils that are 25 cm or longer. **d.** $\emptyset$
19. $E \cap F^c$ 21. $F^c \cap E^c$ 23. $E \cap F \cap G^c$
25. $E \cup F \cup G =$ all 26 letters. $E^c \cap F^c \cap G^c = \emptyset$. $E \cap F \cap G = \emptyset$. $E \cup F^c \cup G = \{a,e,i,o,u,b,c,d\}$
27. $S = \{r,b,g,y\}$, $E = \{b,g\}$

4.4 EXERCISES
1. $1/2$ 3. $2/3$ 5. $1/13$ 7. $1/2$
9. $3/26$ 11. $1/4$ 13. $2/3$ 15. 0.15
17. **a.** 0.12 **b.** 0.8 **c.** 0.08 19. 0.56
21. A: 0.125, B: 0.175, C: 0.4, D: 0.2, F: 0.1
23. 0.55 25. $1/2$ 27. $1/2$ 29. $3/8, 7/8$
31. $1/12$ 33. $1/36, 1/12, 5/36$ 35. $1/3$

4.5 EXERCISES
1. 0.50, 0.90 3. 0.18, 0.63, 0.62 5. 0.25
7. $1/6$ 9. $7/30$ 11. 0.60, 0.80, 0
13. 0.70, 0.70, 0, 0.30, 1 15. 0.60, 0.10
17. 0.20, 0.10 19. 0.20, 0.10, 0.15
21. 0.85 23. **a.** 3:17 **b.** 1:3
25. 2:3 27. 7:5 29. 0.20
31. 0.04, 0.96 33. 0.039, 0.049, 0.951
35. **a.** 0.009 **b.** 0.001 **c.** 0.006 **d.** 0.974
37. 0.20
39. You do not know what the actual probability is. You do know that the empirical probability is $165/1000 = 0.165$. This represents the best guess for the actual probability. But if you tossed the coin more times, the relative frequency and the new empirical probability would most likely had changed.
41. The probabilities in the game are constant and do not change just because you are on a winning streak. Thus no matter what has happened to you in the past, the probability of winning any one game remains constant at 0.48. Thus if you continue to play, you should expect to win 48% of the time in the future. You have been lucky to have won 60% of the time up until now.
43. After reading the first discussion problem above, we know that it is, in fact, impossible to determine with certainty the actual probability precisely. Since the die has been tossed

a total of 2000 times and a one has come up 335 times, our best guess at the probability is $335/2000 = 0.1675$.

4.6 EXERCISES
1. $3/7, 3/5$ 3. $2/3, 4/5$ 5. 1, 0
7. $2/3, 1/2$ 9. $1/3, 1$ 11. 0, $1/2$
13. No 15. Yes 17. No
19. Yes 21. $2/11$ 23. $1/7$
25. **a.** $\frac{10,200}{132,600} \approx 0.077$ **b.** $\frac{49}{25 \cdot 33} \approx 0.059$
27. 0.12, 0.64, 0.60 29. $1/3, 3/10$
31. No 33. 0.65 35. 0.72
37. 0.02, 0.017 39. 0.026
41. 0.000001 43. $5/7, 5/21, 1/21$
45. Yes 47. No 49. 0.057818
51. For E and F to be independent, they must satisfy $P(E) \times P(F) = P(E \cap F)$. From the Venn diagram, we must have: $(p_1 + p_2) \times (p_3 + p_2) = p_2$. So,

$$p_1 p_3 + p_2 p_3 + p_1 p_2 + p_2^2 = p_2$$

$$p_1 p_3 = p_2(1 - p_3 - p_2 - p_1) = p_2 p_4$$

The above steps can be reversed, so if $p_1 p_3 = p_2 p_4$, we will have $P(E) \times P(F) = P(E \cap F)$.
If the sets are mutually disjoint, then $p_2 = 0$. This implies that $p_1 p_3 = p_2 p_4 = 0$. Then either p_1 or p_3 or both are zero. Thus either $P(E) = 0, P(F) = 0$, or both.
53. Since E and F are independent, $P(E) \times P(F) = P(E \cap F)$.

$$P(E^c \cap F^c) = 1 - P(E \cup F)$$
$$= 1 - (P(E) + P(F) - P(E \cap F))$$
$$= 1 - P(E) - P(F) + P(E) \times P(F)$$
$$= (1 - P(E)) \times (1 - P(F))$$
$$= P(E^c) \times P(F^c)$$

Hence, if E and F are independent, so are E^c and F^c.
55. Since E and F are exclusive, $P(E \cap F) = P(\emptyset) = 0$. Since $P(E)$ and $P(F)$ are both nonzero, then $P(E) \times P(F) > 0$. Therefore, E and F are not independent.
57.

$$P(E^c|F) = \frac{P(E^c \cap F)}{P(F)}$$
$$= \frac{P(F) - P(E \cap F)}{P(F)}$$
$$= 1 - P(E|F)$$

59. $P(E|F) = \frac{P(E \cap F)}{P(F)} = \frac{P(F)}{P(F)} = 1$
61. $P(E|F) + P(E^c|F) = \frac{P(E \cap F) + P(E^c \cap F)}{P(F)} = \frac{P(F)}{P(F)} = 1$

4.7 EXERCISES
1. $3/7, 57/93$ 3. $3/19, 1/3$ 5. $4/11$
7. **a.** $2/23$ **b.** $21/23$ 9. $2/17$
11. **a.** $1/56$ **b.** $5/28$ 13. $2/7$
15. $4/19$ 17. $13/51$ 19. $13/51$
21. $6/17$ 23. $100/136 \approx 0.74$
25. $396/937 \approx 0.42, 5/937 \approx 0.005$

27. $5/7$ **29.** $10/19$ **31. a.** $1/12$ **b.** $1/4$
33. $P(1|N) = 6/20, P(2|N) = 4/20, P(3|N) = 6/20, P(4|N) = 4/20$

REVIEW EXERCISES

1. a. Yes **b.** No **c.** Yes
2. $\{x \mid x = 5n, n \text{ is an integer and } 1 \leq n \leq 8\}$
3. $\{0, -\sqrt{2}, \sqrt{2}\}$
4. $\emptyset, \{A\}, \{B\}, \{C\}, \{A,B\}, \{A,C\}, \{B,C\}, \{A,B,C\}$

5. a. **b.** **c.**

6. $A \cup B = \{1,2,3,4\}, A \cap B = \{2,3\}, B^c = \{1,5,6\}, A \cap B \cap C = \{2,3\} \cap \{4,5\} = \emptyset, (A \cup B) \cap C = \{4\}, A \cap B^c \cap C = \emptyset$
7. a. My current instructors who are less than 6 feet tall. **b.** My current instructors who are at least 6 feet tall or are male. **c.** My current instructors who are female and weigh at most 180 pounds. **d.** My current male instructors who are at least 6 feet tall and weigh more than 180 pounds. **e.** My current male instructors who are less than 6 feet tall and weigh more than 180 pounds. **f.** My current female instructors who are at least 6 feet tall and weigh more than 180 pounds.
8. a. M^c **b.** $M^c \cap W^c$ **c.** $M \cap (H \cup W)$
9. $\{1,2,3,4\} = \{1,2,3,4\}$
10. The shaded area is $(A \cap B)^c = A^c \cup B^c$.

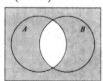

11. 120   **12.** 10   **13.** 50
14. a. 40 **b.** 45 **c.** 19
15. a. 0.016, 0.248, 0.628, 0.088, 0.016, 0.044   **b.** 0.892
c. 0.264
16. a. $5/30$ **b.** $15/30$ **c.** $20/30$
17. $P(E \cup F) = 0.60, P(E \cap F) = 0, P(E^c) = 0.75$
18. $P(E \cup F) = 0.55, P(E^c \cap F) = 0.35$,
$P((E \cup F)^c) = 0.45$
19. $P(B) = 1/6$ **20.** 0.75
21. a. 0.09 **b.** 0.91
22. a. 0.13 **b.** 0.09 **c.** 0.55
23. $P(E|F) = 0.40, P(E^c|F) = 0.60, P(F^c|E^c) = 4/7$
24. Not independent
25. $(0.05)^3$
26. 0.254
27. a. $2/31$ **b.** $4/31$
28. 0.50

5.1 EXERCISES

1. $5 \times 4 \times 3 = 60$ **3.** $8 \times 7 \times 6 \times 5 \times 4 = 6720$
5. $7! = 5040$ **7.** $9! = 362,880$ **9.** $9 \times 8 = 72$
11. n **13.** $4 \times 30 = 120$ **15.** $4 \times 10 \times 5 = 200$
17. $10^6 = 1,000,000$ **19.** $2 \times 10 \times 5 \times 3 = 300$

21. $(26)^3(10)^3 = 17,576,000$ **23.** 96
25. $5 \times 4 \times 4 \times 3 \times 3 \times 2 \times 2 = 2880$ **27.** $5! = 120$
29. $2!4!6! = 34,560$ **31.** $9!5! = 43,545,600$
33. $3!4! = 144$ **35.** $12 \times 11 \times 10 \times 9 = 11,880$
37. 1,814,400   **39.** $(10 \times 9 \times 8)(8 \times 7 \times 6) = 241,920$
41. $P(11,4) \times P(9,3) \times P(5,2) = 79,833,600$
43. $P(n,r) = n(n-1)(n-2)\cdots(n-r+1)$

$$= n(n-1)(n-2)\cdots(n-r+1)\frac{(n-r)(n-r-1)\cdots 2\cdot 1}{(n-r)(n-r-1)\cdots 2\cdot 1}$$

$$= \frac{n(n-1)(n-2)\cdots(n-r+1)(n-r)(n-r-1)\cdots 2\cdot 1}{(n-r)(n-r-1)\cdots 2\cdot 1}$$

$$= \frac{n!}{(n-r)!}$$

45. 24

5.2 EXERCISES

1. $\frac{8\times 7\times 6}{3\times 2\times 1} = 56$ **3.** $\frac{8\times 7\times 6\times 5\times 4}{5\times 4\times 3\times 2\times 1} = 56$ **5.** 12
7. 35   **9.** 105   **11.** n

13. $(a,b,c) \leftarrow$
$(a,b) < \begin{matrix}(a,b)\\(b,a)\end{matrix}$
$(a,c) < \begin{matrix}(a,c)\\(c,a)\end{matrix}$
$(b,c) < \begin{matrix}(b,c)\\(c,b)\end{matrix}$

15. 10
17. $C(46,6) = \frac{46!}{40! \times 6!} = 9,366,819$
19. $C(20,5) = \frac{20!}{15! \times 5!} = 15,504$
21. $C(20,4) = \frac{20!}{16! \times 4!} = 4845$
23. $C(40,5) = \frac{40!}{5! \times 35!} = 658,008$
25. $C(11,3) \times C(7,2) = 3465$
27. $C(20,7) \times C(6,3) = 1,550,400$
29. $C(12,3)P(9,3) = 110,880$
31. $C(11,4)P(7,2) = 13,860$
33. $C(9,5) = 126$
35. $C(8,5) = 56$
37. $2^8 - C(8,0) - C(8,1) = 256 - 1 - 8 = 247$
39. $C(12,3)C(8,3)C(4,2)2 = 147,840$
41. $C(4,3) \cdot 48 \cdot 44/2 = 4224$
43. $C(4,2)C(4,2)C(13,2) \cdot 44 = 123,552$
45. $C(n,r) = \dfrac{n!}{(r!)(n-r)!}$

$$= \frac{n!}{(n-r)!(n-(n-r))!}$$

$$= C(n,n-r)$$

5.3 EXERCISES

1. $3/10, 1/3$ **3.** $(6\cdot 7\cdot 8)/1330$ **5.** $20/323$ **7.** $6/1326$
9. $78/1326$ **11.** $208/1326$ **13.** $4/2,589,960$
15. $624/2,589,960$ **17.** $10,200/2,589,960$
19. $123,552/2,589,960$
21. 0.0833; 0.2361; 0.4271; 0.6181
23. 1   **25.** $6/45$ **27.** $56/2^{10} \approx 0.0547$
29. $5/11$ **31.** 420   **33.** 34,650   **35.** 2520
37. a. 6 **b.** 3 **c.** 24 **d.** 12 **e.** 6   **39.** 3780

5.4 EXERCISES

1. $5(.2)^4(.8) = .0064$ **3.** $35(.5)^7 \approx 0.273$

5. $70(.25)^4(.75)^4 \approx 0.087$ 7. $20(.5)^6 \approx 0.3125$

9. $35(.1)^4(.9)^3 \approx 0.00255$ 11. $10(.1)^3(.9)^2 \approx 0.0081$

13. $45 \times (0.5)^{10} \approx 0.044$ 15. $56(0.5)^{10} \approx 0.0547$

17. $11(0.5)^{10} \approx 0.0107$ 19. $7(0.6)^6(0.4) \approx 0.1306$

21. $7(0.6)^6(0.4) + (0.6)^7 \approx 0.1586$

23. $(0.4)^7 + 7(0.6)(0.4)^6 + 21(0.6)^2(0.4)^5 \approx 0.0962$

25. $1 - (0.633)^4 \approx 0.839$ 27. $(0.839)^{10} \approx 0.173$

29. $1 - (0.915)^4 - 4(0.085)(0.915)^3 \approx 0.03859$

31. $(0.0386)^3 \approx 0.0000575$

33. $12(0.05)(0.95)^{11} \approx 0.341$

35. $(.95)^{12} + 12(.05)(.95)^{11} + 66(.05)^2(.95)^{10} \approx 0.980$

37. $C(20,10)(0.8)^{10}(0.2)^{10} \approx 0.002$

39. $190(.8)^{18}(.2)^2 + 20(.8)^{19}(.2) + (.8)^{20} \approx 0.206$

41. $190(0.05)^2(0.95)^{18} \approx 0.189$ 43. ≈ 0.984

5.5 EXERCISES

1. $a^5 - 5a^4b + 10a^3b^2 - 10a^2b^3 + 5ab^4 - b^5$

3. $32x^5 + 240x^4y + 720x^3y^2 + 1080x^2y^3 + 810xy^4 + 243y^5$

5. $1 - 6x + 15x^2 - 20x^3 + 15x^4 - 6x^5 + x^6$

7. $16 - 32x^2 + 24x^4 - 8x^6 + x^8$

9. $s^{12} + 6s^{10}t^2 + 15s^8t^4 + 20s^6t^6 + 15s^4t^8 + 6s^2t^{10} + t^{12}$

11. $x^8 + 4x^6y^3 + 6x^4y^6 + 4x^2y^9 + y^{12}$

13. $a^{10} - 10a^9b + 45a^8b^2, 45a^2b^8 - 10ab^9 + b^{10}$

15. $x^{11} + 11x^{10}y + 55x^9y^2, 55x^2y^9 + 11xy^{10} + y^{11}$

17. $1 - 12z + 66z^2, 66z^{10} - 12z^{11} + z^{12}$

19. $1 - 12x^3 + 66x^6, 66x^{30} - 12x^{33} + x^{36}$

21. $1024a^{10} + 5120a^9b + 11520a^8b^2, 180a^2b^8 + 20ab^9 + b^{10}$

23. $1, 7, 21, 35, 35, 21, 7, 1$ 25. 16   27. 32

REVIEW EXERCISES

1. $5040, 210$ 2. 6   3. $5!6! = 86,400$

4. $P(6,3)P(5,3) = 7200$ 5. $C(5,3) \times C(6,4) = 150$

6. 44   7. $C(10,7) = 120$

8. $32 - 80x + 80x^2 - 40x^3 + 10x^4 - x^5$ 9. $-36x^7 + 9x^8 - x^9$

10. $369,600$ 11. $(10 \cdot 5 \cdot 15)/C(30,3) \approx 0.185, 1/6$

12. $C(10,3) \cdot C(5,4) \cdot C(15,2)/C(30,9) \approx 0.0044,$
$\quad C(9,3)C(6,4)(10/30)^3(5/30)^4(15/30)^2 \approx 0.009$

13. $C(6,3)(0.3)^3(0.7)^3 \approx 0.185$ 14. $\approx 0.0049.$ Yes.

6.1 EXERCISES

1. infinite discrete   3. continuous

5. finite discrete   7. infinite discrete

9.

A	B	C	D	F
.12	.20	.38	.22	.08

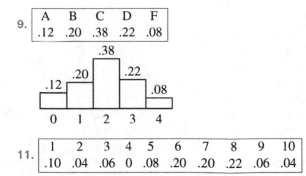

11.

1	2	3	4	5	6	7	8	9	10
.10	.04	.06	0	.08	.20	.20	.22	.06	.04

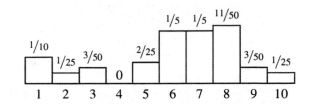

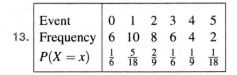

13.

Event	0	1	2	3	4	5
Frequency	6	10	8	6	4	2
$P(X=x)$	$\frac{1}{6}$	$\frac{5}{18}$	$\frac{2}{9}$	$\frac{1}{6}$	$\frac{1}{9}$	$\frac{1}{18}$

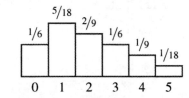

15.

x	-5	-2	1	4	7	10
$P(X=x)$	$\frac{1}{32}$	$\frac{5}{32}$	$\frac{10}{32}$	$\frac{10}{32}$	$\frac{5}{32}$	$\frac{1}{32}$

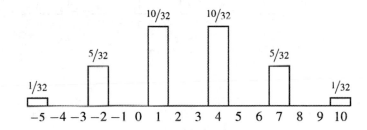

17.

x	0	1	2
$P(X=x)$	$\frac{21}{45}$	$\frac{21}{45}$	$\frac{3}{45}$

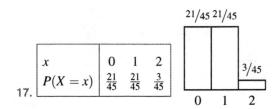

19. $z = 0.30$

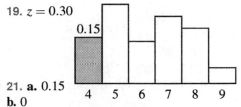

21. **a.** 0.15
b. 0

c. 0.40

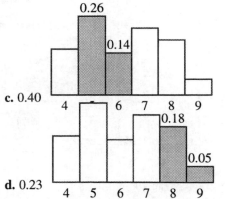

d. 0.23

23.

y	0	1	2	3	4	5
$P(y = x+2)$	0.20	0.15	0.05	0.35	0.15	0.10

25.

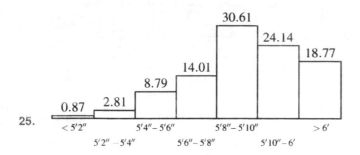

27.

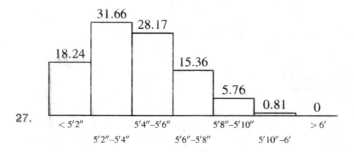

29.

x = total defective	0	1	2
$P(X = x)$	$(0.95)^2$	$2(0.95)(0.05)$	$(0.05)^2$

0.9025

0.095 0.0025

0   1   2

6.2 EXERCISES

1.

0	2	4	6	8	10
.50	.05	.10	.05	.20	.10

$E(X) = 3.4$

3. 0 **5.** 0.847 **7.** 0, −25%

9. −$0.19 **11.** −$1/19 **13.** −$1/19

15. $0.80 or −$0.20 accounting for the cost of the $1.00 ticket.

17. $1/6

19. Yes. Let $F = (a_1 + a_2 + \cdots + a_{99} + a_{100})/100$ and $S = (a_{101} + a_{102} + \cdots + a_{199} + a_{200})/(100)$. Then

$$\mu = \frac{F+S}{2} = \frac{F}{2} + \frac{S}{2}$$
$$= \left(\frac{a_1 + a_2 + \cdots + a_{99} + a_{100}}{2 \times 100}\right) + \left(\frac{a_{101} + a_{102} + \cdots + a_{199} + a_{200}}{2 \times 100}\right)$$
$$= \frac{a_1 + a_2 + \cdots + a_{99} + a_{100} + a_{101} + a_{102} + \cdots + a_{199} + a_{200}}{200}$$

which is the average of the 200 numbers.

21. Yes.

$$\mu = \frac{1234 + 1235 + \cdots + 1333}{100}$$
$$= \frac{(1234 + 0) + (1234 + 1) + \cdots + (1234 + 99)}{100}$$
$$= \frac{1234 + 1234 + \cdots + 1234 + 0 + 1 + 2 + \cdots + 99}{100}$$
$$= \frac{100 \times 1234}{100} + \frac{0 + 1 + 2 + \cdots + 99}{100}$$
$$= 1234 + \text{Average of integers from 0 to 99}$$

23. a. $E(Y) = E(X - c)$

$$E(X) = x_1 p_1 + x_2 p_2 + \cdots + x_n p_n$$
$$= (x_1 - c + c)p_1 + \cdots + (x_n - c + c)p_n$$
$$= (x_1 - c)p_1 + cp_1 + \cdots + (x_n - c)p_n + cp_n$$
$$= (x_1 - c)p_1 + \cdots + (x_n - c)p_n + cp_1 + \cdots + cp_n$$
$$= [(x_1 - c)p_1 + \cdots + (x_n - c)p_n] + c(p_1 + \cdots + p_n)$$
$$= E(X - c) + c$$

This means that $E(Y) = E(X - c) = E(X) - c$.

b. 13.1 **c.** 0.1

25. 0.09

27. 10/3, 2.5, 2

29. 436/7 ≈ 62.3, 20, 18 and 29

31. 8.5, 8.5, no mode

33. 0.83 **35.** $1800, $100 **37.** 2.5

39. $300, $255, the first

41. 156 **43.** 1.29 **45.** 6.6 **47.** 22.5

6.3 EXERCISES

1. a. $\mu = 3$, Var = 2, $\sigma = \sqrt{2}$

b. $\mu = 3$, Var = 1.2, $\sigma = \sqrt{1.2}$

3. Jane: 69.333, 1.556, 1.247; Cindy: 69.667, 0.222, 0.471; Amy: 69.667, 2.889, 1.700: Jane has lowest average, Cindy the most consistent.

5. −0.30, 2.01, 1.418 **7.** 1.5, 3.850, 1.962

9. 1, second

11. a.

$$\text{Var}(cX) = (cx_1)^2 p_1 + (cx_2)^2 p_2 + \\ \cdots + (cx_n)^2 p_n - [\mu(cX)]^2$$
$$= c^2 [x_1^2 p_1 + x_2^2 p_2 + \cdots + x_n^2 p_n - (\mu(X))^2]$$
$$= c^2 \text{Var}(X)$$

b. 3.24 **c.** $\text{Var}(X/3) = 0.36$

13. 0.96 **15.** $c = 10$

17. Bank: 0, 0, 0. Bond: −0.16. 0.034, 0.185. The bond varies more and carries more risk.

19. Utility 2.33, Tech 12.834. Tech more risky

21. A: 0.83, 1.121. 1.059. B: 1.3, 1.810, 1.345. Salesman B sells the most, but Salesman A is more consistent.

23. G:789.333, 7531.5, 86.8. S:95.17, 560.5, 23.7. The number of G cases is varying the most.

25. San Diego: 71, 21.5, 4.6. Chicago: 58.75, 375.2, 19.4. Chicago.

27. Marijuana: 23, 52.3, 7.23. Cocaine: 5.67, 6.56, 2.56. Marijuana.

29. Males: 431.8, 13.36, 3.655. Females: 421, 6.000, 2.449. Males.

31. Carbon monoxide: 6.48, 0.162, 0.402. Ozone: 0.124, 0.0001, 0.010. Carbon monoxide.

33. Viral hepatitis: 0.5, 0.015, $\sqrt{0.015}$. Meningitis: 0.6, 0.015, $\sqrt{0.015}$. They are varying the same.

35. $1 - 1/(1.5)^2 = 0.56$

37. 0.75

6.4 EXERCISES

1. 0.6915　3. 0.3821　5. 0.0668　7. 0.7881
9. 0.0919　11. 0.1498　13. 0.9332　15. 0.0228
17. 0.1151　19. 0.2417　21. 0.9544　23. 1.24%
25. **a.** 15.87%　**b.** 25.14%　**c.** 25.86%　27. 62.93%
29. 6.68%
31. **a.** 2.28%　**b.** 50%　**c.** 47.72%　33. 0.9332

6.5 EXERCISES

1. **a.** 0.1102　**b.** 0.7977　3. 0.0192
5. **a.** 0.9901　**b.** 0.9307　7. **a.** 0.9744　**b.** 0.8793
9. **a.** 0.1539　**b.** 0.7891　11. **a.** 0.9969　**b.** 0.9326
13. 0.9876
15. Yes, since under the old system the probability of 18 or less defectives is 0.0166.
17. Yes, since the probability of this response before the change was 0.0000 to four decimal places.
19. **a.** 1139　**b.** 113,906　21. **a.** 6765　**b.** 676,500

REVIEW EXERCISES

1.

X	0	1	2	3	4	5
$P(X)$	0.168	0.360	0.309	0.132	0.028	0.002

2. **a.**

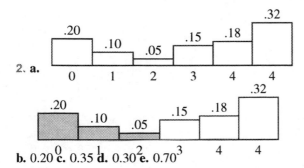

b. 0.20 **c.** 0.35 **d.** 0.30 **e.** 0.70

3. 2.97
4. $1.12 or $0.12 if the cost of the $1.00 ticket is subtracted.
5. $400
6. Wins: $\mu = 28$, $\sigma^2 = 21.2$, $\sigma = 4.60$ Loses : $\mu = 12.6$, $\sigma^2 = 13.44$, $\sigma = 3.67$
7. 13–19: 3862.4, 501,978.64, 708.5; 30–39: 9338.2, 4,050,740.6, 2012.6. The 30–39 year old group.
8. 3.709, 1.926　9. 0.96
10. **a.** 0.8078　**b.** 0.1922　**c.** 0.4993
11. $c = 2.33$　12. 0.0228　13. 38.3%　14. 0.0107

15. 0.1539　16. 0.0181　17. 0.0803

F.1 EXERCISES

1. $26.67　3. $480　5. $2046.67　7. $1120.00
9. 8.57%　11. 3.5%　13. $1980.20　15. $5357.14
17. 5.11%　19. 7.12%　21. $16.67, $983.33
23. $500, $4500　25. 2.5 years　27. 12.5 years
29. $1666.67, $48,333.33

F.2 EXERCISES

1. $1100.00
3. **a.** $1080.00 **b.** $1082.43 **c.** $1083.00
d. $1083.22 **e.** $1083.28
5. **a.** $21,724.52 **b.** $23,769.91 **c.** $24,273.39
d. $24,472.28 **e.** $24,523.94
7. **a.** $3262.04 **b.** $7039.99 **c.** $14,974.46
d. $31,409.42 **e.** $93,050.97 **f.** $267,863.55
9. **a.** $1538.62 **b.** $2367.36 **c.** $3642.48
d. $13,267.68
11. **a.** 8.16% **b.** 8.24% **c.** 8.30% **d.** 8.32% **e.** 8.33%
13. **a.** $1784.31 **b.** $1664.13 **c.** $1655.56
15. **a.** $3183.76 **b.** $2769.32 **c.** $2740.89
17. $31,837.58　19. $26,897.08　21. About $3 trillion
23. 8% since this doubles every 9 years
25. About 36 years
27. About 7 years　29. $1104.79
31. At 8% $1000 doubles in 9 years and at 9% doubles again after 8 years, ending with $4000.
33. 8.26%, 8.32%, second　35. $70,485.40

F.3 EXERCISES

1. $17,383.88　3. $18,120.60　5. $98,925.54
7. $15,645.49　9. $2,045,953.85　11. $1316.40
13. $148.36　15. $7.23　17. $675,764.89
19. $206,348.77
21. $1210.61, $28,209.02, $18,392.71, $1418.71
23. $265.17. Equity: $3316.64, $6944.40, $10,912.47, $15,252.77, $20,000.00
25. $14,836.23. Equity: $129,611.03, $287,529.47, $479,937.77, $714,368.74, $1,000,000.00. Interest carned is $406,550.80. Interest earned during the 18th period is $7738.85

F.4 EXERCISES

1. $339,758.16　3. $286,748.03　5. $245,453.69
7. $2296.07, $3776.42　9. $2642.37, $5854.22
11. $665.30, $139,508.00　13. $804.62, $189,663.20
15. $898.83, $61,789.40　17. $1014.27, $82,568.60
19. $253.63, $2174.24　21. $263.34, $2640.32
23. $34.18, $230.48　25. $36.15, $301.40
27. $85,812.06, $88.92, $588.80
29. $77,412.95, $332.45, $750.54

End of Per.	Repayment Made	Interest Charged	Payment Toward Principal	Outstanding Principal
0				10,000.00
1	2296.07	1000.00	1296.07	8703.93
2	2296.07	870.39	1425.68	7278.25
3	2296.07	727.83	1568.24	5710.01
4	2296.07	571.00	1725.07	3984.94
5	2296.07	398.49	1897.58	2087.36
6	2296.10	208.74	2087.36	0000.00

31.

End of Per.	Repayment Made	Interest Charged	Payment Toward Principal	Outstanding Principal
0				10,000.00
1	2642.37	1500.00	1142.37	8857.63
2	2642.37	1328.64	1313.73	7543.90
3	2642.37	1131.59	1510.78	6033.12
4	2642.37	904.97	1737.40	4295.72
5	2642.37	644.36	1998.01	2297.71
6	2642.37	344.66	2297.71	0000.00

33.

35. 70 payments

37. The first. The present value of the first is $67,100.81, which is higher than that of the second, which is $63,817.96

39. The present value of the first option is only $320,882.88. Accept the lump sum.

41. **a.** The first saves the most, $24,781.30
b. The second saves the most, $35,383.35

43. Your monthly payment in the first case will be $295.24, while using the rebate and the credit union will give payments per month of $292.56. The second is better.

REVIEW EXERCISES

1. **a.** $1469.33 **b.** $1485.95 **c.** $1489.85 **d.** $1491.37
e. $1491.76

2. **a.** $1610.51 **b.** $1638.62 **c.** $1645.31 **d.** $1647.93
e. $1648.61

3. **a.** 9.20% **b.** 9.31% **c.** 9.38% **d.** 9.41% **e.** 9.42%

4. **a.** 11.30% **b.** 11.46% **c.** 11.57% **d.** 11.62%
e. 11.63%

5. **a.** $4631.93 **b.** $4505.23 **c.** $4496.05

6. **a.** $4224.11 **b.** $4106.46 **c.** $4066.15

7. $214,548.21   8. $6499.31   9. 9.05%

10. $408,922.62

11. $33,111.50; $675,540.00; $14,179.87

12. The present value of the 19 payments of $100,000 each, plus the immediate disbursement of $100,000 is $1,060,359.90.

13. $839.20, $1014.27, $151,760.00, $82,568.60, $95.40, $282.65, $217.03, $642.99

Bibliography

Antle, J. M. and S. M. Capalbo (2001). Econometric-process models for integrated assessment of agricultural production systems. *Amer. J. Agr. Econ. 83(2)*, 389–401.

Bell, F. W. (1986). Competition from fish farming in influencing rent dissipation: The crayfish fishery. *Amer. J. Agr. Econ. 68*, 95–101.

Berstein, P. L. (1980). Productivity and growth: Another approach. *Bus. Econ. xv(1)*, 68–71.

Besanko, D., J.-P. Dubé, and S. Gupta (2003). Competitive price discrimination strategies in a vertical channel using aggregate retail data. *Manag. Sci. 49(9)*, 1121–1138.

Blake, J. T. and J. Donald (2002). Mount Sinai Hospital uses integer programming to allocate operating room time. *Interfaces 32(2)*, 63–73.

Blau, D. M. and H. N. Mocan (2002). The supply of quality in child care centers. *Rev. Econ. and Stat. 84(3)*, 483–496.

Briano, J. A., R. S. Patterson, and H. A. Cordo (1995). Long-term studies of the black imported fire ant infected with a microsporidium. *Environ. Entomol. 24(5)*, 1328–1332.

Brown, C., L. Lynch, and D. Zilberman (2002). The economics of controlling insect-transmitted plant diseases. *Amer. J. Agr. Econ. 84(2)*, 279–291.

Brown, G., J. Keegan, B. Vigus, and K. Wood (2001). The Kellogg Company optimizes production, inventory, and distribution. *Interfaces 31(6)*, 1–15.

Caixeta-Filho, J. V., J. M. van Swaay-Neto, and A. de Pádua Wagemaker (2002). Optimization of the production planning and trade of lily flowers at jan de wit company. *Interfaces 32(1)*, 35–46.

Carlyle, W. M. and B. C. Eaves (2001). Underground planning at Stillwater Mining Company. *Interfaces 31(4)*, 50–60.

Cohen, R. B. (1995). The economic impact of information technology. *Bus. Econ. xxx(4)*, 21–25.

Cotterill, R. W. and L. E. Haller (1997). An economic analysis of the demand for rte cereal: Product market definition and unilateral market power effects. Technical report, Food Marketing Policy Center. University of Connecticut.

Dean, J. (1976). *Statistical cost estimation*. London: Indiana University Press.

D'Unger, C., D. Chapman, and R. S. Carr (1996). Discharge of oilfield-produced water in Nueces Bay, Texas: A case study. *Environ. Manage. 20(1)*, 143–150.

Epstein, R., L. Henríquez, J. Catalán, G. Y. Weintraub, and C. Martínez (2002). A combinational auction improves school meals in Chile. *Interfaces 32(6)*, 1–14.

Featherstone, A. M., M. R. Langemeier, and M. Ismet (1997). A nonparametric analysis of efficiency for a sample of kansas beef cow farms. *J. Agric. and App. Econ. July*, 175–184.

Fuller, S., M. Gillis, C. Parnell, A. Ramaiyer, and R. Childers (1997). Effect of air pollution abatement on financial performance of Texas cotton gins. *Agribusiness 13(5)*, 521–532.

Gilligan, T. (1992). Imperfect competition and basing-point pricing. *Amer. Econ. Rev. 82*, 1106–1119.

Grafton, Q., L. K. Sandal, and S. I. Steinhamn (2000). How to improve the management of renewable resources: The case of canada's northern cod fishery. *Amer. J. Agr. Econ. 82*, 570–580.

Gupta, V., E. Peters, and T. Miller (2002). Implementing a distribution network decision support system at Pfizer/Warner-Lambert. *Interfaces 43(4)*, 28–45.

Hickman, T. (1970). School rezoning to achieve racial balance: a linear programming approach. *J. Social Econ. Planning Sci. 3*, 127–134.

Johnston, J. (1960). *Statistical cost analysis*. New York: McGraw-Hill.

Kaitibie, S., F. M. Epplin, B. W. Brorsen, G. W. Horn, J. Eugene G. Krenzer, and S. I. Paisley (2003). Optimal stocking density for dual-purpose winter wheat production. *J. Agr. App. Econ. 35(1)*, 29–38.

Keefer, D. L. (2001). Planning the United Parcel Service Air Network. *Interfaces 31(6)*, 66–68.

Kekhora, T. and L. M. J. McCann (2003). Rice versus shrimp production in thailand: Is there really a conflict? *J. Agr. App. Econ. 35(1)*, 143–157.

Ledyard, J. O., M. Olsen, D. Porter, J. A. Swanson, and D. P. Torma (2002). The first use of a combined-value auction for transportation services. *Interfaces 32(5)*, 4–12.

Lyon, P., R. J. Milne, R. Orzell, and R. Rice (2001). Matching assets with demand in supply-chain management at IBM microelectronics. *Interfaces 31(1)*, 108–124.

Misra, S. K., B. D. McPeek, and E. Segarra (2000). Optimal structure of the ginning industry in the southern high plains of texas. *Rev. Agr. Econ. 22(1)*, 120–133.

Nero, A. (2001). Measuring market power in the ready-to-eat cereal industry. *Econometrica 69*, 307–342.

Price, G. K. and J. M. Conner (2003). Modeling coupon values for ready-to-eat breakfast cereals. *Agribus 19(2)*, 223–243.

Roberts, R. K., B. C. English, and S. B. Mahajashetti (2000). Evaluating the returns to variable rate nitrogen application. *J. Agr. Appl. Econ. 32*, 133–143.

Rogers, C. E. and J. O. G. Marti (1994). Effects of age at first mating on the reproductive potential of the fall armyworm. *Environ. Entomol. 23(2)*, 322–325.

Rogers, D. S. and J. T. Akridge (1996). Economic impact of storage and handling regulations on retail fertilizer and pesticide plants. *Agribusiness 12(4)*, 327–337.

Rondeau, D. and J. M. Conrad (2003). Managing urban deer. *Amer. J. Agr. Econ. 85(1)*, 266–281.

Rowe, A. J., R. O. Mason, K. E. Dickel, R. B. Mann, and R. J. Mockler (1994). *Strategic management*. Addison-Wesley.

Saur, K., J. A. Fava, and S. Spatari (2000). Life cycle engineering case study: Automobile fender designs. *Environ. Progress 19(2)*, 72–82.

Schmitz, A., D. Sigurdson, and O. Doering (1986). Domestic farm policy and the gains from trade. *Amer. J. Agr. Econ. 68*, 820–827.

Shafer, E. L., A. Upneja, W. Seo, and J. Yoon (2000). Economic values of recreational power boating resources in Pennsylvania. *Environ. Manag. 26(3)*, 339–348.

Shea, J. (1993). Do supply curves slope up? *Quart. J. Econ. cviii*, 1–32.

Stiving, M. (2000). Price-endings when prices signal quality. *Manag. Sci. 46(12)*, 1617–29.

Suzuki, N. and H. M. Kaiser (1998). Market impacts of Japanese rice policies with and without supply control. *Agribusiness 14(5)*, 355–362.

Talekar, N. S. and C. P. Lin (1994). Characterization of resistance to lima bean pod borer in soybean. *J. Econ. Entomol. 87(3)*, 821–825.

Tauer, L. W. (1994). The value of segmenting the milk market into bST-produced and non-bST-produced milk. *Agribusiness 10(1)*, 3–12.

Timmins, C. (2002). Measuring the dynamic efficiency costs of regulators' preferences: Municipal water utilities in the arid West. *Econometrica 2 (March)*, 603–629.

Tolley, G. S. and V. S. Hastings (1960). Optimal water allocation: The north platte river. *Quart. J. of Econ. 74*, 279–295.

Velazquez, A., G. Bocco, and A. Torres (2001). Turning scientific approaches into practical conservation actions: The case of Comunidad Indegena de Nuevo San Juan Parangaricutiro. *Environ. Manag. 27(5)*, 655–665.

Yokomi, R. K., R. Lastra, M. B. Stoetzel, V. D. Damsteegt, R. F. Lee, S. M. Garnsey, T. R. Gottwald, M. A. Rocha-Pena, and C. L. Niblett (1994). Establishment of the brown citrus aphid in central america and the caribbean basin and transmission of citrus tristeza virus. *J. Econ. Entomol. 87(4)*, 1078–1085.

Index

$'$, 187

$\bar{}$, 187

$\cap$, 188

$\cup$, 187

$\emptyset$, 186

$\in$, 185

$\not\subseteq$, 185

$\subset$, 185

$\subseteq$, 185

$\{\}$, 186

^{c}, 186

Addition of Matrices, 89
Advertising promotion, 313
Alcohol, 327
Amortization formula, 380
Amortization schedule, 381
Amortizing, 380
Annuity, 369
Arrangement, 258
Asteroid, 69
Average, 303

Basic variable, 52
Bayes' theorem, 239
Bayes, Thomas, 239
Bayesian filtering, 238
Bernoulli trials, 279
Bimodal, 308
Binomial distribution, 295
Binomial Theorem, 285
Boole, George, 185
Bounded feasible region, 160
Break-even quantity, 21

Cardinality, 195
Ceres, 69
Certainty event, 205
Chebyshev's inequality, 319
Cigarettes, 327
Cobweb, 84
Cocaine, 327

Column matrix, 88
Combinations, 265
Comparing Rates at Banks, 367
Complement
    rules, 187
Complement of a set, 186
Complement of an event, 204
Compound interest, 361
Compounded, 359
Conditional probability, 226
Constraint, nonnegative, 143
Constraints, 143
Constraints, problem, 143
Continuous random variable, 292
Correlation analysis, 70
Correlation coefficient, 70
Cost
    fixed, 6
    total, 6
    variable, 6
Cournot, Augustin, 3
Crayfish, 15

Daily numbers game, 313
Dantzig, George, 143
Demand curve, 9
Demand curve for milk, 22
Demand equation, 9
Dependent variable, 4
Depreciation
    straight-line, 11, 15
Diagram
    tree, 255
Dice rolling, 313
Discount, 355
Discount rate, 355
Disjoint, 189
Distinguishable permutations, 274
Domain, 3
Doubling times, 364

Echelon matrix, 53

Effective annual yield, 362
Effective interest rate, 357
Element of a set, 185
Element of symbol, 185
Elementary equation operations, 33
Elementary events, 203
Elementary probability rules, 216
Empirical probability, 211
Empty set, 186
Encoding matrix, 120
Equilibrium point, 22
Equilibrium price, 22
Equilibrium quantity, 22
Equity in a sinking fund, 372
Event
    certainty, 205
    elementary, 203
    impossible, 205
    mutually exclusive, 205
    simple, 203
Events, 203
Exclusive or, 187
Expected value, 304
    lottery ticket, 313
Experiments, 201

Facility location, 29
Factorials, 258
Feasible region, 143, 159
Feasible region, bounded, 160
Federal Trade Commission, 17
Fermat, Pierre de, 210
Fertilizer plant, 13, 26
Finite discrete random variable, 292
Finite stochastic process, 228
Fixed cost, 6
Free variable, 52
Function, 3
    definition, 3
    dependent variable, 4
    domain, 3
    independent variable, 4
    range, 4
Function, linear, 143
Function, objective, 143
Future value of the annuity, 369

Gauss elimination, 32
Gauss, Carl, 69
Gauss-Jordan method, 41, 117
General multiplication principle, 257

General solution, 51

Half-plane, 157
Heart operations, 314
Herschel, Sir William, 69
Histogram, 293

IBM, 146
Identity Matrix, 104
Impossible event, 205
Inclusive or, 187
Independent events, 230
Independent variable, 4
Inequalities, linear, 143
Infinite discrete random variable, 292
Input–Output matrix, 129
Interest, 353
Interest per period, 359
Interest rate, 353
Intersection, 188
    symbol ∩, 188
Intersection of two events, 204
Irrigation water, 17

Jan de Wit, 142

Kellogg Company, 147
Killing the debt, 380

Law of large numbers, 344
Law of supply and demand, 22
Laws for Set Operations, 190
Leading one, 51
Lenape Indians, 361
Length of loan, 355
Linear cost model, 6
Linear function, 143
    definition, 5
Linear inequalities, 143
Linear inequalities, several, 159
Linear inequality, graph, 159
Linear programming, 143
Linear revenue model, 7
London Life Table, 211
Lottery, 313
Louisiana Purchase, 367

Machine shop operation, 30
Make or buy decision, 27
Manhattan, 361
Manufacturing cost, 16
Manufacturing profit, 16

Manufacturing revenue, 16
Marijuana, 327
Mathematical models
    evaluation, 6
    formulation, 5
    manipulation, 6
Matrix
    addition, 89
    column, 88
    echelon, 53
    encoding, 120
    equality, 89
    identity, 104
    input-output, 129
    multiplication by a number, 89
    multiplier, 128
    order, 87
    row, 88
    singular, 115
    square, 88
    subtraction, 89
    transpose, 89
    zero, 90
Maturity value, 355
Mean, 303, 304
Median, 308, 348
Member of a set, 185
Method of Corners, 172
Method of least squares, 68
Milk
    supply and demand, 22
Mode, 308
Multiplication principle, 256
    general, 257
Multiplier matrix, 128
Mutually exclusive events, 205

Newsletter copies, 338
Nominal rate, 362
Nonnegative constraint, 143
Normal probability, 333
Not a subset symbol, 185
Number of subsets, 186

Objective function, 143
Odds, 220
Optimal solution theorem, 171
Optional solution
    existence theorem, 172
Or, 187
    exclusive, 187

    inclusive, 187
Order of a Matrix, 87
Ordinary annuity, 369
Outcomes, 201
Outstanding principal, 382

Parameter, 51
Parametric solution, 51
Particular solution, 51, 52
Pascal's triangle, 287
Pascal, Blaise, 210
Payment toward principal, 382
Permutations, 258
    distinguishable, 274
Pfizer, 159
Piazzi, Giuseppe, 69
Plywood, 17
Present value, 355, 363
Present value of an ordinary annuity, 378
Principle, 353
Probability, 209
Probability distribution, 212
    normal, 333
Probability rules
    complement, 218
    elementary, 216
    union, 217
Probability tree, 228
Problem constraint, 143
Proceeds, 355
Process selection and capacity, 30
Product Rule, 227
Profit, 7
Proper subset, 185
    symbol, 185

Quality control
    ball bearings, 338
    steel beam, 338

Rail freight, 17
Random variable, 291
    continuous, 292
    finite discrete, 292
    infinite discrete, 292
Range, 4
Real Estate Appreciation, 367
Reduced row echelon form, 57
Regression analysis, 70
Repeated Bernoulli trial, 279
Risk, 321

Roster notation, 185
Roulette, 313
Row matrix, 88
Russell, Bertrand, 185

Sample space, 202
    uniform, 209
Saving for Machinery, 367
Scalar, 89
Scatter diagram, 68
Scrap value, 11
Sears, Roebuck and Co., 145
Set, 185
    complement of, 186
    disjoint, 189
    element of, 185
    empty, 186
    member of, 185
    union, 187
    universal, 186
Set-builder notation, 185
Several linear inequalities, 159
Simple event, 203
Simple interest, 353
Singular matrix, 115
Sinking fund, 371
Sinking fund payment, 371
Smith, Adam, 9
Solution
    general, 51
    linear programming problem, 171
    parametric, 51
    particular, 51, 52
Square matrix, 88
Standard deviation, 318
Standard normal distribution, 331
Straight-line depreciation, 11, 15
Subset, 185
    proper, 185
Subset symbol, 185
Subsets
    number of, 186
Subtraction of matrices, 89
Supply curve, 10
Supply curve for milk, 22
Supply curves in industry, 10
Supply equation, 10
Supply-chain management, 146
Sylvester, James, 87
Symbol
    element of, 185

    empty set, 186
    intersection, 188
    not a subset, 185
    proper subset, 185
    subset of, 185
    union, 187

Tape manufacturing, 338
Term, 369
Total cost, 6
Transpose of a matrix, 89
Tree diagram, 203, 255
Trials, 202

Uniform sample space, 209
Union, 187
Union of two events, 204
Union Rule, 195
Union rule for probability, 217
United Parcel Service, 148
Universal set, 186

Variable
    basic, 52
    dependent, 4
    free, 52
    independent, 4
Variable cost, 6
Variance, 318
Venn diagram, 186

Wheat, 13, 26

Zero matrix, 90